MEXICO

BOUNDARIES

—··—··— International		—·—·—·— State or Territory

LEGEND

⊛ National Capital

o Capital of State or Territory

• Other City

Piedras
Negras

Nuevo
Laredo

R. Sabinas   Mier   Rancherías
nas Cerralvo   Camargo
oria

Monterrey   Reynosa
Matamoros

NUEVO
LEON

TAMAULIPAS

dley   Ciudad
Victoria

Llera

rcas   Tula

Guadalcázar   Monte Chijol
uis Potosí   Ebano   Tampico
LUIS   Valles   Ciudad Madero
POTOSI   Río Pánuco   Pánuco
chu   Tamazunchale
JATO   Piñal de   Potrero   Tuxpan — Cobos
mán   Querétaro   Amoles   Alamo   Ezequiel Ordoñez
O   Limapan   Poza Rica
QUERETARO   Tecolutla
HIDALGO   Gutiérrez Zamora
Real del   Papantla
Monte   Teziutlán   Misantla
gue   Pachuca   TLAXCALA
MEXICO   Tlaxcala   Jalapa
México   Tlalnepantla   Veracruz
Toluca   Orizaba   Soledad de Doblado
Puebla   Córdoba   Alvarado
Cuernavaca   Ciudad Mendoza   Río Blanco
Taxco   Tehuacán   Minatitlán
Iguala   Huitzuco   Río   El Plan
Papaloapan   Río   Cuichapa
RELOS   Coatzacoalcos
Chilpancingo   OAXACA   Jesús
La Dicha   Tlaxiaco   Matías   Carranza
Acapulco   Atoyac   Oaxaca   Romero   Jalapa
Taviche
RELOS   Río   Salina Cruz
Puerto
Angel   ISTHMUS OF
TEHUANTEPEC

GULF   OF

MEXICO

Isla de
Mujeres

Progreso   Dzilam
Celestún   Mérida
Cozumel

YUCATAN   QUINTANA ROO

Campeche

Carme   CAMPECHE   Chetumal

Frontera   Xcalac

Coatzacoalcos
Tabón Grande
Tonalá   TABASCO   Villa
Hermosa
Jose Colomo

Tuxtla   San Cristóbal
Gutiérrez   de las Casas

CHIAPAS

Río Usumacinta

Río
Chiapa

GUATEMALA

Tapachula

C OCEAN

Puerto Soconusco

RRERO

Balsas

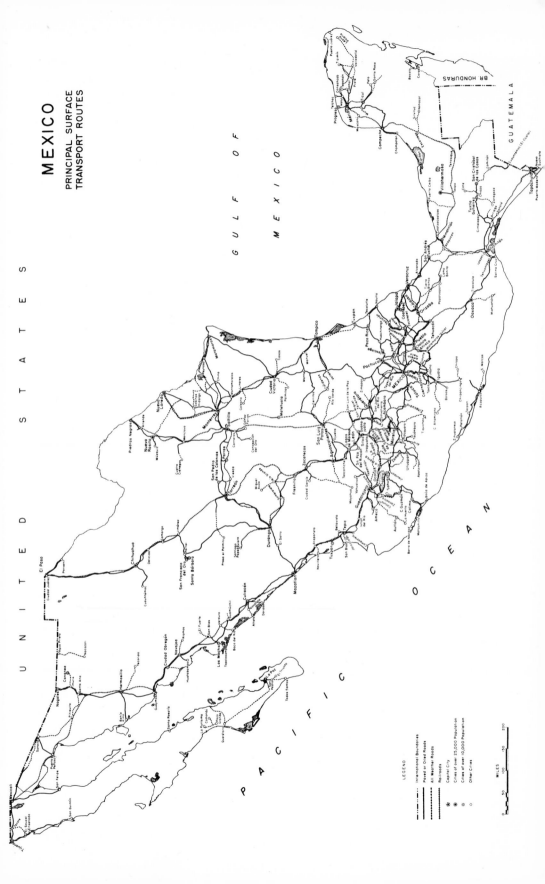

MEXICO

PRINCIPAL SURFACE
TRANSPORT ROUTES

GULF OF

MEXICO

UNITED STATES

PACIFIC OCEAN

GUATEMALA

BR HONDURAS

LEGEND

International Boundaries
Paved or Oiled Roads
All Weather Roads
Railroads
Capital City
Cities of over 25,000 Population
Cities of over 10,000 Population
Other Cities

MILES
0   50   100   150   200

THE MEXICAN MINING INDUSTRY

1890–1950

THE
MEXICAN
MINING
INDUSTRY

1890-1950

A Study of the Interaction of
Politics, Economics, and Technology

by MARVIN D. BERNSTEIN

1964

STATE UNIVERSITY OF NEW YORK

This book is respectfully dedicated to
My Mother,
MRS. THERESSA BERNSTEIN
whose sacrifices made my education possible
and to
DR. ERICH W. ZIMMERMANN
late Distinguished Professor of Resources
at the University of Texas
who gave my education meaning

Preface

MY objective in writing this volume has been to examine in detail four aspects of the history and economic organization of the Mexican mining industry: (1) the economic and historical setting of the industry; (2) the evolving technology and economic organization of the production of gold, silver, copper, lead, and zinc in Mexico; (3) the effects of the activities of the mining industry upon Mexico and its economy; and (4) the policies of the Mexican government to encourage and control the industry to its own ends. An opening date of 1890 was chosen in order to give full scope to my study of the interplay of these forces, particularly the effects of evolving technology and economic organization upon the changing policies of first, Díaz' regime, and second, revolutionary and postrevolutionary Mexico. From this study there emerges a picture of an industry responsive to world-wide technological and economic pressures and changes which must adapt its operations to conform to the socioeconomic policies of the Mexican government. At first we see the effects upon the industry as a result of its influencing the Mexican government to shape legislation to fit mining's operations and needs. The industry received at this time a sympathetic hearing because the government's laissez faire socioeconomic policies seemed to indicate that "what was good for mining was good for Mexico." Later we see the reasons for, and the effects of, the growing political impotence of the mining industry. Throughout this study the fact is emphasized that economic activities in Mexico are carried out in an atmosphere thick with politics and pressure in which each side attempts to use the other for its own interests. Defining who wins and who loses is ultimately determined by the viewer's social and economic attitudes and prejudices.

The idea of undertaking a study of the Mexican mineral economy was first suggested by Professor Eastin Nelson's course at the University of Texas, "A Survey of the Economy of Mexico." Encouraged by Professor Erich W. Zimmermann, under whom I was studying world resources and industries, I expanded my first short paper on Mexico's export metals into a full-scale study of the structure of the Mexican mineral industry and its relations with the government and economy of that nation. After several revisions, this book is the fruit of that endeavor.

In producing this work I am indebted to a number of people whose help and advice were invaluable. *Lic.* José F. Campillo Saenz, now Vice-President of the Compañía Fundidora de Fierro y Acero de Monterrey and formerly Executive Secretary of the Mexican Chamber of Mines, spent hours in his office discussing with me the problems of the industry, its labor relations, and the constitutional questions raised by the industry's operations and the government's policies. *Lic.* Campillo was also kind enough to allow me free use of the library and archives of the Chamber of Mines. Talks with *Lic.* Oscar Morineau concerning property rights in American and Mexican law were invaluable in orienting my thinking in that technical field. *Lic.* Martínez Sobral of the American Smelting and Refining Company, *Lic.* F. Roel of the Compañía Minera de Peñoles, *Lic.* Carlos Sánchez Mejorada of the Compañía Minera Real del Monte y Pachuca, and Mr. Benjamin Silbert of the Mexican Corporation were all cooperative in answering my enquiries concerning their respective companies. To Messrs. J. H. Ashley, Charles Veale, Bernard Dobsavage, and Dr. Stone of the Fresnillo Company, I owe a special debt for the hospitality and patience shown me in making my visit to Fresnillo memorable and instructive. Thanks are also due to the management of the Loreto mill in Pachuca for furnishing me with a guide and giving me permission to inspect the mill, and to Ings. Luis Torón Villegas and Adrian Esteve Torres of the *Departamento de Investigaciones Industriales* of the *Banco de México* for information concerning their work and for making available to me printed material from the very small supply provided by the bank. Mr. W. H. Triplett of Peñoles gave generously of his experience in communicating with me concerning the manuscript.

Without the unflagging assistance of a number of librarians, this work would not have been possible. The staff of the Science and Technology Division of the New York Public Library rendered aid and service beyond any expectations on my part. I should also mention the help of Dr. Nettie Lee Benson of the Latin American Collection of the University of Texas and Sr. Francisco X. Rojas of the Biblioteca de la Secretaría de la Economía Nacional. Other libraries which have been of great assistance to me have been the Library of Congress, Washington, D.C., which provided me with private study facilities while I availed myself of the resources of its collection; the Engineering Societies Library of New York; and the Love Library of the University of Nebraska. The staff of the library of the State University of New York at Fredonia helped in securing a number of items. I am also grateful to Mr. Sumner Anderson of the United States Bureau of Mines, who supplied me with several important pieces of data and documents from his office files.

I cannot fully express my obligation to Dr. Erich W. Zimmermann, late Distinguished Professor of Resources at the University of Texas, and Professor Bailey W. Diffie, of the Department of History of the City College of the City University of New York, for their kindness in reading the manuscript, tendering suggestions, and encouraging me in my work. Professor Charles H. Behre, of the Department of Geology at Columbia University, graciously read and criticized in detail my chapter on the geology of Mexico in addition to reading the entire manuscript. Mr. Francis Bellamy's advice concerning revisions was of inestimable value in preparing this manuscript for publication. The responsibility for any errors of fact or judgment which may have crept into this book is entirely my own.

The final research and preparation of the manuscript was made possible by a grant-in-aid awarded me by the Research Foundation of the State University of New York.

The three typists who worked on various versions of this manuscript— Mr. Aram Severian, Mrs. Alice Sloane, and Mrs. Bertha Glaberman— are due a special mention of gratitude for putting up with my numerous drafts and producing accurate copy.

Dr. Zach Bowen of Harpur College merits special mention for words of advice and encouragement delivered in a parking lot conversation at a very dark moment.

The extent to which I am indebted to my wife for her patience and faith during many trying hours, and her work over many weary months, can be known only to both of us.

M. D. B.

State University College
Fredonia, New York
September 19, 1964

Contents

List of Tables

Note

In this study the weights cited are those used by the author of the source. American and British authors have usually used the British system of weights, while Mexican authors have used the metric system. The following table of mass equivalents is provided to facilitate conversion from one system to the other.

TABLE 1. Mass Equivalents

Metric			English		
1 gram =	0.001	kilograms	1 ounce avoirdupois =	0.0625	pounds avdp.
	0.03527	ounces avdp.		0.9115	ounces troy
	0.03215	ounces troy		28.35	grams
1 kilogram =	1,000.0	grams		0.3732	kilograms
	.001	metric tons	1 pound avoirdupois =	16.0	ounces avdp.
	35.27	ounces avdp.		14.58	ounces troy
	32.15	ounces troy		0.0005	short tons
	2.205	pounds avdp.		0.00044	long tons
1 metric ton =	1,000.0	kilograms		0.4536	kilograms
	2,205.0	pounds avdp.	1 short ton =	2,000.0	pounds avdp.
	1.102	short tons		0.8929	long tons
	0.9842	long tons		907.2	kilograms
				0.9072	metric tons
			1 long ton =	2,240.0	pounds avdp.
				1.12	short tons
				1,016.0	kilograms
				1.016	metric tons

SOURCE: John H. Perry, *Chemical Engineer's Handbook* (3d ed.; New York, McGraw-Hill, 1950), p. 40.

Introduction

SINCE the dawn of the first metal age, man has known that immediate wealth could be had by digging in the earth for ores. Whether in the ancient conquests of the Pharaohs for the copper mines of Sinai and the silver and gold mines of Nubia, or on the fabled expedition of Jason for the Golden Fleece, which symbolized the gold of the Crimea, mines and mining have irresistibly attracted men—and trouble.

If mining offered great wealth to the individual in the twinkling of an eye, to the State it has offered resources to yield revenue and materiel to support government policy; and to mankind it has offered a universal medium of exchange and a stimulus to trade in a large number of indispensable commodities. Man's interest and stake in mining is enormous. The drive to discover mines; the struggle of individuals and governments to control mines; the fixing of relationships between the State and the miners; the technology of mining and smelting; the development of world metal markets; and the modern industrial system dependent upon international lines of commerce—all are part of the prodigious influence of mining upon history and the economic structure of the world.

This study will examine the history and structure of the Mexican mining industry through five metals: gold, silver, copper, lead, and zinc. It will also consider the relation of mining to various facets of Mexico's political, economic, and social life, and national history. To understand Mexico's complex mining problems, we must consider the configuration of the Mexican mineral deposits, the history of the opening of mines, the attitude of the government and the people toward mining law and mine labor, the changing technology, the availability and nationality of mining capital, the history of individual enterprises, and the place of Mexican minerals in world markets. All of these facets have to be viewed against Mexico's political evolution, from the personal dictatorship of Porfirio Díaz, to the socialist-nationalism of Cárdenas, to today's mixed economy in a society slowly developing democratic institutions.

My objective has been to study and explain the changes in the Mexican mining industry from the laissez faire days of the Díaz administration to the tightly controlled phase which marks the 1950's. I have attempted to analyze the intricacies of a modern industry whose beginnings lie in the sixteenth century. I hope that my study will help the reader to understand the attitudes of both Mexicans and foreigners toward an industry of ancient vintage but declining importance, which has been a great fount of national wealth, the object of large foreign investments, an important employer of labor, and a source of economic instability. Today the mining industry presents a paradoxical problem to Mexico. Although highly paid workers, using the latest modern equipment, efficiently turn out metals for coinage, metals for export which produce foreign exchange, and metals which support the industrialization of Mexico, this same industry epitomizes for the Mexican the evil heritage of his history: forced labor, contrasts of opulence and poverty, inflation, foreign intervention, and the depletion of the country's natural wealth. Mining has long held a dominant place in the Mexican imagination, and hence it has been the center of much governmental attention and a bellwether in Mexican socioeconomic thinking.

Unfortunately, most studies of Mexico's mining industry have been written from a polemicist's point of view. They exhibit little appreciation of either the basic economic problems of the international mineral industry or the constructive work of foreign investors. Even from an ardent nationalist's standpoint it is difficult to deny the positive achievements of this foreign-dominated industry in stimulating the Mexican economy and the nation's economic development. Little understanding is shown for the position of the foreign mine investor who put his money into a Mexican enterprise in good faith with the expectation that in return, for producing wealth by utilizing the resources of the country, he would be permitted to take out a profit. It is easy to understand the anger and bewilderment of these investors when they are accused of villainy and the crime of stealing Mexico's wealth under the sanction of a false economic philosophy. While not denying the robber-baron aspects of the activities of some promoters, it would be patently unjust to ignore the prevailing climate of opinion and the positive achievements of the majority of these men. Nor can one ignore the fact that most investors lost their money. I have tried to redress the balance by examining both the industrial accomplishments and the economic progress due to foreign enterprise, as well as the punitive measures taken against them by the Mexican government in its policy of nationalization.

I have tried to grind no axes but rather to present an account of the industry, and Mexico's reaction to it, in as objective a light as possible. For if mining is ever to achieve again a major role in the economy of Mexico, it must be studied objectively and with understanding.

M. D. B.

PART I

THE SETTING

CHAPTER 1

The Physical Structure
of Mexico

ONE of the oldest clichés among Latin Americanists is the saying, "Mexico is a rugged country." Repetition has robbed the saying of originality but not of truth, for, in its relation to man, Mexico is a hostile land. Only a few areas of its mountainous terrain are readily amenable to exploitation.

Generally speaking, most of Mexico is composed of a high plateau dotted with intermontane basins, bordered by two rugged belts of varying widths. The eastern belt consists of folded mountains; the western is, for the most part, a deeply dissected plateau with true mountains only locally visible. The plateau's altitude tends to offset the hot and dry climate associated with the country's latitude, but there is a high loss of arable land because of the topography. Transportation and communication have always been a problem. Today, after three thousand years of habitation and over four hundred years of European occupation and influence, large areas are still isolated and backward. Although the motorbus and truck have gone into regions closed to the railroad, the roads soon end and farther travel is done on horseback or with the ever-present burro. Enforced isolation is a national problem. Not only the people and the economy, but the entire nation suffers. Only the tourists are delighted, and they overlook the toil represented by the highways over which they speed so blithely.

Mexico can be divided into eleven physiographic regions or provinces (map printed on endpapers at the back of the book) which constitute the major geologic divisions of the country.[1] Two of these regions—Yucatan and the Pacific Coastal Plain—are unimportant as mineral areas. Tehuantepec, the Gulf Coastal Plain, and Baja California (Lower California) are provinces of lesser importance as mineral sources. In the Tehuantepec region only one gold mine—the defunct La Fé in Chiapas State—ever developed notably; today, however, there are indications of lead-zinc deposits which merit further exploration. Like its Texas counterpart, the Gulf Costal Plain is composed of young sediments, little deformed structurally, and of minor importance in the production of metals. Its southern part contains most of Mexico's oil deposits, and, with parts of Tehuantepec, has given indications of containing important deposits of sulphur and salt. The northern section of this province, spreading through parts of the states of Tamaulipas, Nuevo León, and Coahuila, contains several small metal deposits and a number of depleted districts. Lower California, the long peninsula off the west coast, is composed of older rocks. Except for the now depleted El Boleo copper deposit near Santa Rosalia, a manganese occurrence, and a few small scattered gold mines, it presents little of interest to the metal mining industry today.

Of the other six major geological provinces, the Sierra Madre Oriental and the Mesa Central (Central Plateau) are the most closely related. The Sierra Madre Oriental is a southern extension of the American Rockies, rising abruptly along the western edge of the Gulf Coastal Plain to elevations as high as 11,000 feet. The Mesa Central resembles the Sierra Madre Oriental, although the rocks found here are mostly slightly older. At different places rocks of greater age have been exposed, including some possibly of Pre-Cambrian age, as at Catorce, San Luis Potosí. Physiographically, and probably structurally, the Mesa Central is analogous to the Great Basin in the United States—a wide upland area of basin-and-range topography. In relation to the Sierra Madre Oriental, the Mesa Central is less mountainous and much of the surface cover is alluvium. As to mineralization, the two provinces closely resemble each other, but the Sierra Madre Oriental is definitely less important than the Mesa Central, "the Heartland" of Mexico's mineral provinces. Some good mines have been opened in the Sierra Madre Oriental, but they have never been of extraordinary size or value and most of them are now closed. Prevailing deposits in the Mesa Central are zinc-lead sulphides with silver content and smaller deposits of gold and copper, oxidized in the upper reaches. While the gold and copper content is generally low— Mexico is not to be regarded as a major producer of these two metals— silver is found in almost all deposits and frequently constitutes the major economic product. Hundreds of mines of this type, of all sizes, produced the oxidized ores which formed the original base of the Mexican smelting industry. Today these ores are mostly exhausted, and the mines are either working their sulphide zones or are abandoned.

The Sierra Madre Occidental—the Sierra Madre proper—is a separate lava-capped plateau, some 1,200 kilometers long by 300 kilometers or less wide, rising above the western edge of the Mesa Central. This plateau has been built up of thousands of feet of lavas, with some volcanic ash, of Tertiary age. Along its western edge this province has been highly dissected, making the topography extremely rough. The central area itself is marked by several great faults. Mineralization in the Sierra Madre Occidental consists principally of veins carrying gold and silver values of the "bonanza" type. Most of the veins bear much silver with relatively small amounts of gold; some are chiefly gold veins. Small quantities of base metals may be found in the ore. As a generalization, there is an increased ratio of silver to gold in the eastern mines, and those ores which carry very little gold but much silver usually are relatively higher in base metal contents. These latter may represent deposits transitional to those of the Mesa Central.

The northwestern corner of Mexico is occupied by the province of Sonora which is not a coastal plain but an area leveled by erosion. Its "porphyry" type of disseminated copper deposits is strongly suggestive of southern Arizona. Mineralization is widely variable, but the deposits of chief value are found almost everywhere in the older rocks. The two northern copper districts of Cananea and Nacozari are actually extensions of the Arizona metallogenic province and not truly representative of Mexico, although they contain the bulk of Mexico's copper resources. The greatest regions of copper mineralization are Cananea, with its Colorada ore body, and Nacozari, with the famous Pilares mine, now depleted. Molybdenum and tungsten occur in some localities, and some gold has been taken out; however, silver mines are of relatively minor importance. Sonora has provided a multitude of prospects and a few successful small and medium-sized operations, but nothing of top importance beyond the two giant copper producers.

In central Mexico lies the province of the Sierra de los Volcanes (Volcanic Mountain Range). This region occupies an area some 150 to 300 kilometers wide and 900 kilometers long. Mineralization here is principally in veins carrying silver and gold values. This area is the great, precious metals section of Mexico; most of the veins are silver bearing with small amounts of gold, but some are chiefly gold veins. Small amounts of base metals may be found in the ore, and they apparently have a higher base-metal sulphide content in depth. The veins are numerous and some have become quite famous: the twin districts of Pachuca and Real del Monte in the state of Hidalgo; Guanajuato, said to have produced over 1,000,000,000 pesos in silver; and El Oro, whose output exceeded 5,000,000 ounces of gold.

Just to the south of the latitude of Mexico City, a high ridge cuts due east and west from the Sierra Madre Oriental to the Sierra Madre Occidental, marking the southern limits of the Sierra de los Volcanes and the northern end of the province of Sierra del Sur (Southern Range). This complex range of old, eroded mountains covers most of the states of Oaxaca, Guerrero, and Michoacan. The province is anything but homogeneous, and its topography is very rugged. It is rich in many metals and nonmetallic minerals in great diversity, but they do not occur in large, economically workable deposits.

Maps locating the deposits of various minerals in Mexico tend to foster the belief that Mexico has many major mineral areas. Too often, however, these maps are based upon a geologist's notes, the existence of a small mine, or even the mere registry of a mine claim. The masses of dots which cover such maps indicate only the physical existence of mineral deposits; they generally disregard the fact that the mass-mining methods of modern industry and the prolonged period of former operations have robbed these miniature pockets of their value as reserves. In his maps of Lower California, Jenaro González Reyna has twenty gold areas marked; in Hidalgo he has only two.[2] Yet Hidalgo is a major gold producer—gold being a by-product of its huge silver output—and Lower California is only a minor producer. By their very nature Lower California gold deposits are unsuited to modern mining methods. One mine manager observed:

> From time to time, small pockets of gold-bearing quartz of great richness have been found and a small gold production made from many different locations. Led on by hopes induced by an assay of picture values, mine workings have been established, mills built, and large expenditures incurred. The peninsula is literally dotted with these monuments to optimism. There seems to be one fatal flaw in the veins: fine looking veins are usually barren; if not, the ore occurs in small bunches or in narrow stringers of material of later age than the general vein deposition—small amounts of material too low grade to work or entirely barren. This condition, which has been persistently overlooked or ignored, has made this peninsula the graveyard of many mining hopes.[3]

The state of Oaxaca has been the Mexican "Land of Tomorrow" for over a century. Most of the Oaxacan deposits indicated on mineral maps are within a radius of fifty miles of Oaxaca City, not too far to discourage a chance purchaser looking for a likely prospect. Despite a tremendous number of deposits indicated on mineral maps of the state, Oaxaca has always been a modest and erratic gold and silver producer because of unfavorable geologic factors, such as shallow veins and excessive faulting. In Sonora, where the mineralized areas are deeply eroded, many promising sites have proved to be little more than "holes in the ground."[4]

Despite the frequent disappointments attendant upon Mexican mining ventures, the torch of hope still burns brightly for investors. Celebrated by Alexander von Humboldt—whose works were translated and pressed into service to sell stock in British mining ventures in Mexico in the 1820's—the fame of Mexican mines moved Cecil Rhodes to declare poetically that out of her hidden vaults of gold, silver, and precious stones (!) would come the materials "to build the empires of tomorrow and make future cities of this world veritable new Jerusalems."[5] To the popular mind, typical Mexican ores would seem to be of the following grade:

. . . a mass of 18 metric tons, or 39,600 lbs. avoirdupois, . . . came from the Calaverita mine in eastern Durango, Mexico. It ran 75 per cent silver, and was so nearly pure metallic silver (which is noted for its soft ductility and malleability) that it couldn't be blasted, hammered, or broken. It had to be cut with knives and saws.[6]

A shipment from the San Francisco del Oro mine was described in which 20-ton carload lots assayed 40 per cent lead and over 3,000 ounces of silver per ton. "The native silver stuck out from this soft, yellow, crumbling ore literally in chunks—pieces ounces in weight."[7]

Unfortunately, the ores of Mexico have gained an undeserved reputation. H. W. Pudan, in studying Mexican ores, remarked that popular imagination set them at some 20 grams gold and 2 kilograms silver per ton with 30 per cent lead, while the correct figure was more likely to be 2.6 grams gold and 300 grams silver per ton with 5.5 per cent lead. While many of the mineral deposits are of huge dimensions, most of them are low-grade deposits best exploited on a large scale.[8] The ores of the Fresnillo Company, running about 5.25 ounces of silver per ton, were at one time considered the lowest grade silver ore in the world being worked.[9] During the twentieth century the Guanajuato mines produced ores averaging only 200 grams of silver and 1 to 2 grams of gold per ton.

Mexican mines are frequently a combination of much lean ore and a number of bonanza pockets; the public imagination thrives on the stories of the bonanzas. Because of the low ore grade, Mexican mines as a rule need large and extensive underground workings and beneficiation plants. But too often such mines have been developed and exploited haphazardly in the hope that a bonanza will be struck, often to the detriment of later scientific exploitation. For that reason unsupervised native workings have made economically unfeasible the recovery of tons of ore otherwise commercially valuable. For ages the Mexicans who invest and work in mines have regarded the industry as a lottery, living only on the hope that their excavation will hit a rich pocket and make them wealthy. In fact, with luck, everyone could win a grand prize! Scientific workings traditionally appeared to be a waste of time; a small amount of capital, plenty of strength, and a stroke of good fortune were felt to be enough. In such haphazard ways have fortunes ultimately been poured into holes in the ground by optimistic investors. Only the advent of large-scale capital investment and modern management secured the sound development of Mexican mining. The poor Mexican prospector, the *gambusino*, can make many rich strikes of small deposits, but the solid success of a long-range business venture has eluded him because his efforts and methods have not been in harmony with the nature of his nation's mineral deposits.[10]

CHAPTER 2

Mining
from the Conquest to 1870

DEEPLY embedded in legend is a myth of rich "Indian mines." However, while there is no doubt concerning the Indians' ability to work gold, silver, copper, tin, and lead by hammering, casting, welding and soldering, sheathing, inlaying, and even alloying, there is no evidence in Mexico of the working to any extent of subterranean mines for their ore. Smelting—the reduction of ore to metal—was probably known by the Mexican Indians but was practiced only on a small scale. Used mostly were pure native metals found as nuggets or powder which were hammered or melted and cast. The so-called treasures of the Aztecs were accumulated throughout ages of hoarding metal found as nuggets or native metal. Chroniclers of aboriginal life note that the Indians worked placers but not mines or smelting furnaces.[1] As evidence that mines were worked by Indians, some writers cite the use of hammer-and-wedge methods of fire-setting (heating the rock with fire and then dashing cold water on the ore face to shatter it) without realizing that, even in Europe, gunpowder was not regularly used in mining operations until the seventeenth century, a full hundred years after Cortés' conquest of Mexico.[2] In any event, the great mines which formed the basis of Mexico's mineral wealth were discovered by Spanish prospectors or were outcrops brought to the Spaniards' attention by friendly Indians knowing of the Europeans' interest in strange rocks. Significantly, in a few years following the first great Spanish mineral strikes in 1545, Mexican mines produced more silver than had been taken in plunder during the entire conquest.[3]

Mining stimulated the Spanish conquest of Mexico as it later stimulated the "Forty-niners" who carried the flag of the United States into the Arizona desert, the farthest reaches of the Rockies, and the gold fields of California and Alaska. The Spaniards' interest in mining was a part of the psychology which motivated the Europeans' land hunger, their grasping for trade, crusading religious zeal, and desire for adventure and glory in the service of expanding national states. Spain needed precious metals to finance the Hapsburg policy of territorial aggrandizement, the

8

defense of Catholicism, and to help meet the needs of Europe's expanding commerce. As for the effect of mining upon Mexico, it served as a stimulus to colonial economic life, providing markets for agricultural produce and livestock in addition to specie for domestic and international trade under the prevalent mercantile system. Buoyed by a flood of precious metals from the New World, the Spanish government tended to ignore the notions of maintaining a favorable balance of trade or increasing manufacturing, since anything from Flemish lace to armies of mercenaries could be purchased with American silver. Undoubtedly a factor contributing to the decline of Spanish power was the overextension of political commitments in European wars financed with bullion from the Indies. Mining was a patriotic duty as well as an individual enterprise. To the Crown, mining held a great fiscal interest; therefore, miners were regarded as special agents of the Royal Treasury. Tools, gunpowder, mercury, salt, supplies, and labor were provided for at cost by the Crown either through its monopolies or at subsidized and controlled prices. The mining of precious metal was too important to be left to the vagaries of free enterprise.[4]

Plunder provided the Spaniards with their first supply of Mexican riches. But the ease and rapidity with which these were gained has led to an exaggeration of their value. For some 20 years after the conquest only small mines were opened, thus further magnifying the size of the plunder. Of the 22,600,000 pesos coined by the Mexico City mint between 1537 and 1550, the bulk was struck after 1545 when the annual output reached 3,000,000 pesos.[5] Compostela in Nueva Galicia was the scene of the first large strike, purportedly revealed to a poor widow by an Indian to whom she had been kind. Its owner was soon a countess while the Crown established a mint nearby. New strikes followed one another with amazing rapidity as Spanish prospectors began to comb the hills. Zacatecas was opened in 1546 followed by Guanajuato, Pachuca, Sombrerete, and Proaño Hill near Fresnillo. A Mexican counterpart to the fabulous Potosí mine of Peru was opened in 1591 at the Cerro de San Pedro whose district was named San Luis Potosí.[6] By 1600 Mexico was well on her way to becoming the leading silver producer of the world.[7]

Contemporary European mining techniques were introduced by the Spaniards.[8] Iron tools, gunpowder, and draft animals facilitated excavation. Horse whims were sometimes used by the larger mines to raise water to the surface in huge rawhide bags. So many of the poor beasts died under the strain that the devices were called "blood-hoists." Ore was packed to the surface by men carrying loads of from 150 to 200 pounds in bags of leather or *ixtle* fiber supported by a tumpline passed under the bag. Their loads startled and aroused the admiration of visiting Europeans. Many contemporaries were highly impressed by the quality of work done by the common miner, especially since most mine supervisors were chosen for reasons other than professional proficiency.[9]

In the year 1555, Bartolomé Medina discovered the famed "patio amalgamation process" which achieved a high rate of extraction from low-grade silver ores. Essentially the process consisted of grinding the ore very fine, mixing it with water, adding salt and magistral (a complex of copper and iron sulphates), and finally mercury. This *torta*, or cake, was stirred for from 20 to 30 days by men and horses wading in the knee-deep muck until the "mercury men" judged that the amalgamation of silver and mercury had gone as far as could be expected. The lighter elements were then flushed into the tailings dump, and the amalgam, which settled, was collected and retorted to separate the silver and mercury. Medina's process permitted the economical working on a large scale of low-grade ores and did not require any scarce fuel, although the loss of mercury was a sore trial. While the exact chemistry of the patio process is still unknown, it was not displaced as the major Mexican silver beneficiation method until the introduction of the cheaper cyanide process in the twentieth century. And even then its use persisted in remote areas until the 1920's.[10] Since trade in salt and mercury were Crown monopolies, the government was often hard pressed in deciding whether to ask a high price for the chemicals and make an immediate profit, or to sell at a lower figure and collect larger sums in taxes on the silver produced. Smelting was little utilized in colonial Mexico because of the high cost of fuel and lack of base metal ores to be smelted. But some small efficient "Castilian furnaces" were erected in remoter areas.[11]

By the end of the eighteenth century, mining in Mexico had become a complex business afflicted with many iniquitous practices. If large amounts of capital were necessary, mineowners were notorious for their prodigality. When working a bonanza the miner spent his money lavishly; when working lean ore he continually borrowed money. In the words of Francisco Xavier Gamboa in 1761: "The miner's chief enemy is the miner himself. He is, generally speaking, prodigal, unlimited in his indulgence in expense, luxuries, superfluities, and even vices. . . ."[12] Because of the aleatory nature of mining and the unstable character of the miner, creditors had to be cautious and demanding. Interest rates typically ran 33⅓ per cent. Debts were frequently unpaid, including money owed the Crown for mercury. Merchants, therefore, milked the miners at every opportunity. Driven by the dread of the consequences of his mine not paying, the mine operator undertook little systematic ore development but concentrated on getting out the ore in sight. During "dead work," merchants were particularly sparing of supplies.[13] Other arrangements might be made whereby an orebuyer would borrow on his credit from a merchant, then lend money to a mine operator with the understanding that the ore would be sold to the orebuyer at a price far below the market value. In this manner the buyer was able to reduce the ore, repay the merchant in silver, and reap a handsome profit.[14]

Interest rates were ruinous and the available capital was small. Capitalists and merchants were not willing to take risks with miners, and those who did lost their credit ratings with their colleagues. Finally, in the 1770's, the miners petitioned the Crown for a reorganization of the methods of financing and regulating mine exploitation. The petitioners noted that miners, in common with other factions in Mexican society, were not interested in accumulating capital or investing in mines, but in purchasing an estate and livestock because this practice was both a highly commendable social action and a duty to one's heirs. Because of a lack of capital, they contended, many excellent mines were closed. Money for dewatering equipment and ore development was not obtainable. And if a man would develop a profitable mine, they reported, his children almost invariably turned to some other kind of employment.[15]

Incessant demands upon the Crown to stabilize conditions in the industry and regularize relations between the miners and their creditors, resulted in the promulgation of the famous mining *Ordenanzas* of 1783, the capstone to Spanish legal pronouncements in the field of mining.[16] Title V fixed the legal position of the industry:

> ARTICLE 1. The mines are properly of my Royal Possessions, [being] thus by their nature and origin, as well as by their reunion in accordance with law IV, title XIII, book VI of the *Nueva Recopilación* [New Compendium of the Laws of the Indies].
>
> ARTICLE 2. Without separating them from my Royal Patrimony, I concede them to my vassals in property and possession, in such a manner that they may sell them, divide them, lease them, bestow them, and leave them in testament by inheritance or gift. . . .

In return for the royal favor of being permitted to exploit the subsoil, the Crown obliged miners to register their mines and work them regularly in order that royalties could be paid in silver or gold.

The Ordenanzas was the most complete mining code compiled by any nation up to that time. It laid down the broad base of royal authority and its relation to the individual miner, and it minutely detailed the methods of working mines. It was not a spontaneous creation but the product of years of experience, framed with the aid of practicing miners, the Mining Guild of New Spain—men who were intimately acquainted with the Mexican mining situation. The administrative organization of the industry was centered in a *Tribunal General de Minería* in Mexico City. In every mining district local miners elected a *Diputación Minera* which was in charge of all local affairs, including the distribution of mercury, and responsible to the central Tribunal, which also acted as a

court of appeals. Mineowners were granted numerous social and economic privileges; School of Mines graduates had the right to claim the
privileges of nobility, and the law accorded all mineowners and employees
special treatment when they went into bankruptcy or were jailed. An
especially important section provided for setting up a tax-supported
Supply Finance Bank, to give credit to miners on the recommendation of
the Tribunal General. One of the duties of the bank was to support a
tuition-free School of Mines which was opened in 1792—the first technical school in the New World.[17]

After 1790 mining operations increased in size and importance until
the Revolution of 1810.[18] Contrary to popular belief, the colonial period
ended in an upsurge of economic activity. Population growth, national
expansion, and the opening of new mines—particularly the mines of
Catorce in San Luis Potosí and the Valenciana at Guanajuato—promised
more favorable circumstances for the miners. Several scientific commissions and expeditions sent from Europe spread the Enlightenment in
Mexico. Fausto Elhuyar carried on research in mine problems and
established the School of Mines in Mexico City.[19] Crown policy also
changed after the promulgation of the Ordenanzas. Mercury and gunpowder prices were lowered while expanding trade increased the demand
for silver. Also, the emergence of a class of professional Indian wage-
earning miners made possible a larger output. And over all sat the Tribunal General de Minería, regulating and supervising the industry's
workings and dispensing justice and loans.[20]

The quantity of gold and silver extracted by the Spaniards in Mexico
will never be known. Clandestine production, smuggling, corrupt officials, falsified and destroyed reports all conspire to obscure the record.
During the first two decades of the eighteenth century, Mexico's annual
output of gold averaged 524 kilograms and of silver 163,800 kilograms.
But the first decade of the nineteenth century saw output rise to 553,800
kilograms of silver and 1,763 kilograms of gold. Baron Alexander von
Humboldt set the total Mexican production of bullion from 1522 to 1803
at 2,028,000,000 pesos. Whatever the exact amount, the total was stupendous.[21]

Disaster struck the industry with the War of Independence in 1810–21.
Raids destroyed mine towns, the workings, the mints, and the archives.
Transportation of bullion and supplies was hazardous at best. Mines
filled with water, timbers rotted, shafts collapsed, roads fell into disrepair,
and isolated mines were forgotten while prospectors left off their work.
Finally, the Peninsular-born Spaniards and wealthy Creoles (American-
born whites), who held the best mines and most of the capital, were
either expelled from Mexico by discriminating laws passed by the new
government or confirmed in their predilection for landowning. "Mexico's
greatest fount of wealth" had ceased to flow.

After the War of Independence, mining recovered slowly. Capital was lacking, the commercial impulse was inhibited, the clergy monopolized the wealth of a closed feudally oriented society, and mass apathy was linked to political instability. Without national discipline or ambitious aggressive leadership, the Mexican government looked toward Europe for aid.[22] On October 7, 1823, the legal prohibitions against foreigners owning mines in Mexico were eased. They were allowed to enter into contracts to rehabilitate old mines but were not permitted to register new ones.[23] Starting in 1824 a number of British companies were formed to work Mexican properties. Humboldt's works, which extolled Mexico's mines, were translated into English, and a covey of writers (including young Benjamin Disraeli) ground out pamphlets to whet the appetite of the British investing public. English investors alone financed seven companies, the largest ones capitalized at over 1,000,000 pounds sterling. Scores of mines were acquired by the British, while German and American investors obtained leases on a lesser quantity.[24]

But the next 25 years brought disappointment. Mexico was plagued by an unstable government, and European shortsightedness also contributed to the debacle. In a land where labor and horses were cheap, transportation miserable, and fuel dear, the companies imported many heavy power-driven machines. Fortunes were spent on poorly conceived drainage adits and inefficient pumps. Cornish miners brought to the workings in Pachuca were a dubious success as teachers or foremen over the independent Mexican workers. Many hastily written leases were unfavorable to the new investors, and the new mine managers were often ex-naval and military officers whose talents may have been of use against bandits but were not adapted to solving technical mining problems. To add to the difficulties, several boards of directors in London and their agents in Mexico demonstrated a folly, extravagance, and incapacity which became matters of constant amazement to those on the spot. Possibly the condition of the mines was such that the technology of the day could not make them profitable. In any event, the failures were so shocking that to the end of the century British investments functioned under a cloud of suspicion.[25]

Large quantities of silver were extracted by the British companies, but the costs exceeded the money realized. Only a few small companies reported profits. By 1840 mining was in sore straits. Complaints to the British government by its nationals consisted largely of lists of murders and robberies.[26] In 1842 and 1843 President-Generals Santa Anna and Bravo expanded the policy of aiding mining by permitting foreigners to acquire mining enterprises on almost the same terms as Mexicans and offering bounties for mercury discoveries. While the program produced little mercury, the output of precious metals did increase and in the decade 1841–50 surpassed the production of the previous ten years by as much as a third in silver and 250 per cent in gold. But it was still a far cry from the output of the last colonial days.[27]

War with the United States, the bloody warfare of "the Reform," and the period of French intervention and Maximilian's empire discouraged new investment, although some of the older companies still managed to operate. Juárez's final triumph in 1867 found the industry in a bad state. Silver was smuggled out of the country because it was cheaper to pay the smuggler than the legal taxes. Mining was reduced to a hand-to-mouth affair, and many properties reverted to ownership by Mexicans who worked them fitfully and haphazardly. With the added risks to the industry, merchants and money lenders imposed well-nigh impossible terms on the mineowners or forced them into highly unprofitable arrangements. The miner took heavy losses and fell deeper into debt, while the creditor secured his ore for a song and reaped a good return after beneficiating it.[28] At this nadir, Mexico's economic renaissance began.

PART II

THE DÍAZ ERA

CHAPTER 3

Stability
and New Foreign Investments

DURING the decade of the 1870's Mexico enjoyed an unaccustomed period of comparative political stability which ushered in the era of the *Pax Porfiriana,* the consulship of Porfirio Díaz. This era coincided with a growth of European and United States investments abroad. Mexican mining expanded again under the stimuli of internal peace and foreign investment. However deplorable Díaz's methods, tremendous material progress took place during his 35 years in office. Condemnations of his economic policies often do not take into account that his regime coincided with the triumph of nineteenth-century Liberalism in economic thought. Promotion of a laissez faire economy had become government policy in the 1850's, after the final expulsion of Santa Anna, and was enshrined in the Constitution of 1857. The Liberals believed that free individualism would be the answer to the political power of the Church, the army, and reactionary landlords. With the approval and encouragement of Juárez, this constitution attempted to bring personal and economic liberty to Mexico by curtailing the power of the state and privileged corporate organizations. When Díaz came to power his vigorous pursuit of laissez faire principles only intensified a trend started under Juárez.

Except for the term of his hand-picked candidate, President González (1880–84), Díaz held the presidency of Mexico from 1876 to 1911. Building upon foundations laid by his predecessors, Díaz restored political peace. He kept the army in hand, maintained at strategic points loyal garrisons whose mobility was increased by the growing railway system, placed trusted cronies in key positions, and organized the *Rurales,* a national mounted police force, to suppress banditry and local political disturbances.

Financial and tax policies inaugurated by Matías Romero, in 1869 during Juárez's administration, continued. Romero had simplified and reduced the tax rates; economic expansion and effective collection methods raised the total collected. He paid particular attention to the problem of mine taxes which took an estimated 25 per cent of the value of the gold and silver mined. Previous administrations had given leases on the mints to private enterprises in return for loans and by law prohibited the export of bullion. Miners had to pay the minting fee even if the coins had to be melted down afterwards. In addition there was a "minting loss" of 5 per cent of the weight of the metal, and long and risky detours were occasioned by the minting requirement. Under Romero's direction the state retrieved the mints, mining taxes were unified, and bullion could be exported directly if the minting fee was paid directly to the treasury. Romero's first term (1868–72) yielded little in tangible results; his second term (1877–79) was more successful. Government revenue rose from 13,600,000 pesos in 1869–70 to over 30,000,000 in 1878–79. Romero's plans for mining did not bear final fruit until the passage of the Mine Tax Law of 1887 and the Tax Law of 1905.[1]

With Mexico safe and stable, the government favored the "economically active" to develop the nation and especially desired foreign capital "to build the nation" since native capital was scarce.[2] It paid no attention to the possible effects of foreign domination of the Mexican economy. Díaz's administration disposed of huge tracts of public land for incorporation into large estates. Although a national railroad system was talked of, the lines actually built were those promising the greatest profit. National development was a by-product of individual enterprise. A group of high-ranking government officials calling themselves *científicos* (the scientific ones) spoke of an inner order to the hectic building. Following the philosophy of Positivism, they exalted order over liberty and yet they also espoused the Spencerian ideal of turning economic development over to private individuals. The latter ideal, at least, ran counter to the many traditional collective and paternal facets of Mexican life and government. Catered to for their political influence, many científicos were placed in enterprises by promoters and accumulated large fortunes. Their bequest to Mexico was a possibly less chaotic governmental system ruled over by a business oligarchy.[3]

New law codes were necessary to implement the new philosophies of government. Amended many times, the Ordenanzas of 1783 still constituted the basic mining law of Mexico. The Constitution of 1857 gave the individual states jurisdiction over mining, but only Hidalgo and Durango framed new codes. An attempt in 1867 to draw up a new code failed. Congress finally federalized mining legislation in 1883 and then passed a new code on November 22, 1884.[4] Admittedly a rewriting of "the ancient and wise Ordenanzas," the *Código Minero* had a number of revisions designed to appeal to foreign investors. While the new code kept the requirements of regular workings to retain title and of close government inspection, it made no direct mention of the nation's retention of ownership of the subsoil, an omission which stirred up some vehement protests. The code still did not grant a fee simple title, but a major concession of title security was made to the liberal economists' concept of property rights. It expressly resigned government pretentions to ownership of bituminous and other mineral fuels as well as nonmetallic minerals, and it gave the surface proprietors ownership of these deposits. Unlike most Mexican codes, this one declared void all previous mining legislation, including the Ordenanzas, whether or not it was in conflict with the new code. In one stroke the Mexican government completely unified all its mining legislation.[5]

Two and one-half years after the new mine code was enacted, on June 6, 1887, the Díaz government revised the mine tax law. The new law aimed at easing the tax burden of the silver miners, since the price of silver had fallen from $1.145 an ounce in 1880 to $0.995 in 1886. It exempted coal, iron, sulphur, and mercury from all mine taxes, while only a seigniorage duty was placed on precious metals, plus 2 per cent of their value (mostly for state governments), plus the stamp tax on commercial transactions. The law set low tax rates on plants and real property, and it prohibited all other taxes. Article 10 provided for special concessions to encourage new enterprises. Finally, the law provided for lowering freight rates on mineral products destined for export.[6] The Code of 1884 and the Tax Law of 1887 set Mexico well on her way toward a laissez faire mining policy.

Confident that Mexico had joined the community of laissez faire nations, foreigners began to invest large sums in her future. To England and France, already embarked upon programs of political and commercial imperialism, Mexico appeared an excellent outlet for their capital. The United States, fast reaching industrial maturity, also had capital available. Englishmen, Frenchmen, and Americans diligently searched for likely prospects and mines inefficiently worked by "backward natives." Because of the Maximilian incident, the Mexican government refused to restore diplomatic relations with Great Britain and France until 1884, which effectively blocked expansion of their investments up to that time.[7] The success of the Americans was not due to pressure on the part of their government but rather to individual ambition, initiative, capital, and techniques. American dominance over production, capital, and the export market was an accident, albeit a highly advantageous one. But the future political implications of control of the sources of supply as well as the major market escaped the foreign investors' attention.[8]

Prospectors from the United States entered Mexico after 1849. Over 30 American companies were operating in Mexico by 1865 and an estimated 40 companies twenty years later. Some 5,000 Americans were said to have joined the rush to Sierra Mojada in the late 1870's. First mines in northern Mexico at San Dimas, Guarisamey, Santa Eulalia, Batopilas, and Sierra Mojada, and, finally, the El Oro mine near Mexico City, came under American control. New smelters built north of the Rio Grande, as far away as Colorado and Missouri, depended upon Mexican ore delivered over the new railroads. Mexican mining began to prosper.[9]

Mexicans holding mining properties found the foreigners' offers to buy too tempting to reject. Encouragement to sell came from a Mexican government anxious to stimulate the economy and increase its tax receipts. Mexican capitalists held on to a few large properties. Only after the mining industry fell into the hands of foreigners did a latent nationalism burst forth, to accuse the outsiders of mulcting poor Mexicans who were either ignorant or lacked capital. Actually Mexican mines fell to foreigners through default.[10]

With few exceptions Mexican mines had been exploited in a haphazard, uneconomical fashion. The capabilities of Mexicans as shrewd, economical, and persistent miners showed up well in small erratic deposits or familiar formations. Traditionally, they "followed the outcrop," which resulted in "labarinthine [sic] mazes of unmapable [sic] chambers, caverns, squeezes, etc.," none of which penetrated to deep levels.[11] Antiquated techniques continued to be used: the stone drag mill, as inefficient as it was cheap to construct and run, and the Castilian furnace smelting only two to three tons of ore a day. Mexicans did not organize companies to explore and exploit mines systematically or to build efficient mills; this required capital and a knowledge of modern chemistry and machinery.[12]

With the foreign owners came new machinery—including the stamp mill for crushing ore—and new processes of ore treatment. Where fuel was not too expensive, pan amalgamation—a process to speed up the action of mercury upon silver ore through the use of steam—was popular. Oskar Hofmann in the 1880's and 1890's introduced the lixiviation process of roasting and leaching silver ores, which successfully challenged the venerable patio process throughout northwestern Mexico.[13]

Foreign investors did not fall onto a bed of roses. Many mines simply could not be made to pay. Frauds and swindles were commonplace; prospect holes were offered as genuine "antiguas" worked by the Aztecs and Spaniards. "Salting" was practiced with a finesse a California expert might envy. In one famous case in 1888–89, two Mexican brothers cheated a San Francisco firm out of $1,500,000. Only a disgruntled employee's confession and President Díaz's intervention saved their money.[14] Pigs in a poke were sold to the credulous as Ophirs, and many a likely looking prospect petered out after a few hundred yards of development. Abandoned mines, dating back to colonial times, were cleaned out and retimbered only to run out of ore or yield a refractory product.[15] Working a good mine was not always easy. John Hays Hammond, one of the most noted mining engineers of his day, told of working a mine in Sonora in 1882–83 which was two hundred miles from the nearest telegraph station and shipping point, and plagued with low ore reserves, corrupt local officials, inexperienced workers, untrustworthy subordinates, Indian raids, bandit attacks, and miners with long-standing grudges. Only the abilities of the Yaqui Indians could be praised. After fifteen months Hammond gratefully returned to the United States for more orthodox work.[16]

Local landlords, the *hacendados,* were stubborn foes of the mine operators. They showed no interest in exploiting the mineral wealth under their feet. Traditionally, their haciendas were organized for the exploitation of cheap labor, not for efficiency or profits. These land-holders were land conscious because of the importance of land in deter-mining social position. Hence the opening of a mine in their district posed a double threat: higher wages with freer and better labor condi-tions lured away their workers, and mineowners might ask for easements on their property in order to develop mine workings. Wages might rise from 25 centavos a day to 50 centavos (about 25 cents, U.S.). Landlords bitterly opposed the entrance of miners, bogging them down in lawsuits and even filing false "opposition claims" in efforts to have the mine titles declared invalid. Because of the industry's favored legal position, miners could get easements on landed estates for roads and for mine and mill sites. Experienced miners, however, privately recommended to new companies that they would do better to sign a lease or reach an amicable settlement with the local landlords, even if the cost were greater, rather than incur their enmity by taking legal action to obtain an easement.[17]

During the decade 1880–90, three large developments were begun in Mexico: at Sierra Mojada, Coahuila; Batopilas, Chihuahua; and El Boleo at Santa Rosalia, Lower California. A lucky find of exceptionally rich silver-lead ore in 1878 started a rush to Sierra Mojada. By 1885 the population reached 5,000. Output totaled 1,000 tons of ore a week, run-ning 20 ounces of silver per ton and 25 per cent lead. By 1920, S. F. Shaw estimated that 3,500,000 tons of lead ore and 2,000,000 tons of copper and silver-lime ore had been shipped, yielding a total value of from $50,000,000 to $75,000,000.[18]

Working costs at Sierra Mojada were fantastically high. O. H. Hahn wrote in 1890 that there was no water, no flux, no fuel, no cheap labor, and that the smelters were poorly managed. Before the railway opened, lead ore had to run over 1 kilogram of silver per ton to pay; the average ore contained 1.5 to 3.0 kilograms of silver per ton plus 30 per cent lead. Several primitive smelters were succeeded by one of the first large mod-ern blast-furnace plants in Mexico, set up by the Purcell Brothers at the La Constancia mine in 1890–91. But the La Constancia smelter shut down when Robert S. Towne opened the Mexican Northern Railway which connected Sierra Mojada with the smelters at El Paso, Texas, and San Luis Potosí—the latter built by Towne through the Compañía Metalúrgica Mexicana. When the Torreón smelter was built in 1902, freight rates ran from 5 to 10 pesos a ton according to grade, and the district mines shipped from 6,000 to 10,000 tons each month.[19]

Sierra Mojada silver-lead ore had a far-reaching effect upon the

American mining industry. Robert S. Towne, the builder of the Mexican Northern Railway, was destined to influence the development of Mexican mining for the next 30 years. Towne started working for the Kansas City Smelting and Refining Company. He organized the Mexican Ore Company which bought Sierra Mojada ore, shipping it out by mule train to the Kansas City company's smelter at Argentine, Kansas. He also obtained control of two of the largest mines for the Kansas City company. In June, 1887, Towne supervised for his employer the construction of a smelter at El Paso, Texas, to work Sierra Mojada ores. Although a jerry-built affair—the original plant was constructed in 100 days—by 1891 it produced 12,000 tons of lead bullion and 4,000 tons of copper matte. Some 40,000 tons of rich self-fluxing carbonate ore was received from Sierra Mojada. Ivan Ragaz claimed that the Sierra Mojada ore was so rich that El Paso contracts read: "No ores received with less than 28 per cent lead; no payment made for lead contents." [20] El Paso paid for the silver content alone. Because of El Paso's location at the crossroads (where American ore moved east and Mexican ore north) and the prevalence of cheap labor, which offset fuel and transportation costs, the financial success of the plant was assured. Even after a partial reorientation to the use of Mexican smelters after 1900, Sierra Mojada shipped large amounts of ore to El Paso.[21]

Believing themselves threatened by Sierra Mojada ore, American lead-mine operators, over the opposition of smelter owners, prevailed upon Congress to insert a duty on lead imports in the McKinley Tariff of 1890. Towne completed the Mexican Northern Railway the same year. Despite an exemption from Mexican silver export duties, other taxes on Sierra Mojada ore ran 50 to 60 per cent of their value which paid 30 per cent of the income of the state of Coahuila. Soon Mexican smelters at San Luis Potosí, Torreón, and Monterrey took a large portion of the district's output of 4,000 tons a week. By then the entire district was under American ownership and supervision.[22]

Alexander R. Shepherd, ex-Governor of the District of Columbia, organized the Consolidated Batopilas Silver Mining Company in 1880 to buy out the Batopilas Silver Mining Company and exploit silver deposits in southern Chihuahua.[23] San Antonio, Texas, was the nearest railroad terminal. On his Mexican visit in 1879 Shepherd crossed the Isthmus of Panama, sailed up the west coast to Ajiabampo, and proceeded by muleback into the Sierra Madres. After completing the deal, he returned the next year leading a caravan from San Antonio with his family, engineers, mechanics, and a doctor.[24]

Starting with the San Miguel mine, for which he paid $600,000 in January, 1880, Shepherd bought other mines in the district. He was given a concession by the Mexican government in 1886 (renewed in 1906) to full mineral rights in an area of 61 square miles. He also controlled other mines as well as ranch and timber lands. Shepherd merged his various interests into the Batopilas Mining Company capitalized at $5,175,000.[25]

Batopilas was an excellent but erratic producer with much native, or "black," silver mixed with ordinary ore. In ten years the previous owner had extracted $3,000,000 in bar silver. There was generally little "ore in sight." A day's work could bring in barren rock or valuable stringers of native silver. Once when bullion was needed to cover a $90,000 bank draft, the mine superintendent called on the last day to say that he had only three loads of lean rock. An hour later he called for every mule on the property. A bonanza had been struck, so rich that there was not enough rock to blast; a shop crew with cold cutters had to carve it out.[26]

Shepherd started remodeling by erecting a 20-stamp mill—one of the first modern ore crushers in Mexico—costing $17,000. It was shipped from San Francisco with amalgamating pans and settlers able to process 40 tons of ore a day. During its erection the old mill produced some $500,000 in silver, paying the construction costs and part of the purchase price. Originally designed to work by water or steam power, depending on the season, a later mill expansion to 100 stamps included building a dam and water wheels to provide 800 horsepower. An extraordinary exploratory tunnel, El Porfirio Díaz, was driven for several kilometers through sterile rock to tap several bonanza veins which produced over 20,000,000 pesos in silver. By 1920 over 30,000,000 pesos of silver had been shipped out to Chihuahua City by muleback. Shipments of from 50 to 100 bars valued at from $60,000 to $120,000 were made about once a month. During the entire period of Shepherd's operation, up to the Revolution of 1910, not a single bar was stolen although it was a 300-mile trip to the railroad. The only guard consisted of a squad of Mexicans.[27]

Only the personality of Governor Shepherd kept the enterprise going. The original capitalization did not provide enough working capital to cover the periods between bonanzas, and after a first period of good profits the development costs ate up any further profits. Governor Shepherd continually cajoled creditors and bondholders to extend their due dates. Profits from the later bonanzas were absorbed by the accumulated debt. Under Shepherd's management Batopilas produced an estimated 24,539,244 pesos in silver. In 1909 the mine began to play out. The Revolution of 1910 forced a shutdown. An English corporation could not resuscitate the enterprise, and in the 1920's the town of Batopilas began to disintegrate.[28]

Most famous of the early enterprises was the French Compagnie du Boleo in Lower California. Legend has it that the ore body was discovered by a local rancher who found blue and green nodules—"boleos" —in an arroyo south of Santa Rosalia. Exhibited as curiosities, they were recognized as a complex copper ore: chalcopyrites mixed with small amounts of cobalt, nickel, molybdenum, pyrite, barite, and carbon in a clayey material. The rancher sold his rights for a song, and a horde of ranchers and merchants soon worked the area with Indian labor. A group of Frenchmen and Germans in Lower California and the United States became interested, and between 1875 and 1884 they organized a number of small companies. Three major ore beds had been discovered and the principal claims were in the hands of the Compañía Minera Elhuyar y Sontag and Srs. Guillermo Eisenmann and Eustaquio Valle. From 1872 to 1884 they mined 60,000 tons of high-grade ore—20 to 25 per cent copper—by taking rock from the outcrop and hauling it by wagon to the beach where it was loaded on Europe-bound ships. Some 120,000 tons of 8 per cent ore were in the dump. They organized the Negociación del Boleo in 1884 which employed 250 men, including 80 Frenchmen who lived in a settlement built over the deposit. Labor was expensive; peons received 75 centavos to 1 peso (on par with the dollar) for a ten-hour day. The company held 110 hectares of mineral land containing deposits of at least 12 per cent copper. Without pumps or mining machinery, it reported profits of 35 pesos a ton on ore shipped to Swansea, Wales, for smelting. On the basis of that showing they made contact with European capitalists.[29]

A French commission arrived in 1884 to study the district and advise French investors. It was greatly impressed with the ore body, which was estimated at 700,000 tons of 12 per cent copper, quite clean and amenable to smelting. The commission found the climate to be *"sec y chaud."* It commented on the excellent quality of the Yaqui Indian labor and the ease of labor recruitment on the west coast of Mexico. Only supervisory workers would have to be brought from France. For an investment of $1,000,000, the commission estimated that the mine could be modernized, a $575,000 smelting plant erected, and sufficient circulating capital provided.[30]

Shortly afterward, on July 7, 1885, the Mexican government granted an exploitation concession to the Boleo company, including land to erect a village and a large number of tax and financial concessions. In turn, the company agreed to improve the harbor of Santa Rosalia, build the necessary government buildings, and carry government goods and employees on company ships at half price. This contract was turned over to the Compagnie du Boleo, controlled by the House of Rothschild, which was formed in Paris on May 16, 1885, with a 12,000,000-franc capitalization.[31] The company built a port at Santa Rosalia and a town near each of its four mines. By the early 1900's the company supported a population of over 8,000, including 200 Europeans. Although the houses resembled packing cases, they were well built with a kitchen, bathing facilities, a zinc roof, and rented for from 2 to 7 pesos a month. European quarters were larger, with high ceilings and open verandas more suitable for a tropical climate. Running water was not piped to the houses, and the sewer system left much to be desired. In addition, a separate colony of miserable Yaqui Indian and Chinese huts constituted another health hazard. But the streets were straight and broad, there were schools with company-paid teachers, churches, a roofed market place, a circus, and a theater. A hospital and pharmacy cared for the health of workers, their families, and the local inhabitants. The total cost was estimated at about 13,500,000 pesos.[32]

El Boleo constructed a harbor with slag, and a dredge kept the port clear. A small company-owned fleet of vessels serviced the plant and the needs of the population. Because of the surrounding desert, a great deal of food had to be imported. El Boleo planted orchards, opened an irrigation system on the company's 600,000 hectares of grazing land, and grew vegetables. It developed a herd of several thousand cattle from imported stock. Local fisheries added to the diet.[33]

For its plant the company built over 45 kilometers of railroad to haul 1,500 tons of ore a day. A power plant, installed in 1897, produced 2,000 horsepower by 1912. Originally El Boleo erected 10 furnaces in 1886 with a capacity of 940 tons of ore per day. By 1894 this plant turned out 10,537 tons of copper matte and black copper a year. In 1901–2 the company rebuilt the plant with 10 furnaces of 150 tons capacity each. Copper output reached 11,000 tons a year, about 75 per cent of the total Mexican production. Until the opening of the Cananea copper mines in Sonora, El Boleo was the largest copper producer in Mexico. Despite losses during the first years of operation, because of a depressed copper market, between 1900 and 1912 El Boleo paid investors from 25 to 200 per cent a year.[34]

El Boleo continued to produce between 10,000 and 12,000 tons of copper a year until the 1940's. In order to offset an unstable labor supply, the mine was fully mechanized. An exploration campaign in 1927 discovered the San Luciano vein about nine miles south and west of Santa Rosalia. Brought into production in 1932, the San Luciano remained the mainstay of the enterprise despite its medium-grade ore and poor working conditions. El Boleo presented a peculiar problem in its later years because the deposit—once referred to as "a mass of rubber"—needed extensive timbering. Of the 9-peso-per-ton extraction costs, 2 pesos were charged to timber. El Boleo rebuilt the smelter in 1922, installing six 250-ton reverberatories and two 40-ton converters. Blister copper was sent to Tacoma, Washington, for refining, and timber was brought in on the return trips.[35] Following a period of relative prosperity in the late 1920's and 1930's—which resulted in a bettering of wages, working conditions, and housing—the company started to go into liquidation in 1938. War contracts and tax concessions, however, kept the operation going. The population of Santa Rosalia fell from some 15,000 to 8,000, and only the

San Luciano mine was worked regularly. As early as 1938, *poquiteros* (10 to 20 men working under an independent operator) began clearing out the older mines. With company guidance they began, in 1950, to work the San Luciano. El Boleo went through several reorganizations, finally emerging as Cia. Minera Santa Rosalia, S.A., with a mixed capital from private sources, and the government's Commission for Mining Development. Rising copper prices in the 1950's kept the enterprise going, but it was painfully apparent that the social problem of caring for the workers was the overriding factor in the government's interest in continued operations.[36]

According to the records of the Compañía del Boleo, between 1886 and 1947, it extracted 13,622,327 metric tons of ore which yielded 540,342 metric tons of copper valued at approximately $166,000,000.[37]

CHAPTER 4

Modernizing
the Mining Economy

A CONTINUING decline in the price of silver in the 1890's brought a crisis to Mexican mining despite the increasing investment. In order to attract and encourage capital, the científicos advocated a more liberal and "scientific" mining law. Consequently, the Mine Law of June 4, 1892, grafted mining law onto the general property law. The entire eleven-page introduction to the law was a panegyric for free and unhampered work and enterprise and a denunciation of the "anti-economic and anti-social" effects of the regalistic ideas of the laws of 1783 and 1884. Emphatically the drafting commission declared the object of the law to be: "Facility to acquire, liberty to exploit, and security to retain."[1]

In conformity with liberal economic principles, the state was reduced to a passive level. All standards and implications of government owner-ship of the subsoil were dropped, and all matters of business conduct were regulated by the general commercial code. Administration was centralized; mine agents, appointed by the federal government, simply sent the papers supporting the claim to Mexico City for processing. Of key importance was the omission of the proviso that an ore sample be shown before a title could be granted. Now a title would be granted to the first claimant merely on the merits of the application without inspec-tion. Regular working of the property was no longer required to maintain title. A mine title could be declared forfeit only for nonpayment of taxes on the claim area. The Mexican government resigned any interest in whether or not the claim produced ore. With the suspension of the regu-lar working clause, mineowners were permitted to stake large areas without evidence of mineralization in the hope that the land might be sold by them later at a speculative profit.[2]

Americans often erroneously thought that the lack of a direct statement of government ownership of the subsoil made mine titles equivalent to fee simple titles. First, the government's revocation of a title was simply an administrative matter. Second, the titleholder possessed no equity in the claim. In addition, Article 2 of the "Ley de Bienes Inmuebles" of December 18, 1902, made it clear that the government still regarded the subsoil as part of its patrimony by referring to "the deposits of minerals whose eminent domain belongs to the Nation."[3]

Legal terms for mining, still in use today, were first standardized in 1892. Mining titles are held to *fundos,* the equivalent of a claim area. A "title" covers a fundo which may be comprised of any number of *pertenencias,* an area measurement equal to one hectare (100 by 100 meters) or 2.47 acres. The number of pertenencias that may be claimed at one time depends upon the provisions of the current mine code. Claim-area taxes are levied by pertenencias. To claim more land a new title must be obtained. Mines that have had their titles legally cancelled, or are forfeit for any reason, are said to be *en caduca.* Americans have anglicized the term and refer to mines as "caducated" or "in caduca."

The effect of the Mine Law of 1892 was far reaching. Since miners were free to claim as much land as they could pay taxes on; work a mine in any manner they might see fit; open or close as their economic or personal desires dictated; and employ any number of men they might wish, the mineowner and the speculator in Mexico attained a position of almost complete liberty of action. The break with the old tradition had been abrupt, and many Mexicans were not prepared to go along with the radical change. Gilberto Crespo y Martínez reported:

> Upon [the law's] appearance, a tempest arose. Some, terrified, called the Minister a revolutionary, and others, among them many miners, attacked the law terribly. In the meanwhile, a few, better versed in the material, brought themselves to resist the torrent, being certain of the definite triumph of the liberal and scientific principles.[4]

W. H. Trewartha-James insisted before the Institution of Mining and Metallurgy of London that it was the best of all extant laws and urged its application to all parts of the world. To illustrate the law's security of title, he told of his negotiations with a prospector, Henry Baer. With great approval he quoted Baer's closing remark: "One thing I must remind you of: I shall be able to hand over to you the clearest and best title in the world to my 42 claims. My title has only two names on it—President Porfirio Díaz and Henry A. Baer."[5]

A mine tax law passed on June 6, 1892, ordered for the first time the registration of titles held under the provisions of previous laws and the payment of 10 pesos for each pertenencia upon registration and an annual tax of 10 pesos per pertenencia.[6] Mineowners registered 2,829 fundos covering 34,499 hectares. From 1893 to the end of 1900, 12,871 new fundo titles covering 135,478 hectares were issued by the Ministry for Development (Secretaría de Fomento). President Díaz also granted 48,693 hectares directly through contracts issued under the law of June 6, 1887, while Congress granted great zones directly to the El Boleo and El Progreso companies in Lower California, the Mulatos company in Sonora, and the Batopilas and Pinos Altos companies in Chihuahua. From 1900 to 1905, the number of mining titles in force increased from 10,234 titles covering 109,426 pertenencias to 20,111 titles covering 256,243 pertenencias. Obviously the fundos were increasing in size. Silver output increased from an annual mean of 39,800,000 million pesos in the period 1886–90 to 56,300,000 million pesos in the period 1892–96.[7] Growth should not be attributed to legal changes alone for new smelters and railroads made an increase inevitable.

On March 27, 1897, Mexico fixed the tax on gold and silver at a 3 per cent internal stamp tax and a 2 per cent coinage tax. Increased production of complex metals necessitated including a clause taxing silver sulphides, argentiferous lead, and copper in ores or concentrates. However, small amounts of silver in lead bullion or impure copper bars were exempt. It also exempted up to 250 grams of silver and 10 grams of gold per ton in ores to be exported. The law levied no production or export tax on any other metal or mineral.[8]

Changes in monetary policy paralleled changes in mine policy.[9] Traditionally, Mexico based her monetary system on the silver peso, the famous (and still lamented) *peso fuerte* with an intrinsic silver value of one peso and at par with the dollar. When the price of silver began to decline after 1880, Mexico functioned on a bimetallic basis with gold pesos quoted at a premium over silver. But since gold was little used internally, and the prestige of Díaz's government and the stability of the price level hid this weakness from the people, they did not exchange their silver for gold. Market prices for a kilogram of silver fell from 33.628 gold pesos in 1890 to 17.232 gold pesos in 1903. However, the monetary law obligated the government to maintain the value of the silver peso by buying domestically mined silver at a high fixed price. Only heavy exports of silver coins to the Far East, fluctuating prices which kept hope of a rise alive, the apathy of the lower classes, and the advantages derived by some sectors of the economy made the situation tolerable. And the resulting inflation, coupled with railroad expansion and Díaz's reign of law and order, sparked economic expansion. Export industries, of course, profited while industries dependent upon imports, such as the railroads, suffered. Inexorably the price level rose, and the cost of imports rose fastest of all. While the middle and upper classes could readjust to the inflation, particularly with the gains of economic growth, the Indian laborer and peasant received no wage boosts. They would have to wait for the "trickle down" effect of economic growth and prosperity among the upper classes.

Silver mine owners had a good thing of it. They sold their depreciated product to the mint at a high guaranteed price and then paid their workers the traditional wage and settled their taxes in silver. If they needed gold, they could obtain it for silver pesos at any bank. Since the nonferrous mining industry exported virtually all of its output, it received payment in the world market in gold, exchangeable in Mexico at a premium for the needed silver pesos. Therefore, a bad exchange rate for silver might even mean a better price *in silver pesos* for copper, lead, and gold sold abroad. Internal costs—transport, taxes, domestic supplies, power and labor—rose slowly while production costs with improved technology declined rapidly.

A conference in 1903 decided that despite the effect on the politically powerful henequen planters—who depended upon a favorable exchange rate from their profits from exported fibers to pay their large mortgages—the burden on the national treasury, the draining away of Mexican resources, and the fear of inflation necessitated a change in monetary policy. Such a change would also satisfy the financiers and científicos who did not wish to raise doubts concerning Mexico's credit among foreign bond purchasers. Perhaps it was but the appearance of weakness rather than an actual weakness which afflicted the monetary system. Certainly the fluctuating silver price frightened the Mexican financiers, and the científicos believed that the apparent weakness was enough to raise doubts in the minds of the government's creditors abroad. The result was the Monetary Law of 1905 which placed Mexico on the gold standard. Underlying this coup was a subtle, yet most significant, change in attitude destined to affect profoundly the economic history of Mexican mining; despite their vehement protests, the silver miners would have to accept a position of equality with other segments of the Mexican economy.

The new Monetary Law of March 25, 1905[10] set up a gold peso worth 49.75 cents (U.S.) and reduced silver coins to 800 fine to make them subsidiary coinage. This latter action saved silver coins from export by raising the bullion point (the level at which the metal content of the coin has greater value than its face value). Limantour handled the demonetization of silver most adroitly, selling 60,000,000 old pesos for gold without harming the silver market and netting the government an 8,100,000-peso profit on the seigniorage.

Social costs of deflation were another matter. As gold replaced silver the price level rose, and the government found it difficult to obtain enough gold for free convertibility. With the usual inflationary pressures upon prices which operate in periods of national expansion, workers found their silver pesos buying less and mineowners faced higher working costs. Limantour, realizing that some adjustment would be necessary to compensate the silver miners for the removal of their subsidy, overhauled and unified the entire tax structure. On March 25, 1905, he had the tax laws of 1892 and 1897 extensively amended.[11] His changes simplified federal taxes, repealed the old mintage tax, and reduced the stamp tax. He continued the principle of lower tax rates for metals more highly refined in Mexico before export. The law set title taxes at 5 pesos per pertenencia when registered and an annual tax of 6 pesos for the first 25 pertenencias and 3 pesos each above that number. It also set assay, melting, and refining dues at exceedingly low rates. States were given permission to tax mines up to only 1.5 per cent of the value of their output plus 25 per cent extra for the account of the federal government. Finally, importers did not have to pay duty on mining or beneficiating machinery imported before June 30, 1908. This law, which remained in effect until 1913, also established two important precedents. First, there was a tax differential between large and small holdings. Although the differential was regressive, it made a pattern for progressive taxation at a later date. Second, the tax differential between the export of ores and the export of refined metal became the basis of a policy to encourage beneficiation and refining of metals in Mexico.

Because of the tax reduction, government collections declined from 9,500,000 to 5,500,000 pesos.[12] While welcoming the lighter tax burden, miners complained that it was still too large. They disapproved particularly of the collection of the production tax upon gross output, reputedly an inheritance of the terms of the "King's Fifth."[13] One miner contended that the direct tax came to 7.5 per cent on gross output—not counting the many stamp taxes and local taxes or the taxes on dynamite, machinery, and the fundo—which could push the total burden up to 11.5 per cent.[14] Later government concessions permitted the duty-free import of fuel oil, and Limantour postponed raising freight rates to aid the silver miners.[15]

Not government interest but an improving market for silver in 1906–8, coupled with the spread of the cyanide process, saved the silver mining industry. Unfortunately, this improvement turned out to be but a temporary reprieve, for the price of silver soon fell again. Furthermore, cyaniding released larger amounts of cheap silver than ever before and flooded the market. Only low-cost producers, strong companies, or miners working exceptionally rich ore were able to survive. Ironically, the great expansion of silver production in Mexico in the twentieth century coincided with the industry's decadence. Mexico's giant silver industry was perched upon a rapidly decaying foundation as Mexico entered the full flush of modernization.

As long as the mule and the burro were the backbone of Mexican transportation, moving in mining machinery required patience and ingenuity.[16] Sectionalized machinery was standard. One traveler in the Sierra Madre Occidental observed that the machinery looked as if it were built mainly of bolts, seams and rings, with plates the size of postage stamps.[17] An engineer bringing machinery to the Lluvia del Oro mill in Chihuahua in 1906 had to build eleven miles of expensive road, construct several power boats of different designs with steel bottoms to resist the river rocks, and install a gasoline engine for hauling the boats.[18] Neither the railroad nor the ubiquitous motor truck have yet done away with the mule or burro in mountain terrain.

Railroads constituted the foundation of the modernization of Mexico. They knit the national economy together, brought goods and machinery to all parts of the republic, and made bulk exports economically feasible. Furthermore, railroads finally did away with the antiquated local fiscal systems and trade barriers.[19] Unlike in the United States, Mexican railroads were introduced into a country already centuries old and with fixed economic patterns. They did not build up as much as they rejuvenated Mexico. In only a few instances did railroads serve to promote new regions; custom was too firmly established in Mexico. Colonists did not flock into new lands, and old centers responded slowly. Heavy capitalizations and competition, by parallel lines on the profitable routes, bogged down the roads.[20] Settling the question of whether the pattern of Mexican railways was good or bad—neglecting considerable sections and overrailroading others, as Limantour charged in 1906[21]—is an impossibility since there was no economic planning. Planning was limited to estimates of profits by individuals as condoned by liberal economic theories. Foreigners financed and built the railroads of Mexico because Mexicans were unprepared for the task. (Today these men are condemned by a new generation of socially conscious and ultranationalistic Mexicans. While it is impossible to deny either the scandals accompanying the construction of the roads—which also occurred in many other countries—or the predilection of the railway companies to employ their own nationals as trainmen, it must be remembered that the railroad men were simply acting according to the accepted principles of their day with the encouragement of the legitimate government of Mexico. It is unfair to judge the railroad builders by the attitudes and values prevailing in later years.

Railroad transportation is particularly suited to mining: large loads are handled swiftly and rates for bulky items are generally low. Since railways are a diminishing-cost industry, when minerals become a mainstay of a system they are frequently carried close to cost because they are counted on to pay the fixed charges. Mineral shipments are well adapted to railroad service: they come in carload lots; delivery is often in trainload lots; claims for loss or damage are rare; and the loads are compact, carrying a good value per unit of weight. Furthermore, mining contributes more traffic than is generally supposed because of reshipments from mine to smelter to refinery to fabricating plant to seaport or to market. Finally, machinery, supplies, and camp provisions constitute a lucrative traffic for the railroad. In some ways, the low cost of carrying minerals is but a subsidy to be repaid by other freight.

Mining has often been charged with perverting the railroad system of Mexico. While the most heavily railroaded area is the south-central plateau centering on Mexico City, the immediately adjacent area, and the region toward the Gulf of Mexico, the important northern mineral states tend to be underrailroaded, particularly on the west coast.[22] Promising mineral areas in the Sierra Madre Occidental have never been served by railroads. Feeder lines generally were not built by the railroads but by the mining companies.[23] On the other hand, railroad building has always been the precursor of increased mine activity. It was the configuration of railway routes and junction points—particularly those of the Mexican Central and the Mexican National—which determined the sites of the modern smelters. In any event, Mexicans tend to look upon enterprises built to serve the "foreign-owned ephemeral mining industry" as having less social value than enterprises serving the "eternal occupation" of agriculture.

Smelters are completely dependent upon the railroads. Large central plants were not constructed until after the railway network was completed. Only then did it become feasible to smelt the so-called "minerales de exportación" in Mexico.[24] Larger smelting companies obtained substantial rate concessions on freight destined for their works. Miners claimed that reductions in freight rates did not benefit them since the smelters "adjusted" their rates accordingly. Smelter officials denied these charges and asserted that low freight rates and low treatment charges created more business for them and helped many mines to operate.[25]

Railroads aided mining from their very inception. They opened remote sectors; reduced freight charges on ore and supplies; made possible the introduction of large and heavy machinery into remote areas; tapped a hinterland from which the large smelters could draw even low-grade ore; helped solve the fuel problem by making possible the opening of a coal mining industry and the importation of American and British coal; and, finally, they cheapened both the cost of exporting mineral products and importing materials from abroad.[26] Of the 44 railroads listed in the *Mexican Year Book for 1908,* 21 were engaged mainly in hauling minerals and 3 more had extensive mineral business. Out of a total of 22,822 kilometers of track, 3,749 could be called "mineral railroad," although most railroads counted upon mineral shipments.[27]

Before the completion of the Mexican network of railroads, frequent shipments of high-grade ore to Europe were reported. Copper ores were sent to Swansea, Wales, from points as distant as Oaxaca and the west coast of Sonora. Completion of the Mexican Central and the Mexican National's northern divisions, between 1883 and 1885, gave the northern mining districts an outlet to American lead smelters in Colorado and in the tri-state district of Kansas, Missouri, and Oklahoma.[28] Cheap Mexican ores were welcomed in Kansas and Missouri, and the Kansas City Smelting and Refining Company even built another smelter for them at El Paso. In Colorado the ores were a godsend. Their high lead content offset the "dryness" (low lead content in relation to silver) of the Colorado ores. Smelters a thousand miles from the Mexican border would pay more for these ores than the lead content was worth and make up the loss by heavier treatment charges on the local "dry" ores.[29] Ore exports tapered off after the passage of the McKinley Tariff of 1890, but new developments counteracted the effect of the tariff. Smelters were constructed in Mexico, and coal was mined in sufficient quantity to power the railroads and to fuel the smelters.

Coal mining in Mexico is of rather recent origin. An expedition in 1880 uncovered little of importance.[30] Although deposits of varying geologic ages have been found in scattered sections,[31] only the northeastern Coahuila fields, first described in detail by Jacobo Küchler in 1866,[32] have been commercially developed. Knowledge of the Coahuila coalfields spread slowly; Santiago Ramirez, the leading Mexican mining geologist of his day, referred to them in 1884 on the basis of secondhand information.[33]

The Coahuila coalfields, six in number, stretch in a line south from Eagle Pass, Texas. Northernmost is the Fuente basin, part of the southern Texas coal fields. It can produce a fine grade of gas coal but is abandoned today. The Sabinas basin, 117 kilometers south of Piedras Negras, measures 54 by 24 kilometers in area and is broken into several subdivisions. It contains the best coking and steam coal in Mexico. In the center lies the Hacienda Soledad, abandoned after an explosion. A long outcrop lying along the northern rim of the basin is subdivided into three fields: Rosita, Cloete, and Agujita. Southwest of Sabinas lies the Palau district which was worked by the Coahuila Coal Company and more recently by a miners' cooperative. A small ridge of mountains divides the southern part of the Sabinas Valley from the Esperanzas basin, which is about 35 by 5 kilometers in area containing some 8,000 hectares of the richest coal land in Mexico. The three basins south of Esperanzas are of little commercial importance. A subsidiary of the Monterrey Steel Company exploited the twin Saltillito y Lampacitos basins on a small scale. In 1908 the company turned its attention to the Sabinas basin, and with its subsidiary Compañía Carbonífera de Monterrey, worked the El Menor mine in the southern edge of the valley. South of the Saltillito basin are the San Blas and San Patricio basins. Neither of the latter has been extensively explored.[34]

Luis Reyes Soto estimated that the three major coal basins of Coahuila (Esperanzas, Sabinas, and Saltillito) contained 2,625,000,000 metric tons in calculated reserves and 613,000,000 metric tons in exploitable reserves. His estimates for the individual basins were: Esperanzas, calculated, 175,000,000 metric tons, exploitable, 52,000,000 metric tons; Sabinas, calculated, 2,000,000,000 metric tons, exploitable, 281,000,000 tons; Saltillito, calculated, 450,000,000 metric tons, exploitable, 280,000,000 metric tons.[35]

Early coal production reports are vague.[36] Perhaps 80 tons a day were mined in 1884 by companies controlled by Collis P. Huntington. Huntington had built the Mexican International Railroad, paralleling the Mexican National south into Monterrey, to secure coal for his Southern Pacific Railroad. The International, passing directly through the major coal basins, opened the first mines and operated them through a number of subsidiaries. In 1884 the Sabinas Coal Mines Company opened the Sabinas River outcrop. It was succeeded by the larger Coahuila Coal Company in 1886. Huntington also controlled the Alamos Coal Company and the Fuente Coal Company organized in 1888 and 1894 respectively. The output of these mines totalled 256,000 tons of coal in 1904, and the company operated 120 beehive coke ovens. Plans to use Mexican coal on the Southern Pacific did not bear fruit; the line continued to be operated on Texas-mined coal.

Coahuila's first large coal mining company was the Mexican Coal and Coke Company, organized by James T. Gardiner in 1899, which owned newly discovered veins in the Esperanzas basin. Edwin Ludlow, who was hired to open the property, later wrote:

> The writer arrived on the property on the night of November 5, 1899, and the view that met him next morning was not entirely encouraging. He saw a cactus and mesquite desert with no trees, no houses (except a few "jackals" [sic]), and no water; but he was told that a small spring, two miles away, would furnish enough for drinking. The work already done consisted of prospect-holes about half a mile apart along the outcrop; and, as few of these had gone through the surface coal, the outlook, from a mining point of view, was not flattering. The instructions from the New York office were to open mines and obtain a production of 5,000 tons per day as soon as possible. That is what we all have been trying to do ever since.[37]

Ludlow produced over 500,000 tons of coal and 52,000 tons of coke from 226 beehive coke ovens by 1904, and built a 15-mile railroad, the Ferrocarril Carbonífera de Coahuila, to run through the Esperanzas basin into the Palau district. By a contract, the International Railroad's subsidiary Coahuila Coal leased its Fuente, Soledad, and Palau holdings to Mexican Coal in return for a lease on Mexican Coal's railroad. (The railroad was later incorporated into the Mexican National Railway system along with the International.) Between 1902 and 1904, the Esperanzas mines employed 2,000 men and the district had a population of 10,000. All told, the Mexican Coal Company held 30,000 hectares of coal lands and produced 40,000 tons of coal and 6,500 tons of coke a month.[38]

Following the Mexican Coal company's success, a number of other enterprises started working the northern rim of the Sabinas Valley outcrop. Largest of all was the Compañía Carbonífera "Agujita," S.A., organized with Mexican capital, which produced 45,000 tons per month and had 469 coke ovens in 1910. To exploit adjacent mines, William B. Cloete organized the New Sabinas Company, Ltd., in 1905. One mine and 60 coke ovens were in operation at Cloete's death, and the company passed to the Mazapil Copper Company to fuel its two smelters. Ernesto Madero held a large claim next to the Cloete holdings, to supply coal for the Torreón smelter which the Maderos had opened in 1902. His Compañía Carbonífera de Sabinas held a plot 11 by 4.5 miles and set its capitalization at 5,500,000 pesos in 1907. Stock had been floated in London, and the Board of Directors included a number of distinguished English mining investors. The company installed 60 Belgian by-product coke ovens; the outbreak of the Revolution of 1910 prevented the installation of 60 more. Guggenheim interests bought the mines in 1919 to fuel their chain of smelters. The Maderos also controlled two other companies. Ernesto Madero also organized the Compañía Carbonífera Lampazos, capitalized at 1,300,000 pesos, to work mines in the Monclova district of Coahuila; his nephew, Francisco I. Madero, headed the National Coal Company, with a 1,000,000-peso capitalization, to work the San Blas basin. Neither enterprise amounted to much.

Mexican coal production probably never did quite reach 2,000,000 tons per year. Coal imports ran about 1,000,000 tons per year and coke about one-third as much. Many weaknesses plagued the coal industry. Production costs were high. The mines required expensive imported timbering. There was too much water in the mines and not enough potable water. Slate in the coal made the ash content high, and cleaning it out was expensive. Coal companies retained antiquated machinery and charged high prices which drove consumers to oil or imported fuel. Finally, getting good coal miners was always a headache.

Railways in the north and the metallurgical plants were the best customers for coal. Consumers in the central areas imported coal via Tampico or Vera Cruz, since transportation charges from Coahuila raised the price over 200 per cent. Hydroelectricity and oil cut deeply into coal markets. Smelters frequently found it more convenient to import coke. After the merger and nationalization of the Mexican National Railways, Limantour discriminated against imported coal by adding a flat $1-per-ton charge. Before the Revolution, Mexico consumed annually somewhat less than 4,000,000 tons of coal and half as much coke.

After 1880 a number of large smelters doing custom and private work opened in Meixco. They were built because first the newly imposed United States duty on imported lead ores made the opening of silver-lead smelters in Mexico appear feasible, and second, because American smelting companies saw additional opportunities south of the border. E. E. Olcott, President of the American Institute of Mining Engineers, even thought that the Mexicans should be grateful for the new smelting industry built by American capital and American protectionism.[39]

Although the Tariff of 1873 levied a duty on lead ores, the so-called "Windom customs decision," based on a technicality in the wording of the act, virtually exempted Mexican silver-lead ores. Colorado lead miners complained bitterly of Mexican "pauper labor" and protested that Missouri Valley smelters working Mexican ore undersold them. Nearer at home, the Colorado miners of straight lead ores believed that lead-rich Mexican ore would undercut their monopoly on the ore needed to balance the furnace charges. Pressuring Congress, the lead miners had the McKinley Tariff of 1890 set a rate of 1.5 cents per pound on the lead content of imported ores. (See Appendix II(A).) Still the Colorado lead miners were not happy since some Mexican ore came in over the tariff wall, and with higher prices Missouri lead ores could compete in Colorado smelters. Ultimately, it was the Colorado producers of siliceous silver-lead ores who had to pay the smelter higher rates for processing their "dry" ore.[40]

New railways in northern Mexico opened possibilities for expanding the exploitation of silver, lead, and copper mines. Stimulated by good transportation, cheap labor, cheap ore, and an amenable government, at least five custom smelters were built in Mexico by 1895. In addition, smaller plants were built at La Constancia in Sierra Mojada; Velardeña, Durango; Las Trojes, Michoacan; and Terrazas, Chihuahua.[41]

Three smelters were authorized at Monterrey as early as 1890. Samuel Lederer, with American and English backing, built the first one. Granted a concession as partner with Joaquin Maíz, who owned the nearby San Pedro mine, Lederer opened the Fundicíon Número Uno for the Nuevo León Smelting, Refining & Manufacturing Company (Compañía Minera, Fundidora y Industrial, Nuevo León) in 1888–89 with six furnaces treating 240 tons of ore a day. Poorly designed and incompetently constructed, the smelter was also inefficiently managed. A bullion-parting plant was erected after 1890 to separate the lead from the precious metals and then cast lead pipe for export to Europe. Failing in March, 1892, the plant was dismantled.[42] Vicente Ferrara, who had once built a small smelter at Sierra Mojada, erected Fundicíon Número Dos in 1890 for the Compañía Minera, Fundidora y Afinadora de Monterrey. His six-furnace plant opened on May 18, 1891, with four water-jacketed blast furnaces. Doubled in size by 1899, it had a rated capacity of 500 metric tons of ore a day yielding 60 tons of lead bullion. The American Smelting and Refining Company (ASARCO) later leased the plant, and in 1920 it was sold to Minerales y Metales, an American Metal Company subsidiary. Ferrara later built the plant of the Monterrey steel works.[43]

Smelters numbers one and two were soon overshadowed by the Guggenheims' Gran Fundición Nacional Mexicana. Edgar Newhouse, who had learned the Mexican mining business under Robert S. Towne, introduced Daniel Guggenheim to Mexico in 1890. On October 9, 1890, Díaz granted the Guggenheims a concession for the construction of three smelting plants, two of at least 300 tons daily capacity and one of 100 tons. They chose Monterrey because its railway connections linked Sierra Mojada and Monclova ore, Sabinas coal, and coke imported via Tampico. Governor Bernardo Reyes granted a concession in 1891 which included municipal and state tax exemptions in return for a 300,000-peso investment. Building the smelter was troublesome, but after the first year, profits totalled $60,000 per month. All capital expenses were realized within one year.

The Guggenheims opened the Gran Fundición in February, 1892, with six small, water-jacketed shaft furnaces (or cupolas) and two long-hearth roasting furnaces. They soon expanded this well-designed and soundly constructed plant. By 1897 it comprised 10 cupolas of larger dimensions and six long-hearth roasting or calcining furnaces, as well as the most modern buildings and equipment. From 1892 to 1896 the plant smelted 10,000 tons of ore a month. By 1900 it processed 35,000 tons, and by 1904 it was ASARCO's second largest works.[44]

The Guggenheims built a second plant in 1895 at Aguascalientes to treat both lead and copper ores. Guggenheim capital then entered mining by purchasing the nearby Tepezala and Asientos mines. They provided enough copper ore for Aguascalientes' four converters to treat 50 tons of copper matte a day. By 1900 the plant had four lead furnaces of 125 tons daily capacity each, four copper furnaces with a total capacity of 680 tons, and three copper converters. It was the largest custom smelter in North America by 1908, with a capacity of 1,500 tons of ore daily in its eight copper and two lead furnaces and four copper converters.[45] Later the Guggenheims operated two more smelters in Mexico, at Avalos, Chihuahua, and Velardeña, Durango.

Aguascalientes was of great importance in Guggenheim family history, for this smelter was the lever which enabled them to enter and gain control of the American Smelting and Refining Company. When ASARCO —called "the Smelters Trust"—was formed by H. H. Rogers in 1899, it included all the major American silver-lead smelters except the Guggenheims'. Meyer Guggenheim, the family patriarch, would not allow his sons to enter the trust unless they were assured of control. Since the Guggenheims owned only one smelter in Colorado and two in Mexico, the trust would not hear of it. When excessive stock watering brought ASARCO into financial difficulties, the Guggenheims cornered much of the independent ore in Colorado while their Mexican operations threatened to swamp the trust's purported monopoly. Guggenheim smelters turned out 40 per cent of all the lead and 20 per cent of all the silver produced in Mexico! After integrating their Aguascalientes copper production by constructing a refinery at Perth Amboy, Guggenheim copper sales abroad threatened the Lewisohn-controlled United Metals Selling

Company. Under heavy pressure from its financial backers to reach an agreement with the maverick Guggenheims, ASARCO arranged a settlement whereby the Guggenheims obtained control by purchasing $45,-200,000 in ASARCO common and preferred stock, agreeing to sell their copper through "orthodox channels" and to merge their smelters and refinery. But the mines, railroads, steamship line from Perth Amboy to Tampico, and the Guggenheim Exploration Company remained in the family's hands. Since 1901 the story of ASARCO has been mainly the story of the Guggenheims, and stockholders have often alleged that ASARCO was used as a catspaw or receiver for many of the family's extraneous ventures. On the other hand, the aggressiveness and financial acumen of the Guggenheims were the paramount reasons for the pre-eminent status of ASARCO.[46]

With the fusion of ASARCO and the Guggenheim interests, a change in the pattern of the Mexican smelting industry took place. Consolidated Kansas City's plant at El Paso (already merged into ASARCO) and its small plant at El Carmen, Texas, integrated economically with the Guggenheims' two smelters, while its mines in Sierra Mojada and Santa Eulalia (also part of ASARCO) found alternate outlets in the Guggenheims' Mexican smelters. Guggenheim smelters now obtained Sierra Mojada's lead-fluxing ores without depending upon independent miners. Expenses decreased as overhead costs were cut, and closer coordination between mines and smelters brought greater economies.[47]

Other entrepreneurs followed the Guggenheims' lead. Robert S. Towne chartered the Compañía Metalúrgica Mexicana in New Jersey in 1890. He obtained a concession to open five smelters in Mexico but actually built only one plant at San Luis Potosí in 1892. It became an immediate success working ores from Sierra Mojada, Aguascalientes, and San Luis Potosí. The plant processed Towne-owned ores and did custom work for independents.[48] To treat ores from their Ojuela mine, the Peñoles company at Mapimí, Durango, opened a smelter consisting of six water-jacketed furnaces with a daily capacity of 150 tons each.[49]

Ernesto Madero organized the Compañía Metalúrgica de Torreón, the only large Mexican-owned plant, and opened its smelter in 1901. After doubling its starting capacity, the plant comprised two copper and eight lead furnaces and could treat 200,000 tons of ores and fluxes a year. The Mazapil Copper Company built two smelter plants, one at Concepción del Oro, Zacatecas, for copper ores and another at Saltillo, Coahuila, for lead, each with a daily capacity of about 500 tons. They were connected by Mazapil Copper's Coahuila and Zacatecas Railroad. At Matehuala, San Luis Potosí, a small custom smelter processed lead and copper ores from local mines. ASARCO absorbed Matehuala in 1909. Only three other smelters of any size existed in Mexico. They were controlled by the large copper companies and worked almost exclusively on company ore: El Boleo in Lower California; the Cananea smelter in northern Sonora; and its short-lived neighbor, the Nacozari smelter.[50]

Smelters rejuvenated and reorientated the Mexican mineral industry. In their hunt for siliceous ores to balance the rich straight silver ores of the south in their furnace charges, the smelters brought about a tremendous expansion of the lead-silver camps of southwestern Chihuahua. James W. Malcolmson estimated that while 90 per cent of the gold and silver produced before 1885 had been treated locally, by 1905 over 75 per cent was shipped over railways to smelters. Treatment losses declined from 20 to 5 per cent. Custom smelters gave mineowners a financial boost, for despite ore prices—lower than those paid in the United States—the final returns were much higher than those received from the old processes which lost all of the lead and most of the gold.[51] Even the silver camp of Guanajuato gained. Formerly ores assaying over 300 ounces of silver a ton were shipped to Europe. In 1887, shipments were started by rail to a smelter at Omaha, Nebraska. Treatment costs dropped from $50 a ton to between $38 and $40 a ton. With the opening of the smelter at Monterrey, they fell to between 25 and 30 pesos a ton.[52]

Between 1880 and 1900 the lead-refining industry in the United States underwent a reorientation. Mexican lead smelters at Monterrey, Aguascalientes, San Luis Potosí, and Mapimí could send lead bullion economically by rail to Tampico and by steamer to New York for refining, under bond, at Newark and Perth Amboy. The ships returned to Mexico with coal and coke. Since this method of transport was cheaper than by railroad from the Middle and Far West, the older eastern refineries were able to compete with their new Rocky Mountain and Pacific Coast rivals for the export trade.[53]

By official count there were 53 smelters in Mexico in 1905. With few exceptions most of them did private work exclusively. ASARCO controlled half the custom-smelter capacity, much to the dismay of many small mine owners. San Luis Potosí and Mazapil did custom work, but largely processed their own ores. Dr. Peñafiel, the Mexican Director of Statistics, deprecated ASARCO's position by citing the total number of plants in the country—without noting their capacities. Then lumping private and custom plants together, he arrived at a figure of 14,500 tons daily capacity for the "Independents" and 4,000 tons for ASARCO, representing "the Trust." Dr. Peñafiel neglected to indicate that most of the Independents worked only their own ores, which did little to help the small miner. Consequently, many of these Independents—for example El Boleo and Cananea—were in out-of-the-way places close to their owners' mines and hence were in no position to receive economically custom ore. Also, many of them sold their bullion to ASARCO for refining and marketing. Finally, ASARCO was in a pool with the San Luis Potosí and Torreón smelters to fix rates, quotas, and territories.[54]

In 1913 the *Engineering and Mining Journal* surveyed the silver-lead and copper-smelting works of North America. Of 124 silver-lead blast furnaces, 3 were in Canada, 76 in the United States, and 45 in Mexico. Of the last, 20 were in ASARCO plants: 10 at Monterrey with an annual capacity of 475,000 tons of charge; 2 at Aguascalientes with 100,000 tons; 5 at Chihuahua with 274,000 tons; and 3 at Velardeña with 140,000 tons. The Compañía Metalúrgica Mexicana at San Luis Potosí had 11 furnaces with 385,000 tons annual capacity; the Compañía Metalúrgica Torreón at Torreón had 8 with 360,000 tons; and the Compañía Minera de Peñoles at Mapimí had 6 with 325,000 tons. All told, Mexico's total of 2,059,000 tons of annual charge capacity was slightly over 40 per cent of the United States annual total. In copper smelting, ASARCO's annual capacity totalled 1,282,000 tons of charge. It owned 8 furnaces at Aguascalientes with an annual charge capacity of 730,000 tons; 3 at Matehuala with 325,000 tons; and 3 at Velardeña with 227,000 tons. In addition, Aguascalientes had 4 copper converters. Mexico's other copper plants were: the Compagnie du Boleo at Santa Rosalia, Lower California, with 8 furnaces having 650,000 tons annual charge capacity; Cananea Consolidated Copper Company at Cananea, Sonora, with 868,000 tons, 2 reverberatories with 153,000 tons, and 5 converters with 35,000 tons; Mazapil Copper at Saltillo, 4 furnaces with 350,000 tons, 1 reverberatory with 52,000 tons, and 4 converters; Teziutlán Copper Mining and Smelting Company at Teziutlán, Puebla, 2 furnaces with 250,000 tons and 3 converters; and the Compañía Metalúrgica de Torreón, 2 furnaces with 175,000 tons and 2 converters.[55]

Not everyone regarded smelters as an unmitigated blessing. Mexican miners thought the smelter rates were high. Let it be noted, however, that the smelters paid for ore on delivery, not within thirty days as was customary with the patio process. They also advanced money to miners and paid well for the gold content. But as the patios closed and the smelters were established, the mineowners found themselves in a squeeze. V. M. Braschi lamented:

> But the smelter . . . formed the natural monopoly under such circumstances, accumulating large reserves of cash, paying large dividends and buying and leasing and controlling large mining properties. The smelter began by helping the Mexican mining industry, but it was ending by throttling its very life. . . . The Mexican mining industry was giving evident signs of becoming soon simply a series of large mines controlled by the smelting interests and a few independent large companies.[56]

Braschi, however, did see a glimmer of hope in two innovations after 1900. Electric power came into general use, and the cyanide process made silver and gold camps independent of the smelters. Costs fell sufficiently to allow the reworking of millions of tons of dumps and old mine fills. Electric motors made possible the transmission and utilization of power into every nook of a mine—for lighting, pumping, hoisting, tramming, and running air compressors and mill machinery.

Electricity for illumination was first used in mines in the 1880's. Electric pumps quickly displaced the nineteenth-century Cornish pumps, which were always a bother and usually denuded the district of wood for fuel.[57] Electric power was installed in a mine at Batopilas some time before 1889, where two hydroelectric turbines and two steam generators produced 30 horsepower.[58] Sam Traylor installed an electric system at the Bustamente mine near Villaldama, Nuevo León, in 1887, and later Sam Lederer hired him to install the power plant for his Monterrey smelter. The Santa Ana mine, in the Catorce district of San Luis Potosí, was electrified in 1892. Following the flooding of the Carmelia mine in 1897, Real del Monte made its first electric installation. Generating power from the Barranca de Regla waterfall, the Compañía de Potencia Eléctrica de Hidalgo sold it to the major mines and *haciendas de beneficio* in the district. Large scale installations came after 1900; by 1910 almost all of the important mines were electrified.[59] At El Oro, Mexico State, milling costs fell from .296 pesos to .110 pesos a ton when electricity replaced steam.[60] Pneumatic drills and power machinery displaced the gambusino who worked on his own and permitted the large scale exploitation of low-grade deposits. Peons no longer had to carry 200-pound loads up ladders in suffocating temperatures; hoists did the lifting and ventilating fans could make mines more livable.[61]

In Guanajuato, the Guanajuato Power and Electric Company and the Michoacan Power Company—two allied American-owned companies which included General Electric interests—started operations in 1902 and developed a 2,250-horsepower plant the next year.[62] From the Duero River, Guanajuato Power sent power 101 miles to Guanajuato City and included Irapuato and León in its system. Through Michoacan Power, they also obtained two concessions on the Angulo River. At the Brunel Concession, a 4,000-horsepower plant with a 90-mile line to Guanajuato was built. At the Noriega Concession, a 10,000-horsepower plant was completed in 1911 to supply power to ASARCO's Asientos and Tepezala mines.[63] The Chapala Hydro-Electric and Irrigation Company of Guadalajara and the Guanajuato company agreed in 1910 to split the west-central Mexican territory. Guanajuato supplied San Luis Potosí and the adjoining mining camps; Chapala transmitted power to Aguascalientes and Zacatecas.[64] Central Jalisco's mining camps were reached in 1910–11 by the Chapala company. The Guanajuato company with the Central Mexican Light and Power Company increased its capitalization to $5,000,000 and bought out most of the small companies of west-central Mexico, adding San Luis Potosí, Siloa, Celaya, and Salamanca with their surrounding mining camps to its list. Between them, the Chapala and

Guanajuato companies controlled all the power installations in south-west Mexico from Jalisco to Sinaloa.[65]

Guanajuato is an excellent example of the revolutionary effect of electric power and cyaniding upon Mexican mining, for they were introduced almost simultaneously. Annual silver output had fallen from 7,000,000 to 3,750,000 pesos between 1898 and 1904. Production began to rise with the introduction of electricity in 1904, reaching a total of 4,500,000 pesos in 1906. With the cyanide process, silver output reached 8,250,000 pesos in 1908 and a peak of 9,900,000 in 1911. Although a decline set in thereafter, 1914 saw 8,000,000 pesos turned out; not until the anarchy of the Revolution did silver production sink to 2,000,000 pesos.[66]

A Canadian-British corporation, the Mexican Power and Light Company, bought out the growing Mexican Electric Works (organized in 1897 with £400,000 in paid-up capital) and the Mexican Gas and Electric Light Company, and built a large dam on the Necaxa River in Puebla. It supplied power to the cities of Mexico City, Puebla, and Orizaba as well as to the mining centers of El Oro, Tlalpujahua, Pachuca, and Real del Monte. After expanding its installations in Mexico City and El Oro in 1905, Mexican Power extended its lines to mines in the state of Hidalgo. For the El Oro undertaking the company had to issue 2,400,000 pesos in stock.[67]

Paul Ginther, a mine operator, obtained a concession in 1905 to build a dam on the Río Conchos and sell power to the mining camps of southern Chihuahua and the city of Torreón. Ginther sold his rights to S. Pearson & Son who formed the Northern Mexican Power Company in 1909 in Montreal, Canada, with a $1,500,000 capitalization. The development, finished in 1915, created a 175-square-kilometer lake. The Boquilla Dam contained the generating equipment; its 36,000 horsepower was first utilized in 1921 when mining resumed after the Revolution of 1910. Mining enterprises at Parral, Santa Barbara, Santa Eulalia, San Francisco del Oro, Naica, and the Chihuahua smelter were the major power consumers.[68]

Several small electric companies operated to supply local needs, and many mining companies opened their own plants. For example, at Nacozari, Sonora, the Phelps Dodge subsidiary, the Moctezuma Copper Company, built a 4,000-horsepower steam plant to supply the mine, mill, and company town.[69] In northwestern Sonora, the Tigre Mining Company built a 65-mile transmission line in 1911 to "import" power from its plant built in Douglas, Arizona, where it claimed fuel was cheaper.[70]

Electric companies and mines developed a mutual dependence. Power failures, particularly to the distant camps, were not infrequent and these mines maintained stand-by power plants to work their pumps. In the 1920's, due to high rates and undependable service, private electrical generators of 220,000 horsepower came into use, 90,000 horsepower of which belonged to mining companies. In turn, the power companies could not afford to depend upon the mines alone. While they favored opening power plants near mining centers because of the assured demand —mines consumed about one-third of all the power generated—any decline in metal prices would leave the electric companies with unsalable power.[71] To combat this uncertainty mining companies were required either to guarantee a fixed minimum consumption or to finance the construction of the transmission lines, the mineowner to be reimbursed by deductions on his electric bill.[72]

Electricity made possible great savings. Ernesto Galarza noted that Dos Estrellas reduced its power costs per horsepower from 388 to 102 pesos, El Oro from 400 to 100 pesos, and some mines in Guanajuato from 400 to 60 pesos. Hoisting costs fell, in some areas from 8 to 1 centavo per ton; pumping costs dropped from 282 pesos per week to 82 pesos; drilling costs went down from 58 to 19 centavos per ton. Dos Estrellas found electric bulbs saved 50 per cent over the cost of candles. Such savings were possible despite the high rates charged by the power companies.[73]

Originally invented to treat gold ores, the cyanide process revolutionized Mexico's silver-mining industry. Wherever power was available to run fine grinding mills, cyanidation made the extraction of gold and silver from amenable ores amazingly cheap. Ore containing as little as 8 ounces (250 grams) of silver to the ton could be treated profitably. Cyaniding and smelters finally doomed the patio process. Many great haciendas de beneficio closed their doors between 1905 and 1910; later some of them reopened as cyanide mills. Ironically, the last mill to adopt cyanidation in Pachuca was the Purissima Grande where Bartolomé Medina had invented the patio process.

The cyanide process is based upon the solubility of gold and silver in solutions of potassium and sodium cyanide. First, fine grinding of the ore crushes both the precious metals and the worthless gangue to a powder. Then, this powder is "slimed" with water and cyanide is added. Next, the mixture is agitated until the cyanide forms a compound with the gold and silver particles. Adding fine zinc dust causes the cyanide compound to break down; the precious metals precipitate out of solution and are melted into bars. In the gold camps of El Oro and Tlalpujahua, the silver mines of Pachuca, Real del Monte, Guanajuato, and the west coast region, cyaniding displaced all other methods. Since it did not work well on complex ores, the lead-silver camps continued to ship ore to the smelters.

In a cyanide plant all ore containing over 100 grams of silver was milled. Mining costs fell because ore could be mass-mined and did not have to be meticulously hand-sorted. Silver losses were small, all the gold was recovered, and cyanidation cost only four pesos a metric ton.

With a mill on the mine property, there was no freight charge.[74] While not wholly successful in emancipating the smaller miner from the "clutches" of the smelters, cyanidation introduced an element of independence for those who could afford a plant.

Cyaniding did not come into general use until some ten years after its introduction into Mexico, despite its advantages and the greatest mining boom Mexico had ever experienced. Fixing the exact date for the first cyanidation of silver ores is difficult. Burton Hunt and H. W. Trewartha-James, equipped with a portable assay outfit and testing plant, toured the republic in 1891 and discovered that oxidized silver ores could be treated with a strong solution of cyanide and that sulphide ores could be made amenable by the use of an oxidizing agent.[75] However, the Mexican Gold and Silver Recovery Company, which held the Mexican patent rights, directed its attention toward the Mexican gold fields.

Exactly how many cyanide plants were built before 1900 is not known. E. A. H. Tays constructed a plant to treat 1,500 tons of ore per month at San José de García, Sinaloa, for the Anglo-Mexican Co., Ltd., during the period 1895–97.[76] James B. Haggin introduced gold cyaniding to the El Oro district in 1894, erecting his first mill as an annex to a lixiviation plant in a converted mule stable. It was a success, and the El Oro mine paid $1,000,000 in dividends by 1898.[77] The El Oro district was one of the most productive gold fields in the world by 1905, and the El Oro plant remained the outstanding cyanide plant in Mexico until the opening of the large silver workings at Guanajuato.[78] Cyanide processing at El Oro had a pronounced effect upon Mexican mining, particularly when E. M. Hamilton discovered that regrinding ores to crush them yet finer made for better extractions.[79] Hamilton worked for Charles Butters whose group previously had designed "the first [mill] in Mexico to treat slime by agitation and cyanidation," at Las Prietas, Sonora. At the same time, a 200-ton cyanide mill was opened by the Creston-Colorado Mining Company at Minas Prietas, Sonora and a 100-ton mill by the Pan-American Mining Company, also in Sonora.[80]

Between 1900 and 1903 the cyaniding of silver ores slowly spread. F. J. Hobson estimated that about 500 tons of silver ore alone were handled daily by the cyanide plants during this period. Early methods did not yield good results and were replaced by Hamilton's superior sliming methods.[81] But many operators believed that the original cyanide mills were so much better than the older methods—particularly straight pan amalgamation and lixiviation—that wisdom dictated leaving well enough alone. However, there was one triumph when the Palmarejo & Mexican Goldfields Company erected a large-scale plant in 1902 that was not an annex to a lixiviation plant—the first such in Mexico.[82]

In 1902–3, the tenacious prejudice against cyaniding silver ores finally broke down. Guanajuato ores tested by the Mexican Gold and Silver Recovery Company in 1899 had proven refractory, and as late as 1903 the company's manager declared Mexican silver ores, on the whole, unsuitable for cyaniding.[83] However, E. M. Hamilton had achieved satisfactory results the year before while working for the Charles Butters Company, and the Guanajuato Consolidated Mining and Milling Company decided, in 1904, to build a 200-ton mill on Hamilton's recommendations. It was a success, but the company had retained the old pan-amalgamation mill until the cyanide mill was fully proven.[84]

In the same year, F. J. Hobson obtained favorable results working Guanajuato's Valenciana ores, and a mill was installed the following year. A cyanide plant was erected at the El Cubo mine in 1904; the next year George W. Bryant built another plant for the Peregrina Mining and Milling Company. By 1907 the Peregrina mill was cyaniding over 200 tons a day and had a capacity for 350 tons. Of the 34 patios in Guanajuato in 1887, only 2 were working by 1907; 205 tons of ore a day were being treated by cyanide and only 25 to 30 tons by the patio process.[85]

Cyanidation was not introduced to Pachuca and Real del Monte until later, probably because of the delayed entrance of foreign companies. Up to 1907 the area's methods could be discounted as antiquated.[86] During that year the San Francisco hacienda, which had been closed for six years, reopened as a cyanide plant to treat ores from the La Luz mine. The La Unión patio also began renovations. At the end of 1907, the United States Smelting, Refining and Mining Company rebuilt the Loreto hacienda, on their recently acquired Real del Monte property, as a cyanide plant. This 300-ton mill was followed shortly afterwards by their new 350-ton Guerrero mill, which cost 818,000 pesos and was considered the most up-to-date cyanide plant in Mexico.[87] Three other cyanide mills opened the next year: the San Rafael and the Maravillas with 400 tons capacity each, and the La Blanca with 500 tons capacity. In rebuilding the San Francisco mill in 1910, the Maravillas Mining Company introduced the so-called Brown, or Pachuca, tanks for the agitation of the slime with cyanide, a design copied in plants the world over.[88] The British-controlled Santa Gertrudis Company erected the largest mill which, starting with 600 tons, was soon raised to a capacity of 1,100 tons per day.[89] As in Guanajuato, the patios closed as ore treatment charges fell.

On the basis of cyanide consumption, the Mexican Gold and Silver Recovery Company computed in 1908 that 300,000 tons of ore a month were being cyanided: 53,000 tons at Guanajuato; 71,000 at El Oro; 38,500 at Pachuca; 25,300 in Chihuahua; 15,000 in Durango; 14,000 in Zacatecas; and 20,500 in Sonora, with the rest scattered.[90]

Zinc was a new metal when its exploitation in Mexico started at the beginning of the twentieth century. Demand was small and could be satisfied from the production of straight zinc ores which are not too common since most zinc occurs in lead or copper-bearing ores. Zinc in complex ores cannot be extracted by lead or copper smelters without prior treatment. In fact, its presence leads to furnace difficulties.[91] Hence some companies in Santa Barbara, Chihuahua, in 1904, tried a system of magnetic separation to clean the zinc out of their complex ores.[92] But a cheap and effective process was not perfected until after 1920, with the advent of selective flotation. Mexico did possess a number of straight-zinc ore mines whose product was well adapted to zinc smelting—a rather complex process requiring a great deal of skilled labor and cheap fuel.

Mexican zinc production grew rapidly, although only the Calera mine, west of Miñaca, Chihuahua, could be called a real mine. The rest were "holes in the mountain sides," planlessly exploited, with peons carrying the ore to mules, which in turn carried it to the nearest railway station.[93] In 1909 the United States consuls at Saltillo and Monterrey, stressing the planlessness and remoteness of the mines and their marginal economic position, correctly predicted that the cost of fuel would weigh heavily against the creation of a Mexican zinc-smelting industry.[94]

Small amounts of zinc ore were first mined in Mexico in the 1890's. In response to exceptionally high prices in 1904, the first zinc ore was exported to the United States. Its high quality and low price made it a favorite with the Kansas smelters. Missouri zinc miners attempted to stop its import by having the Treasury Department reinterpret the Tariff Act of 1897, but their effort failed when challenged in the courts.[95] Meanwhile, American imports climbed from 2,264 tons of ore in 1904 to 102,005 tons in 1907 despite freight costs interdicting shipments of ore of less than 30 per cent zinc. Reviewing the proposed tariff duty in January, 1909, the *Mexican Mining Journal* cited a study of the Joplin, Missouri, zinc producers' association which showed that Mexican ore could be laid down at Kansas smelters at over $20 per ton cheaper than Missouri ore. Cheap labor and the lack of royalty and amortization charges more than offset the high freight rates.[96]

Zinc imports from Mexico declined after the Panic of 1907 only to rise again in 1909 when smelters stocked Mexican ore before a tariff duty was placed on it. Finally, the Tariff of 1909 set a duty of one cent a pound on the zinc content of all ores assaying over 25 per cent zinc and provided a sliding scale for other contents. Importers of copper and lead ores had to pay for the minute amounts of zinc in their ores even though it was lost in processing.[97]

To offset the effect of the American zinc tariff, the Díaz government changed the railroad rates in December, 1909, to make it more profitable to ship zinc ore to Tampico for export to Europe than to American border points. This move killed whatever market might have been left for Mexican ore in the United States.[98] Zinc discoveries at Butte, Montana, and the poor condition of the best Mexican zinc mines adversely affected Mexican zinc mining.[99] Despite the government granting a number of concessions, zinc-smelting plants did not materialize.[100] The new freight rates did help, for contracts were made to ship ores from many sections of northern Mexico. Belgian and German orebuyers took ores and concentrates from the Mazapil Copper Company and the San Francisco del Oro Company in Chihuahua. Belgian investors organized the International Ore Company, with a capital of 4,000,000 Belgian francs, to erect a calcining plant at Saltillo for shipping the concentrates to Belgium. Zinc mining had started to show signs of recovery when the Revolution paralyzed the entire mining industry in the north. Zinc was not sent out of Mexico in large quantities again until 1916–17, when the revolutionary fighting subsided and the high prices induced by World War I made shipments again profitable.[101]

CHAPTER 5

Foreign Capital, 1890–1912

MEXICO'S mining industry entered its era of greatest expansion after 1900, for up to then its growth had been relative rather than absolute. During the decade 1900–1910 metal production almost doubled despite a metal market panic lasting from 1906 to 1908.

Mexico became El Dorado, and the words "Mexican mines" launched many a success and many a swindle. Most intriguing to a new investor was a genuine "antigua," an ancient abandoned bonanza. Most districts had someone holding a property whose spiel to probable purchasers started with the words: "The Indians say . . . ," followed by a long recital explaining why the ancient mine was abandoned—the reasons usually including murder, revolution, Indian raids, and a general lack of capital—to which was appended a list of figures attesting to the mine's productivity in colonial times. A British mining engineer, commenting on mine investment psychology, wrote that if a hole one hundred years old is worth one, a hole two hundred years old will be worth four. Hence, from a sales point the best mines were "Aztec workings."[1] At best, profitable exploitation of an antigua was problematical. Large sums of money could be spent on the hazardous dewatering and timbering of a flooded mine only to reveal that the Spaniards had thoroughly cleaned out the vein. A buyer might consider himself lucky if he found that the mine had been abandoned because the ore was too refractory for the old methods.[2]

Two other types of enterprises preferred by foreigners were low-grade deposits needing large scale operations and the reworking of mine dumps.[3] Since these deposits were too lean or too refractory to be amenable to the older beneficiation processes, they literally created ore. Dumps and old mine fills, on the other hand, were sources of mined ore only awaiting a cheap extraction process. Cyaniding and later flotation were perfectly suited to this type of work. Reworking tailings was one of the first tasks of the cyanide process in Pachuca and Guanajuato. At the latter old tailings were dredged out of the river bed.

But foreign investors did not ignore newly discovered mines. The oft-repeated complaint that newly discovered mines were immediately bought up by foreigners was generally true. El Boleo, Cananea, Naco-zari, Sierra Mojada, the Coahuila coal fields, the extensions of Santa Eulalia, Parral, San Francisco del Oro, El Oro, and Tlalpujahua all came under foreign domination. The Mexican generally looked upon mining as a steppingstone to becoming a landlord; the role of capitalist had little appeal.[4]

Mexican governments actively encouraged foreigners to invest in mines on a large scale. A Mexican Information Bureau was opened in London in 1900.[5] In 1901 the American Institute of Mining Engineers held its annual convention in Mexico City, and a delegation of 165 engineers from the United States came in two special trains. They visited Chihuahua City, Parral, Santa Eulalia, Zacatecas, Mexico City, Pachuca, Guana-juato, San Luis Potosí, Monterrey, and toured the adjoining mine regions. Feted at every stop, they were literally overwhelmed with dinners, balls, serenades, concerts, speeches of welcome, and "interesting and informa-tive" brochures and pamphlets.[6] At the meeting in Mexico City the papers presented were studies of Mexican mining districts and the in-dustry's organization and methods. Together with some prepared pamphlets, these made a bulky volume of *Transactions* for the year 1901. In 1906 a similar trip arranged for the Tenth International Geologic Congress emphasized the extent of mineral deposits rather than their profitability.[7] Propagandizing Mexican "treasure chests" successfully turned the attention of mine investors to Mexico.

Of all the enterprises expanding in Mexico, the group known as the "Guggenheim Interests" was by far the largest and most important. Not all of the Guggenheim properties were under the American Smelting and Refining Company's (ASARCO) flag. Some properties were held di-rectly by the Guggenheim family under the title "M. Guggenheim's Sons," while their Aguascalientes Metal Company controlled the Tepe-zala-Asientos copper mines. Mines in Parral were controlled through the Mexican Ore Company, which had merged with ASARCO along with its parent, the Consolidated Kansas City company. A subsidiary, the American Smelters' Securities Company (ASSCO), held other im-portant properties. Finally, the Guggenheim Exploration Company (Guggenex) and its subsidiary Mexican Exploration Company were key corporations, founded with the object of controlling and promoting im-portant mines in the Western Hemisphere on the pattern of the Roths-childs' successful Exploration Company of London. Guggenex's interests ranged from Utah Copper to the Tecolotes silver-lead mines at Santa Barbara, Chihuahua, to the famous Esperanza gold mine. Under able men, such as John Hays Hammond and Pope Yeatman, Guggenex han-dled the cream of Mexico's innumerable mines. Although the epigram, "When you think Mexican mines, think Guggenheim," was not abso-

TABLE 2
PRODUCTION OF THE MEXICAN MINING INDUSTRY:
1891–1912
(*Selected Metals for Selected Years*)

Year	Silver (Kgs.)	Gold (Kgs.)	Lead (Met. Tons)	Zinc (Met. Tons)	Copper (Met. Tons)
1891	1,087,261	1,477	30,187		5,650
1895	1,456,773	8,017[c]	68,000	500	11,806
1900	1,776,410	12,697	63,828	1,100	22,473
1903	2,018,652	15,993	100,532[d]	1,000	46,040[h]
1905	1,890,970[a]	24,306	101,196	2,000	65,449[i]
1908	2,221,137[b]	32,028	127,010[e]	15,650	38,173[j]
1909	2,212,983	34,370	118,186	3,000[g]	57,230
1910	2,416,669	41,420	124,292	1,833	48,160
1911	2,518,202	37,120	116,758[f]	1,593	56,072
1912	2,526,715	32,431	105,160	1,266	57,245

a. Passage of Monetary Reform Law of March, 1905.
b. Completion of major Guanajuato cyanide mills; start of cyaniding in Pachuca; completion of lead-silver smelters.
c. Start of cyaniding at El Oro.
d. Smelter expansion.
e. Velardeña and Chihuahua lead-silver plants completed.
f. Start of disturbances in northern Mexico; Chihuahua, Mapimí, Torreón, and Velardeña smelters work intermittently.
g. Imposition of U.S. Tariff on zinc imports.
h. Cananea starts full-scale operations.
i. Nacozari starts full-scale operations.
j. Financial panic; smelters close to sell surplus stocks.
N.B.—During this period the Mexican government had no direct method of ascertaining the yield of the mines. The figures are based upon exports and production reported for tax purposes, and the assumption was made that the consumption of metals in Mexico was insignificant. The figures, taken from the *Boletin de estadistica fiscal* are therefore only approximations. See *The Mexican Year Book for 1909–1910*, p. 472; and *Mexican Mining Journal* (Jan. 1909), 12. For a general critique of Mexican official statistics, see Secretaría de la Economía Nacional, Dirección General de Estadística, *Informes sobre las principales estadísticas mexicanas* (Mexico, 1941), pp. 100–106, SOURCE: J. González Reyna, *Riqueza minera y yacimientos minerales de México* (Mexico, 1956), p. 448.

lutely true, the limitation to its veracity could not be charged to lack of effort.

One key to the success of the Guggenheims was the capital at their disposal. An index of the activities of Guggenex can be inferred from the report that between the summer of 1902 and March, 1903, it had bought mines at Velardeña, Durango ($5,000,000); the Hidalgo Mining Co., Chihuahua ($6,000,000); the Promontorio Mine, Durango ($2,000,-000); the Avino Company, Durango ($3,000,000), and the Escuadra mine, Oaxaca ($2,000,000). In addition, the Veta Grande mine in Chihuahua was almost repaying monthly its $200,000 purchase price and was valued at $5,000,000.[8]

Another key to the success of the Guggenheims was their good relations with President Díaz, dating from the interview with Daniel Guggenheim in 1890 which led to the concession for the family's smelters. John Hays Hammond maintained the cordial relationship. He later remarked that his mines never had any trouble with petty officials; letting it be known that he was going to Mexico City generally brought the local men to heel.[9] Finance Minister Limantour was a major thorn in the Guggenheims' side. As a Pachuca mine owner on the Board of Directors of the Real del Monte y Pachuca Company and an antimonopolist, Limantour opposed the Smelters Trust, as he did American domination of the Mexican railroad system. He is said to have stopped the Guggenheims from dominating any major district south of Aguascalientes.

Smelters were the most important of the Guggenheim Mexican properties. We have already noted the building of the Monterrey and Aguascalientes plants to which El Paso ought to be added, for even after the McKinley Tariff it continued to handle Mexican ores in bond, and ASARCO regarded it as part of its Mexican operations.[10] By 1910 ASARCO added three more plants to its holdings. Between 1906 and 1908 ASSCO built the works at Velardeña, Durango, and ASARCO erected the Avalos, Chihuahua, plant. A small smelter at Matehuala, San Luis Potosí, was bought in 1909. Also, at this time, ASARCO controlled the Fundidora y Afinadora smelter at Monterrey. These smelters effectively blanketed northern and central Mexico as far south as Aguascalientes and even drew ores from Oaxaca. Only the smelters at San Luis Potosí and Torreón offered any competition, for the Mapimí and the Mazapil Copper Company smelters worked largely on their own ores, custom work being of minor significance. Furthermore, Towne's San Luis Potosí works processed mainly ores from his mines. Finally, ASARCO made a pooling agreement with the San Luis Potosí and Torreón smelters to contain any possible competition.[11]

Later, the Torreón works offered some competition. It was reported in 1905 that Ernesto Madero had offered to sell the plant to ASARCO for 5,000,000 pesos; ASARCO offered 4,500,000 pesos. Madero, "active for the directors and stockholders, absolutely refused to consider the figure. . . ." ASARCO's agent left for New York, and the Torreón interests started to buy a number of lead properties in Chihuahua and Coahuila to strengthen their position. With the collapse of negotiations, the Maderos were reluctant to re-enter the smelter pool, and Torreón negotiated a number of desirable contracts as an independent.[12]

A survey made in 1904 sparked ASARCO's determination to expand its Mexican operations. A 25 per cent increase in ASARCO's Mexican output between 1902 and 1904 had marked that country for particular attention. A growing need for lead ores to balance the company's "dry" silver ore intake became the basis of a recommendation to buy lead mines to supplement ASARCO's custom purchases. The survey also stressed the economic advantages accruing to smelters that owned mines. At the same time, the intake of copper ores had reached a point which necessitated the building of another refinery. ASSCO was founded in 1905 to buy lead-silver mines to assure the company's future ore supplies and also to acquire copper mines and plants for ASARCO's expansion into that field.[13] But ASSCO soon became principally occupied in acquiring smelters for ASARCO along with a few mines. ASARCO described their relationship in 1910: "They both have mining interests, but in the case of the Securities Company these are of an importance inferior to the smelting, while in the case of [ASARCO] they are almost insignificant."[14]

In 1905-7 ASSCO rebuilt the Velardeña copper-lead smelter originally held by Nash, Barton, and Matthews, who were closely connected with the Omaha and Grant Smelting and Refining Company. Until 1894 Velardeña ore was shipped to Omaha for smelting, but after the passage of the McKinley Tariff the company erected a smelter in Mexico.[15] When Omaha and Grant became part of ASARCO, it did not surrender its Velardeña holdings. Guggenex was reported to have received a 60 per cent interest in May, 1904, in return for $5,000,000 and a promise to invest $1,000,000 in improvements. Daniel Guggenheim called the figures incorrect, but since the matter was a private deal he refused to give any others. Guggenex sold the properties, which included the smelter and two copper mines, to ASSCO, in 1905, through the Velardeña Mining and Smelting Company. Starting with two copper stacks of 600 tons daily capacity, ASSCO invested $1,500,000 between 1905 and 1907, to increase production to 1,000 tons, and added lead furnaces. The completely electrified plant was one of the best mechanized properties in Mexico. A 2.5-mile aerial tramway and a 3-mile railroad connected the mines and the smelter. Its main function was to smelt ASARCO ores; custom work was subordinate. ASSCO built a copper refinery at Baltimore to handle the increased Mexican output. But Velardeña proved to be a white elephant. Except for profits from the treatment of custom ores, it lost millions.[16]

The Chihuahua smelter has an interesting history. ASARCO fairly well dominated silver-lead smelting in the western Sierra Madre, with plants at El Paso and Aguascalientes, but the Governor of Chihuahua was anxious to have a plant erected in his state. Governor Creel authorized a study to be made of the situation and offered government concessions. ASARCO bought out a small copper plant, La Descubridora, and obtained a 20-year concession from Governor Creel to build a smelter in Chihuahua. Finally, at the Rancho de Avalos, about five miles south of Chihuahua City, ASARCO began to erect in January, 1906, an 800-ton plant with two lead stacks and one copper stack. ASARCO announced that the plant labored under the handicap of an uncertain future ore supply which prompted it to keep its investment at a minimum. Surplus and secondhand equipment from El Paso and Monterrey was used, and ASARCO officials referred to the installation as "the Junk Heap." It comprised only the essentials of a lead smelter and was devoid of labor-saving devices. ASARCO believed that the Chihuahua smelter would cripple its Monterrey, El Paso, and Aguascalientes operations. Henry F. Wagner, who was in charge of ASARCO's northern Mexican operations, candidly remarked in his autobiography:

> Unfortunately, the smelter had been built never to run. It was only a bluff to avoid the construction of a competitive plant by some other concern. Consequently, all the scrap from all the other plants had been used in its construction and there was some doubt as to whether it could be made to run.[17]

Wagner thought its operation economically feasible, but other ASARCO officials opposed him. Governor Creel's insistence forced ASARCO to open the plant. During the first 18 months it produced only 6,000 tons of lead bullion; not until mid-1910 were mechanical operations untroubled. The proximity of a plant stimulated mine activity in western Chihuahua; ASARCO's own ore reserves increased; and soon more ore was offered than the smelter could handle. Since increased tonnage meant lowered costs, ASARCO expanded and modernized the plant after 1914 until, in the 1920's, it had become the largest lead smelter in the world. As a result of this reorganization ASARCO rebuilt El Paso as a copper smelter to treat Guggenheim-controlled ore from Arizona.[18]

ASARCO acquired the small Matehuala smelter in 1909. It consisted of a 200-ton copper stack and a 100-ton lead stack. But it occupied a highly strategic position in the heart of the Matehuala copper district where ASSCO had several mines. An American firm, the National Metallurgical Company, owned the plant in addition to 51 mining claims. Its capital was small; building costs were high; and only one stack was completed before the company was in difficulties. The smelter was designed to work local low-grade ores which could not pay shipping costs to Aguascalientes or San Luis Potosí. ASSCO's Dolores mine, which sent its high-grade ore to Aguascalientes, was the largest shipper. When ASSCO stopped shipping ore from the Dolores mine, during the financial panic of 1907–8, the smelter fell into desperate straits. ASARCO acquired control in 1909. Plans were immediately launched to increase the capacity of the smelter to 800 tons to handle the ore output of all ASSCO mines in the district. ASSCO increased the capacities of its mines and developed the newly acquired units.[19]

Ownership of a large chain of smelters brought concomitant responsibilities. ASARCO owned or operated a number of railway lines, many grouped in the Mexican Union Railway. The American Smelters Steamship Company carried copper matte and lead bullion from Tampico to the United States for refining and returned with cargoes of coal, coke, and general merchandise for the smelters.[20] Guaranteeing sufficient ore for the smelters constituted another problem. Miners complained that the smelters bought control of mines because their financial power and economic position made it possible for them to pick up bargains; the smelters answered that mine ownership was only a way of maintaining adequate ore supplies. Deliveries of independently mined ore often were irregular because of a scarcity of workers during various seasons, shutdowns, and shortages of working capital which forced small operators to close or curtail operations.[21] In any event, ASARCO's declared policy was to acquire mines in Mexico but not in the United States. A survey of ASARCO properties in 1922 showed that of its fifteen metal mines, two were in the United States, one in Canada, one in Peru, and eleven in Mexico.[22]

Guggenheim mining interests blanketed northern Mexico. They first secured the Reforma mine in the Monoclova-Cuatro Ciénegas district, to supply the Monterrey smelter, and then the Tepezala copper mines in Aguascalientes. Soon after they obtained a lease on the Encantada mine in Sierra Mojada.[23] After merging with ASARCO, the Guggenheim holdings expanded with mines bought by ASARCO, ASSCO, and Guggenex. With the Consolidated Kansas City and the Mexican Ore Companies' holdings, ASARCO controlled five mines in Sierra Mojada producing 33,000 tons a year, and the Pachuqueña and Cordero mines in Parral, Chihuahua, producing over 500 tons a day. In Santa Eulalia ASARCO held seven mines and a 1,000-ton mill. Later a larger number of silver-lead properties acquired by Guggenex were dumped into the ASSCO holdings, leaving Guggenex free to expand its own copper holdings.[24] Because of ASARCO's and ASSCO's policy of concealing exact figures and details, an authoritative listing is impossible. ASSCO holdings were reported to consist of five mines in Aguascalientes producing 58,000 tons a year; the Veta Grande mine at Parral producing 15,000 tons a year; the Tecolotes mine at Santa Barbara, Chihuahua, producing 15,000 tons a year; the Bonanza mine in Zacatecas just starting production in 1909; the Jibosa mine at Jímenez, Chihuahua, producing 11,000 tons a year; the Terneros-Copper Queen-Velardeña group producing about 200,000 tons of ore a year; and the Zaragoza mine near Monterrey producing 5,500 tons a month. These company figures are not comparable, since, except for the Velardeña group, they probably represent the sum of the copper and lead metallic content.[25]

In 1902 an ambitious scheme was launched under which Guggenex would buy out all the important properties on the Veta Colorada in Minas Nuevas, Chihuahua. The rationale of the plan was that the area was closely tied to ASARCO's smelters and that possession of the mines would forestall any rival's chance of opening a successful smelter in Chihuahua. Only the Quebradillas, Veta Grande, and Verde mines were finally purchased. By 1920, however, the scheme in its original form was consummated.[26] The backbone of the company's Mexican holdings were in the states of Chihuahua, Durango, Coahuila, Nuevo León, and Aguascalientes.

ASARCO made two very important acquisitions in 1910 and 1911. In

1909 it leased the Angangueo mines in Michoacan and the 60-mile railroad connected with it. A Mexico City capitalist, Sebastian Camacho, owned these mines which employed 3,000 men and shipped 200 tons of high-grade silver ore to Aguascalientes every day. ASARCO purchased the mines the next year.[27] In August, 1911, ASARCO bought the Tiro General mine in San Luis Potosí for about 1,500,000 pesos. Its ore, originally treated at Charcas by the patio process, had been sent to the Aguascalientes smelter since the opening of the plant in 1895. In 1902 the Compañía Minera de Tiro General had been organized with a capitalization of $375,000. Shipments rose from 1,000 to 5,000 tons a month, and the mine became the largest remitter to the smelter. Guggenex held an option on the mine in 1903 but had allowed it to lapse. In 1911 ASARCO finally bought the mine, the dump, and the 15-kilometer railway and immediately started to enlarge the workings. It made Tiro General a subsidiary of the National Metallurgical Company which also controlled the Matehuala smelter. The Revolution cut the work short, and the mine did not become a steady producer again until after 1920.[28]

It is impossible to leave the Guggenheim interests in Mexico without some comment on their interest in the Esperanza mine in El Oro, Mexico. Discovered by August Sahlberg in 1893, the Esperanza quickly became a profitable venture: extraction cost twelve pesos while the ore sold for twelve dollars a ton. In 1897 the Esperanza paid 110 per cent on its capital. John Hays Hammond examined the mine for Guggenex and recommended its purchase; there was ore worth $4,000,000 in sight. Daniel Guggenheim at first was cool to the proposition. He finally agreed that Guggenex would take 49 per cent and sell the balance of the stock in London through Weetman Pearson (later Lord Cowdray) and Robert J. Price, who controlled the Mexican Gold and Silver Recovery Company and the Venture Corporation. The mine cost over $2,000,000 and was capitalized at £450,000 in 1903. With power from the Necaxa dam, construction was begun on a 120-stamp mill and cyanide plant. A bonanza was hit shortly afterwards and shares went up to £300 in London. In 1906 dividends equalled 160 per cent of capitalization; from 1904 to 1910 they averaged 68.8 per cent. When Guggenex dumped its holdings into ASSCO in 1905, only the Esperanza was retained. In 1905 the mine yielded 10,292,530 pesos in value; in 1906 it yielded 15,357,690 pesos and employed 3,200 men. Because of the decline in ore grades, the yield in later years fell from 5,000,000 to 4,000,000 pesos a year despite a high mill extraction rate. Guggenex divested itself of control in 1912, allowing it to gravitate to London.[29]

By far the most swashbuckling figure in the history of the Mexican mining industry was "Colonel" William C. Greene. While the Guggenheims built an empire based on financial acumen and sound metallurgical practice, Greene founded an empire on prospectuses and bluff. He opened the largest copper mine and smelter in Mexico and yet drove his company into bankruptcy.

Greene had bought a small ranch near Tombstone, Arizona, but it was an indifferent success.[30] While wandering in northern Sonora in 1898, he came across the Cananea copper mine which had been known since colonial days but whose remoteness precluded any sizeable development. In the middle of the nineteenth century, General Ignacio Pesqueira had worked the mines and opened a small smelter. Several other fitful workings in the district were unsuccessful. Greene recognized a potential mountain of ore, and for $47,000 he obtained an option on the "Cobre Grande" from the General's widow.[31]

Greene had only a few hundred dollars. But with the aid of two friends and his ability as a prospectus writer, he managed to get the mine going, float the Cobre Grande Copper Company, and start a 100-ton smelter. His troubles now began. A venture in obtaining more capital from J. H. Costello of Pennsylvania almost cost him the mine. Costello did not know that since their agreement was not registered in Mexico it had no legal standing there. An armed force provided by the friendly Mexican authorities ousted Costello's men and gave Greene possession of the enlarged mine workings and a 200-ton smelter. Cutting out Costello also cut out the Cobre Grande stockholders, and Greene set out to mend his fences.[32]

In September, 1899, Greene organized in Mexico the Cananea Consolidated Copper Company, S.A. to run the enterprise, while a West Virginia corporation—the Greene Consolidated Copper Company—handled financing in the United States. Selling stock in the new company involved Greene in deals which continually led to lawsuits. At one time the copper promoter, Tom Lawson, almost caught him over a barrel, but John W. Gates bailed him out.[33] Greene then started to sell stock from a lavish Wall Street office. His settlement with the old Cobre Grande stockholders was accepted by the majority, but an eastern group took the matter into court. Greene's legal talent soon tied up that move in the Arizona courts.[34] Meanwhile, he became notorious by reason of his phenomenal ability to sell stock and spend money in New York and at Cananea.

Greene built a spur line to Cananea in 1901; two new ore bodies were opened; a 600-ton concentrator was built; and in the same year six furnaces treated 1,000 tons of ore per day. But he had constant trouble with finances and with his Board of Directors. Plagued by stock raids, speculative manipulations, and "copper panics," he had to juggle the Board constantly to restore confidence and offset rumors of failures while seeking more money for his own market adventures.

Meanwhile, Cananea worked increasingly leaner ore which could still yield handsome profits if intelligently exploited. Despite the presence of excellent metallurgists on the Cananea board and the services of Louis D. Ricketts—the leading copper engineer in the Southwest engaged as consultant to supervise the rebuilding of the mill—a new, progressive mine manager at Cananea wrote that he found himself stymied by the poor over-all design of the jerry-built workings, Greene's autocratic methods, and the presence of Greene's cronies whose connections were better than their abilities. While the thriving town of Cananea, Greene's tax exemptions, his concession which included 900 square kilometers of mineral land, and his promotion of gold and silver companies with a $25,000,000 capitalization might make for confidence, Cananea's methods were woefully inefficient. By forcing 5 or 6 years development into one, too much was unplanned and uneconomical. One of his contractors remarked that Greene could bring copper from the New York market cheaper than he could produce it at Cananea. A labor force of 3,500 men, 8 furnaces, and a concentrator capable of handling 2,500 tons of ore a day signified that all of Greene's talk was not bluster. But his purchase of a ranch—measuring 40 by 100 miles with 40,000 head of Herefords—while paying dividends out of stock sales, did not speak well for the company's stability. The Rockefeller-Amalgamated Copper interests, captained by Thomas Cole and John D. Ryan, appreciated Greene's position, and started to buy into Cananea, first with a $2,000,000 loan and then with stock purchases.[35]

From 1904 to 1906 Greene rode the crest of his wave. He had collected about $12,000,000 from his various promotions, confidently looked forward to producing 6,000,000 pounds of copper a month from Cananea, and planned to rehabilitate a series of old gold and silver mines in northern Mexico. Suddenly a bolt hit Cananea: the workers went on strike.

Díaz's clandestine opposition,[36] the Liberal party, organized the strike. Taking advantage of the miners' grievances over the large number of Americans employed, the wage differences between the two nationalities, and the lack of promotions for Mexicans, the Liberal party members at the mine called a strike on May 31, 1906. They demanded a basic 5-peso-per-day wage, a limit of 25 per cent on the number of Americans in any department, and promotions for Mexicans. Greene's paternalistic pleas for the workers to return to their jobs fell on deaf ears. Nor did the management's offer to consider the matter placate the men. At the lumberyard the supervisors opposed the demonstrators calling the men out.[37] In the ensuing riot the American supervisors and seven strikers were killed, touching off a civil war between the strikers and the company police. For two days pitched battles were fought in the streets. Governor Yzabal of Sonora invited American troops to cross the border, and only prompt orders from Washington stopped a cavalry troop from Fort Huachucha from crossing over. With the Governor as an escort, a group of men from Douglas and Bisbee, Arizona, including United

States Rangers, entered Mexico. Luckily, they had no part in the fighting. The arrival of Rurales broke the strike. The leaders were exiled or impressed into the army. Two hundred soldiers were stationed in Cananea. On June 7th work resumed, and ten days later the plant was in full operation. "President Díaz," said Greene, "has ordered me not to raise wages, and I dare not disobey him."[38]

The political effects of the strike were far reaching. Francisco Madero in his criticism of the Díaz regime called the horror of the strike, in spite of all the concessions given to Greene, a national scandal. Americans were disabused of the idea that dissatisfied Mexicans moved on instead of trying to redress their grievances by striking back. Cananea remained a seedbed of the Revolution in northern Mexico. Today the union local there is named: "The Great Workers' Syndicate 'Martyrs of 1906.' "[39]

Cananea's labor policies also changed. The company cut the workday from nine to eight and one-half hours while the average Mexican's wages rose about 100 pesos a year. In an economy move, Americans employed fell from 34 per cent in 1906 to 13 per cent in 1912.[40]

Later, in 1906, the final blow hit Greene: stock sales collapsed and the Amalgamated Copper interests forced a merger. On the basis of a few mediocre mines, which Greene had turned over to them, the Cole-Ryan group had organized the Cananea Central Copper Company. Now they merged the two companies as the Greene-Cananea Consolidated Copper Company. Cananea Central was given two-fifths of the new company's stock, although its holdings were hardly worth a small fraction of the value of the Cananea mine and plant. Amalgamated holdings assured control of the new company, while the cash settlement given to Greene as part of the deal went to pay the debts of his pet lumber company. Three months later Greene was forced out of the company.[41]

In March, 1907, Louis Ricketts took charge of remodeling the plant and cut operating costs by 9 cents a pound. Necessary improvements cost $2,500,000 and included completely rebuilding the smelter. A poor market for copper during the Panic of 1907 made it economically feasible to close the plant for repairs. By October, 1911, Cananea produced 6,000,000 pounds of copper a month at a cost of 9.5 to 10 cents a pound. It paid its first dividend on March 1, 1912, with the year's profits amounting to $1,026,951.[42] Cananea had become a member of the fraternity of the great copper mines of the world.

Greene met death in befitting turbulence. Always proud of his horses, he was thrown from his carriage by a pair of runaways. A special train was rushed from El Paso with a team of doctors and nurses. Their efforts were in vain. On August 5, 1911, Colonel William C. Greene passed away.[43]

East of Cananea lay another large body of copper ore named Pilares de Nacozari. About 1890 the Moctezuma Concentrating Company sold the mine to Colonel John Wein, who in turn sold it to the Guggenheims.[44] Louis D. Ricketts visited the camp in 1895 and found that the ore was rather good—6 per cent copper—but results and returns were poor because the plant was 90 miles from the railway and the copper smelter was worked on a silver-lead system. Rickets thought the plant was experimental and was surprised to learn that a profit was expected. When the Guggenheims finally declared that they were not copper miners and put the mine up for sale, Ricketts recommended it to James Douglas of Phelps Dodge. Phelps Dodge purchased the mine in 1897 for a price equal to the bonded debt plus the amount the Guggenheims had lost.[45]

To develop the property Phelps Dodge formed the $3,000,000 subsidiary Moctezuma Copper Company and also bought 35,000 acres of timberland. A large power plant, two 200-ton mills, two 150-ton furnaces, and two 5-ton Bessemer converters were erected a few miles from the mine. A ridge of hills separated Pilares from the milltown, named Nacozari de García.[46]

In 1901 the smelter turned out 4,300 tons of copper, 8,091 pounds of silver, and 60 pounds of gold. A 121-kilometer railroad line was built to Agua Prieta to meet the El Paso and Southwestern owned by Phelps Dodge. The company embarked, in 1900, on a program of integrating Nacozari with its Copper Queen workings in Arizona by building a smelter in Sulphur Springs Valley, 25 miles southwest of Bisbee. With the railroad completed, the Nacozari smelter was abandoned in December, 1904, and a huge 1,500-ton concentrator was erected in its stead. Although the ore grade fell, the concentrator's extraction was 85 per cent, and the amounts of ore mined rose from 86,660 tons in 1901, to 348,630 tons in 1908, and to 542,363 tons in 1912.[47]

Robert Safford Towne was an empire-builder almost unknown outside mining circles.[48] Born in Ohio in 1858, he received a degree in mining engineering in 1880. Gaining experience in Colorado mining camps, Towne joned the Kansas City Smelting and Refining Company. He established its ore-buying agencies in Sierra Mojada and organized the Mexican Ore Company to buy mines there and in Parral. Towne then helped build the El Paso smelter and the Mexican Northern Railroad, serving as president of the railroad. The El Paso smelter and the Mexican Ore Company (but not the railroad) were merged with several other units to form the Consolidated Kansas City Smelting and Refining Company. When it joined ASARCO in 1899, Towne disposed of his holdings to devote himself exclusively to Mexican affairs.

The heart of Towne's enterprise was the Compañía Metalúrgica Mexicana, a corporation chartered in New Jersey in 1890.[49] He built a smelter in 1891–92 at San Luis Potosí to take advantage of the railroads tapping the mines of Sierra Mojada, the northwest Pacific coast area, and the many mining camps in San Luis Potosí, Aguascalientes, Hidalgo,

Guanajuato, and Oaxaca. Although the bulk of the ore came from the Towne-controlled San Pedro mines, the excellent rail connections overcame the distance from other sources of ore, and the smelter prospered. By 1900 it had eight lead and two copper furnaces. Two furnaces added in 1905 brought the plant's capacity to 1,000 tons of ore a day, 800 of them in lead. Peon labor was paid 37 centavos (17.5 cents, U.S.) a day. All work was done by hand, necessitating a force of 1,300 men beside clerical help.[50]

Towne's interests were very extensive. To supply the smelter and service his neighboring mines, he controlled the Potosí & Rio Verde Railway and the Mexican Mineral Railway, as well as the Mexico Northern. His Alvarez Land and Timber Company supplied the needed lumber. To assure a basic ore supply for the smelter, he leased mines in the San Pedro district of San Luis Potosí. Towne also held the Veta Rica at Sierra Mojada, which sent about 2,500 tons a month to San Luis; the Montezuma Lead Company, controlling lead mines in Santa Barbara, Chihuahua; and the rich Sombrerete mines in Zacatecas. With the Mexican Lead Company, the Sombrerete Mining Company had additional holdings in La Noria and Chalchuites, both in Zacatecas. Later Towne acquired the tremendous Proaño Hill in Fresnillo, Zacatecas. He organized the Fresnillo Company and opened a 700-ton cyanide plant to treat the silver ores and the old dumps. To help supply the copper furnaces at San Luis, Towne held the Cerro Prieto and the adjoining mines at Concepción del Oro, Zacatecas, and the San Pedro and San Pablo mines in Nuevo León. He acquired minor interests in properties in Guachinango, Jalisco, the Urique district of Chihuahua, and a lease on properties in Flojonales, Hidalgo. Towne also headed the Teziutlan Copper Company in Puebla, which he had bought from George D. Barron. A copper smelter had been erected at Aire Libre, Puebla, to treat the ore. Through the Teziutlan company, Towne acquired the Ocotes mine in Oaxaca, which promised well until the ores proved too refractory. When Towne died in August, 1916, he left an estate appraised at $2,500,000. The value of the property under his control, but not owned personally, was greater.[51]

Guanajuato is the center of a major group of mines in west-central Mexico.[52] By the beginning of the twentieth century, the Guanajuato mines were 350 years old. Spaniards had extensively exploited them until defeated by the falling ore grades and flooding. British efforts to revive them in the nineteenth century were not notably successful. Although the deepest shaft in Guanajuato was only 2,000 feet—a full 1,000 feet less than shafts at Comstock—it had produced more silver than any district in the United States. Its long life may be attributed not only to the ore mass but also to the fact that the mines had not been worked with modern machinery, nor with the energy of United States mineral conquistadors. Formerly the owners had opened only shafts and galleries and turned miners loose on a share basis. Ore was carefully sorted to find the pieces of highest value. At one time the prices offered made ores containing less than one-half kilogram of silver per ton unprofitable. Plenty of good ore was left in the mines, mine fills, and dumps for modern processing.[53]

Americans were attracted to Guanajuato primarily by the dumps, which still contained huge amounts of silver, and only secondarily by the mines. The size of the dumps and the ease of working them offset the fact that they were worth only $4.00 a ton, containing 4 to 6 ounces of silver and 1.5 grains of gold to the ton. The promoters, George W. Bryant and George W. McElhiney, figured that 2,000,000 tons of dumps would yield $1.00 profit per ton, while richer waste fill in the mine would yield up to $1.50.[54] To obtain control, the new enterprises acquired the old leases. Mexicans were skeptical of American operations since earlier the British had come to grief and had quickly sold their holdings. They looked upon the idea of removing the old dumps and working abandoned mines with amusement, and local merchants shied away from investments.[55]

Guanajuato started to boom in the late 1890's. Bryant and McElhiney became interested in Guanajuato after Leonard E. Curtis of Denver had visited the town. Convinced that introducing hydroelectricity could transform the entire district, Curtis pioneered the organization of the Guanajuato Power and Electric Company. Bryant and McElhiney, followed by the MacDonald brothers, journeyed to Guanajuato to look for likely properties. Within a short time five companies organized by these men completely dominated the district.[56]

The MacDonalds purchased the La Sirena mine in 1898, and organized the Guanajuato Consolidated Mining and Milling Company with a capitalization of $3,000,000 to hold the La Sirena group; 50 per cent of the Barragana, Constantina, and Cardonas groups; 51 per cent of the important El Carmen mines; and 63 per cent of the San Vicente. M. E. MacDonald was general manager of the Republic Mines Company which owned the balance of the Barragana and Cardonas mines. Guanajuato Consolidated erected a stamp mill and a 100-ton pan-amalgamation plant, and in 1905, after cheap electricity became available, it introduced cyaniding to Guanajuato. No matter how low silver prices might fall, the gold content alone insured a dividend.[57]

On the basis of calculations of the value of dumps and mine fills, Bryant and McElhiney bought a number of properties as a development speculation. Frank G. Peck, John H. House, and J. J. Welch joined in promoting this group of holdings. They formed a series of corporations, rotating the positions of president, vice-president, secretary, and treasurer among them, with Bryant usually acting as general manager. These promoters finally united the enterprises into the Guanajuato Development Company, a holding company chartered in New Jersey in February, 1906.

Guanajuato Development controlled 14 companies capitalized at $20,000,000, plus the 16,000-acre San Isidrio ranch with its valuable water rights, timber, and 5,000 head of cattle.[58]

Bryant and McElhiney also organized the Guanajuato Reduction and Mines Company after buying out the leases held by the mine financiers, the Rule estate. Financiers in the past had steadily milked the mine by the high charges for ore treated at their patios until the accumulated debt amounted to 6,000,000 pesos, and the original owners could not claim a penny until the entire amount was paid to the leaseholder. "In plain English, the legal ownership [was] a legal figment."[59] Bryant and McElhiney secured the deep levels by filing for more claims along the mother lode. A number of famous mines, including the Valenciana, Cata, Rayas, Mellado, and Purísima, covering 514 hectares and operating through 20 main shafts, comprised the main properties. The stamp mill and the cyanide plant could handle 600 tons of ore a day. In common with most other Guanajuato workings, mine production was balanced with ore taken from the dumps. In November, 1904, they sold control to Columbus, Ohio, and Colorado Springs capitalists.[60]

El Cubo Mining and Milling Company, just north of Guanajuato, was the last independent company of importance. Americans bought the property in 1902 from the British-owned United Mexican Mining Company, the only company left of the group organized in the 1820's. They chartered El Cubo in New Jersey the next year with a $500,000 capitalization and 21 properties covering 325 hectares. When electricity came into Guanajuato, a stamp mill and a 50-ton cyanide plant were opened at El Cubo which was later enlarged to 100 tons capacity.[61] A number of small Mexican properties still operated in the district, but most of them were either leased to Americans or had their small production custom-milled.

While American companies took over Guanajuato, a similar change of ownership took place at the Real del Monte and Pachuca districts in Hidalgo, among the largest operations in Mexico. After the failure of the British lessees, the major mines had again passed into Mexican control, but British influence remained. American engineers were astounded by the antiquated design of new machinery imported from Britain.[62] Flooding was the greatest difficulty, and pumping costs ate deeply into the companies' profits. Nevertheless, they appeared prosperous.[63] In the year 1906 returns ranged from 7.5 per cent on the Real del Monte y Pachuca shares, to 16.6 per cent on Santa Gertrudis, 18.4 per cent on San Rafael, and 23.4 per cent on Soledad.[64]

Earlier American investments in Mexico had not touched the Hidalgo districts since the mines were profitable and the selling price was too high. Shoestring operators were naturally excluded while smelter owners were fully occupied in northern Mexico with ores containing base metals.

The growing success of cyanidation, the government's monetary policy, and the declining price of silver put several of the Pachuca companies into a financial squeeze. Money for modernization was not easily obtainable. As a result, the Real del Monte y Pachuca and Santa Gertrudis groups were put up for sale.

The Real del Monte y Pachuca Company owned 116 mines in the two camps, some of which were opened over 350 years ago. They produced about 65,000 metric tons of ore per year averaging 1.2 kilograms of silver to the ton. Most of the production was treated at the company's Loreto hacienda and the rest was sent to its San Antonio mill. Ore was carried in baskets to the Loreto patio where the high grade was sorted out by hand for shipment to a smelter and the remainder was treated by the patio process.[65]

Bernard MacDonald of Guanajuato and F. W. Baker of the Venture Corporation of London negotiated the sale of the property. Options could be secured because an unreturned investment of $1,000,000 in improvements had discouraged the stockholders. Finding a buyer with enough cash to purchase the stock and develop the workings was the next step for the promoters. The United States Smelting, Refining and Mining Company (USSR&M) of Boston was interested. Subsidiaries of USSR&M took up the options in early 1906 and after a brief examination immediately purchased almost all of the Real del Monte stock. Subsequently it acquired the remaining shares. The *Mexican Mining Journal* observed that MacDonald and the Venture Corporation netted a handsome profit, and continued:

> The new owners, of course, did not buy a pig in a poke. An examination of the Real del Monte mines was arranged for. Some twenty mines were working, but after examining six of them the engineers reported that there was in sight in those alone more than three times the price of the option.[66]

USSR&M planned a very extensive development of the mines covering many years. It brought electric power into the district to eliminate the old steam-driven Cornish pumps, hoists, and other equipment. Fourteen of the 50 or more deep shafts on the property—some of which had been idle for over 40 years—were renovated and equipped. It rebuilt and converted the Loreto mill to a cyanide plant of 200 tons daily capacity. A new mill—the Guerrero, of like capacity, below the town of Real del Monte—was constructed and finished in March, 1908. By June 30, 1907, when the property once more started operating, nearly $1,700,000 had been spent on equipment and development work. During the first two years some high-grade ore was sorted and shipped to smelters, but improved mill metallurgy made this step uneconomical. These mills were later enlarged, first to a combined capacity of 600 tons and, in 1911, to 1,200 tons per day. Silver production in 1911 was reported to be 9,000,000 ounces.[67]

Santa Gertrudis was the next Pachuca mine to be sold. Discovered in 1867 by two Cornishmen, it had fared poorly during its first 10 years and few men had the faith to invest in it. A number of Mexicans bought shares in 1877. Shortly afterward the 24 shares rose in value from 80 to 5,000 gold pesos each, and by the next year 28,000 gold pesos in dividends had been paid. In the early 1900's the company found itself in financial straits similar to Real del Monte. It owned 243 hectares of mineral land which produced, in 1907, about 975 tons of ore per week averaging 1.1 kilograms of silver per ton. It treated its milling ores in the Hacienda Guadalupe patio, probably the largest in existence at the time.[68]

Meanwhile, an English firm that had made money in Colorado was looking for a likely investment. Like USSR&M, the Camp Bird Company did not buy a pig in a poke. E. E. Chase, one of the surveyors of the Santa Gertrudis, later wrote:

> [The mine was] opened up for 2000 feet on the 1700 foot level averaging 15 feet wide (one place 35 feet) of $30.50 ore (U.S. value), with silver at 65 cents; all clean argentite and no base metals. I could have endorsed that on even 30 cent silver, for I figured $10,000,000 to $15,000,000 ore in sight, and the price was only $4,500,000.[69]

R. J. Frecheville, who was in charge of the examination, made a more conservative estimate of a profit of 20 pesos per ton on 160,000 tons annual production or a yearly profit of 3,200,000 pesos—enough to repay the purchase price in three years.[70] Santa Gertrudis' final price was 9,350,000 pesos, and the check for 9,114,825 pesos was said to be the largest ever drawn in Mexico. London sources reported the price as £922,000, excluding commissions.[71]

Santa Gertrudis' problem was threefold: inefficient labor, flooding, and a heavy ore body with a bad hanging wall. Fortunately, the discovery of new ore reserves made up for the extra money needed. By 1911 the company completed a new mill to process 1,100 tons of ore a day, and from June, 1911, to June, 1912, it paid a dividend of 15 per cent on the invested capital.[72]

About 100 miles west of Pachuca lies the most famous gold districts of Mexico: El Oro, Mexico State, and Tlalpujahua, Michoacan. Their only separation is the state line; geologically and geographically they are one. El Oro's wealth led to its nickname—"The Golden Mile of Mexico." These mines, lying in a straight line over the San Rafael vein, have yielded fabulous amounts of gold. Today the district is gutted.[73]

Although the Spaniards worked the district, the thick andesite capping prevented the detection of the mother lode until the 1890's. On the basis of surface indications, a number of mining engineers individually proceeded to open underground workings. Once they pierced the capping they discovered the extension of the San Rafael and opened the Golden Mile.[74]

El Oro became a British and French stronghold. The story of the sale of Esperanza stock in London has been told. In 1899 the Exploration Company of London bought the holdings of J. B. Haggin and General John B. Frisbie in the American Mining Company and the American Railroad and Lumber Company which included the El Oro mine, a 47-kilometer railway upon which the entire district depended, and 40,000 acres of timber land. This property cost the Exploration Company £820,084 cash plus £65,988 in shares in the new company. It then organized the El Oro Mining and Railway Company with a paid-in capital of £859,000. A new mill costing £20,000, and using Necaxa power, gave the company a total of 200 stamps capable of handling 1,500 tons a day. In 1902 a new strike at the Somera shaft was bought for £125,000, and the Somera Gold Mining Co., Ltd., set up to develop that section. Immediately adjacent to the Somera was the Esperanza. On the farther border of the Esperanza, the Tiro Mexico shaft again struck the mother lode. It became the center of Weetman Pearson and Robert J. Price's organization of the Mexico Mines of El Oro. They sold it to the Exploration Company in 1904. Price was made a director, and Pearson was paid 38,000 shares of the 180,000 £1-par-value shares issued. Development work paid for itself by the ore uncovered in explorations. A 40-stamp mill with a cyanide plant yielded profits of £12,000 per month by 1907. It remitted its first dividend, 50 per cent, in 1908 and its highest dividend, 110 per cent, in 1917. For two decades, beginning in 1908, its nominal average return was 62 per cent!

These companies were bound together by interlocking directorships. In 1911 several of the major British holdings in Mexico were merged under one management: the Guggenheims withdrew from active participation in the Esperanza, and the Camp Bird mines—including the Santa Gertrudis—entered a "community of interest." From 1900 to 1910 the El Oro Mining and Railway Company paid 11,613,100 pesos in dividends, which was equal to its book value. In its first two years of paying dividends, 1909 and 1910, Mexico Mines of El Oro paid almost 3,000,000 pesos, or 165 per cent of its book capital value. While not equal to King Solomon's mines, the El Oro district could give any other group in the world a run for its money.[75]

The Dos Estrellas mine was discovered by a Frenchman, F. J. Fournier, who deduced from geological evidence that the vein system of El Oro might cross into Tlalpujahua. Fournier's predictions proved correct, but he lacked enough capital for development. At this point, in 1898, José L. Requena, who had been active in reopening and finding financing for the Borda Antigua mine, helped form a corporation with a paid-up capital of 200,000 pesos.[76] Work was started on December 27, 1899, and two minor veins were cut before striking the major vein at the 660-meter level. The bonanza Veta Nueva (New Vein) was two meters thick and

700 meters long with some ore assaying 3 kilograms of gold and 85 kilo-grams of silver to the ton! Much of it ran 200 to 225 grams of gold and 2 to 2.5 kilograms of silver. Later the Veta Verde was found, and the ore settled down to an average of 25 grams of gold and 300 grams of silver to the ton.

Don Estrellas' original 3,000 shares shot up to fantastic values. Keeping the capital at its original figure, the 100-peso par shares were called in and divided into one-peso shares. These shares averaged a quotation of 85 on the exchange! Yearly dividends ran from 480 to 510 per cent of the capitalization. The company started its first mill with 20 stamps in 1902. It enlarged the plant to 130 stamps and a capacity of 700 tons of ore a day and erected a second plant, El Cedro, to treat another 700 tons. All the ore was cyanided. In 1907 financial control passed into French hands, but the management remained Mexican. Five years later Dos Estrellas declared a dividend of 6,000,000 pesos without increasing its capitalization. After 1913 a decline set in as the bonanza days passed. Control passed to English investors who efficiently exploited the known veins.[77]

The Exploration Company of London was active in many sections of Mexico. Its major function was to purchase likely looking prospects or small companies, develop their holdings, and then either sell them to going concerns or float new companies. Arrangements for new companies were often handled through the Venture Corporation. Selling prices usually included enough cash to cover exploration expenses and a block of stock. The Exploration Company itself held control of the Buena Tierra mine in Santa Eulalia, Chihuahua; the Santa Rosa mine in Con-cepción del Oro, Zacatecas; and the El Oro companies. In addition, it held or examined properties in Minas Prietas, Sonora; Cusihuiriachic, Chihuahua; Sierra Morada and Taxco, Guerrero; Sultepec, Mexico; and Charcas, San Luis Potosí. However, the company concentrated on buying mines and made no attempt to enter the smelting business or to integrate its holdings.[78]

In northern Mexico, several large silver-lead enterprises grew up inde-pendent of the "chains" developed by ASARCO and Towne. Most impor-tant was the Compañía Minera de Peñoles, at Mapimí, Durango. The Spaniards discovered the Mapimí mines in 1598. In the late nineteenth century they passed to A. B. Sawyer, who sold them to the Durango-Mapimí Mining Company of Council Bluffs, Iowa, while he remained in charge of operations. Durango-Mapimí united the principal mines and smelted some 20 tons of ore a day. Despite the fact that the ore ran about 20 per cent lead and 30 ounces of silver with some gold values, high initial costs precluded any profits and the American and Mexican capitalists who had financed the venture gave up. Charles Reidt reor-ganized and modernized the equipment, developed some promising areas with capital provided by José María Bermejillo, a Spanish capitalist of Mexico, and found a bonanza.[79] Jacob Langeloth, who was buying ores in Mexico at the time, promoted the new company in the United States. Through Langeloth, it became closely connected with Minerales y Metales, S.A. and the American Metal Company, a concern controlled by the Metallgesellschaft of Frankfurt-am-Main. The Cia. Minera de Peñoles was organized on March 1, 1887, and by 1903 it was referred to as the largest independent base-metal enterprise in Mexico.[80]

Large scale operations started in 1893–94 after the company introduced electricity, built a successful cog-railroad to connect the mines and smelter, and constructed an impressive railroad suspension bridge 313 meters long. It also erected 10 water-jacketed furnaces of 60 tons capacity each. K. B. Heberlein, the General Manager, described the enterprise in 1910 as consisting of 6 silver-lead blast furnaces with a normal rating of 150 tons capacity and 2 reverberatories which held from 60 to 80 tons. An arsenic plant produced 1,500 tons of refined white arsenic a year.[81]

Peñoles' mines and smelter were one of the most highly mechanized operations in Mexico. Its output increased from 672,977 pesos in 1893 to 4,037,866 pesos in 1899. Dividends were stabilized at 100,000 pesos per month—on a total capitalization of 250,000 pesos![82] To encourage custom smelter work, the company installed new lead stacks in 1907 which increased its daily capacity from 1,500 to 2,000 tons. In 1909 Peñoles' gross profit was 597,141 pesos. In 1910, after paying a dividend equal to 300 per cent of its capitalization and with an undivided profits account of over 1,000,000 pesos, Peñoles increased its capitalization to 4,000,000 pesos in order to acquire likely properties. With its huge profits Peñoles and its subsidiary, the Mexican Metal Company, proceeded to buy mines in Sonora, Durango, Chihuahua, and Nuevo León. In 1911 the capital was increased to 6,000,000 pesos; the Higueras mine in Coahuila was acquired the following year. Peñoles was strong enough, with its affiliation with the American Metal Company, to ride out the Revolution and emerge as ASARCO's largest competitor.[83]

Ernesto Madero opened the largest independent custom smelter in Mexico at Torreón in 1902. He increased the original capitalization until by 1905 it had reached 4,000,000 pesos. The plant with an ore capacity of about 1,500 tons a day had 12 furnaces for lead and copper and a 15-ton copper converter. Little more than half the capacity was ever used at one time. In addition to their coal lands, the Maderos owned the Cabrillas mine near Saltillo; the San Diego mine in Santa Barbara, Chihuahua; and the Voladora mine in the Mitra Mountains of Nuevo León. Torreón's major value, however, was as a custom plant for mines in northern and west-central Mexico. It maintained ore purchasing agencies at Parral, Chihuahua City, Guanaceví, and Zacatecas, making it one of the few competitors of ASARCO. After several attempts to buy control, ASARCO realized the political advantage of being able to point out a competitor to a dissatisfied ore shipper.[84]

The Mazapil Copper Company grew out of the holdings of William Purcell, who had made his start in the Sierra Mojada district in the 1880's. Purcell afterwards acquired the valuable Aranzazú, Zacatecas, copper mines. He set up a Mexican company, William Purcell y Cia., and sold his holdings to the Mazapil company, which was formed in England in 1893. Starting with its major holdings at Mazapil, Zacatecas, the company soon shifted its interest to Concepción del Oro, Zacatecas, where in 1894 it acquired control of the San Eligio mines.[85] It also acquired holdings in the neighboring San Pedro silver-lead field. After 1896 it became a paying concern. Later, Mazapil bought a number of smaller properties for silver-lead ore and smelter fluxes, being more interested in smelting than in mining. All in all it held about 220 properties and had a capitalization of £750,000. Closing the smelter at Mazapil, it built a larger plant at Concepción del Oro in 1901, where four copper furnaces smelted 25,000 tons of ore a month. The company sold its own silver-lead ore at first to custom smelters. Before it could open a lead smelter, Mazapil had to attract additional ores. A lead smelter was finally built at Saltillo, Coahuila, the northern terminus of the company's Coahuila and Zacatecas Railroad, which had been opened in September, 1898, to bring supplies into northern Zacatecas and to take out copper matte. The $650,000 Saltillo lead smelter had a daily capacity of 300 tons. Both smelters shipped their output to England via Tampico. Mazapil was only moderately successful until 1902 when a rising copper market allowed yearly dividends equal to 20 per cent of capitalization. Its workings were highly mechanized and attracted 8,000 employees despite the refusal of the company store to sell liquor to employees.[86]

An interesting combination grew up in Sonora with the expansion of the Creston-Colorado Company, organized in 1886 by Cleveland, Ohio, capitalists. This group in the state of Sonora eventually included the Creston and Colorado mines and the famous Minas Prietas. Continuous expansion enabled the company to erect a 170-ton mill to treat its own ores by pan amalgamation with cyanidation of the tailings.[87] Adjoining it was the Grand Central Mining Co., Ltd., organized by the Exploration Company in 1896 to unite the Grand Central mine and a number of others surrounding it. The mill could handle some 150 tons a day, but the company was more interested in custom work than in mining.[88] In 1902 the Mines Company of America acquired control of Creston-Colorado and also absorbed the Grand Central mines and mill. Capitalization increased from $2,000,000 to $9,000,000 to finance the undertaking. The venture was quite successful. In 1910 profits of over $1,000,000 were reported, while 1912 yielded $581,757 in profits and showed a surplus reserve of $2,426,268. These profits were due in large measure to the economies effected by centralizing the milling operations of the various enterprises. Revolutionary activities in the district and the destruction of property at the Dolores mine curtailed later earnings.[89]

One of the few successes in mining achieved by a Mexican came about when Pedro Alvarado, a mine worker of Parral, Chihuahua, struck a bonanza in his Palmilla claim. Stories concerning Alvarado's prodigality are legion. He built a 100-room house, and it is said that he ordered a piano for every room. He even offered to pay off the Mexican national debt as an expression of his gratitude. John Hays Hammond examined the Palmilla for Guggenex but found it no longer worth the price Alvarado was asking for it. When Hammond turned down the sale, Alvarado offered first to buy out ASARCO, then to hire Hammond to work for him. Finally, he confessed that he was really interested in owning Hammond's private railroad car! Alvarado supported hordes of relatives and friends in grand style. In addition to the nearly $2,000,000 produced by the mine, a tremendous amount was stolen by his employees, while smelter agents boasted that they never paid him more than 60 per cent of his ore's real value. A British engineer reported taking a grab-sample from some "unsacked second-class ore" which assayed over 3,700 ounces of silver and 90 ounces of gold per ton![90]

Eventually the bonanza was gone and the mine had to settle down to a workaday existence. A fire in the summer of 1907 destroyed an estimated $150,000 worth of buildings, shaft houses, and timbering. Now bankrupt, Alvarado had to lease his beloved mine to a Boston company for a cash bonus of $100,000 and a 15-year lease which would give him 45 per cent of the profits, from which he would repay, with 7 per cent interest, a loan of $300,000. A new company named the Alvarado Consolidated Mining and Smelting Company erected a stamp mill and cyanide plant. Later it merged with the Palmilla Milling Company to form the Alvarado Mining and Milling Company. Alvarado's share from the mine lease just about paid his debts, and in later years he lived in his empty house supported by the charity of friends.[91]

Charles Schwab, after his rebuff in the Chihuahua smelter plan, purchased the San Toy mine in Santa Eulalia for 8,000,000 pesos. It produced 1,410,630 ounces of silver and over 9,000 tons of lead in 1910. Schwab also held the Cananea Western Copper Company in Sonora.[92]

Charles Butters, the cyanide pioneer, owned a number of properties in Sinaloa and Sonora, including what was purported to be the oldest silver cyaniding plant in Mexico. The Butters-Copala Syndicate, chartered in England but including American investors from California, processed about 450 tons of ore a day in two plants.[93]

The El Tigre Mining Company in Sonora, situated near the railway line running from Nacozari to Douglas, Arizona, was an excellent silver producer. Discovered by two Americans in 1902, it was owned by the Lucky

Tiger Combination Gold Mining Company, controlled by Kansas City, Missouri, capitalists who had bought the property for $850,000. Despite litigation over the purchase, the company prospered and by 1907 its $10 par stock was selling for as high as $40. In that year $167,644 was paid in dividends. A 100-ton concentrating mill was built the next year, and its capacity was doubled in 1911 when a cyanide plant was added. Dividends increased to $357,601. El Tigre shipped metal valued at 9,000,000 pesos in 1913.[94]

Two large enterprises in Jalisco were operated by Americans: the Amparo Mining Company at Etzatlán, owned by the Marcus Daly estate of Philadelphia, and the Cinco Minas at Hostotipaquillo, owned jointly by the Daly estate and James Gerard, the last United States Ambassador to Imperial Germany. When the Amparo company purchased the Santo Domingo mine, the *Engineering and Mining Journal* correspondent called it "a mine by the grace of buscones robbing the pillars regularly," and wondered how the owners had obtained $320,000 for it. Another correspondent, however, believed that it had been undervalued. A dark future was predicted for the $3,000,000 Philadelphia corporation—which had turned in 800 per cent on its book capitalization by the time it closed during the 1930's. The 530,000 pesos paid for the Cinco Señores mine, however, was said to "scarcely cover the cost of the dumps." A new vein struck in 1909, while the mine was under bond, raised its value to an estimated 2,000,000 pesos. Other large workings in Jalisco did not prosper. The attempt of the Ameca-Magistral Copper Company to exploit mines in the Magistral district was never conspicuously profitable.[95]

Although many mines were registered in Oaxaca, the state remained essentially a promoter's paradise. The Taviche boom of 1905 opened a smelter near Oaxaca city, but the mines petered out.[96] A short resurgence during the 1920's brought some properties to life; the first dip in the market, however, led to the wholesale dropping of options and the termination of leases.

It is not possible to accurately determine the amount of money invested in Mexican mining. Any attempt to estimate the figure on the basis of capitalization is foredoomed to failure, since the mining fraternity issues stock on the basis of hope of future gain. To make the task more difficult, many companies refuse to give out figures except on a "lump basis," combining all parts of a far-flung enterprise. Furthermore, companies with world-wide interests are not too certain regarding the value to be placed upon any given branch. There always exists a great difference between the value represented by the stock, book capitalization, or cash invested and the true value of the property. Continuing depletion and the flexibility of development accounts—whose funds come from the mine itself—prevent any accurate determination of value except for short periods.

Before World War I, the United States was more interested in its indebtedness than in its assets abroad. As a result, few estimates and even fewer figures exist for this early period. Since the statistics were not collected regularly, it is impossible to trace changes closely and explain precisely their causes and significance; only major changes can be indicated. To make matters worse, they were collected by untrained men following their individual methods and ideas. Figures given by an "authority" are often the last estimates "with something added."

In the case of Mexico, we have only a few surveys. Evaluating the available surveys, J. Fred Rippy estimates that in 1890 the United States had $125,000,000 invested in Mexico. That sum had risen to $205,000,000 by 1897, when Mexico was the largest recipient of United States foreign investments. In 1868 there were some 13 American-owned mining companies in Mexico. An estimate of February, 1888, reported that American mining men had approximately $20,000,000 invested in that country. American mining investments by the end of 1897 had shot up to $68,-000,000.[97]

The first detailed survey was made in 1902 by Consul General Andrew Barlow, who assembled reports sent to him by the various consuls concerning American companies in their districts.[98] A perusal of the report indicates that much of the data, which was "cheerfully given," is composed of promoters' capitalizations with little attempt at deflation. Its tone is naively boastful, and doubtless an impressive total rather than accuracy was the objective. Figures for a number of larger companies were given in creditable detail. However, the tables do not cross check, and the division among categories is erratic.

TABLE 3

ESTIMATED CAPITALIZATION OF SOME MAJOR
UNITED STATES COMPANIES IN
MEXICAN MINING: 1902

(*In U.S. Dollars*)

Company[1]	Holdings	Estimated Capitalization
Aguascalientes:		
M. Guggenheim's Sons	Tepezala mines	$ 2,500,000
Chihuahua:		
Candelaria Mining Co.	Candelaria mines	600,000
Batopilas Mining Co.	Batopilas silver mines	12,053,353
La Descubridora Mng. Co.	Copper mines	666,667
Santa Eulalia Mng. Co.	Silver and non-ferrous metals mines	1,000,000
Cia. Beneficiadora del Cocheno	Smelter	666,667
Rosario Mng. & Milling Co.	Guadalupe y Calvo district	1,000,000
Hidalgo Mining Co.	Parral district—18 mines, 2 mills	666,667
Coahuila:		
Fuente Coal Co.	Fuente coal fields	500,000
Jimulco Mining Co.	Jimulco copper mines	500,000
Mexican Coal & Coke Co.	Las Esperanzas coal fields	5,000,000

TABLE 3 (Continued)

Company[1]	Holdings	Estimated Capitalization
Durango:		
Descubridora Mining & Smelting Co.	Descubridora (near Conejos)	250,000
San Luis Mining Co.	Pánuco de Coronado	350,000
Lustre Mining Co.	Santa María del Oro	1,000,000
Gurney Mining Co.	Topia district	1,000,000
Miller & Sibley Mining & Smelting Co.	Topia district	500,000
Mary D. Grace	Vacas mines	500,000
Velardeña Mining & Smelting Co.	Velardeña	1,333,333
Federal District:		
American Smelting & Refining Co. (Mining properties)	Sierra Mojada............$750,000 Chihuahua, Chih......... 600,000 Parral, Chih............. 250,000 Asientos, Ags............. 250,000	1,850,000
Guggenheim Exploration Co.		616,638
Cia. Metalúrgica Mexicana	San Luis Potosí Smelter; The Mexican Lead Co.; Montezuma Lead Co.; San Luis mining properties	4,000,000
Guanajuato:		
Guanajuato Mining & Milling Co.	Silver mines and treatment plant	266,666
Nuevo León:		
San Carlos Copper Co.	Mining and smelting of copper	350,000
Puebla:		
Teziutlan Copper Co.	Copper mines and smelter	1,000,000
Sinaloa:		
Sinaloa & Sonora Mining & Smelting Co.	Properties in Sinaloa, Sonora, and Chihuahua	600,000
Tajo Mining Co.	Rosario district	1,000,000
Sonora:		
Greene Consolidated Copper Co.	Cananea copper mines	7,500,000
Creston-Colorado Gold Mng. Co.	Gold and silver mines in northwest	2,222,222
Moctezuma Copper Co.	Nacozari copper mines	2,222,222
American Smelting & Refining Company (Office in New York)	Six ore buying agencies $ 105,877 Customs settlement agcy. 80,358 Monterrey smelter 2,679,321 Aguascalientes smelter 3,164,383	$6,029,939

[1]Listed under states where central business offices were located.

SOURCE: A. D. Barlow, "U.S. Enterprises in Mexico," *Commercial Relations of the United States*, I (1902), pp. 442–444, 471–484.

In June, 1907, Consul General Alfred L. M. Gottschalk reported from Mexico City that since 1902 approximately $64,000,000 more had been invested in mining enterprises. Guanajuato led with $12,000,000 invested in five years; Jalisco and Oaxaca were next with $10,000,000; and the states of Guerrero, Hidalgo, Puebla, and Zacatecas followed with an estimated $5,000,000 each. Not going into details, he set the total American investment at between $750,000,000 and $800,000,000.[99]

Using Gottschalk's estimates of the United States' share of Mexican mining, John R. Southworth and Percy G. Holms, in their officially authorized *Directorio,* placed investments in Mexican mining at 363,-000,000 pesos. On a national basis they listed them as: Mexico, 148 companies capitalized at 28,000,000 pesos; the United States, 840 companies capitalized at 250,000,000 pesos; Great Britain, 40 companies capitalized at 73,000,000 pesos; and France, 2 companies capitalized at 12,000,000 pesos.[100] (The peso was then valued at about two to the dollar.) In itemizing British companies, Southworth and Holms listed 11 properties capitalized at £300,000 or more: Avino Mines of Mexico (£1,000,000); El Oro Mining and Railway Company (£1,150,000); Mazapil Copper Company (£300,000); Mexican Mining Company (£350,000); Cherokee Gold Fields (£400,000); Palmarejo and Mexican Gold Mines Company (£700,000); Salinas of Mexico (£325,000); San Francisco del Oro Mining Company (£375,000); Somera Gold Mines (£500,000); Somona Mines of Mexico (£500,000); and Tominil (Mexican) Mining Company (£350,000).[101] To this list the *Mexican Mining Journal* added thirteen other English concerns whose capitalization totalled £2,864,600. The largest of these were: British and Mexican Trust (£500,000); Esperanza Mining Company (£455,000); Mexican Mining and Industrial Company (£153,750); San Carlos Gold, Zacatecas (£100,000); and W. S. Pearson and Company (£1,500,000).[102]

The Banco Central Mexicano made a listing in 1908 of Mexican owned and incorporated mines with the object of separating bona fide Mexican enterprises from those representing foreign capital with a Mexican corporate title. But even in this case it did not sort out the foreign elements in the Dos Estrellas and Agujita enterprises. The total came to 22,461,440 pesos, about 5,500,000 pesos less than Southworth and Holms' total. Among the major companies on the list (with authorized capitalization) were the following: Cia. Fundidora de Fierro y Acero de Monterrey (10,000,000 pesos); Cia. Minera Fundidora y Afinadora (8,000,000 pesos); Cia. Carbonífera "Agujita" (1,250,000 pesos); Neg. Minera de "San Rafael" y Anexas (834,440 pesos); Cia. Minera Ignacio Rodríguez Ramos (700,000 pesos); Cia. Minera "La Reina" y Anexas (400,000 pesos); Cia. Minera "Asturiana" y Anexas, Zacatecas (350,000 pesos); Cia. Minera "Dos Estrellas" (300,000 pesos); and Cia. Beneficiadora de Metales "La Union" (300,000 pesos).[103]

The most frequently cited estimate of investments in Mexican mining is the "Letcher Report" of 1912.[104] William H. Seamon, who "had long experience in Mexico as a mining engineer," drew up the report in 1911 from government and company reports, directories, periodicals, reviews, and encyclopedias. Consul Marion Letcher forwarded it to Washington and it has since appeared under his name. The report placed the wealth of Mexico at $2,434,241,422, with Americans owning $1,057,770,000, or approximately half. In mining the following breakdown was made:

TABLE 4

NATIONAL DIVISION OF OWNERSHIP OF MINES AND SMELTERS IN MEXICO: 1911
(*In Thousands of U.S. Dollars*)

Classification	American	British	French	Mexican	Other
Mines	223,000	43,600	5,000	7,500	7,830
Smelters	26,500	.....	.....	7,000	3,000

SOURCE: M. Letcher, "Wealth of Mexico," *Daily Consular and Trade Reports* (July 18, 1912), p. 316.

The foregoing table is not too satisfactory. For example, the British-owned smelters at Concepción del Oro and Saltillo (Mazapil Copper Company) and the French smelter at El Boleo must have been lumped under "Mines." Hence, the classification "Smelter" might refer solely to custom smelters. In this event, the $3,000,000 in smelters listed as owned by "Others" is unexplained. The figure may include the Mapimí smelter owned by Peñoles—a German-American firm—which was certainly not a custom smelter. Seamon's figures have the additional disadvantage of not being comparable in time due to their varied sources. Also, exactly how ownership in joint enterprises was divided among Americans, British, French, and Mexicans is not clear.[105]

Senator Albert Fall in a U.S. Senate investigation of Mexican affairs in 1919–20 made the most severe critique of the Letcher Report.[106] Senator Fall criticized the method of compiling the report and set American ownership of the total wealth of Mexico at $1,500,000,000. He also believed the value of the mines to be greater but offered no concrete figure. In the course of the investigation, ex-Ambassador Henry L. Wilson estimated that out of 75,000 Americans resident in Mexico in 1910, 5,000 were engaged in mining. Senator Fall's critique, however, should be taken with a grain of salt since his attempts to discredit the revolutionary government of Mexico would lead him to present an inflation of the figures in order to increase both the amount of the damage and the size of the American interests.

Cleona Lewis of the Brookings Institution, in 1938, made a new estimate of American holdings in Mexican mining.[107] Unfortunately the sources are not given, the figures do not cross check, and the actual basis of classification is not clear. However, they do indicate an important trend.

British investments in Mexican mines after the debacle of the early post-independence period were considerably smaller than the American share. Of the early British companies only two with a nominal capital

TABLE 5

United States Investments in Mining and Smelting in Mexico: 1897–1929

(*In Millions of Dollars*)

	1897	1908	1914	1919	1924	1929
Precious Metals[1]	50.0	119.0	140.0	100.0	112.0	116.0
Industrial Metals	18.0	115.0	162.0	122.0	124.0	132.8
Total	68.0	234.0	302.0	222.0	236.0	248.8

[1]Includes mine railways and other facilities built in connection with the industry.

Source: Cleona Lewis, *America's Stake in International Investments* (Washington, D. C.: The Brookings Institution, 1938), pp. 583–584.

of £1,381,721 existed in 1880, and only one—the United Mexican Mining Company in Guanajuato—still operated. The British Companies Register List in 1876 showed 8 companies with a paid-up capital of £1,435,348. By the end of 1884, 14 more companies had been organized with a paid-up capital of only £246,176, but several of them did not survive so the total stood at 16 companies with a paid-up capital of £1,642,902—almost all of which belonged to the United Mexican Company.[108] By 1890 a growing demand for copper and the resumption of British-Mexican diplomatic relations were reflected in increased British capital in Mexican mining. At the end of that year there were 47 companies with an "aggregate nominal capital" of over £8,500,000; 17 of them were capitalized at over £200,000 each. Their actual paid-in capital in 1891 came to £2,760,835. A decade later, at the end of 1900, there were 39 companies with a nominal capital of £5,020,000 but the paid-in capital had risen to £3,790,319. By 1911, 65 companies were registered with a nominal capital of £11,690,000 and, as of 1910, a paid-in capital of £4,522,755. As for the paid-in totals, Alfred Tischendorf noted that they included all shares issued, but the amount subscribed in cash did not exceed two-thirds of the total paid in. Following are some of the largest British enterprises and paid-in totals: Santa Gertrudis Company (£1,368,000); El Oro Mining and Railway Company (£1,147,500); Esperanza, Ltd. (£454,993); Palmarejo and Mexican Gold Fields (£413,121); and Mazapil Copper Company (£401,660). Tischendorf estimates that of 210 companies registered between 1885 and 1910, 57 actually mined ores, 15 returned some dividends, and only 3 paid dividends for longer than 5 years.[109]

French investments were smaller. In 1902, there were an estimated 50,000,000 francs invested in Mexican mining. By 1910, 16 mining companies were nominally French. British capital, however, was invested in many of them, and French capital could be found in many British enterprises. An estimate made in 1914 placed the French interest in mining and petroleum at 391,635,000 francs, but this figure was probably exaggerated in order to bolster French claims for damages during the Revolution against Díaz.[110]

In order to restore our perspective, it is well to realize that investment figures *per se* mean little. The realities of mineral economics are such that many companies hold on to land as reserves or for speculation. Also, most properties are marginal in comparison with the large producers. For example, Southworth and Holms estimated that out of the 25,000 titles outstanding, 50 to 60 per cent "have been taken up by their owners to be worked if convenient and to be sold if possible." At least a third of the 12,500 titles remaining were held by large companies or individuals "for reasons of strategy." Of the remaining 8,750 properties, at least half might "be in a state of semi-development," while most of those actually worked would be under large companies holding a number of titles for each unit.[111] Therefore, the actual activity would be much less than the raw data might indicate.

During the decade 1900–1910, "Mexican mines" held an understandable fascination for American investors. The *Wall Street Summary* summed up the situation by commenting that three-fourths of the dividend-paying mines in Mexico were held by Americans, and they paid a sum 24 per cent in excess of the aggregate net earnings of all the National Banks in the United States, or about $95,000,000. While bank stock paid an average of 5.46 per cent, "sixth-rate mines of Mexico are paying ten to fifteen per cent per annum."[112] With all due respect for the *Summary's* optimism, Díaz was in his heaven, all was right with the world.

The course of development of the Mexican mining industry from 1890 to 1912 is of transcendental importance, for the pattern set then has endured to this day. Today stamp mills have been replaced by crushers and tube mills; the flotation process has displaced, or has become a companion to, cyaniding; and smelting activity has been centralized as some plants closed and others were enlarged. But these changes are superficial, making for greater technical efficiency without affecting the basic structure and pattern of the Mexican nonferrous metals economy. The industry has been living on the districts and the plants developed forty years ago.

CHAPTER 6

Reaction to Foreign Control:
The Mine Law of 1910

POPULAR accounts which state that the Díaz regime was in a conspiracy with foreign interests to ransack Mexico miss the point through oversimplification. While the regime believed that economic liberalism was the best policy, it wished foreign capitalists to join with wealthy Mexicans in the development of Mexico. Having more capital, foreigners managed to secure control over a large part of the economy. The influx of foreign capital and its influence on the Mexican economy did not go unnoticed. After 1905 a change in the Mexican attitude was apparent. Rapid growth of foreign investments roused the latent ire of Mexican nationalists. Nationalization of the major railroads, adoption of the gold standard, and the Panic of 1907 brought questions concerning the relation of Mexico to the outside world to national attention. Anti-Americanism was particularly strong among the hacendados who disliked the encroachment of American land companies. Political "outs" found that anti-Americanism made excellent political tinder. Theodore Roosevelt's "trust busting" and the exposés of the muckrakers had repercussions in Mexico where American capital was active; Limantour engaged in Yankee-baiting on antimonopolistic grounds. Some of this resentment came out in the debates during the passage of the Mine Law of 1910.

In 1904 a committee was appointed to begin framing a new mine law. Miners were riding high then and even talked of a law to grant titles in perpetuity if a mineowner paid his taxes regularly for a stipulated period of time.[1] One of the leading lights of the committee was Rodolfo Reyes, son of General Bernardo Reyes, Governor of Nuevo León. In later years, when Governor Reyes dreamed of running for President upon Díaz's retirement, his platform contained a long section on the abuses of foreign mining companies.[2] Olegario Molina, a wealthy henequen planter from Yucatan, seconded young Reyes. Henequeneros were known for strong antiforeign views.[3]

In February, 1907, the committee presented a draft proposal embodying principles to guide the Minister of Development.[4] It stated that a change was necessary because of the lack of definite regulations in the

78

short and vague Law of 1892. In addition, the regulatory bylaws were too long, and the numerous circulars and directives had to be incorporated to bring the law up to date. The committee attempted several things. It wished to keep the liberal spirit of the Law of 1892 but at the same time wanted a certain amount of control over the activities of miners, particularly the foreigners. Hence, the draft contained a nationalist proscription against foreign miners securing claims in the frontier states without special permission—an idea carried over from a law passed in 1856. Claiming that enough concessions had been granted to give the industry the impulse it was supposed to have needed, the committee recommended a policy of "parsimony in [granting] concessions."[5] Their draft increased the powers of the Ministry of Development in regulating internal mining affairs. It proposed that the Minister himself scrutinize both oil and mine concessions and deny them if he believed them to be contrary to the public interest or if they were held for speculation.[6] It also placed all bitumens, including petroleum, under special federal jurisdiction, thus reversing the Mine Laws of 1884 and 1892. The committee added a section titled "On the responsibilities for mine accidents," which made mineowners civilly responsible for all accidents in their mines by voiding the "fellow-servant" defense.[7] This section was justified by citing the daily spectacle of crippled and killed miners—which amounted to a national disgrace—and charged that Mexico was far behind all other civilized countries in protecting workers from industrial hazards. Finally, the committee recommended empowering the Public Attorney to prosecute all injury cases and to act as the plaintiff's attorney if requested.

Minister of Fomento Molina worked on the draft for another year before presenting it to President Díaz, who had already secured Congressional consent to enact the draft into law by decree. But the outcry that greeted the draft made Díaz adopt a cautious attitude; his cabinet held long discussions at which interested parties made their objections known. He finally decided to permit the pros and cons of the bill to be fought in public. Molina's major addition to the draft was a section which dealt with foreigners holding mining property.[8] Articles 141 through 143 provided that no foreigner or joint foreign-Mexican enterprise could hold mining property in the border states without prior permission. In case of inheritance or possession through liens, the new owner would still have to obtain permission. Article 144 bluntly stated:

Foreign corporate bodies are incapable of denouncing and acquiring henceforth, by any process, either mining properties or liens thereon within the territory of the Mexican Republic.

While Articles 141 through 143 could be defended on precedent,[9] Article 144 was quite disconcerting. However, foreign investors were better off in Mexico than in the United States. In Mexico there were no restrictions in nonborder states, and any corporation could set up a Mexican subsidiary quite easily. United States laws allowed no one to file claims on public lands until he had announced his intention to become an American citizen. In any event, Molina had already started to put teeth into his proposals by changing the possessive clause in special concessions from "to the individual named or the company he might organize," to "to himself or by way of the Mexican company which might be organized for this purpose, in conformity with the laws of the Republic."[10]

Attacks upon the Mexican government, and upon Molina himself, appeared in American and Mexican mining journals. The major complaint —or threat—was that since the law would rob foreigners of confidence in Mexico by taking away the protection of their home governments, the number of mine claims filed would drop. On July 20, 1908, Molina defended his views in a letter to the *Mining and Scientific Press* of San Francisco.[11] He first restated the legal precedent for Articles 141 through 143, adding his fear that unscrupulous "adventurous spirits" might use their property in border states to foment trouble between nations (a jibe barbed by the actions of Americans during the Cananea strike of 1906). As for Article 144, Molina said that the Mexican government had to exercise more control over companies operating in Mexico, because companies organized abroad could call any regulation in the Mexican national interest a violation of their rights and appeal to their home government for aid—which had happened before in Mexican history. In other words, they had rights in Mexico denied to Mexicans themselves! Therefore, although Mexico desired to have and appreciated the work of foreign capital, Molina felt that some regulation was necessary in the national interest, particularly in the case of "trusts" organized outside Mexico. Other than this, said Molina, there were no restrictions on companies operating in Mexico; the law would not be retroactive; and mines in the border regions could always be worked under leases.

The Mexican Chamber of Mines approached the problem of the new law warily. It sent a long petition to Díaz and Molina listing the many things it liked about the new law, but condemned the clauses on the civil responsibilities of mineowners and the antiforeign clauses. Claiming that foreign investors would turn to other regions, the Chamber insisted that the cry of "México para los mexicanos!" would be most disturbing after the financial Panic of 1907. José Luis Requena, a member of Congress, was elected President of the Chamber to carry out the fight. In November the Chamber triumphantly announced that, as a result of its petition made at a cabinet meeting with Díaz, Article 144 and the mining accidents clauses had been deleted. Molina admitted as much. The disability of foreign companies to denounce claims in frontier states was not done away with completely, but the state-wide prohibition was restricted to 80 kilometers. Predicting a field day for antiforeign deputies in Congress when the law was discussed, the Chamber still felt quite proud of its work.[12]

Final debate on the bill began in the Chamber of Deputies in December, 1909, after being deferred to the committee for further study.[13] Manuel Calero, a leading mine attorney; José Luis Requena, President of the Chamber of Mines; and Jenaro García, a mineowner quite active in the Chamber of Mines, shepherded the bill. However, the floor leaders were not completely in favor of the bill, and when it suited their purpose they pressed for changes. Molina gave as the basic reasons for changing the Law of 1892 a need for greater centralization and federalization, even to putting the mercantile aspects of the industry under the Civil Code of the Federal District.[14] Precepts taken from regulatory bylaws and technical circulars issued since 1892 were placed in the body of the law. The bill sharply curtailed the discretionary powers of the local mining agents in granting claims (with the resultant errors), and more power was placed directly in the hands of the Minister of Development. It made special allowances for assessments levied on mining securities. Finally, the draft gave inspectors for the Ministry the power to visit mines to check compliance with the code and the concession, and to gather statistical data not of a financial nature.[15]

Despite earlier discussions and revisions, the debate was long and acrimonious. Opposition concentrated on the sections relating to the new powers given the Ministry of Development and the federalization of all aspects of mining. Administrative law was thoroughly examined after many deputies objected to the power of the bureaucracy over the courts in the matter of easements. This clash was but a phase of the larger fight kept in the background: the conflict between the landlords and the miners. Molina's draft contained an article prohibiting further exploration for new mines on the excuse that in view of the building of railroads, the extension of mapping and geological knowledge, and the long record of abuses by prospectors, no need for further exploration existed. Requena attacked this proposal vigorously, denouncing it as a device of the Minister to play on the landlords' prejudices. He stressed the viewpoint of the landlord, who, he said, regarded the economic gains of a larger market for his foodstuffs more than offset by the evils resulting from the presence of a local mining enterprise. Then, shifting to a "national viewpoint," Requena passionately exclaimed that as Russia is known as the granary of Europe, Mexico will be known as the "metalliferous deposit of the world"—but only if further explorations were actively encouraged and the greedy desire of the landlord to simply hold on to land were curbed.[16] Despite Calero's attempts to defend the Minister's proposition, Requena carried his point and they compromised by providing that the explorer, before being given permission to prospect, would be required to make a deposit to cover the damage which might result from his diggings. This settlement was in favor of the large exploration companies since the independent prospector would find the deposit and legal fees beyond his resources.[17]

Also discussed was the relationship of the mineral industry to the government. Although the Law of 1892 was silent regarding ownership of the subsoil, the "Ley sobre división de los Bienes Inmuebles" (Law concerning the division of Real Property) of December 18, 1902, stated in Article 2 that the subsoil belonged to the nation. In any event, the traditional status of the subsoil had not altered, for to legalize such a change would require a renunciation by the government, as in the case of bitumens in the Code of 1884.[18] To describe the government's rights, Molina's draft used the term "dominio eminente," taken from the Ley de Bienes Inmuebles. When the Congressional Commission protested that the phrase was misused and inaccurate, a compromise term described the government as holding the subsoil "dominio directo."[19] Also, while the Law of 1892 had merely described possession as coming from a title issued by the Ministry of Development, Article 11 of the new law very explicitly stated: "Mining property (la propiedad minera) is acquired originally from the Nation, by means of a title issued by the Executive Power. . . ."[20] However, the question of ownership of the "ore in place" in property covered by a title appeared to be settled in favor of the miner. Calero, President of the Congressional Commission, said:

> . . . the mines with their deposits, minerals and their workings, are the property of the miner during the times in which he complies with the law, pays the mining tax and under the sanction that the State will withdraw them the day on which the miner fails to pay the tax.[21]

(Repossession by the government, however, was only an administrative matter once the facts of nonpayment were established.) This interpretation differs fundamentally from the present-day concept which holds that only extracted ore belongs in equity to the miner; ore in place in the concession still belongs to the state.[22] During the debate an attempt was made to include petroleum among the minerals covered by the mining law. Congress rejected the motion on the grounds that the conditions established by the Code of 1884 had led to property rights which could not be abrogated and would lead to trouble with the Supreme Court.

Although unsuccessful, the strong demands for greater control over the subsoil by the government foreboded ill for the future. During the final sessions, debate on the floor caused over 20 articles to be revised and several chapters to be rewritten. On many chapters the vote was far from overwhelming, particularly on those enlarging the power of the Ministry of Development. Opposition votes in some cases went as high as 47 and 48 while government support fell to 75—a safe margin but one indicating strong opposition.[23]

When the new mining law went into effect on January 1, 1910, the future never seemed brighter. There were the usual chronic complaints about the tariff-protected dynamite monopoly and the multiplicity of taxes;[24] but the world was recovering from the Panic of 1907, and Mexico was entering its centennial year of independence with production reaching new peaks every year. Silver cyaniding, new smelters, more capital, expanding railroads, the revival of old districts, and the opening of strong new ones, all augured well. Under such circumstances a slight display of antiforeign feeling by Mexicans could be overlooked.

CHAPTER 7

The Mine Worker:
Pre-1910

NEXT to fabulous mines, cheap and docile labor was the siren attraction of Mexico to investors. Mexican mineowners mouthed the dictum that low-cost labor was not necessarily cheap labor, but they found that with patience and training Mexican labor stood up well under competition.[1] Prejudice often led to the importation of skilled foreigners who could not communicate with their illiterate and underfed subordinates, although ASARCO used Mexican mechanics wherever possible, employing Americans only as master mechanics.[2] Employers were free of one major difficulty in Mexico. E. E. Olcott, the President of the American Institute of Mining Engineers, wanted to discover their secret when he remarked to his Mexican hosts:

> We want to learn, while here, why it is that in this happy land strikes are unknown. It must be that sweet contentment blesses the hearth-stone, and a man is free to go to his work as his needs and inclinations direct. May the blessings of this peace rest long upon you.[3]

Mr. Olcott received no prize for irony. No one informed him that strikes were illegal and that the Rurales were vigilant in enforcing the law. As for the Mexican going "to his work as his needs and inclinations direct," any mine manager could have pointed out the number of drawbacks arising when such freedom is given to "indolent and child-like" people.

The nature and character of the Mexican laborer has been the topic of endless discussions. The attitude of many "old hands" has been well summarized by E. K. Judd:

> Principal drawbacks to Mexican labor are: (a) Inefficiency due to low vitality, unhygienic living, indulgence in liquors, warm climate and high altitude in some localities; (b) insistence on observing numerous fiestas or saints' days. While a Mexican miner can carry excessive loads on his back or shoulders he is often inefficient as a driller, trammer or shoveler, and is usually unskillful as a mechanic. Best results with Mexican labor are attained by: (a) placing as much work as possible on short-term contracts; (b) improving living conditions of mining camps, with special attention

to sanitation; (c) contributing to the support of the local church; (d) allowing reasonable opportunity for sports and entertainment; (e) discouraging the sale of liquor.[4]

Others thought differently. W. H. Triplett, of Peñoles, remarked:

> Inefficiency has no doubt been due to a low standard of living, warm climate and high altitude in many instances, but this criticism does not apply universally. I am an old hand who marvels at the amount of work native drillers, muckers and hammermen can turn out and do when there is an incentive.[5]

A Mexican's seeming irresponsibility often derived from a unique set of circumstances, such as the desire to return home for corn planting and harvesting.[6] His lack of initiative, inability to save, absences while celebrating too many holidays, willingness to work only three or four days a week if that paid for necessities, insatiable desire for alcohol—all were pointed out as proof of a natural inferiority. Few employers could understand that a penniless peon, with a heritage of personal and economic oppression on the hacienda, could not rise to the level of discipline expected of European or American workmen. A manager's impatience must also be understood; he could not wait out the years necessary to re-educate his employees; he had to produce ore and bullion today.[7]

Smelters had to run furnaces 24 hours a day and felt the burden of unreliability most heavily. E. P. Mathewson recounted his experiences working for the Guggenheims at Monterrey by telling how on rainy afternoons he would send the watchmen out to round up the night shift. Even then he counted noses to determine how many furnaces would be run and how many banked.[8] The Esmeralda smelter in Sierra Mojada in the 1880's procured labor for night and Sunday work by impressment and used its control over the local water supply to control malingering: those who did not work received no water ration.[9] Writers noted at the time a tendency to favor smaller furnaces which could be handled more easily with less labor.[10]

Feast days were annoying. They included Sundays, national feast days, the day of the patron saint of the locality, days of the patron saints of nearby churches and villages, birthdays of owners and administrators as well as the men's own and members of their family, plus baptisms, weddings, and funerals of friends or relations. To which might be added *San Lunes*—the Saint Mondays—needed to sober up from the week-end. However, as the twentieth century progressed there was a reduction in the number of holidays.[11]

Determining the wage scale of Mexican miners is almost impossible. The lack of reliable over-all figures is complicated by the great variance in wages in different areas and the changing wage levels during the 20 years preceding the Revolution of 1910. Mine operators were responsible for generally raising agricultural wages. Customary hacienda wages of a peso a week and a ration of corn were replaced in the mines by straight cash. Nineteenth-century mine wages ran about 50 centavos a day. Between 1892 and 1902 wages in mining rose 27 to 33 per cent and in beneficiation plants from 29 to 52 per cent. By 1910 only peons doing unskilled work received less than a peso a day. Constant demands for labor from new mines, smelters, railroads, textile mills, and other industrial establishments drove field hands' wages up to 50 centavos a day, and most mine workers received from 1 to 3 pesos.[12] Industrial enterprises still complained about a lack of labor despite the higher wages offered, for hacienda peons were not free to move and less cultured native groups were not readily amenable to wage-labor. A basic difficulty with the wage problem was that it was a political one linked to bad social conditions beyond the power of foreigners to alter.[13]

Generally speaking, wages tended to be highest in the north and along the Pacific coast region, gradually becoming lower in the central district around Mexico City.[14] Wages in Oaxaca were probably the lowest in Mexico. Cananea's 3 pesos a day was unusual and excited much adverse comment among mine operators. A "typical" wage—if such a thing existed—might be found in Guanajuato, where the Guanajuato Mining and Milling Company, in 1908, reported paying the few highly skilled piston-machine drillers and machine-tool sharpeners 3 pesos a day; the more general types of workers (hand drillers, skipmen, timbermen, trackmen, pipemen, conductors, timekeepers, motormen, and watchmen) received from 1 to 2 pesos a day; and the most unskilled labor (muckers, ore sorters, peons, crushermen, and helpers) got from 50 to 75 centavos a day.[15]

Mining companies employed few women and children. A census of Guanajuato in 1884 showed that less than 10 per cent of the workers were women or minors.[16] Doubtless cheap adult male labor and prevalent superstitions deterred attempts to use females except for ore sorting. In the twentieth century the number of women employed declined further. In 1901 some 92,187 men and 5,595 children, but only 414 women, were employed in the entire industry. Companies employed children for simple tasks at from 20 to 35 cents (U.S.) per day.[17]

The common remark that a Mexican worker was paid what he was worth actually served to cover vicious attitudes which had developed concerning his health. An untutored Mexican peon was generally underfed and as a consequence physically incapable of performing a day's labor by foreign standards. If he were married, it was a moot question whether or not he would have sufficient money—even after giving up drinking and gambling—to feed, clothe, and shelter himself and a family. As a result, mineowners had to hire two men to get one man's work. Undoubtedly a good meal every shift at the employer's expense would have paid for itself in increased output.[18] With malaria, hookworm, tuberculosis, silicosis, pellagra, and venereal diseases rampant, the mineworker was probably as often sick from preventable diseases as he was hungry.[19]

The debilitating effect of the Mexican diet was aggravated by poor housing. Mineworkers were not singled out; they shared the common lot of the Mexican poor. Houses with damp floors caused pneumonia and rheumatism, while stuffing the cracks to keep out the cold resulted in carbonic acid asphyxia which sapped the workers' vitality. Housing varied with the district. Towns in older mining areas were built of stone, brick or adobe but had little else to commend them. In remote camps, housing could hardly rate as shelter. At zinc camps in the north-central district, the American Consul in Monterrey wrote of seeing men living in "caves, holes in the ground, or in thatched huts." Covering was insufficient during inclement weather; clothes were rudimentary and water, packed to the camp, was used only for cooking. Food purchased at the company store consisted of wheat or corn tortillas, beans, coffee, goat meat, and sometimes beef.[20] On the other hand, in places such as Santa Rosalia and Mapimí, decent houses were built by the company. In Cananea the company provided the municipal facilities and left the actual development to individual owners. Although company town houses often resembled a series of oversized packing cases, they offered electricity, potable water, baths, and toilet facilities. A sanitary organization of sorts existed, and a doctor often provided free medical attention.

A critical note was injected by Ralph M. Ingersoll, a young Yale graduate, who spent a year in Nacozari, a company town built by the Moctezuma Copper Company, a Phelps Dodge subsidiary. Ingersoll found the company houses to be "one-room shacks about fifteen feet square" and felt that they differed little from the houses built by the men for themselves, except that they did not live two families to the room.[21] A company spokesman in rebuttal wrote that the houses were "substantially built," the roofs were tight, the rent was less than the interest on the investment, and living conditions were "infinitely better than in the majority of Mexican towns." Moctezuma was also proud of its water and sewage system which cost $100,000 to install.[22]

Ingersoll's key charge went unanswered: the company was doing nothing to combat the traditional Mexican attitude toward modern sanitation and diet but acted as though its responsibility stopped with safety-first training and medical service. Putting in a bath was not enough, for the Mexican who never had a bath was not too interested in experimenting.[23] Phelps Dodge, however, did maintain a sanitary mine and an exemplary first-aid program. At Pachuca, mine hygiene was so poor that hookworm was endemic in every mine in the area and had spread to the town population.[24]

In the matter of accidents, the callous attitude of some companies was beyond belief. For years the customary compensation for fatal accidents was 50 pesos ($25, U.S.). Fifty pesos in coin paid all at once was believed to be ample: "The average Indian mind could not think more than fifty pesos worth." Small wonder that death was an incidental affair; safety campaigns were more expensive than compensation.[25] Injury to a worker was merely another statistic and accepted as part of the enterprise. An enthusiastic American doctor reported:

> A Mexican mining camp is the delight of a young American doctor; what with the number and variety of diseases and surgical cases resulting from mine accidents, he is certain of an interesting and varied practice.[26]

On the appointment of a state mine inspector in Hidalgo, the *Mexican Mining Journal* observed that mine accidents in Pachuca were too frequent; one mine was responsible for over six hundred accidents, one-quarter of which were fatal! Companies countenanced workers drinking pulque (agave beer) in unlimited quantities. At one time a one-inch pipe facilitated the distribution of pulque underground at Pachuca. If a man happened to doze near a winze after a meal punctuated by frequent visits to the pigskin, the fact was likely to be reflected in the week's accident statistics.[27] Workers displayed an attitude of cheerful optimism tempered with fatalism.

Accident compensation was usually a token payment. Ernest Gruening met a begger in Guanajuato who had lost both legs in an accident in 1908. His company had paid the hospital expenses and had given him in addition 5 pesos; he had been begging ever since. In east-central Mexico, an American company officer told Gruening that before the Revolution the company paid hospital expenses and 10 or 15 pesos if the man were badly crippled—"if he lost an arm or a leg, for instance." Also an attempt was made to find him a job as porter or watchman, "but if there was no such job he was out of luck."[28]

Companies in isolated districts often provided free medical attention for their workers. Others, in more populated areas, used ingenious health plans. Fabulously wealthy Dos Estrellas provided medical care for its workers and their families: hospitalization and 2 pesos a week until a worker could report for work again. Death benefits ranged from 50 to 100 pesos, depending upon the man's job and length of service; the company paid the funeral expenses. Dos Estrellas financed this paternalistic program from the profits made selling dynamite at full retail price to their *contratistas* (foremen over piecework squads), thus avoiding payroll deductions.[29]

Employers found it a trying experience to train green labor. Edwin Ludlow recorded this experience in the Coahuila coal fields.[30] Americans were used at first, but they became addicted to the local brandy. A select few, kept on beer and light wine, were retained as foremen. The company tried Mexicans, Japanese, Chinese, Negroes, and Italians with varying results. Mexican peasants had no concept of continuous labor; some would follow the mine car out of the pit to see it weighed before loading another. Mexican metal miners, puzzled by the large amounts mined, found it difficult to adjust to coal mining. Ludlow rated the different groups by the number of tons per day loaded. By his ratings white Americans loaded 10 tons per day, Negroes 8 tons, Italians 6 tons, Japanese 5 tons, Chinese 4 tons, and Mexicans only 2 tons. He based the Mexican showing perforce on "green miners" since good men became contratistas, employing and supervising 6 to 20 laborers. Ludlow hoped that the young boys might grow into a generation of coal miners as in the United States, England, and Germany. The Revolution ended those plans.[31]

Mexican workers were not essentially mercenary; they only lacked industrial initiative. "Day's-pay" systems were unworkable, for the men would stall at every opportunity. Hence it was best to put as many jobs as possible on a contract basis.[32] Sometimes employers figured the contract on a "*tarea*," or task, system in which a man was assigned a daily quota and permitted to go home when he completed it. Opportunities to earn extra money by doing more than the task were almost universally ignored.[33] At times the contract was for straight piecework. A superintendent at Nacozari evaluated that system:

> But given a contract and the assurance that he will get so much money for each ton he mines, and that it doesn't matter how long he takes doing it, or how often he sits down to contemplate life, he will work with a vigor which is remarkable.[34]

Most mines let their contracts through contratistas. A job would be laid out at a rate to give the average workman the amount he would earn on day's-pay. A contratista recruited the men—no alien shift boss could hope to bring as many men as regularly to work as a Mexican recognized by his men as a leader—and kept them at work to meet the time schedule.[35] He made whatever terms he could with his men; sometimes they worked as a team sharing the money. Whether the contratista worked or not, he was expert at the job and his close supervision was highly effective in cajoling work out of the men. Usually he made a good wage out of the margin between the company's estimate and the actual labor cost. A particularly rapid job might yield a bonus to be shared among the men. Contratistas were the backbone of the labor system in many mines and generally made four or five times as much as the men they hired. They were well worth the money they earned as supervisors.

Miners had to be paid every week, since paying wages for longer periods undercut the men's spirit and made awards for speed or efficiency appear chimerical. Still the men often spent their earnings in a few days and had to borrow against the next week's wages. Even today a system of *prestamos* (loans) is part of even the largest payroll offices. This extra burden is repaid by the stimulation it gives the men.[36]

Thievery was a constant headache. T. A. Rickard remarked that while peon labor is cheap, material stolen by the workers made it costly.[37] Francisco Gamboa had complained in 1761 that Mexican miners conjugated the verb *rapar* (to snatch) in all its moods, taking picks, crows, candles, clothes, ore, and silver.[38] In twentieth-century Guanajuato, church altars blazed with the companies' candles on the local saint's day. Mineowners regularly asked the priests to preach sermons on the horrors of hell for those who stole their employers' property after they were paid honest wages. "The next day those mining tools reappear as silently and mysteriously as they had disappeared." In return, "The priest is generously treated by the mineowners and managers. . . ."[39]

Ore stealing was an accepted practice—on the part of the workers at any rate. Tradition states that Antonio Obregón, between 1765 and 1785, built the Valenciana cathedral in Guanajuato by persuading the miners to put their stolen ore in a huge pile as they emerged from the mine.[40] Methods of getting pilfered ore out of the mine were legion, although searching miners was routine, even in some cases examining the men's mouths.[41] Many mines had a professional searcher reputed to have a "nose for stolen ore" that was aided by timely tips from supervisors. At Batopilas, "old Don Romulo" would dramatically knock the ashes out of a man's pipe in front of his companions to find silver dust underneath.[42] No matter how the men might rail against affronts to their dignity, the dealers who bought stolen ore did well.[43] Often owners accepted the losses as part of the business. Catching a thief in *flagrante delicto* was not always wise. Local sympathy lay with the thief, and the owner might be in difficulties if anyone were hurt in a fracas.[44]

Relations between mineworkers and their employers before 1910 were not on an organized basis. Peons drifted into mining when the industry's demands for labor exceeded the supply of trained miners. Helpless and bewildered by the new life, the peon's illiteracy did little to aid him in making an adjustment. Loyalty to a *patron* (employer) could not offset his irresponsibility. To worsen matters, many of the foreigners brought in as supervisors never learned more than a "pidgin Spanish." Some Americans crossing the Rio Grande gave up ideas they may have had concerning the equality of men and let their prejudices run free. They looked upon Mexican labor as a particularly unsatisfactory brand of commodity: "The peon represented exactly to them what the hoists and pumps did, only the former were more unstable, less fixed and calculable, and therefore more exasperating and depraved."[45]

Peons responded with sullenness and disobedience. They had no organization since the Constitution of 1857, reflecting economic liberalism, gave little comfort to strike organizers. Mexico's Penal Code provided for imprisonment and fines for any one who used physical or moral force "with the object of increasing or decreasing the salaries or wages of the workers or to impede the free exercise of industry or labor."[46] One mine manager wrote from a practical point of view:

> Strikes . . . can never take place under the present system of government in Mexico. There is no objection to a man or any number of men striking, but the moment these begin to interfere with other men taking their places, or the moment they begin to destroy property, the Federal Government takes a hand, and the leaders will, in all probability, be shot without trial. . . . The Mexican laborer appreciates the methods of the Federal Government, and is a great respecter of property, and of the individual as well as public rights.[47]

Mass protests were generally handled by calling the *jefe político* (prefect) of the district, who would round up the men, have the Rurales crack a few skulls and arrest the leaders if they were identifiable. Mine managers openly boasted of these methods to timid investors.[48]

The Cananea strike with its wholesale violence was a great shock to Americans: the dissatisfied miners should have moved on. Traditionally, Mexican workers protested in a personal manner. Although strikes were reported from time to time, a more common method of protest was the one used against a foreman employed by the Guggenheims who, during the building of the Monterrey smelter, attempted to get as much work out of the Mexicans paid 50 centavos (25 cents, U.S.) as out of the Americans paid $5 a day. One night five men chosen by lot by the work gangs from among themselves broke into his room and stabbed him to death. Rurales moved in, caught five men, and shot them without trial the next day. Troops were then stationed at the plant to prevent any further disturbance.[49]

The Revolution of 1910 completely changed the character of Mexican labor. Strikes became commonplace as unions won recognition and a place for themselves in the Mexican economy. During the 1930's, under President Cárdenas, the last vestiges of docile labor disappeared, and the employers had to deal with aggressive labor leaders.

PART III

THE REVOLUTION
OF 1910-1920

CHAPTER 8

Miners' Problems,
1910–1917

WITH hindsight we can see the shortcomings and weaknesses of Díaz Mexico. Social jealousy, hidden political rivalry, and economic conflict bred out of rapid change undermined the social order. As Díaz aged, oblique challenges to his power appeared, and he resorted to a series of stratagems before the election of 1910 to flush out his opponents. Two of them, General Bernardo Reyes and Francisco I. Madero, had pointedly denounced the influence of foreign mining interests and particularly mentioned the Cananea incident.[1] Reyes finally went into honorable exile as an ambassador; Madero, a stubborn idealist and scion of a wealthy landholding and business-minded family, ended up in prison.

Francisco Madero, a moderate Liberal, believed that "freedom" and "free elections" were the panaceas for Mexico. Madero escaped and fled to San Antonio, Texas, where he issued a declaration denouncing Díaz. His brother Gustavo came to his support with money embezzled from a railroad company that was building a line to serve several mine districts in Zacatecas.[2] After setbacks in the fall and winter of 1910, other dissident elements arose, and the Díaz regime collapsed. In May, 1911, Madero entered Mexico City.

The Mine Law of 1910 was little over a year old. Madero preserved this law with the addition of the "Police and Security Regulations for Mine Workings," enacted on October 4, 1912.[3] After striking from the mine code the section covering employers' responsibility for mine accidents, the legislative drafting committee had substituted an article providing for a future series of police regulations; these regulations constitute Madero's contribution to Mexican mining law.

"The Police and Security Regulations" comprised a complete set of safety rules. They required the employment of a competent engineer, a first-aid attendant, and the maintenance of a complete set of mine maps. They detailed instructions for the handling, storing, and distribution of dynamite. Digging exploratory pits and all tunneling work could be done only if the operation did not endanger surface property or improvements. Rules required adequate ventilation, good timbering, and machinery guards to prevent injury. A special section covering coal mines prescribed margins of safety for the gaseous and weak-structured Mexican mines. The law punished violators by jail sentences as well as by fines. Enforcement was sporadic until the late 1920's when a series of government safety campaigns put the Regulations into full effect. They still serve as Mexico's basic mine safety ordinance.

Problems plagued Madero's regime. Local rebellions continued under the pretext of land reform or became sheer banditry. His finances were shaky and the bureaucracy, carried over from the old regime, was lukewarm in its loyalty. And the American ambassador was not too friendly.[4] In his memoirs, Ambassador Henry Lane Wilson wrote that Madero's receptions "were attended by only a few members of the diplomatic corps and by others of doubtful origin and peculiar appearance." This contrasted with the Díaz receptions, "which though simple and democratic, had a dignity and repose which imparted to them a definite character."[5]

General Victoriano Huerta, an army leader held over from the Díaz administration, was the strong man who appeared. He was the prime mover of a triumvirate organized to overthrow Madero. In the melee which followed, Madero was assassinated and Huerta emerged as leader of Mexico. Immediately a revolt broke out. Venustiano Carranza, Governor of Coahuila, took the leadership supported by several military chiefs which included Alvaro Obregón, formerly a small landholder in Sonora, and Doroteo Aranago, better known as Pancho Villa, a bandit chief of no particular political persuasion turned general.

The revolutionaries called themselves "Constitutionalists"; Carranza assumed the grandiloquent title, "First Chief of the Constitutionalist Army Entrusted with the Executive Power." They refused to recognize Huerta's *de facto* control or the legality of any official acts emanating from Mexico City. Despite the recognition of Huerta by several European powers, President Wilson withheld recognition and committed the United States to a policy of "watchful waiting."

Huerta at first contained and defeated his opponents, but the financial burden of the war proved too much and an American arms embargo particularly hurt him. News of an attempt to land arms at Vera Cruz led to the American occupation of that port, an incident which completely alienated the two countries; Carranza became as rabidly anti-Yankee as he was anti-Huerta.[6]

Huerta's installation as strong man had unexpected side effects. To stop the outflow of bullion, he taxed the export of gold 10 per cent and later embargoed it. He raised the tariff 50 per cent and doubled the stamp tax. The public hoarded silver coins. To secure money for their needs, mining companies sent bullion to the Mexico City mint. When Huerta stopped sending back coins, the miners hoarded or smuggled out their bullion. With gold at a high premium and world silver prices up 20 per cent, some optimists believed that large profits could be made by precious metals miners who paid their taxes and wages in depreciated money. Pachuca and El Oro took advantage of the situation until the smelters closed and the railroads broke down.[7] By September, 1913, Huerta plagued businessmen for forced loans. At Monterrey ASARCO was "assessed" $12,500; the Monterrey Steel Company, $10,000; and the Waters-Pierce Oil Company, $7,500. ASARCO attempted "a company policy not to pay blackmail." But when a spokesman was asked whether the demands were met, he answered, "We had to, or he'd take us by the throat."[8] Between December, 1910, and December, 1913, mining stocks on the Mexico City exchange fell on the average 25 to 50 per cent. No matter how stable the company, only by uncovering a bonanza with a possibility of disposing of the ore could it resist the trend.[9] In July, 1914, Huerta went into exile and Constitutionalist troops occupied Mexico City.

Carranza's alliance with Pancho Villa did not last. By the fall of 1914 the men were at loggerheads; Obregón supported Carranza. Working with the peasant leader, Emiliano Zapata, who did not trust Carranza's agrarian program, Villa drove Carranza back to Vera Cruz but could not crush him. Ultimately Carranza's stubbornness and Obregón's armies won out.[10] Villa fell back to his bailiwick in the north and ruled the area until Obregón reduced him to guerrilla status. After the Pershing Expedition of 1916 withdrew, Generals Plutarco Calles and Lázaro Cárdenas chased Villa over northwestern Mexico. He finally made his peace in 1920. Meanwhile, Zapata retreated into the Sierra Madre del Sur where he held out until his assassination in 1919.

It is surprising that Americans could not appreciate Carranza's conservatism. Blinded by his failure to control his armies and by his ardent nationalism, they could not see that he was not their real enemy. In order to raise fighting forces and to appease the social revolutionary leaders, Carranza had to espouse a new cause. Only under Obregón's prodding did he adopt programs calling for land redistribution and labor reforms in an effort to attract new allies to fight a total war against Villa and Zapata. He also finally accepted a new Constitution embodying the ideals of the Revolution.

Hardships suffered by mining enterprises varied with the course of the Revolution. When Madero revolted against Díaz in 1910 and 1911, the cutting of a few railroad lines and the rerouting of bullion shipments were slight inconveniences. Low metal prices and the American zinc tariff were greater problems, along with the shortage of dynamite caused by a government embargo.[11] Americans were impressed by the pains revolutionaries took to avoid molesting foreigners and their property. In the light of later actions, it is difficult to suppress a sardonic smile over the report:

The revolutionists have treated the people and especially the foreigners with every consideration, even better in instances than the federal troops. It has been the most gentlemanly revolution I have ever heard or read about.[12]

The fighting over, Mexico awaited the election of Madero in November, 1911. Many mineowners paid their taxes in advance to receive a 5 per cent reduction.[13] Suppressing banditry and restoring confidence seemed minor points. Miners expected fair treatment, a curtailment of special concessions and privileges, the encouragement of small enterprises, and more frequent strikes and higher wages. Abraham González, provisional Governor of Chihuahua, summed up the government's general viewpoint:

> I am well . . . aware that a few rich Americans and other foreigners interested in great syndicates and Mexican concessions regret the overthrow of the Díaz oligarchy, but their number is insignificant. Heretofore, only the rich syndicates could get a concession. These great concessions have worked an injury to the great masses of the people, the foreigner of small means as well as the Mexican. . . . We are going to begin some legislation that may be expected to put an end to the inequitous [*sic*] system of giving away the heritage of the people to the big syndicates.[14]

No new plans were made for the future; the gossip undermining Madero was already starting.[15]

Revolution to the workers meant a chance to strike for higher wages and demand a redress of grievances. Mineowners complained in March, 1911, that instead of working steadily the men were spending time discussing the Revolution. Some men deserted the mines to become soldiers for 2 pesos a day.[16] By June, 1911, a wave of strikes hit Mexico. Smelters at Velardeña, Chihuahua, Aguascalientes, Monterrey, Torreón, and Mapimí, as well as the mining camps of Santa Eulalia, Parral, Naica, El Oro, and Cananea were all closed. At Chihuahua, for example, the men received from 1 to 2 pesos for a 10-hour day. They demanded 25 per cent increase in wages, lower house rents, the abolition of hospital fees, company police, and company stores. These strikes were settled by concessions and compromises. ASARCO, "to help the new administration," ordered a minimum wage of a peso a day at its smelters. The head of the Mining Department refused to extend the order to his division. In an ensuing strike the Tiro General shaft, which was being dewatered, was flooded and several hundred thousand dollars in construction work was lost.

In January, 1912, the Western Federation of Miners announced its intention to enter Mexico.[17] In an attempt to pacify the antagonists, the Director of the Department of Labor issued a circular noting that the workers were within their rights in forming unions. Employers, he said, had no grounds for fearing that the men would try to persecute them or take control of the enterprises just because they had formed a union.[18] The appeal had little effect. The companies took a stronger stand. They threatened the workers with lockouts "rather than grant unreasonable wage demands." An unsympathetic reporter summed up the miners' plight quite succinctly:

> Without organization, without funds, living absolutely from hand to mouth, and with the excess of labor over demand, the striker must quickly come to terms. What little success strikes may have had in isolated cases, was due to the desire to avoid encounters and aggravations at the present state of affairs, not to the efforts of the strikers.[19]

In December, 1912, Peñoles broke a strike by threatening to close for six months. Later, Maderist leaders appealed to the men to be more reasonable; a smelter strike would put four times as many miners out of work, and the government could not stand the strain. At El Oro a strike was quelled by troops and trouble "avoided." Cananea reduced the workday to 9 hours and raised wages to 3.50 pesos. Later strikes were all effectively broken.[20]

Despite labor unrest, 1911 and 1912 were good years for the mining industry, and a number of production records were set. In 1912 a number of mines came into bonanzas. ASARCO reported that the smelting department profits were the largest ever earned in Mexico.[21] But without an efficient rural police force, the government forces held only the larger towns and cities, and guerrilla bands roamed the countryside. For its readers' information, in August, 1912, the *Mexican Mining Journal* printed an illustrated article entitled "Armored Blockhouses and Portable Steel Shields," describing easy-to-construct defenses for railroads, mines, and haciendas.[22] Orozquistas attacked the El Tigre mine in September, 1912, causing $30,000 damage. They looted the town and carried off $50,000 in gold and silver bullion. An alert mine manager saved the bullion by casting it into 400-pound ingots whose weight caused the mules of the retreating revolutionists to collapse. All the bullion was recovered.[23] Before a raid at Pachuca, one company buried its bullion in a bed of concrete. Afterward it took two days to blast it out.[24]

In the years following Madero's assassination, news dispatches from Mexico were filled with lootings, kidnappings, and murder. Railroads failed; the United States embargoed the export of dynamite; camp supplies gave out; and smelters worked intermittently as coke and ore shipments became unpredictable.[25] When ASARCO notified its employees that all who wished might request transfer to safer plants, no one applied. ASARCO doubled its usual 10 per cent bonus.

The ensuing revolutionary anarchy shut down most of the major mining areas in the country. Pachuca, the Jalisco camps, and the copper properties along the border managed to continue operations, but even they suffered during the Vera Cruz incident and Villa's vengeance campaigns. Only the Amparo and Cinco Minas properties in Jalisco operated regularly during the entire disturbance, exporting their silver through Pacific coast ports.[26]

Northern copper producers enjoyed a peculiar situation. While World War I boomed copper prices, El Boleo was completely untouched by the revolutionary fighting and Cananea and Nacozari had only a few close scrapes. Their location near the border gave them some protection and they even expanded. Cananea installed new converters equalled in size only by those at Butte. When Villa dominated the district, he encouraged full operations for the taxes.[27]

Between battles the Villistas and Carrancistas (followers of Villa and Carranza) lived off the country and effected working arrangements. Carranza in 1914 and 1915 was not able to occupy the west coast effectively, but his generals raided it "to restore law and order." The United States Consul at Guadalajara related that when the Carrancistas raided the Magistral mine for horses and saddles, the mine manager had the local Villista leader request their return on the pledge that "the Villista would, in turn, bind himself to extend similar courtesies to the Carrancista when opportunity offered." On the strength of the note the property was returned.[28]

Extraordinarily good markets during the war years tempted many companies to keep their properties open, so keeping experienced administrators at the mines was another problem. Some camps became battle sites. Kidnapping, murder, robbery, or the settlement of old grudges became commonplace.[29] Almost every operating mine was held up at one time or another with demands for horses, supplies, and "hard money." Compliance could mean the ruination of a small operator's life work; resistance could mean death. Although during the Revolution the ASARCO staff at the Tiro General mine (Charcas, San Luis Potosí) had to escape under cover of darkness after an all-day battle with revolutionists, the company prided itself on the fact that none of its men was killed. Mazapil Copper got its people out by paying £2,500 for permission to run a train into Saltillo on its own line. In 1914, mining men fleeing Mexico flooded the United States employment market with job applications. Fortunately, some plants were able to continue operating with Mexican personnel during the absence of the foreign staffs.[30]

ASARCO declared no earnings in Mexico in 1915 and 1916: employment was down from 12,000 in 1912 to 6,000 and production off some 75 per cent.[31] Greene-Cananea skipped dividends from 1913 to 1915 and then kept them small despite good earnings to build up a reserve fund for "contingencies."[32] The Exploration Company of London reduced its capitalization in 1916 from £750,000 to £375,000 "on account of depreciation of its Mexican investments."[33] The Mines Company of America dipped into reserves to pay dividends.[34] Mazapil Copper sus-

TABLE 6
PRODUCTION OF THE MEXICAN MINING INDUSTRY: 1910–20[1]

Year	Silver (Kgs.)	Gold (Kgs.)	Lead (Met. Tons)	Zinc (Met. Tons)	Copper (Met. Tons)
1910	2,416,669	41,420	124,292	1,833	48,160
1911	2,518,202	37,120	116,758	1,593	56,072
1912	2,526,715	32,431	105,160	1,266	57,245
1913	1,725,861	25,810	68,343	960	52,592
1914	810,647	8,635	5,703	793	26,621
1915	712,599	7,358	19,971 [sic]	5,806	20,598[2]
1916	925,993	11,748	19,971 [sic]	37,449	28,411
1917	1,306,988	23,542	64,125	45,181	50,986
1918	1,944,542	25,313	98,837	20,699	70,223
1919	2,049,898	23,586	71,376	11,560	56,172
1920	2,068,938	22,864	82,518	15,651	49,192

[1]The figures from 1913 to 1917 are estimates. No national statistics were compiled during those years. On July 18, 1918, an order was sent to all mine agents, asking them to estimate the production of the mines in their districts from 1913 to 1917, and enclosing forms for the estimate. (*Col. de leyes . . . 1918*, pp. 201–202.)

[2]Due to a typographical error, this figure was given as 205,978 kgs. in the estimates published by the *Boletin minero* in 1920. The error was corrected in later editions of the *Anuario de estadística minera*, but González did not make a correction in his compilation.

SOURCE: *Boletin minero*, X (Sept.–Oct. 1920), 288–289; J. González Reyna, *Riqueza minera y yacimientos minerales de México* (Mexico, 1956), p. 448.

pended operations from 1913 to 1917 and reopened with its reserves fallen to £42,927.[35] Mines in Pachuca did rather well. Real del Monte y Pachuca struck a bonanza vein which ran over $50 a ton in silver compared to $8 in its original veins. Reputedly it contributed 20 per cent of the earnings of its large parent, the USSR&M, which earned a net of $4,300,000 in 1915. In fact, the mine was said to have a value greater than the entire capitalization of USSR&M.[36] Although not doing as well as Real del Monte, Santa Gertrudis managed to work at full capacity and return handsome dividends to its parent, Camp Bird Ltd.[37]

Collapse of the railroads was the most disruptive feature of the Revolution. Antigovernment forces, realizing that a functioning transportation system made the federal forces supreme, did their best to halt the railroads by destroying bridges, bending rails, and burning ties.[38] Each side seized rolling stock and lived off the country for fuel and supplies. By 1916, only 16 per cent of the rolling stock was available for commercial use.

Mining companies forced to buy their own trains still paid full rates for the use of the track alone. ASARCO, which owned 44 locomotives and over 600 cars, put more than $1,500,000 into its rolling stock and repair facilities in addition to spending $600,000 a year to run the outfit. It met part of the expense by shipping ore from independent mines to its smelters at cost. The American Metal Company in 1919 had 25 locomotives and from 600 to 900 cars. At least five other companies also owned railroad equipment.[39] Some concerns, such as the Real del Monte, rented trains in the United States under bond and ran them with supplies to their mines.[40] Some firms arranged with the government railroads to rehabilitate stock for the privilege of leasing it exclusively for from one to two years. Smaller companies paid "charter companies" 60 to 75 per cent over regular freight rates for bonded trains. Service was usually satisfactory; the brother of the general manager of the railroads operated the largest company.[41] Those unwilling or unable to play the game found their freight buried in hopelessly congested train yards.[42] Smelters, dependent upon adequate coke supplies, were hard hit. With the Coahuila coalfields closed, importing coke was problematical, and there were constant reports that the smelters had ore on hand but not enough coke to smelt it.

To add to Mexico's troubles, World War I disrupted international trade channels and markets. The entire mining community mourned the lost German markets until the Allies' war needs more than made up the loss.[43] But the loss of German cyanide was not so easily taken care of: Mexico consumed 3,600 metric tons a year while the United States used only 3,250 short tons. In 1914, a French scheme to manufacture cyanide in Mexico City fell through, and the United States market alone absorbed the increased output of the American Cyanimid Company. However, Mexican mining activity had fallen off drastically, and the few camps in operation usually could obtain enough of the chemical. The lack of dynamite imposed even greater hardships. One estimate was that the United States embargo on dynamite shipments alone caused mine production to fall 50 per cent. Even after its export was regularized, government and rebel forces frequently sequestered it. Loss of the Mexican market was a prime cause of hard times in the American mine supply industry.[44]

Rampant inflation played hob with wages. After Madero's revolution, specie steadily disappeared. Mexico, producer of one-third of the world's silver, went on a paper standard.[45] Under ordinary circumstances the common people did not trust paper; now they would take it only under compulsion. Coinage was almost at a standstill. In the case of gold, 5,010,000 gold pesos were coined in 1910; none was minted from 1911 to 1915; in 1916, only 260,000 gold pesos were struck. With recovery, in the years 1917 and 1918, over 100,000,000 gold pesos were struck. Silver coinage followed a similar trend: from 1911 through 1914 a total of 17,304,000 silver pesos were minted; none was coined in 1915; 23,640,000 silver pesos were coined in 1917 and 1918; and coinage from 1919 to 1922 annually averaged over 25,000,000 silver pesos.[46]

Cruder revolutionists confiscated and stole property. Those more sophisticated paid their debts with paper currency—exacting forced loans and capital tax levies in gold or silver "for the support of the Army." Bills were turned out by the ton after 1913. Some were mimeographed; others were manufactured on a typewriter. Mining company representatives coming to Carranza to exchange New York bank drafts for currency waited a few days in local hotels while bales of bills were printed "to order."[47] Carranza broke a strike of government printers with the claim that the presses were part of the military establishment since the bills were needed to pay his troops! It was difficult to keep up the value of paper money, and often strong-arm methods were used—even the penalty of execution—on anyone not accepting the local paper money at an exchange rate set by the commanding general.[48] To establish a metallic base for their currency, some revolutionists struck coins from confiscated or stolen bullion. Some of these pieces had a greater intrinsic than face value because of small amounts of gold mixed with the silver. Carrancistas even melted trolley wires at the Parral mines to make copper centavo pieces.[49]

Villa issued paper as prolifically as Carranza, but military setbacks made his currency decline in value more rapidly. He worked his presses day and night to pay with his money for the goods he took. After Villa's defeat some companies found themselves stuck with large amounts of his currency. They carried it on their books as an asset for years but finally wrote it off and destroyed it.[50]

Carranza issued unlimited amounts of continually depreciating currency as a deliberate plan to force loans from the merchant class which would not buy his bonds. He later repudiated his own money, claiming to have saved Mexico from a tremendous bonded indebtedness due to revolutionary needs! In a gesture of ironic magnanimity, Carranza retired part of his currency by requiring taxes usually payable in gold to be paid with an additional paper peso for every gold one![51] As for the mineowners, base metal producers suffered while the precious metal miners prospered. And everyone played the exchange market with smelter receipts.

Wages rose, but they did not keep pace with the declining value of the paper peso. Both Carranza and Villa unsuccessfully tried to force mineowners to put gold or silver in circulation by decreeing that wages must be paid in metal money.[52] Carranza forced the use of his money by "allowing" workers to be paid in his paper at a rate fixed every ten days. At Pachuca the companies worked out a complex system to combine paper pesos with a bonus plus a corn ration and carfare. Later, during a strike, the Carranza government tried to force the workers to accept half silver money and half Carranza paper; the amount was increased to 75 per cent paper as a penalty for not working five days a week. A riot ensued which required sending in troops, and the government had to promise to force the stores to accept half paper.[53]

Few companies were as fortunate as those in Pachuca. Real del Monte y Pachuca had its Barron shaft concreted in 1916 for about half the estimated cost since the labor, estimated at $7,943, came to only $1,941.[54] Mines in the fighting zones found that higher costs for supplies and shipping ate up the savings on labor. At El Oro, particularly hard hit because of raids by both Zapatistas and Carrancistas, the fabulous dividend payer Dos Estrellas had reported its 1913 profit of 6,537,000 pesos had changed into deficits of 782,000 pesos in 1915 and 155,000 pesos in 1916, while its security fund declined from 4,000,000 to 2,900,000 pesos.[55] Conditions at Guanajuato became a national calamity. Mines employing from 1,000 to 3,000 men kept only 100 or 200 as guards or maintenance men. Prices rose enormously; famine and pestilence broke out while skilled miners left for other camps. A representative at the Constitutional Convention of 1916–17 declared that unless Carranza forced the mines to reopen, it would "signify the death of those workers and the death of the city of Guanajuato." Guanajuato Reduction and Mines complained that treatment costs had doubled and that its profit margin of 2.48 pesos per ton had dropped to a 1.16 peso loss.[56] Mining was moribund; exploration was at a standstill. There were no new developments, and construction was limited to the absolutely necessary. Most companies considered themselves fortunate if they could export enough bullion and ore to make expenses.[57]

To determine the extent of revolutionary destruction is nearly impossible. No total of capital loss through destruction and robbery was ever established. In addition, there were business closings, flooding and cave ins, and general deterioration due to neglect and abandonment. Much of the damage was done only to parts of a plant or were due to suspending operations and maintenance. Raids were usually for supplies or money, and the physical plant was only damaged as an expedient or for spite. Carranza's brother Jesús did a complete job of destruction when he raided the Compañía Carbonífera Agujita in Coahuila to demand a 100,000-peso ransom for the plant. Forced to retreat, he caused $1,000,000 in damages within two hours, and the mines filled with water and gas.[58] After a dispute with the state government over working conditions in 1916, the Mines Company of America closed down and the state reopened the mine for unrestricted exploitation. Prospectors "picked the eyes out of the mines," taking all the rich pockets in sight and robbed the pillars causing sections to collapse. They used timbering for firewood. A visitor later observed:

> Not a nut, valve, rod or rivet is in evidence. And so far as cold chisels could reach the copper on the motors, they too were wrecked.
> The cyanide tanks were all utilized as fire wood. . . . There is not an engine, pump, motor, or other piece of machinery or equipment in the camp that could now be put in operation for less money than it cost originally. Corrugated iron, windows, doors, and even the framing of the buildings have been carried off. I found a man, a woman, and two boys busy getting firewood with a crowbar from the mill floor.[59]

He estimated that reopening the mine would cost $500,000.

The losses of American mining companies during the Revolution will never be known. The State Department refused to release the total of the claims filed with it. Senator Albert Fall's Sub-Committee to Investigate Mexican Affairs, set up in 1919, assembled several volumes of data, but they are rather prejudiced. Fall's report lamented that few representatives of mining companies would appear to press their claims. Some cases reported by the Committee were interesting: one company, with 8,000 stockholders, paid $1,500,000 in bribes and blackmail and another lost $25,000,000 on its investment in 10 years. The Committee's guess set the total American loss at $505,000,000, of which $125,000,000 represented damage to mining property.[60] Wallace Thompson, in a private estimate of revolutionary losses in 1919, set the "physical damage" to mining property at $15,000,000, with an additional $100,000,000 in "actual losses."[61] Cleona Lewis noted that out of 110 American mining companies in Mexico only 14 worked steadily from 1914 to 1919 and that $180,000,000 in capital equipment was idle.[62]

The mining companies' refusal to work with the Fall Committee is understandable in the light of their long-term interests. Owning valuable plants and large ore deposits, they had to plan for future operations. Pressure from Washington might only make matters worse after the fighting: barring American conquest, the Mexican government would have the last word. Consequently, in return for guarantees of security and a "reasonable" attitude by the Mexican government, mineowners willingly waived their claims to get on with operations.[63] British concerns and defunct American companies constituted the bulk of claimants.[64] In 1926 the operating mining concerns agreed to drop their claims, declaring "foreign companies operating in [Mexico] should take 'pot' luck with the natives."[65]

Smaller companies suffered most from the Revolution. Many were wiped out while larger concerns rode out the storm with the aid of cash reserves or operations in other countries. Larger companies often took advantage of the situation by picking up good properties cheaply. George A. Chamberlain, the American Consul-General in Mexico during World War I, reported a conversation he had with an official of a large American mining company which had been issuing optimistic statements on conditions in Mexico and urging the United States government to keep hands off. The official justified his stand by remarking that his powerful company had been quite successful in "fixing" both the Constitutionalists and the bandits:

> Disorder consequently suits us; mining claims are cheap, competition scarce. We yell, "Come in, fellers, the water's fine," because we know they won't come. In our business it's better to be lonely than crowded.[66]

CHAPTER 9

New Taxes, New Laws, and the Constitution of 1917

MEXICO'S Revolution of 1910 was a thoroughgoing social upheaval as well as a political struggle. Exigencies of war bred new taxes to finance armies and new legal concepts to force owners of property to keep their possessions in use to produce taxable wealth and jobs. Mineowners were caught in a welter of conflicting and changing tax laws and innovations in concepts of property rights. Economic liberalism was buried in order to revive the ideas embodied in the Spanish mining Ordenanzas of 1783. Punitive taxes levied for social purposes, demands that foreigners give up their rights of appeal to their home governments, and a requirement that mines be worked or concessions forfeited—all made for new operating conditions for the Mexican mineowner. New governments were determined to be mothers to Mexicans and stepmothers to foreigners.

A tax problem arose soon after Madero's assassination when Carranza, to discredit Huerta, refused to recognize any taxes paid to the Federal Government. Indeed, he construed such payments as "aid to the reactionaries." Neither side would abridge their legal or pretended right to collect taxes, leaving the mineowner in the middle. On November 30, 1913, when Carranza held only northwest Mexico, he ordered taxes to be paid to his collectors ". . . in the knowledge that payments made to the so-called Federal Government since March first of the present year will not be recognized as valid." Since mining was under federal jurisdiction, many owners tried to cover themselves by sending their payments directly to Mexico City. Others deposited them with the American consulates. Some used the impasse as an excuse not to pay taxes at all. Carranza, as a compromise, ordered that taxes be paid only to the agent in the district in which the mine was located.[1]

The United States State Department exchanged a series of notes with Carranza in an attempt to reach a workable compromise for areas in which Carranza had *de facto* control. "Double-tax cases" were dropped when Carranza agreed to accept an amount equal to the last payment to Huerta as fulfilling the requirements of the decree of November 30, 1913. Some companies had already paid double taxes on the assumption that "it was not worth while to take any chances on what is relatively a small matter."[2] Since "equity" as known in English law does not exist in Mexico, missing tax payments could lead to absolute loss of property, a penalty most mine-owners did not wish to chance.[3]

On August 10, 1914, after his victory, Carranza repealed all of Huerta's tax laws, restored the previous rates, and planned a number of new taxes to be an integral part of his finance program. He also voided all mine titles registered under Huerta and all actions taken by the Ministry of Development during Huerta's regime. Carranza stood firm against State Department protests. By extending the revalidation period for Huerta's titles for six months (and eventually until 1917) he solved the problem. To the revolutionaries the mining industry constituted one of the most valuable tangible assets of the Mexican economy; moreover, it was principally owned by foreigners.[4]

During Carranza's struggle with Villa, mineowners felt the first real pressures of total war and revolutionary change. Villa, fighting for his life against Obregón's armies, used all the means in his power to wring money from the industry. As early as July 27, 1914, Fidel Avila, Villa's Governor of Chihuahua, ordered under the threat of forfeiture that the state's mines resume operations. A concession, according to his interpretation, carried with it an obligation to work the mine. Villa ignored Secretary of State Bryan's protests[5] and on March 19, 1915, issued his own Decree No. 5, imposing forced work on the mines under pain of confiscation. He reasoned that the nation granted mining concessions to increase the public wealth and to provide the state with income. Therefore, mining was a public utility which also provided work for the poor. Mining property, Villa decreed, should be forfeited not only for nonpayment of taxes, but "by the voluntary suspension of working of the mines; by the abandonment of such work; and by deficient exploitation." Workings not complying with the law were to be open to denouncement by any individual. Miners were given 120 days to reopen and 90 days to pay their tax arrears.[6] In answer to vigorous protests by the State Department, Villa's representatives ultimately assured the United States that the decree would not interfere with legitimate activities but was designed to prevent speculation in dormant properties. Villa personally assured official American representatives that he did not intend to enforce the decree until he could give guarantees and furnish transportation. In particular, he did not wish to cause any international trouble. The Mine and Smelter Owners' Association of Mexico which was organized in El Paso to deal with Villa, finally arranged a settlement. New taxes were set at reasonable rates in return for a promise to buy Villa's weak currency. Villa's agent, sent to Washington, assured the Americans that the forced-work law would not be enforced at that time.[7]

Relations with Villa were always rather delicate. He confiscated the Naica mine and the Santa Rosalia, Chihuahua, mine and smelter. On the other hand, he was usually ready to bargain, and his businesslike attitude seemed to offer some security. He supplied guards to keep the Chihuahua smelter safe and in operation, and he kept out organizers for the International Workers of the World.

Villa's Achilles' heel was the railroads. In exchange for coal to run his locomotives, he hauled bullion from Chihuahua to El Paso, commenting: "I am protecting the smelter from bandits." Desperate for funds needed for his campaign in September, 1915, Villa, in July and August, 1915, threatened to confiscate all American-owned mines in his territory if he were not granted a loan of $300,000 in gold. General Hugh L. Scott of the United States Army worked out a compromise with Villa by literally buying him off with coal for his railroads. Villa, at one time, threatened to blow up the Chihuahua plant unless ASARCO paid him $1,000,000 as an "indemnity." ASARCO built a system of adobe-and-stone forts, walls, and pillboxes to protect the smelter. Just before his final defeat, Villa seized the plant and unsuccessfully tried to operate it. An ASARCO manager later claimed that the coal which Villa stole from their shipments, and for which they deducted sums from their freight payments, was the only transaction in which aid might be said to have been given.[8]

By the fall of 1915 Villa's defeat appeared certain. In October the Association wrote to Washington asking for advice and protection against Carranza's high taxes.[9] Villa's hopes died hard and American mine operators experienced anxious times. Mining revived only fitfully. Villa's attacks on Cananea, Nacozari, and El Tigre, and the massacre of sixteen mining engineers at Santa Ysabel were forceful examples of their difficulties.[10] But the miners of the northwest did not suffer alone, for all sections of the country shared the same problems.

Carranza levied few new mine taxes until 1915. He raised the export tax on zinc ores in 1914,[11] and specified that the stamp tax on exported gold and silver—and later all federal and state taxes—be paid in gold.[12]

Tax arrears, which plagued Carranza's government throughout the Revolution, constituted his most pressing problem. Carranza, on January 22, 1914, ordered a list compiled of all mines under his jurisdiction with the status of their tax payments during the past fiscal year. In this way he hoped to flush out mineowners who evaded tax payments to his faction.[13] He also ordered his collectors to demand payment for the last tax period before Huerta's overthrow and to forward detailed accounts of those paying tardily.[14] Despite forfeiture penalties, the chaotic state of the country led many mineowners to skip tax payments; others paid only when forced to; and yet others refused to pay as long as conditions did not permit them to resume operations. Officially, Carranza took a depreciatory attitude toward all remonstrances. Actually, circumstances compelled his government to back down continually. At times the threat to caducate would be used in an attempt to activate a developed property or to turn it over to a party willing to pay the taxes. In most cases only penalties were imposed for tardiness in payment, unless an interested party desired to take over the claim.[15] The State Department withdrew from this controversy in 1916 after receiving a promise that parties able to prove their inability to work the mines would be safe from forfeiture.[16]

Because of his desire to collect delinquent taxes, Carranza often played into the hands of his archenemies, the "speculators." By a decree of February 27, 1917, a mine in arrears could be caducated only upon the application of a third party, who would have preference in redenouncing it. Men in Mexico City scanned the tax rolls and grabbed desirable properties on a gamble when they fell into arrears. Eventually the press became so great that mine agents had to be warned not to accept redenouncements of claims not yet fully declared forfeit. To guard the government's interests, a decree of March 31, 1917, provided that any *developed* mine declared in caduca for tax arrears, or for noncompliance with the forced-work decrees, could only be denounced through the negotiation of a special contract with the Ministry of Development. A contract would give a 20-year concession and a tax reduction in return for proof of financial ability to work the mine, a guarantee deposit, and an agreement to pay five per cent of the gross earnings. Lack of knowledge of local conditions in Mexico City, coupled with the difficulty in defining a developed mine and fixing its value, led to delays of up to two years. Only two concessions were actually granted; both were forfeited. Often speculators filed claims in violation of the decree.[17]

After the initial defeats of Villa and Zapata in 1915, Carranza began to rewrite tax laws in earnest. A decree of March 1, 1915, modified the tax law of March 25, 1905.[18] It raised export taxes and placed them on an absolute rather than an ad valorem basis. All metals refined in Mexico were allowed a 20 per cent reduction. There was little protest since metal production was at an ebb. However, the new claim-area, or pertenencia, tax raised a storm of protest. Traditionally, this tax was due triannually; missing three installments automatically cancelled the title to the mine. Even the equity in physical improvements was forfeit to whomever reregistered the title. While production taxes were only due when the mine was working, the area taxes were due under all conditions with delinquents facing the threat of complete property loss. The 1905 tax had been a regressive one: 6 pesos for each pertenencia up to 25 and 3 pesos for those beyond that figure. Carranza first raised the registration tax to 10 pesos per pertenencia and then set the annual tax on a progressive scale of from 12 pesos, for the first 10 pertenencias, up to 24 pesos for the excess over 50.[19] Carranza's objective was threefold: first, to collect more money; second, to force production by making idleness too costly; and third, to force the breakup of large holdings in the belief that it would give employment to small miners or prospectors, most of whom were Mexican.

Arguments over the progressive tax rate were extremely bitter. Small mineowners complained that while the rates were tolerable, the demand to pay in gold made the new tax extremely difficult to meet. Large companies carrying reserves against future production—or practicing preemption under the lenient Díaz tax laws—found most of their holdings in the 24-peso tax category. They claimed that while they did not seek to escape just taxation, the new rates were ruinous and would discourage future development. The State Department insisted that under the circumstances the new tax rate was tantamount to confiscation.[20] In a calmer vein, the economist Díaz Dufoo believed that the nature of Mexican ore deposits made large reserves and large-scale workings an economic necessity and that attempts to whittle down the size of holdings invited waste and disaster.[21] On the other hand, single-tax disciples of Henry George were highly pleased.[22] But even the conservative commentator, T. A. Rickard, noted that production taxes were useless where there was no production: "This evasion can be checked . . . by taxing the claim-area . . . , whether productive or not, to such a degree as to render long idleness prohibitive."[23]

Carranza's area tax proved too severe. Unrelenting pressures exerted by the State Department forced a revision. Its protests emphasized that the "pitiful condition of the mining industry in general," as well as Carranza's own extralegal position, which made the taxes "unconstitutional," all pointed to the need for a more lenient attitude.[24] Carranza backed down on August 31, 1915, giving mineowners a breathing spell. He excused their inability to pay because of civil war, the lack of raw materials, and the effects of the war in Europe. Carranza set a timetable for gradually imposing the new rates to reach full force in February, 1916. The State Department made certain that the areas not under Carranza's control would not have to pay double taxes and would not be penalized at a later date for having paid taxes to Villa.[25] Meanwhile, the State Department managed to obtain a promise that enforcement of the new tax law would be delayed until July 1, 1916, and forfeitures would also be postponed.

Secretary of State Lansing in time became well acquainted with Carranza's stubborn attitude. On February 21, 1916, he demanded that because of the friendly attitude of the United States towards Carranza's *de facto* government, the mining decrees should be annulled or modified as a reciprocal gesture. Three days later Carranza summarily rejected the note, and Lansing pressed for a compromise. In April, Carranza released the text of a new tax law to be promulgated on May 1 for enforcement on July 1, when a forfeiture-for-arrears decree on December, 1915, would also go into effect. Miners protested, demanding that Carranza return to the "constitutional tax level of 1905," while the State Department believed the rates to be too high. However, the law went into effect as scheduled.[26]

The tax law of May 1, 1916,[27] provided for a 10 per cent ad valorem tax on exported gold and silver, and a 5 per cent duty on industrial metals based on monthly market quotations. Metals refined in Mexico continued to receive a 20 per cent reduction. For the pertenencia tax, claims were divided into gold and silver holdings and industrial metal holdings with the former paying a significantly steeper progressive rate. Other articles limited state taxes to 2 per cent, set up a sliding scale for copper taxes depending upon the market price, and wiped the legal slate clean by repealing all previous mine tax legislation.

While the tax law of March 1, 1915, might have been regarded as a temporary expedient, the law of May 1, 1916, saw Carranza firmly in power and the old laws repealed. To the claim that the pertenencia tax was still excessive, the Mexican government answered that it was forcing the large companies to disgorge their excess holdings. It rejected the claim that they would give up only the poorest pieces of land which needed the largest capital to develop.[28] Carranza was adamant in his desire to drive out "unproductive speculators," a term which included any company with undeveloped land. He answered Lansing's protests with the comment that taxation was an internal matter. On January 25, 1917, Lansing inveighed against the law's avowed intention of confiscating the property of people who had invested in good faith, declaring that thousands of pertenencias, on which taxes had been paid for years and which were needed for reserves, had been surrendered. He got no satisfaction. A gradual reduction in the size of holdings became evident.[29]

While official protests over the pertenencia tax were fruitless, meetings between the mine and smelter owners and the Mexican Secretary of the Treasury did lead to a substantial reduction in the export tax on December 8, 1916, for one year, "in order to activate the reconstruction of the country." Allowances were also made for shipping charges on lead and zinc.[30]

Relations between Carranza and the mineowners entered a serious crisis in the summer of 1916 during the Pershing expedition's pursuit of Villa. The mining community had not endeared itself to Carranza by its dealings with Villa or by its support of the expedition. When the expedition's limited objectives became clear, the miners' position deteriorated rapidly. Carranza now put teeth into his laws by ordering first, that all foreigners desiring to obtain concessions in Mexico renounce in advance appeals to their home governments (the so-called "Calvo Clause") and second, that all mines must be worked regularly under threat of forfeiture, for the concession to remain in force. Forfeiture threats were real enough in Mexico from 1913 to 1916. Villa and Carranza confiscated many properties on the pretext that their owners were aiding the enemy. They worked these properties despite the refusal of American smelters to process confiscated ore.[31]

Caranza had demonstrated several times his determination to keep the mining industry under his control and to make mineowners aware of his power. He had cancelled a number of special concessions for noncompliance. When new state laws in Zacatecas and Sonora ordered mine operations, Carranza nullified them on the grounds that mining was under federal jurisdiction.[32] Guanajuato passed a similar law to force employment for its thousands of starving miners. In response to a strong United States demand, the Mexican government agreed on August 21, 1916, to void the law and halt state forced-work orders as long as transportation and protection could not be assured.[33]

The first step in Carranza's new mine policy came on August 15, 1916. His administration required all foreigners desiring to apply for mine concessions to first renounce all rights of appeal to their consuls or home governments on penalty of immediate forfeiture. At the same time, all foreign companies were barred by a blanket clause from applying for concessions unless they "nationalized" themselves—held their Mexican properties through a Mexican subsidiary—and made a similar declaration. Carranza advanced reasons identical with those used by Olegario Molina in advocating Article 144 of his projected mine law in 1908: It was not fair for foreign companies to enjoy a greater protection in Mexico from Mexican laws than Mexican firms themselves. Enforcement of the decree was difficult. Notices had to be sent out continuously to the mine agents reminding them of the order.[34]

A second step came a month later, on September 14, 1916. Carranza reversed the trend of Mexican mining legislation since 1884 by summarily ordering all mines to resume work.[35] The introduction to the decree outlined a new philosophy embodying the accumulated discontent and frustration of the Revolution which was to burst forth in the Constitution of 1917. It stressed the right of the State to intervene in economic matters if necessary to protect the interests of the individual, the nation, and humanity—should their rights of conservation, protection, or progressive evolution be threatened—or whenever an individual or corporate enterprise failed to fulfill the needs of society. It declared this right to be particularly applicable in the case of mining, which was a "public utility" because of its importance in uncovering wealth, employing large numbers of workers, contributing to the national Treasury, and supporting the nation's industry. In 1892, it noted, the State introduced a Liberal philosophy which believed that these interests could best be served by allowing individuals to work mines under their own initiative and management, with the single requirement that taxes must be paid. But the law failed because its effect was to favor speculators; to keep out workers without capital; to concentrate holdings in the hands of wealthy foreigners, who worked only within the limits fixed by the gamble of the stock market; and to encourage land monopolization. Furthermore, these interests interfered in government matters and aided reactionary revolutionists, thus depriving the government of revenue and workers of jobs. And these same interests were uncooperative in seeking peace and good order. Instead, they incited foreign governments to intervene on the excuse of saving property. Therefore, the explanation concluded, free individual initiative and action "has seriously hurt the solidary interests of the country." To remedy this situation all concessionaries were ordered to work their mines under pain of forfeiture (caduca) if they stopped work for more than two consecutive or for three nonconsecutive months a year without just cause and without permission. Caducated mines would be reported immediately to the Ministry of Finance, who would determine whether to open them to redenunciation or to appoint an administrator to work them for the government. On September 26, 1916, the Minister of Development issued a circular to all mining agents, instructing them to prepare a list of all mines in their districts with notations on whether they were being worked. Mines not working would be assigned quotas and given three months to begin operations.[36]

The State Department immediately protested: "American mining companies need no urging to resume operations upon return of normal conditions," and also alleged that under the circumstances the decree was confiscatory. However, it advised the miners to file statements explaining why the mines were closed.[37]

On November 14, 1916, the miners were given until February 14, 1917, to resume operations.[38] This extension quieted State Department protests and permitted a slow resumption of activity. A recession of Villa's activities in the northwest also helped. El Oro Mining and Railway had already reopened in October, 1916, after eighteen months, "having fortified themselves with influential advice." Following a series of conferences with Carranza, ASARCO reopened its Monterrey smelter in February, 1917. In the meantime, the State Department four more times demanded the repeal of the law before giving up. In February, the Mexican government informed the Department that since the law was over five months old, those who could not reopen their mines should have filed explanations. Finally, the State Department asked only that leniency be exercised and dropped the subject.[39] America's entrance into World War I brought on more pressing problems.

Many Americans returned to northern Mexico in March, 1917. Chihuahua noted a general revival. Carranza informed the miners that his policy was not to compromise mining properties: mines not yet in operation because of force majeure (inevitable accident) could obtain extensions.[40] But the booming world metal markets, the United States entering the war, and the gradual suppression of guerrilla activity were great inducements. In any event, it appears that no property was declared forfeit under the law of September 16, 1916.[41] To facilitate mine workings, on March 28, 1917, Mexico ordered all mills and smelters to resume operations within sixty days under the vague threat to use "The means which may be judged convenient to force compliance with this disposition. . . ."[42]

With the writing of the Constitution of 1917, the legal position of the Mexican mining industry changed completely. Legal thought to the present day has been influenced by the circumstances surrounding the adoption of the new Constitution. To appreciate property concepts and the rights of labor in modern Mexico, it is necessary to understand the work done at Queretero in late 1916 and early 1917.

Many of Carranza's lieutenants recognized the need to rewrite the Constitution as early as 1914, but Carranza's conservatism led him to resist a change.[43] With the neutralization of Villa and Zapata in 1915, demands for a new Constitution became more insistent. Furthermore, Carranza's platform—the Plan of Guadalupe—merely declared his political principles and was not a guide to social revolution. Politically powerful leftists demanded that Carranza put the various social reform decrees he had issued into an irrevocable form. In any event, his new labor laws and land distribution schemes had made the old Liberal Constitution of 1857 obsolete.[44] In the summer of 1916, Carranza called for a Convention to meet at Queretero on November 1, 1916, to frame a new Constitution by January 31, 1917.[45]

Under existing conditions elections were far from being fair or representative. Delegates were of the "cleanest political antecedents," and all were identified with the ideals of the Revolution. But they often represented little more than themselves or the faction which wrote out their credentials.[46] Obregón was the acknowledged leader of the leftists as Carranza was of the rightists, and during the two weeks needed to approve credentials the Obregonista majority blocked the seating of many rightist delegates.[47] They also charged the rightists with appointing most of the stenographic corps in order to make it possible for them to appear less reactionary by having their speeches edited and their votes altered.[48] Neither group had any party organization; the following of each was animated by a mixture of personalism and individual idealism.

Carranza addressed the Convention on December 1, 1916, to discuss his proposed reforms.[49] With regard to land and labor questions, he requested that Article 27 of the Constitution of 1857 be amended in several minor points and that it include the insertion of the Calvo Clause. Workers' rights were to be covered in Article 5 which simply guaranteed protection against peonage. He recommended that other reforms be carried out by enacting laws rather than by writing policy into the Constitution.

Bitter debates immediately broke out between the lefists and the rightists, and the former soon showed that they dominated the Convention.[50] Rightists could only protest and attempt to make the Constitution less radical by demanding the inclusion of legal guarantees. Carranza, it is alleged, authorized Pastor Rouaix, his Minister of Development, to use his judgment to try to keep the reforms as prudent as possible.[51] Rouaix, respected by the Convention for his intelligence, modesty, and lack of partisanship[52] was made chairman of the committees to draw up Articles 5, 27, and 123.

Articles 27 and 123 were the catchalls for ideas concerning the rights of workers and property rights. They were inserted after debate on Carranza's draft had shown that his suggestions were inadequate. The Convention empowered Rouaix's committee to draw up a new article to be entitled, "Concerning Labor."[53] The committee met in his hotel room to prepare both Article 123 on labor and Article 27 on property rights. Anyone with suggestions to offer or with ideas on points to debate, was invited in and given a hearing. Unfortunately, records of these discussions—the Convention's real debates—were not preserved. By the time the two articles reached the floor, only the irreconcilables and those whose suggestions had been rejected carried on debates, which tended to be perfunctory. Committee members countered the arguments, and the delegates then voted.[54]

When Article 123 was presented, the committee stated as its ideal that "he who gives and he who receives the labor" should have equal status. In short, the unchallenged right of capital to hire and to fire, to open or to close as the owner may see fit, should be countered by the worker's right to his job at a decent wage. Hence, it was necessary to regulate the employers' right to discharge workers and the methods by which wage rates were determined. Delegates demanded "regular workings" as an expedient: the desire to create work for the large army of men involuntarily idle and threatening the public tranquility. Article 123 was approved unanimously in one afternoon amid shouts of "To a vote!" and "Get on with it!" Twenty-three of the thirty sections were passed without discussion.[55]

Article 27 on property rights had a stormier history. Carranza's proposals did not touch the fundamental problems of land distribution and ownership of the subsoil.[56] After José Natividad Macías denounced the proposed article, the Convention sent it to Rouaix's committee for revision. Rouaix, busily working on Article 123, called in Andrés Molina Enríquez, who was not a delegate but a member of the National Agrarian Commission, and assigned José Inocente Lugo to work with him in drawing up a preliminary draft. Molina Enríquez's draft proved unsuitable, for it was a cross between historical analysis and a statement of principles. Despite his later pretensions to authorship of the article, the committee used the draft only as an explanatory introduction. Rouaix,

Molina Enríquez, Lugo, Macias and Rafael de los Ríos wrote the actual article in ten days. Rouaix held open discussions to hear all sides.[57]

The object of the article, as explained in the introduction, was a return to colonial precepts: the government would have the same control over property as the king. (See Appendix I for the text of the article.) Called an advance over Liberalism, it justified this system because it "permits the Nation to retain under its dominion all that might be necessary for social development."[58] Rouaix forced through the concept of the State's rights being superior to those of the individual. It replaced Molina Enríquez's concept that property ownership resided in the State alone.[59]

Since the revised article was not presented until the afternoon of January 29, 1917, the Convention voted itself into continuous session in order to complete the Constitution before adjourning on January 31st. After dinner the delegates remained in session until the article had been discussed and voted upon. An opening suggestion that peasants be given capital to work their land—with revolutionary fighters having preference—brought on a demonstration by the Carrancistas which the chairman stopped because "[the Convention] might be converted into a cattle pen." Another delegate's suggestion, that indemnifications for expropriation be paid in silver, brought forth shouts of "He's afraid of losing his hacienda." Paragraph 5, which provided for the inalienable dominion of the State over the subsoil and that the subsoil could be held only under concessions which included the obligation to maintain regular workings, occasioned a long debate. The Convention defeated an attempt to write in a royalty clause as a tax measure because the government desired to keep the mine tax structure intact and not endanger that source of revenue in a critical time. Paragraph 7, which embodied the Calvo Clause requiring concessionaires to renounce the right of appeal to their home governments, reopened an earlier debate on Article 32. Finally, the delegates doubled the length of Paragraph 7 to spell out in detail the restrictions on foreign concessionaires. Enrique Colunga, an Obregonista, headed off a demand that foreigners become Mexican citizens before being allowed to hold property in Mexico.[60]

Midnight slipped by and the debate continued. Delegates became restless, and the chairman continually called for order. Finally, a vote was taken and, except for one section, the article passed unanimously. The session recessed at 3:30 A.M. on the morning of January 30, 1917.[61] In this manner, property rights in Mexico were revolutionized; economic liberalism was legally dead.

Reconciling the mining companies to the new Constitution was difficult despite the government's strategy of virtually holding the new basic law in abeyance in economic matters. Revolutionary chaos had made the mineowners sullen and distrustful. Enforcement of the mining provisions of the Constitution has always depended upon the interplay between

Mexico's need for new foreign capital and the foreign investors' existing stake in Mexico and their desire for profits. Only when the latter factor became powerful could the Mexican government implement constitutional policy. Mexico, in 1917 and 1918, was still too disturbed by banditry, civil war, and political rivalry for the government to take advantage of the booming metal markets to frame regulatory laws for Articles 27 and 123.

In late 1917, the Ministry of Industry, Commerce, and Labor *(Secretaría de Industria, Comercio y Trabajo)* called a National Industrialists' Congress to discuss the influence of Articles 27 and 123 upon the Mexican economy. Reports prepared by various committees and the Congress as a whole voiced similar objections, but the report of the Congress was more conciliatory.[62] As for Article 123, the report of the mining committee ranged in attitude from constructive criticism to snide commentary and included the observation that the idea of minimum salaries was hatched by "Socialist schools of thought." But in some instances the miners were willing to accept their legal obligations if they were given a "square deal" by the government. They asked for a delay before new regulatory laws were framed so that a mining chamber might be organized to voice their desires and needs; industrialists objected strongly enough to prevent the framing of a labor code until the 1930's. Practically every facet of Article 27 was attacked by the miners' committee as being socialistic and destroying private property.[63] It even appeared to deny the sovereign power of the constituent assembly! Undoubtedly the Congress felt that the chances of getting Article 27 revised were so remote that they had nothing to lose by stating their implacable opposition. Furthermore, the framing of legislation to carry out the constitutional requirement might be delayed.

At the Congress the government made a noteworthy attempt to present a draft of a new mine law to reconcile the Law of 1910 with the new Constitution.[64] Although nothing came of it as this time—a new mining law was not promulgated until 1926—many of the ideas in the suggested draft were enacted into law in 1926 and 1930. Surprisingly, the miners' committee in this matter accepted about half the government's suggestions, even though they vehemently rejected the rest. Mineowners took a determined stand in declaring that, except for the duties of maintaining minimum workings and obeying the Police and Security Regulations, they ought to enjoy complete liberty of industrial action in working on whatever scale of operations and as fast as they pleased with as many workers as they might wish to hire in accord with the economic and technological circumstances. The Mexican government had to overlook their opposition until a more opportune time arrived for setting the mine operators in their place in the new scheme of Mexican society. The reckoning came under President Calles, nine years later.

CHAPTER 10

The Recovery of Mining, 1917–1920

MEXICO'S mining industry recovered slowly between 1917 and 1919. Despite 1,220 caducations in 1918 and 714 more in 1919, only some 12 per cent of the mines and 21 per cent of the metallurgical plants were operating.[1] Some local officials tried to enforce Articles 27 and 123 of the new Constitution zealously, but Mexico City acted with restraint.[2] Bandits and taxes could not deter miners spurred on by alluring wartime metal prices. The United States and Mexico both embargoed gold shipments abroad and the United States restricted all exports, but the mine companies were constant in their efforts to reopen and continue operations.[3]

Several areas had not fared badly during the Revolution. Cananea and Nacozari worked at full capacity in 1917 and 1918, reaping full benefit from the rising price of copper. Pachuca, and other silver camps, suffered mainly from a shortage of cyanide when Germany was blockaded. Later, the United States supplied Mexico with cyanide, and, after entering the war, permitted it to be exported under license.[4] El Boleo escaped the Revolution unscathed; geographical isolation and managerial tact saved the property. It produced its capacity of 11,000 tons of copper a year through 1916, but output fell off the next year as workers left for better paying jobs in the United States.[5]

Areas damaged by revolutionary warfare began to revive in 1917. Only supply problems and the need to protect American personnel hampered operations. During 1917 and 1918, reports of reopenings came in increasing numbers from Fresnillo, Sombrerete and Mazapil in Zacatecas; from San Luis Potosí, as ASARCO's smelter there reopened; from El Oro and Guanajuato; from all over the states of Chihuahua, Sonora, and Coahuila; and the Coahuila coal mines reported production of half the coal and a third of the coke normally turned out. As smelters were blown in, and as ASARCO expanded its operations, the Northern Mexico Power Company extended its lines in Chihuahua. Only in the south, Zapata's agitation delayed recovery until 1920. Mexico softened its official attitude toward foreigners to encourage greater activity.[6] And in July,

1918, the United States War Trade Board allocated supplies to Mexican mines on the same basis as to mines in the United States.[7]

Banditry in some places still made life exciting for those desiring a dime-novel existence. While the government generally maintained law and order along the railroads, they too were attacked and dynamited from time to time. Mining companies frequently preferred to pay blackmail to bandits or endure their depredations, rather than call for protection from government troops who, often being unpaid, stole from anyone in order to eat. Not only did mine companies find it difficult to maintain commissaries, but army officers often blackmailed them for protection.[8]

ASARCO opened its Monterrey smelter in March, 1917, and Matehuala in April. Tepezala and Angangueo now opened and shipped ore to Matehuala. Villa's activities in Chihuahua, Sonora, and Durango kept the Velardeña and Chihuahua smelters closed until mid-1918 compelling the south-central Chihuahua districts to ship to El Paso. When the Chihuahua smelter finally reopened, ASARCO invested an additional $1,000,000, making it the largest lead smelter in the world. This move was the first step in ASARCO's reorganization of its Mexican operations carried out during the early 1920's.[9]

Of the companies in Mexico, the American Metal Company, through its subsidiaries, Cia. Minera de Peñoles and Cia. de Minerales y Metales, S.A., most improved its position during the Revolution. German ownership led to a corporate reorganization in the United States in 1918,[10] and it also reorganized its Mexican subsidiaries. Minerales y Metales, founded in 1890 and reorganized in 1913, was protocolized in Mexico in 1916 with a 2,500,000-peso capital. It merged in 1920 with Peñoles to form a new company, registered and protocolized in Mexico City, with a capitalization of 9,000,000 gold pesos.[11]

American Metal's extremely profitable holdings in Peñoles had served as a base of expansion after 1905. By use of its cash reserves, the company acquired three additional valuable properties during the Revolution. In 1916, the 1,000-ton Torreón smelter, closed since 1912,[12] was taken over from the Madero family. Minerales y Metales bought the Agujita coal mines[13] and in 1918 leased the smelter of the Cia. Fundidora y Afinadora de Monterrey with a purchase option. Of the mines it acquired, the most important were the San Toy silver-lead property in Santa Eulalia, bought from the Schwab interests, the Concepción-Cocineras, the Cardina, and the Perú lease.[14] Dr. Otto Sussman hired Heath Steele in October, 1917, to integrate and centralize the administration of Peñoles' scattered mines and smelters. C. M. Loeb, President of American Metal Company, Ltd., sent Steele to Monterrey in the summer of 1918. He completed his work in 1920, at which time his "smooth and efficient organization" was second only to that of the Guggenheims.[15]

Peñoles based its reorganization upon the depletion of the Mapimí district and the impending abandonment of the smelter there. By acquiring smelters in Torreón and Monterrey, Mapimí ore was assured favorable smelter accommodations until its depletion. In turn, the rail connections of these smelters made them excellent nuclei for expansion over the entire northern section of the republic.

When the Torreón and Monterrey plants made custom work secondary to their work for Peñoles, miners began complaining: if Peñoles' own plans did not include the operation of these smelters at any time, the miners dependent upon them for custom work found themselves without an ore buyer. There were even demands that the government fix smelter rates and force continuous operation.[16] Peñoles, in turn, pointed out that two-thirds of the ore smelted came from its own mines, and that it had suspended smelter operations only after damage to the railroads. In fact, smelters belonging to other companies, doing a larger portion of custom work, were idle for longer periods. In the years following, Peñoles gradually built up its custom business until it utilized three-quarters of the plants' capacities. To aid its suppliers, Peñoles offered its shippers the services of a mining geologist.

Peñoles was acknowledged as the largest operator in north-central and eastern Mexico by 1919. Its properties included mines in Santa Eulalia, Chihuahua; Guanaceví and Ojuela, Durango; the Minas de Providencia, Zacatecas; Minas Viejas and El Refugio, Nuevo León; the Higueras group and La Parreña at Sierra Mojada in Coahuila; coal mines at Agujita and Lampacitos; large smelters at Mapimí, Torreón, and Monterrey; and two small smelters at Guadalupe and Cerralvo, Nuevo León. It also held a lease on the Mexico Northern Railway.[17]

Carranza adopted a more conciliatory policy towards mining in mid-1917. On August 27, 1918, for example, all mining machinery and parts were admitted into Mexico duty free.[18] While not relenting in his drive for the recognition of Mexican rights, Carranza, by presidential decrees, relaxed laws which were considered handicaps upon recovery.

When the decree suspending the enforcement of the tax law of May 1, 1916, expired, Carranza promulgated a new tax law on April 26, 1918, to lower the 1916 rates.[19] Tax rates differed from metal to metal, ranging from 8 per cent on impure gold and silver, to 3 per cent on most other metals, and 1 per cent on zinc. Copper taxes were placed on a sliding scale. State taxes were limited. On gold for coinage taxes were reduced while the Treasury promised to buy some silver at the daily New York quotation. To keep precious metals in Mexico for coinage, their export in any form required official permission and a pledge that an equal amount of gold would be imported. In the case of silver exports, the imported gold would have to equal only a percentage of the value of the silver. Claim-area taxes were significantly reduced. Finally, the law offered a plan for the payment of tax arrears. If a mine resumed working by January 1, 1919, tax arrears could be paid, with a decreasing penalty, in installments payable at the same time that current taxes were due. The new rates could well be borne by an industry riding the crest of World War I prices.

Carranza also eased restrictions on foreigners seeking concessions. The Department of Mines had sent repeated orders to mining agents not to forward applications for concessions without first obtaining the applicant's renunciation of the right to appeal to his home government—a principle included in the new Constitution. But a new order on July 8, 1918, stated that "taking into account that the suspension of these transmissions is prejudicial, as much for the solicitants . . . as for the Treasury which fails to receive the taxes due it under various concepts," the solicitants filing briefs without the renunciations would be given until August 31st to supply them. In the future, a brief could be transmitted without a renunciation, though the latter had to be supplied before the final title was issued. [20]

One constitutional precept, however, was strictly interpreted. A clause in Article 27 provided: "Within a zone of 100 kilometers from the frontiers and of 50 kilometers from the seacoast, no foreigner shall under any conditions acquire direct ownership of lands or waters." On March 14, 1919, a presidential determination, followed on May 7, 1919, by a circular, ordered that applications for mining concessions in that zone would not be sent to Mexico City until proof was submitted of either Mexican nationalization or of the transfer of the rights to a Mexican citizen or company.[21] This ruling in effect stretched the constitutional prohibition of direct ownership to include concessions. Not until December 19, 1925, was the ruling changed, when the Ministry of Industry, Commerce, and Labor issued special permits upon application.[22] In all other respects, territory in the forbidden zone was to be treated in accordance with the circular of July 8, 1918.

Carranza also began to rehabilitate Mexico's currency. A favorable balance of trade, principally in oil and metals, made possible the importation of sufficient gold to begin to retire the worthless paper money and supply enough gold coin to keep the economy functioning. Although the rising price of silver pushed the silver peso over the "bullion point," Carranza forbade the export of gold and silver coins to keep them in circulation. The United States embargo of the export of gold in September, 1917, also threatened the recovery of Mexico since gold in Mexican ores and base metal bullion sent to the United States for refining could not be returned to Mexico. Mexican mines particularly were affected because of the lack of bullion-refining plants in the country which could separate the precious metals from copper and lead in the bullion ingots. Exporting base metal in bullion form, therefore, entailed the export of the precious metals in the ingots.[23] But Carranza was compelled to halt exports of gold bars and also restrict the export of precious metals in any form. He decreed that if unrefined materials containing precious metals were exported, an equal amount of gold and 25 per cent of the value of the silver in gold had to be reimported within 10 days.[24] Although the government allowed this gold to be applied on tax payments, the new policy started a panic. Silver climbed to $1 an ounce and lead to 10 cents a pound at this time, partially because of the fall in Mexican exports. When Mexican shipments resumed in November, 1917, silver declined to 84 cents and lead to 8 cents.

Mining companies immediately pressured the United States government to allow the export of gold to Mexico. A countersuggestion that Mexico accept gold certificates or U.S. Treasury notes was rejected on the ground that the Mexican people no longer trusted paper money, even that from the United States. In addition, Mexico did not like the idea of having its gold held hostage in the event of trouble between the two countries. After some bargaining in November, 1917, the United States agreed to permit $10,000,000 in gold per month to move into Mexico.[25] Carranza's insistence forced the United States government to grant Mexico this privilege which was necessary for stabilizing her economy. Mexican gold export prohibitions continued until the late 1920's, when they were recognized as being among a large number of similar laws promulgated the world over.

Carranza signed a new tax law on June 27, 1919, setting the pattern for the organization of mine taxes, which has been followed to the present time.[26] It divided taxes into three categories: those levied on mine property, on production and smelting, and on coinage and assaying. The pertenencia tax was not changed; taxes on precious metals were lowered slightly; those on base metals generally remained the same; and the copper tax continued on a sliding scale. The law retained most of the provisions covering state taxes, exemptions, and gold exports. It made an extraordinary concession to those delinquent in tax payments: if a miner resumed working, he could pay all taxes for the years preceding 1919, installment for installment with current taxes, *without penalty*. To aid the delinquents, the Treasury refused to accept any registrations for three months of claims heretofore declared in caduca but not yet reregistered by other owners.[27] Five months later, the booming silver market necessitated some tax revisions by special amendments as the metal rose to over $1 an ounce in the postwar market. When the boom passed, the tax was lowered.[28] These new laws placed silver, like copper, on a sliding tax scale dependent upon the New York market price. A new concept exempted the metal when the price fell below 60 cents, the theoretical average break-even point for Mexican silver producers.

Carranza was assassinated on April 20, 1920, while attempting to flee into exile. His successors were Generals Obregón, Calles and de la

Huerta, leaders of the "Revindicating Revolution" to save the ideals of the Revolution of 1910 from Carranza's conservatism and corruption. Once in power, they built a political machine whose chief object was to regulate political ambitions. De la Huerta attempted to revolt against the organization in 1924 and got nowhere. Down to the present time all revolts have been equally unsuccessful. Mining companies prospered greatly during the 1920's which was a period of rapid recovery, rebuilding, and excellent prices.

PART IV

PROGRESS AND READJUSTMENT, 1920-1933

CHAPTER 11

Post-Revolutionary Difficulties

THE election of Alvaro Obregón in 1922 established the triumphant Revindicating Revolution. Obregón soon started informal conferences with the United States to settle the question of American land and oil holdings under Article 27 of the new Constitution. In May, 1923, in accordance with the Bucareli Agreement, the United States State Department literally sacrificed American landholdings in Mexico in return for confirmation of the pre-Revolutionary oil concessions; it also recognized Obregón's government. While mining benefited by the recognition of Obregón, the legal position of the industry did not change. Mining companies accepted their holdings as concessions, not as fee simple property. (The new doctrine of "forced workings," derived from the laborer's right to work in Article 123 of the Constitution, affected all enterprises, not mining alone.) Politically, mine operators were not in the bad graces of the new Mexican government, as were the oil companies, for they had preferred to settle their differences directly instead of calling for State Department intervention. In turn, the government recognized the importance of mining in yielding taxes, employing workers, and producing bullion for coinage and foreign exchange by exports. Mining was not mentioned in the Bucareli Agreement, and miners did not ask for State Department help during the 1920's.

Following the depression of 1921–22, mining began to expand again despite hardships. However, there existed many problems and difficulties: the growing power of the large companies which bought properties at bargain prices; the concentration of control of custom smelters; bandits; strikes. But the three major drawbacks were: the days of the 1890–1912 boom had passed; new investors refused to enter Mexico; and few large mines were discovered while the development of remote camps was reduced or abandoned.[1] Even the boom of 1924–29 did not overcome the last two problems. With few exceptions, the basic pattern of mineral industry operations hardened into the lines discernible in 1912.

Larger companies acquired numerous properties. ASARCO built up an extensive series of holdings in Parral and Sierra Mojada; American

TABLE 7

PRODUCTION OF THE MEXICAN MINING INDUSTRY: 1521–1954

Year	Gold	Silver	Copper	Lead	Zinc	Coal
	(Kgs.)			(Met. Tons)		
From 1521 to						
1890	272,700	88,427,398	80,000	300,000	. . . . .	1,000,000
1891	1,477	1,087,261	5,650	30,187	. . . . .	200,000
1892	1,735	1,250,661	7,915	47,532	. . . . .	350,000
1893	1,862	1,386,479	9,607	64,000	400	260,000
1894	4,439	1,422,635	11,959	57,000	300	300,000
1895	8,017	1,456,773	11,806	68,000	500	270,000
1896	9,583	1,523,803	11,338	63,000	500	253,104
1897	10,693	1,635,570	11,553	71,637	600	359,070
1898	12,533	1,743,228	15,919	71,442	1,200	367,193
1899	12,711	1,744,075	19,427	84,656	700	409,125
1900	12,697	1,766,410	22,473	63,828	1,100	387,977
1901	14,258	1,794,664	33,943	94,194	900	670,000
1902	14,805	1,898,323	36,357	106,805	700	709,654
1903	15,993	2,018,652	46,040	100,532	1,000	780,000
1904	19,194	1,972,684	51,759	95,010	800	831,762
1905	24,306	1,890,970	65,449	101,196	2,000	920,000
1906	27,365	1,803,330	61,615	73,699	22,566	767,864
1907	28,909	1,953,859	57,473	76,158	23,197	1,024,580
1908	32,028	2,221,137	38,173	127,010	15,650	866,317
1909	34,370	2 212,983	57,230	118,186	3,000	1,300,000
1910	41,420	2,416,669	48,160	124,292	1,833	1,304,111
1911	37,120	2,518,202	56,072	116,758	1,593	1,400,000
1912	32,431	2,526,715	57,245	105,160	1,266	982,396
1913	25,810	2,199,107	52,592	68,343	960	600,000
1914	8,635	856,787	26,621	5,703	793	780,000
1915	7,358	1,230,850	206[1]	19,971	5,806	450,000
1916	11,748	925,993	28,411	19,971	37,449	300,000
1917	23,542	1,306,988	50,946	64,125	45,181	430,820
1918	25,313	1,944,542	70,200	98,837	20,699	781,860
1919	23,586	2,049,898	52,272	71,376	11,560	728,374
1920	22,864	2,068,938	49,192	82,518	15,651	715,789
1921	21,275	2,005,143	15,228	60,513	1,257	734,980
1922	23,276	2,521,832	26,978	110,456	6,142	932,550
1923	24,162	2,824,599	53,372	155,720	18,481	1,261,541
1924	24,647	2,844,104	49,113	165,063	24,659	1,226,696
1925	24,541	2,889,962	51,336	178,662	51,795	1,444,498
1926	24,033	3,057,268	53,763	210,794	105,367	1,309,138
1927	22,556	3,252,688	58,672	243,346	137,724	1,031,308
1928	21,745	3,375,966	65,103	236,486	161,747	1,022,475
1929	20,276	3,381,038	80,560	248,500	174,050	1,054,197
1930	20,808	3,272,288	73,412	240,938	142,901	1,294,259
1931	19,378	2,676,966	54,212	226,780	120,289	922,289
1932	18,183	2,155,613	35,213	137,325	57,256	690,805
1933	19,836	2,118,229	39,825	118,693	89,339	646,838
1934	20,572	2,306,168	44,268	166,333	125,186	782,156
1935	21,223	2,351,087	39,373	184,193	135,921	1,255,058
1936	23,451	2,409,397	29,713	215,724	150,251	1,307,915
1937	26,326	2,633,870	46,077	218,133	154,625	1,242,148
1938	28,734	2,519,967	41,851	282,369	172,218	1,093,252
1939	26,178	2,359,839	44,390	219,506	134,166	876,851
1940	27,468	2,570,394	37,602	196,253	114,955	815,907
1941	24,882	2,437,392	48,716	155,259	154,996	855,697

TABLE 7 (Continued)

Year	Gold	Silver	Copper	Lead	Zinc	Coal
	(Kgs.)		(Met. Tons)			
1942	24,925	2,639,577	50,897	197,019	189,873	914,269
1943	19,643	2,686,456	49,774	218,126	197,199	1,025,326
1944	15,828	2,286,193	41,300	185,282	218,965	904,198
1945	15,530	1,900,352	61,680	205,315	209,940	914,614
1946	13,079	1,345,634	61,053	140,143	139,535	977,874
1947	14,455	1,830,249	62,492	223,135	195,814	1,040,360
1948	11,434	1,789,063	59,076	193,317	179,029	1,057,226
1949	12,614	1,538,219	57,246	220,764	178,402	1,074,707
1950	12,694	1,528,470	61,698	238,078	223,530	911,732
1951	12,255	1,362,262	67,351	225,468	180,064	1,118,710
1952	14,288	1,566,262	58,463	246,028	227,375	1,316,867
1953	15,038	1,489,435	60,148	221,549	226,539	1,432,315
1954	12,033	1,240,919	54,806	216,624	223,749	1,313,609
Totals	*1,496,868*	*220,422,294*	*2,882,364*	*9,293,020*	*5,041,243*	*56,302,361*

[1]See Table 6, n. 2.
SOURCE: J. González Reyna, *Riqueza minera y yacimentos minerales de México* (Mexico, 1956), p. 448.

Metal bought more property in northern Durango and in Santa Eulalia; Santa Gertrudis and USSR&M added to their properties in Pachuca; and the Amparo Company took control of the Mazata mines and the newly discovered Piedra Bola mine in Jalisco.[2] In one week in 1919, the *Engineering and Mining Journal* reported the sale of seven properties to six large established firms.[3] By 1922 most companies had depleted their free cash reserves and had to wait for the new acquisitions to bring in some returns before embarking upon any other projects.[4]

During 1919–20, expansions figured in all reports. Fresnillo reopened with mechanized operations and began an extensive "glory hole." Rechristened the Dolores-Esperanza Company, the old Mines Company of America resumed work and started to build a new power plant. Numerous reports of growth came from the southern Chihuahua camps. In a campaign starting in 1915 ASARCO had managed to buy or gain control of the properties on the Veta Colorada and now opened the largest cyaniding plant in Chihuahua to work those ores. Northern Sonora, El Boleo, Nuevo León, and even Guanajuato reported labor shortages. Railroads were sorely overburdened; 25 per cent of their cars hauled silver and lead ores and bullion as lead production headed for new records. San Rafael of Pachuca summed up its impatience with the slowness of recovery by blaming inefficient railroad service, pilfered shipments, a shortage of labor, the lack of fractional currency for payrolls, and frequent changes in fiscal rulings. It would seem that its difficulties were minor ones encountered in resuming operations.[5]

Changes in the economic structure of the industry vitally affected its recovery. Small miners declined in importance with the concentration of holdings and the entrance of smelter owners into actual mining. A major blow to the small miners was the disappearance of the independent ore buyer, who would buy small lots of ore and combine them into carload lots, dilute the undesirable constituents, and bargain shrewdly with the smelters.[6] To worsen the picture, the needs of the smelters had changed. Ore from the holdings of the smelter owners and the large independents made straight-silver ore—the forte of the small Mexican independent—undesirable since furnace charges were no longer designed for this type of ore.[7] Furthermore, new milling processes employed by the large companies—particularly flotation—weighed against the crude ores of the independents.

Ore shippers on the west coast were in the worst position. Copper miners could only ship to Cananea or to Douglas, Arizona, since the small copper smelters of southern Sonora were all closed. Their lead ores had to be sent either to El Paso or to San Francisco for custom smelting; freight rates were high and shipping to Chihuahua was impossible. Copper producers east of the Sierra Madre found their lot little better. The Matehuala, Teziutlán, and Concepción del Oro smelters did little custom work. The San Luis Potosí smelter worked only on a small scale until ASARCO gained control in 1923. Consequently, shippers on the Mexican Central Railroad were practically tied to the Aguascalientes smelter. Only the lead shippers of the north-central and the northeastern areas had a choice among the smelters at El Paso (for Chihuahua and Coahuila miners), Chihuahua, Torreón, Velardeña, Mapimí (until it was dismantled in 1921), Monterrey, and Saltillo. Prices paid for ores of various grades and qualities were quite important, hence shipping to the nearest smelter was not always most profitable. A smelter had to be found that needed the independents' type of ore to mix with its own ore or with that of its large customers, with whom it had long-term contracts.[8] Several plans were broached, but a solution for the independents' dilemma was not found.[9]

Mexico's recovery was set back by the postwar world depression of 1921–22. A decline starting late in 1920 lasted until the first quarter of 1922. Silver quotations slowly declined between February and September, 1920, while zinc showed weakness. Then—from October, 1920, to March, 1921—silver and zinc prices collapsed completely; copper fell over 6 cents a pound and lead over 4 cents a pound. A bitter and prolonged coal strike during the second half of 1920 and the beginning of 1921 shut many smelters, crippled the railroads, and added to the industry's difficulties. A railroad strike, following the settlement of the coal strike in January, 1921, coincided with the metal price decline of early 1921.[10]

ASARCO closed its Monterrey smelter after the first break, and silver miners deluged Mexico City with appeals for tax relief until the industry could adjust itself. In their case, the sliding-scale features of the new tax laws came into effect. Also, the government decision to accept Carranza paper money (at a 210 per cent premium) helped relieve the initial tension. It then set the silver tax on June 15, 1920, at 5 per cent, when silver sold for less than 60 cents (U.S.), with a 0.5 per cent rise for every 10-cent price rise up to $1.00.[11] In August, 1920, President de la Huerta appointed a commission, composed of government and mining representatives, to study the situation with a view toward reducing taxes and suggesting minor changes in the mining law. During the next month tax reductions were extended to low-grade mining enterprises and remote camps to enable them to temporarily overcome "natural obstacles."[12]

The second market break coincided with the silver tax reduction. Apparently stabilized at 90 cents an ounce in September, 1920, silver fell to 65 cents by December. Copper and lead suffered equally disastrous declines. In November, Minerales y Metales closed its Mexican plants. The closing of mines and smelters by mid-December forced the government to act.[13]

A decree of December 24, 1920, exempted silver from taxation when the price was under 60 cents and set the tax at 1 per cent from 60 to 70 cents with a 0.5 per cent rise for every 10-cent rise up to 90 cents, the old rates to take effect beyond that price.[14] The next day copper was exempted from all taxes when the price fell below 15 cents a pound on the New York market.[15] Lead was given a total tax exemption on April 21, 1921.[16] In March, 1921, the government issued a long list of duty-exempt mining supplies and equipment, although on April 29th it restricted this exemption to any period during which silver sold for less than 60 cents.[17]

As the situation worsened during the first half of 1921, a "conservative curtailment" was noted. Mines worked their men three days a week, cut wages, and took out only higher grade ore. In Durango, mining seemed to shut down all at once. Cananea and Nacozari closed in January. Work in Zacatecas was at a standstill, and ore-buying agencies closed for lack of offerings. Even a mine as strong as Santa Gertrudis had to sell a group of notes at a £10 discount. One encouraging feature was the continuation of new construction work as the industry took full advantage of the lull to prepare for the larger operations anticipated when the market recovered.[18]

Revenue losses to the Mexican government were considerable. Collections fell from a peak of over 15,000,000 pesos in 1919 and 1920, to 4,500,000 pesos in 1921, and 8,500,000 pesos in 1922. However, an interesting fact was observed: tax cuts did not help sustain production. Copper production during the first half of 1920 was 23,914 metric tons.

In the first half of 1921, despite tax exemption, it was only 8,838 metric tons. For the same periods, lead production declined from 44,899 metric tons to 24,151 metric tons, and zinc from 8,543 to 598 metric tons. Only silver showed a most remarkable strength. Despite its being the hardest hit, marketwise, of all the metals, production for the first half of 1921 had declined only to 942,718 kilograms compared with 1,038,995 kilograms during the same months the year before—a fall of only about 9 per cent.

The explanation of this lack of correlation between taxes and production is of tremendous significance in understanding the Mexican mining industry. Mexican metals were an integral part of the world mineral economy, but some metals were more tightly integrated with foreign production than others. The greater the degree of integration, the less effect tax manipulation in Mexico would have upon production, for only a change in the world market could affect Mexican production. Mexican copper was virtually an appendage of the American copper industry. American copper producers were trying to unload huge stocks which had accumulated after the war, and so they completely stopped operations. American-controlled Mexican copper producers followed suit. Mexican zinc miners depended completely upon United States smelters. But after the war, the United States had overexpanded its zinc capacity while the market contracted severely. Zinc was a "sick metal" for years. Recovery depended upon finding new markets to smelt Mexico's zinc ore and concentrates. Silver, however, was in a different position. While falling lead prices curtailed silver production from the lead-silver smelters, silver-cyanide plants at Pachuca expanded and could operate at a profit despite low prices. Therefore, they kept working at full capacity on veins which had been recently discovered and showed a profit on 60-cent silver. To them a tax reduction was only an added fillip.[19] For these reasons, simply reducing metal taxes could not increase production, but it did drastically reduce government income.

By mid-1921, as it became increasingly clear that a new postwar price equilibrium was in the making, the Mexican government's attitude toward mining changed. It realized that it would have to continue aid to mining for some time to permit readjustments. Also, it would have to make a distinction between the problems of high-cost and low-cost producers, so that tax concessions would not deprive the government of revenue from the large low-cost producers who would still be making profit. During the first half of 1921 a strange phenomenon was observed. Mexican silver had become tax exempt in February when the price fell below 60 cents. The price hovered there, just below the taxation point, varying from 56.023 to 59.810 cents on the monthly average; output did not decline. Pachuca's large, new efficient mills could produce silver at less than the assumed Mexican break-even point of 60 cents, and they were saving the payment of even a 1 per cent tax. Despite pleas by marginal producers that they would be forced to close, a new policy went into effect on July 20, 1921. The government repealed the law of December 24, 1920, reinstituted the rates of June 15, 1920, and dropped the tariff exemptions.[20]

Threats to discontinue operations were met with a firm attitude. In August, the *Engineering and Mining Journal* correspondent reported that the miners were told that they "must paddle their own canoes" and not look to the government for special exemptions. Mining would have to adjust to new market conditions instead of expecting the government to do the worrying. For emphasis, President Obregón declared that he would rather see the minerals remain in the subsoil until they could be exploited with a profit than relieve the "transient" and "foreign-owned" mineral industry of its equitable share of the national tax burden.[21] Despite Obregón's nationalistic stand, mining companies allegedly operating at a loss[22] continued to buy new properties. Aside from copper and zinc, production figures remained high.

Mine operations resumed in mid-1921. By September, 1921, railway rolling stock was in short supply; ore pickups and supply deliveries were tardy. ASARCO's western smelters opened first, putting their newly installed equipment to work. El Boleo floated a $1,000,000 issue of gold debentures to install a converter plant and end shipping matte and black copper to ASARCO for converting. Silver rose to 68 and 70 cents. Velardeña and Chihuahua worked at full capacity. Mazapil blew in its furnaces at Concepción del Oro and Saltillo.

Peñoles revealed a major alteration when it announced the reopening of the Torreón plant on January 2, 1922. On September 6, 1921, it had decided to dismantle the Mapimí smelter and use its furnaces to replace the old ones at Torreón. Peñoles permanently abandoned Mapimí as a smelter site because the decline in its siliceous ore production had made it more profitable to concentrate operations at Torreón or Monterrey, where ores from Parral, Zacatecas, and Sierra Mojada could be brought in to balance the charges. A 250-ton flotation plant was installed at Mapimí in 1926 to concentrate lead-sulphide ores before shipment to Torreón.[23]

By the spring of 1922, a full-fledged mine revival was underway. In June, Nacozari and Cananea resumed operations. El Tigre reported the lowest costs since 1916: wages and marketing costs were down and production in tons-per-man-shift was up 17 per cent. ASARCO's Tiro General at Charcas, S.L.P., and the Bacis Gold and Silver Company, reopened after having been closed since the beginning of the Revolution. A new railroad spur from Ardagas to Jiménez, Chihuahua, along with the extension of power lines from the Boquillas Dam, induced several new enterprises to open in the Parral district. Dos Estrellas increased its milling capacity from 1,400 to 2,000 tons per day and replaced its antiquated tube mills with modern ball mills. The Mexican Reduction & Mines Company in Guanajuato resumed treating the tailings in the Guanajuato River with a new plant. A commission from the Société de la Vieille-Montagne of Belgium arrived to look over the zinc-calcining plant at Saltillo and zinc properties optioned to them. By the end of 1923, the freight forwarders of El Paso had their hands full with mining machinery orders, and some hired night shifts. In view of the energy directed toward mine development and equipment, Mexican mining was more active than the production charts might indicate. During the next 5 years the value of Mexican mineral production climbed from 200,000,000 to 345,000,000 pesos.[24]

Mineworkers suffered grievously during the depression and were happy to return to work even with wage cuts of from 10 to 30 per cent. The assistant engineer described the condition of the peons wanting jobs when the Tiro General mine opened:

> Half-starved and ragged, hundreds of peons clamored for work. . . . The peon—utterly poor, living in a rude *jacal* of sticks and thatch . . . wearing leathern sandals, a breech clout, a 2-gallon straw hat, with a serape flung over his shoulder, and a cigarette rolled in a corn husk between his lips— has changed but little. . . . The bitter lessons seared into the memories of the people by nine years of revolution and starvation are still fresh; they know that if the mines shut down, their lot will be hard.[25]

Not until March, 1923, did the government rescind the decrees suspending taxes on lead and copper. Lead was again taxed on the basis of the law of June 27, 1919. When the price of copper reached 15 cents a pound the tax was automatically restored.[26] In June, the copper tax was put on a sliding scale designed to encourage beneficiation in Mexico. If copper rose to over 20 cents a pound, the lion's share of the rise would accrue to the Mexican government in taxes.[27]

Pertenencia tax arrears continued to plague Mexico throughout the early 1920's. From 12,000 to 15,000 mine titles were delinquent in tax payments; the British Consul went as far as to estimate that 49,000 out of approximately 70,000 titles were in arrears.[28] The practice of allowing a title to remain on the books until someone specifically petitioned to have it declared in caduca to denounce it, kept the delinquent rolls quite long.[29] Mineowners employed the ruse of having a dummy third party file a petition, denounce the property, receive a tax-free title, and "sell" it back to the original owner. Under de la Huerta, the policy of not penalizing tax arrears being paid in regular installments was no more successful than Carranza's original proposal. With many official records destroyed, ownership often could not be established until the owner voluntarily presented himself for tax payments.[30]

Villa's surrender, a lenient tax policy, and gestures by the government not to recognize dubious denouncements of property when local turbulence made the payment of taxes or compliance with the law impossible— all tended to bring many properties back into production by the summer of 1920. In October, Obregón prodded the delinquents as part of his "get-tough" policy. He ordered lists prepared of tax-delinquent titles which were to be cancelled immediately if their taxes were not paid up by November 1, 1920.[31] For the next six years the government followed a mildly conciliatory policy while clerks checked the lists of property titles against tax receipts. As many as thirty caducations were made in one day; for the month of April, 1925, alone the number reached 1,072. Sometimes the clerks would become "too enthusiastic" and issue new titles before notifying the owners of the cancellation. Mineowners often found their titles in dispute without any prior hint of trouble.[32] The government made continual allowances for the payment of arrears; it cancelled all taxes due before 1920. Placing a property on the caducation list simply meant that the concession holder had to ascertain first whether the property had been denounced by someone else before being allowed to reclaim it by paying the arrears. Generally, the payment of one or two years' taxes in a lump, and the rest in installments, was sufficient to restore a title to good standing.

In 1924 de le Huerta instigated a revolt against Obregón. The rebellion was soon quashed, but not before conjuring up again visions of the old fighting days. To reassure mineowners, Obregón offered to accept partial payment for tax arrears in depreciated government bonds. At the same time, he placed greater emphasis upon resuming workings before tax arrears would be forgiven.[33] But the rising metal market and the guarantee of law and order encouraged operation of all but the most worthless properties.

Mexico's monetary system gradually regained its stability during the early 1920's. Although the runaway silver market of 1919 necessitated strengthening laws prohibiting the export of bullion to save silver pesos, the collapse of the silver market in 1920 caused gold to circulate at a premium. Mexico attempted to coin enough gold for the nation's monetary needs, but the coinage of silver was still too great and the Treasury continually engaged in local market operations to support the silver peso.[34] Defeat of de la Huerta and American recognition gave Obregón enough stability to open a new government bank—the *Banco de México*— which could start issuing paper currency again. For years Mexico had claimed to be the only modern country whose entire circulating medium was either gold or silver. While the restoration of confidence in paper was not complete, significant strides were made. Laws prohibiting the export of gold were kept until Mexico went on a managed currency system in the 1930's. In 1924 the requirement to reimport 25 per cent of the value of exported silver was repealed for the last time.[35] Until the depression of the 1930's, the conservative deflationary policy managed to keep Mexico's peso at a ratio of two to one with the dollar, or the parity of 1905–12.

CHAPTER 12

New Technical Developments, 1920–1933

DURING the 1920's Mexican mining went on to new production highs based on more modern techniques of mass mining and ore processing; there were relatively few discoveries of new mines. Two mine districts were opened after 1918—Piedra Bola, in Jalisco, and Ahumada, in Chihuahua—but after achieving local prominence neither became more than an interesting development. On the other hand, the recently perfected flotation process revolutionized the base-metals industry and made possible the profitable extraction of zinc. Its effect on two mines in Chihuahua—the San Francisco del Oro and the El Potosí—had a greater impact than the opening of the two new districts.

Ore flotation, like cyanidation, originated in the nineteenth century but was not perfected until about 1910.[1] For this process the ore is fine ground and then washed into cells where it is agitated and mixed with air, oils, and chemicals. Metal particles cling to the oil when it floats to the surface as a froth; the gangue sinks. This froth is skimmed off and the water filtered out, leaving a concentrate. For some unknown reason different metallic compounds have an affinity for specific oils. Thus, by treating complex ores with several oils the different metals can be extracted. This process is known as "selective flotation." Its cheapness and high efficiency suit it admirably for low-grade complex base metal ores. Flotation does not work well on straight gold and silver ores for which cyaniding is still the preferred extraction method. Flotation concentrates were too fine for efficient smelting until the development of processes to agglomerate them.[2] By 1931, flotation concentrates comprised 90 per cent of the ore processed in the Chihuahua smelter.

An experimental plant in Parral introduced flotation into Mexico in 1908, but little more appears to have been done.[3] Its neglect was attributed to the failures occurring in the early development of the process and to the tremendous amounts of available ore which were not amenable to flotation. Copper mines in Sonora adopted the process from parent companies in the United States during the Revolution. In 1917, eight flotation plants operated in Mexico with the two largest at Cananea and Nacozari.[4] Between 1916 and 1918 Real del Monte fruitlessly conducted a series of experiments in floating straight silver ores in an effort to relieve the cyanide shortage.[5]

As the industry gradually depleted the enormous surface oxide ore bodies of Mexico, flotation became as important as cyanidation and gravity concentration. Tariff exemptions for flotation equipment and materials further encouraged the use of the process.[6] Flotation mills increased their daily capacity, between 1925 and 1926, from 6,490 to 17,956 metric tons. In 1926, flotation plants treated 2,112,506 metric tons of ore, 16.66 per cent of the Mexican output; in 1928 they treated 32.30 per cent of the output, some 4,073,413 metric tons.[7] Flotation was now hailed as the saviour of the small miner, and the government tried to encourage the erection of small flotation plants. But the capital, technological skill, and knowledge needed to make them economically successful was beyond the reach of the small operators.[8] Small miners needed an administration ready to provide substantial funds and guidance.

Flotation raised zinc to the level of a major Mexican export metal. It made possible the continued working of old mines, whose ores had been condemned as being too "zincky," and the opening of marginal mines.[9] Smelter penalties for excess zinc had so hampered the lucrative Tiro General mine that one manager despondently referred to it as "the greatest zinc mine in Mexico."[10] Attempts to separate zinc from silver-lead ore at Tiro General and at mines in Parral and Santa Barbara, had all failed. Selective flotation made possible the profitable separation of zinc and silver-lead concentrates. Consequently lead production also increased during the 1920's. Mexico's zinc industry traditionally had been marginal, and the American zinc tariff of 1909 almost dealt it a mortal blow. But in 1912, a Belgian concern, the International Ore and Smelting Company (IO&S)—a subsidiary of the Société Générale des Minerais of Brussels with a capitalization of 4,000,000 Belgian francs—began to export zinc from Saltillo to Belgium via Tampico. It centered its early efforts on a zinc calcining (concentrating) plant with a capacity of from 2,000 to 3,000 tons a month. During the Revolution IO&S closed the plant although a few shipments were still made.[11] In 1919 a 240-retort zinc furnace built to produce 400 kilograms of zinc a day, which it had opened at Saltillo, proved unprofitable.[12] When Great Britain, in order to exclude continental buyers,[13] erected a smelter for Australian zinc ores, the Belgians turned their attention to Mexico. The Société Générale founded the Compañía Mexicana de Minerales in 1924, and raised the IO&S capitalization to 6,000,000 francs. It also announced plans to increase zinc ore purchases, build loading facilities in Tampico, start a monthly steamer service with Antwerp, and send in experts to revitalize the industry.[14] Between 1924 and 1928 the Mexican zinc industry grew rapidly. Despite absurdly low zinc taxes, technological and economic difficulties had made it difficult for Mexican zinc to compete in the world market.[15] But now flotation plants provided the stimulus needed to change the zinc mines from "holes in the mountainsides" to respectable mining installations. Until 1923 zinc production had closely followed the rise and fall of zinc prices. After 1923, with the growing output of by-product zinc from selective flotation plants, Mexico became one of the world's largest zinc producers, and the rate of increase in production far outdistanced the rise in price.[16]

In 1923, IO&S reopened its calcining plant and added a new furnace. ASARCO constructed a zinc smelter at Nueva Rosita, Coahuila, immediately adjacent to its new by-product coke ovens, to use their waste heat to run the zinc furnaces. It also built a model town to house the smelter's workers. Despite ASARCO's increasing the plant's output from 1.5 to 5 metric tons of zinc per day, Mexico remained a minor contributor to the world's supply of zinc metal.[17]

Mexico's zinc industry was designed to export concentrates and high-grade ore to Belgium and Germany. In this trade the Belgian companies at Saltillo held the dominant position because of their calcining plant, purchasing agencies, European contacts, and shipping facilities at Tampico. They handled almost all the straight zinc ore produced as well as much of the flotation concentrates not destined for the ASARCO zinc plant. Even ASARCO concentrates produced at San Luis Potosí were shipped to Belgium. Only the Howe Sound Company's subsidiary, the Compañía Industrial El Potosí in Chihuahua, shipped concentrates to Germany.[18]

Flotation affected the lead industry almost as much as it did zinc. By 1922, at the start of the expansion of her lead industry, Mexico became the second largest lead producer in the world. Production rose from 110,456 metric tons in 1922 to 248,401 metric tons in 1929. Amazingly, this growth took place without the discovery of new mines except for the short-lived Ahumada-Erupción group. Selective flotation in the complex ore camps of Chihuahua, Coahuila, and Zacatecas accounted for most of the increase.[19]

The San Francisco del Oro and El Potosí mines in south-central Chihuahua experienced the greatest expansions and made the highest profits in Mexico from the introduction of flotation. San Francisco del Oro had been a large producer in the nineteenth century, but the increasing complexity of the ores had made treatment difficult. Some ore shoots were fabulously rich. An ore analysis in 1889 showed about 25 per cent lead, 11 to 12 per cent zinc, 6.5 to 7 per cent iron, 1 per cent copper, 0.08 to 0.12 per cent [sic] silver, plus manganese, cadmium, antimony, sulphur, aluminum oxide, calcium carbonate, and some gold which escaped assay.[20] A Mexican syndicate had picked it up for a song at a receiver's sale when it was thought that the surface carbonate ores were gone. In 1903 a London group bought the mine for £200,000 and formed the San Francisco del Oro Mining Company, later renamed the San Francisco Mines of Mexico, Ltd. In floating the company its promotors soft-pedalled the zinc content of the ore and the high smelter penalties involved.[21]

A long series of beneficiation experiments proved fruitless. At first the lack of water necessitated dry concentrating; when water was struck on a lower level, the company opened a 100-ton mill using jigs for wet concentrating. Later examinations raised the estimate of the ore reserves, but after ten years the company had not paid one dividend and was forced to float debentures to obtain working capital.[22]

In 1919 its engineers advised the company either to expand the mill to make a profit on volume or to sell out. An American syndicate took a $3,500,000 option on the property but permitted it to lapse. A record of 16 years without a dividend, despite an excellent Board of Directors and the best engineering advice, occasioned considerable adverse comment. After the Americans' rejection of the option, the company arranged another loan and in 1921 enlarged the mill to 250 tons.[23] A £40,900 loss in 1919 turned into a £33,148 profit the next year, but the sharp postwar depression placed the company in financial straits. The enlarged mill embodied the latest flotation equipment and immediately solved the beneficiation problems. At first it made a silver-lead-copper concentrate; two years later it also produced zinc concentrates. Huge new investments bailed out the company financially and doubled the mill's capacity. The first dividend on the basis of 1921–22 earnings amounted to £112,690, or 15 per cent, and the next year the rate was 32.5 per cent. The company declared in 1924–25 a dividend of £308,148, or 37.5 per cent, despite the cost of increasing the mill capacity to 800 tons, starting an 11-kilometer railway, and buying more property. The dividend rate the next year reached 40 per cent![24]

Flotation converted the hitherto rebellious complex ores of San Francisco del Oro into a veritable treasure. Assay values were converted into economic assets: in 1925 the ore ran 300 grams of silver and 1.25 grams of gold to the ton, with 8.5 per cent lead, 13.8 per cent zinc, and 0.77 per cent copper. The mine shipped lead concentrates to the Velardeña and Chihuahua smelters and zinc concentrates directly to Antwerp. It also acquired the neighboring Clarines unit. San Francisco employed 652 men at an average wage of 3.54 pesos per day.[25]

During the second half of the 1920's San Francisco enlarged its mill to 1,100 tons, and until 1929 the dividend rate was kept between 37.5 and 40 per cent. When metal prices broke, the unit stepped up production to make money on volume, but dividends fell to 10 per cent. Despite milling almost 400,000 tons of ore a year the enterprise lost money. In December, 1931, the mine shut down. With maintenance work and other charges, the management reported an operating loss of £45,452 in 1931–32. Ironically, it announced simultaneously the completion of new additions which raised the mill's capacity to 500,000 tons per year.[26]

San Francisco reopened in 1934, having been closed for over a year. Output rose close to capacity with the revival of metal prices in the mid-1930's. Profits fell during the recession of 1938, from £453,000 in 1936–37 to £60,015 in 1937–38. During World War II profits were not large. The 1943–44 dividend came to £36,404, about 5 per cent per share.[27] A new unit added in 1944, to improve the separation of copper from the lead concentrates by the use of sulphur dioxide, made the mill even more efficient. A survey in 1948 noted that the company now realized 37 cents more per ton of concentrate treated in the mill: the cost of the added treatment was 8 cents, leaving a profit of 29 cents.[28] For 7 years after 1943 San Francisco paid an average dividend of 27 per cent on a capitalization of £900,000; the 1949 dividend was no less than 50 per cent![29]

San Francisco also worked two other units. The Los Azules unit, closed in 1941, and the neighboring Clarines unit, which worked fitfully and in 1946 produced 15 to 20 per cent of the San Francisco's mill feed.[30]

After World War II, San Francisco entered into a long term contract with the Compañía Metalúrgica de Peñoles, a new company which had leased the smelting and refining plants of the Compañía Minera de Peñoles to smelt and refine the lead and copper production of both companies. Peñoles' parent, the American Metal Company, held 37.5 per cent of San Francisco's stock and collected some $653,000 in dividends on it in 1956. In that year San Francisco reported that its mill ground 65,000 tons of ore a month although it was designed for only 60,000 tons, because of improvements in the mill flow-sheet. It employed some 3,000 men, including 35 foreigners. Ore reserves were set at 3,517,970 metric tons of blocked ore and 1,494,940 metric tons of partially blocked ore. In 1953 it reported reserve ore grades of 9.06 per cent zinc, 6.28 per cent lead, 0.66 per cent copper, and about 5.3 ounces of silver per ton.[31]

Before the Revolution the El Potosí Mining Company at Santa Eulalia, Chihuahua, had had a checkered financial history until it came under control of the Howe Sound Company. With an estimated value of $1,500,000, the company in 1919 mined each week 3,000 tons of zinc ore with silver and lead values. It shipped directly to the Chihuahua and El Paso smelters since it did not have a mill. In 1922 El Potosí built a small 50-ton experimental flotation plant while a diamond-drilling campaign explored the ore body. At first the ore presented some difficulty, but the problem was solved. The company built a 600-ton plant— expanded to 850 tons in 1925 and to 1,000 tons in 1929—to handle the increased ore output.[32] The ore was quite complex—300 grams of silver per ton with 9.2 per cent zinc, 9.2 per cent lead, 29.4 per cent iron, 20.8

per cent sulphur, and 8.2 per cent calcium oxide—but beneficiation cost only 2.15 pesos per ton for a concentrate only one-fifth the weight of the ore. El Potosí shipped lead concentrates over its own electric railway to the Chihuahua smelter and zinc concentrates to Europe. After World War II the mine continued to operate although its reserves were low, and any drop in metal prices cut its profit margins drastically.[33]

Flotation plants soon dotted Mexico. Cananea and Nacozari had very large installations which originally presented difficult technical problems.[34] Magistral, La Noria, Mazapil, Mapimí, Santa María de la Paz, Promontorio, Aurora, Teziutlán, Palmilla, Angangueo, Chihuahua City, El Oro, Asientos, Fresnillo, Veta Grande and Guadalupe (Zacatecas), and San Pedro (San Luis Potosí) boasted plants ranging from 100 to 3,000 tons daily capacity.[35] With their combined outputs, Mexico developed its greatest boom in base metals.

Flotation did not destroy the dominant position of large companies in base metal production. Four companies, ASARCO, San Francisco Mines, Howe Sound, and IO&S (in its role of ore buyer and shipper) dominated the zinc industry. ASARCO, American Metal, San Francisco Mines, and Howe Sound produced the bulk of the lead. While flotation had managed to add a number of rivals to the powerful ASARCO and American Metal's chain of mines and smelters it had not, by any means, changed the basic picture of concentration of control of the base-metals mining industry.

Nor did the introduction of flotation mean the demise of cyanidation. Most gold and silver districts found it to their advantage to continue the older process. Large numbers of cyanide plants were still to be found in Pachuca, El Oro, Guanajuato, and in the silver camps of the west coast. Some companies erected "dual plants," removing the precious metals by cyanidation and the base metals by flotation. Several new cyanide plants were built during the 1920's. Of three large plants built in the Parral district, the biggest was ASARCO's 500-ton mill at Minas Nuevas. Fresnillo erected a 2,000-ton plant which could treat 3,500 to 4,000 tons a day. Expansions continued in the Guanajuato and Pachuca districts. The Real del Monte company milled 2,000 tons of ore a day in its two plants. A new plant in San Pedro Analco, Jalisco, treated 750 tons a day, while the Esperanza company in El Oro increased its capacity to 1,000 tons. In addition, the Pachuca and Fresnillo mills added cyanide regeneration equipment to recover the chemical for reuse and to halt stream pollution.[36] Cyanidation remained a most important process in the Mexican mining picture.

CHAPTER 13

Foreign Investments, 1920–1933

DURING the decade of the 1920's foreign investments in Mexican mining continued to increase. One estimate placed Mexican mine ownership at about three per cent of the mines exploited in 1910 and less than two per cent in the 1920's.[1] For the years between 1922 and 1925, the *Anuario de estadística minera* estimated that on an average about five per cent of mine output appeared to have been Mexican controlled.[2] The disparity between Mexican holdings and Mexican production may have been due to the fact that a greater proportion of Mexican-held properties were worked.

Investment trends during the Revolution are difficult to trace. Contemporary comment would indicate that many smaller companies found themselves either wiped out or forced to sell to large companies; water was squeezed out of perennially hopeful bonanzas; and major firms increased their holdings. Cleona Lewis estimated that American holdings declined from $302,000,000 in 1914 to $222,000,000 in 1919, and then increased to $248,800,000 ten years later.[3] (See Table 5, p. 76.)

Paul D. Dickens of the Bureau of Foreign and Domestic Commerce, United States Department of Commerce, made the first authoritative survey of American investments in Mexico in 1929. He set American holdings at $230,421,000 controlled by 97 companies,[4] including $10,000,000 "to cover omissions." Dickens' and Lewis' figures differed by $18,000,000 because Dickens omitted a number of nonproductive enterprises. However, Lewis had estimated that the inclusion of nonproductive enterprises would have raised her figure to $320,000,000. Dickens set the total holdings in precious metals workings at four-fifths of the total, but segregation was admittedly difficult and the two differed on definitions. While not as large as anticipated, $230,000,000 represented a substantial stake. J. Fred Rippy estimates that between 1913 and 1929 British holdings declined from 50 to 19 companies whose paid up capital had fallen from £8,600,000 to £7,680,000.[5]

Undoubtedly the reputation Mexico had gained during the Revolution and the oil and land controversies discouraged much new investment. Rises in metal prices brought out numerous marginal operations but little new capital. Still, a substantial area of agreement grew up between the mineowners and the Mexican government. A reporter in 1926 asked William Loeb of ASARCO to explain why his company got along so well with the Mexican authorities. Loeb answered that ASARCO never knowingly broke a Mexican law no matter how unjust; it never ignored or defied a public official but tried to persuade him that he was taking a wrong position; it never touched a mining property unless it had a sound title; and it made certain that all responsible officials in contact with Mexican authorities could talk things over in a friendly manner in Spanish. Even as caustic a critic as Harvey O'Connor admitted that ASARCO's policy in Mexico during the 1920's, although antiunion, was impeccable and paternalistic. While Mr. Loeb's statement might smack of press-agentry, ASARCO's Mexican relations were excellent and its expanding empire was profitable.[6]

ASARCO embarked upon a number of ambitious projects. In 1919 it acquired from the Maderos the Rosita coal fields near Sabinas, Coahuila, to replace imported coal, and floated a $10,000,000, 24-year first mortgage bond issue at 6 per cent for Mexican developments. It built a battery of by-product coke ovens and zinc retort furnaces to operate on waste heat and illuminating gas from the coke ovens. The project cost over $8,500,000 (17,000,000 pesos). From Rosita's coal reserves of 100,000,000 tons, ASARCO planned to mine 50,000 tons a month and feed 15,000 tons to the coke ovens. The scheme worked, and the ovens produced a long list of by-products as well as substantial profits. Smelting concentrates from northern Mexico, the zinc plant turned out 1.5 tons of zinc metal a day. When the needs of the smelter outgrew the supply of heat and gas from the coke ovens, ASARCO piped in natural gas.[7]

ASARCO built a model town, Nueva Rosita, to gain tax and railroad rate concessions. It set up a complete benevolent program: hospital, medical service, and homes with water and light—all for three pesos a month. The building program included a sewage system, market, church, casino, school, and a cooperative store which sold merchandise at cut-rate prices. This show place for ASARCO—and Mexico—even had a model dairy and provided credit plans to encourage home ownership.[8]

In southern Chihuahua ASARCO developed one of its largest agglomerations of mines. During the Revolution it acquired control of the entire Tecolotes (Veta Colorada) vein system in the Santa Barbara–Minas Nuevas district and built the largest cyanide mill in the state. At Parral, a few miles to the south, ASARCO by 1923 had purchased control of the entire vein system at the foot of the Cerro de la Cruz. Introducing electric pumps and the flotation process, it overcame the water problem and beneficiated the complex ores economically. When four neighboring mines, including the famed Alvarado company, ran into financial difficulties, ASARCO engineered their merger along with the Parral and Durango Railroad into the Mexico Northern Railroad and Mining Company. ASARCO took a block of the stock of the new company, an option on another block, and appointed five of the company officers. By integrating the area's milling operations and improving mining methods, in 1925 ASARCO handled over 1,000,000 metric tons of ore in its 6 mills, shipping the concentrates to either the Chihuahua smelter or to the Nueva Rosita zinc plant. ASARCO also controlled important properties in Chihuahua in the districts of Villa Escobeda, Santa Barbara, La Palmilla, and Parral. It expanded its Coahuila holdings in Sierra Mojada, but they remained second to Peñoles'.[9]

ASARCO's greatest coup was the absorption of a large part of the Robert Towne properties. Towne's death in 1916, the ravages of the Revolution, and the erratic metal market left his Compañía Metalúrgica Mexicana and its subsidiaries in bad financial straits. It leased two of its properties, Fresnillo and Teziutlán, to a British corporation. Finally in June, 1923, ASARCO announced that Metalúrgica had been taken over by a holding company, Towne Mines, Inc., whose activities would be directed by ASARCO, although Towne's heirs still held title to the properties. Under a complicated arrangement ASARCO agreed to provide working capital; spend $1,000,000 to remodel the San Luis smelter; treat 50,000 tons of ore a month; equip the company's Santa Barbara mines and give them special privileges in ASARCO's Tecolotes mill; and pay off $600,000 in receiver's certificates. In turn, ASARCO was given a 60 per cent interest in a number of Towne mines, to integrate with ASARCO's own operations, plus a handsome block of debentures with generous retirement terms. After retirement of the debentures ASARCO was to get 30 per cent of the company's earnings to cover risk and operating and merging charges. ASARCO appointed all officials of the new company with the exception of Towne's old crony and general manager, Donald C. Brown, who was retained as Vice-President to represent the Towne interests.

The key to this large transaction was the San Luis Potosí smelter, the natural outlet for the new 900-ton flotation plant on ASARCO's Tiro General property. ASARCO prepared to abandon the antiquated Aguascalientes plant in 1925 since San Luis offered a better site. Improvements made at San Luis included a white-arsenic plant and a 20,000-ton battery of copper smelting furnaces. A baghouse, for the recovery of metals in the smelter fumes, made it possible to rework the old dumps as well as resmelt much of the old slag which had been used for paving and construction. Many a street pavement in San Luis Potosí found its way back to the smelter.[10]

ASARCO and Peñoles both turned their attention to Oaxaca in the mid-1920's. ASARCO concentrated on the Taviche district; Peñoles worked in both the Taviche and Natividad areas. Between 1924 and 1928 both companies built roads, cleaned out mines, and constructed mills, only to withdraw in 1928 when metal prices began to decline. ASARCO reopened its workings in the 1930's, but closed them for good in 1936.

Peñoles kept pace with ASARCO. Its major income came from the properties organized at the end of the Revolution. In 1923–24 Peñoles reorganized its capitalization to become a wholly owned subsidiary of the American Metal Company with a capitalization of $66,000,000.[11] Although the Torreón smelter drew the bulk of its ore from Mapimí, shipments from Chihuahua State increased and Mapimí's days appeared numbered. Peñoles entered the Santa Eulalia and Santa Barbara camps in Chihuahua in the early 1920's and shipped ore to ASARCO's Chihuahua smelter. But as Mapimí shipments declined, Peñoles diverted its Chihuahua ore to Torreón. Peñoles' ventures in lead mines in the northeast; in Guanaceví, Durango; and in a small flotation plant and smelter in the Guadalupe district of Zacatecas—where it had acquired a few properties—were not successful. Its Natividad venture in Oaxaca was also abortive. Peñoles' Monterrey smelter began to experience difficulties as northeastern lead ores were depleted. To attract trade, it emphasized the advantages of its lead refinery and its proximity to export points. A lease on the Aurora y Anexas mine in Xichu, Guanajuato, was given up and the mine returned to its owners. One bright spot was Peñoles' Suriana property on the Río Balsas in Guerrero State. Its pyritic copper ore was amazingly refractory. Peñoles took the property on option when ASARCO could not find a profitable beneficiation method. It solved the problem with an expensive chloridizing roast and built a 300-ton mill. Despite a number of unsuccessful undertakings, Peñoles kept its place as second only to ASARCO in Mexico.[12]

Not to be outdone by the Americans, the British, under the urging of Fred W. Baker who had controlled the old Venture Corporation, made large investments in Mexico after 1919. Baker worked through the Camp Bird Company, whose subsidiary, the Santa Gertrudis company, had negotiated a number of profitable leases in the Pachuca area.[13] Encouraged by the success of the El Bordo lease, Camp Bird considered entering further Mexican ventures. The urging of Hugh Rose, its Mexican manager, was decisive. Rose noted that the lack of British capital in Mexico allowed choice properties to slip into American hands for a fraction of their value. Baker stoutly maintained that conditions in Mexico were good, and that the unfavorable propaganda was circulated by those wishing to deter others from entering their Mexican preserve.[14]

Baker formed the Mexican Corporation in July, 1919, distributing shares three ways: to the Camp Bird and Santa Gertrudis treasuries; to the stockholders of these companies; and to a group of London mine investment houses. The corporation's possessions consisted of leases on the mines at Fresnillo, Zacatecas, and Teziutlán, Puebla, owned by the Towne estate. They called for an investment of about £1,500,000. Amortization charges had first call on working profits with the balance to be split between the lessors and the Towne heirs; the British company was to receive 40 per cent of Fresnillo's net profits and 37.5 per cent of Teziutlán's. By 1921 the corporation had sent £1,132,813 to Mexico.[15]

Spurred by his success, Baker launched the National Mining Corporation in November, 1919. Its objective was to support British mining ventures throughout the world, particularly to help low-grade and complex-ore operations. Its shareholders and Board of Directors were almost identical with those of the Mexican Corporation plus the Union Corporation of South Africa which also had heavy holdings in San Francisco del Oro. National Mining and the Mexican Corporation were also tightly bound together by a welter of stock and note interchanges, which heavily committed the Camp Bird and Santa Gertrudis companies.[16] Except for its aid in marketing Mexican Corporation notes and stock and its holdings of the Corporation's and Santa Gertrudis' stock, National Mining concentrated its attention on fields outside Mexico.

The postwar depression soon put the British ventures into financial difficulties.[17] To replace the money subscribed for Mexican Corporation stock, Santa Gertrudis issued through National Mining, £300,000 in 8-per-cent notes for new equipment. The notes sold at a heavy discount and were not redeemed until 1925, when the company resumed dividend payments.[18] The Mexican Corporation itself had to issue 10-per-cent notes, and the condition of the metal markets in 1921 when it was ready to begin operations brought forth skeptical evaluations of the company's chances of success.[19] Hugh Rose had to renegotiate the leases of Fresnillo and Teziutlán to give the British 41.5 and 50 per cent, respectively, of the net profits.

The Mexican Corporation completely rebuilt the Fresnillo cyanide mill and raised its capacity from 700 to 2,500 tons per day. Because of the nature of the ore, by 1924 the mill was handling up to 3,500 tons a day at a total cost of 3.70 pesos per ton—a record-breaker for Mexico. At the same time, several minor unsuccessful ventures were started in Oaxaca and Zacatecas.[20]

Conservative financing practices also vexed the company. Its attempts to amortize its capital out of current production while paying off its 10-per-cent notes led to a chronic shortage of working capital. Excellent metal markets in the mid-1920's permitted the corporation to pay off its debts and improve its properties, but the metal market slumped before dividends could be paid. A merger with the Fresnillo Company of New York was arranged, but, after two dividends of one shilling each, the company ceased payments in 1930.[21]

Unlike the newer companies, Santa Gertrudis did quite well for itself in the second half of the 1920's. It purchased the Dos Carlos vein to add to the El Bordo lease, and the Anglo-American Company, eager to participate in a promising development, helped the company retire the last of its notes. More Pachuca silver properties were purchased with the aid of the Camp Bird Company. Dividends rose from £266,462 in 1927 to £317,523 in 1930. Despite a poor silver market and a fire in the Dos Carlos mine, an 11.25 per cent dividend was declared in 1931.[22]

French interests in Mexican mining remained small. Before the Revolution, French capital had been invested in the El Boleo copper and Dos Estrellas gold mines. Some money had gone into the British El Oro holdings, but the French still constituted a minor group. In the 1920's, the Corporation Miniére du Mexique was formed in Paris with a 25,000,000-franc capitalization in order to acquire the Pedrazzini silver mines at Las Chispas, just south of Nacozari, Sonora. Through a Mexican subsidiary, Corporación Minera de México, S.A., the French took over the mine, remodeled the power plant and acquired additional gold properties in Sonora and Lower California. In 1924 the company struck a bonanza vein and by the next year it paid a 25 per cent dividend and increased the capitalization by 10,000,000 francs.[23]

CHAPTER 14

The Calles Administration:
Mining and Labor Legislation

IN contrast with Alvaro Obregón's conciliatory attitude toward mining, Plutarco Calles' administration was marked by an insurgent nationalism. Recognizing the reticence of foreigners to invest in Mexican mines, he also realized that excellent markets would sustain large outputs despite high taxes, a strict mine code, and a vigorous policy of revoking mine titles in tax arrears.[1]

Determined to set his own policies, Calles wished to change the status of foreign-owned enterprises—particularly oil—tacitly recognized by Obregón. Now that the United States no longer held the club of non-recognition, reaching his objective was much easier. American mine-owners were in a dilemma. Expanding markets and rising prices made for handsome profits from their large fixed investments. But Calles' disputes with the oil companies led to an obstructionist policy on the part of the Mexican government toward all foreign businesses. A web of ill will enmeshed the mining companies making them subject to retaliatory practices by both government and labor.

Calles, addressing Congress in the summer of 1925, cited excellent prices for metals and climbing Mexican mine production as evidence of bettering conditions. He insisted that the government was justified in demanding the immediate development of mine claims—a euphemism for forced workings. Furthermore, he believed that before the government issued a title, the claimant, native or alien, should be required to show his financial ability to develop the claim and to observe all safety and hygienic regulations.[2] At the same time Calles had an Office of the Register of Mining Companies opened in which mining companies had to file certified copies of mine titles, ore descriptions, documents dealing with the extent of development and compliance with safety and hygienic regulations, and any legal changes in company organization.[3]

In October, 1925, Calles introduced a bill to implement Section I of Article 27 of the Constitution which provided that foreigners could not hold property within border or coastal regions without special permission. His bill prohibited foreigners from personally owning property or shares of corporations holding property in that area. They had three years in which to dispose of their holdings or to become Mexican citizens. Further, all foreigners holding property anywhere in Mexico would have to sign an affidavit embodying the Calvo Clause. Aimed primarily at the oil companies in the Tampico area, these proposals included mining enterprises. But Congress passed a milder amended version on January 15, 1926.[4] And on December 19, 1925, the Ministry of Industry, Commerce, and Labor had abrogated the orders of March 14 and May 7, 1919, which denied foreigners the exemption necessary in applying for concessions in border and coastal regions.[5] Breathing a sigh of relief, the mining community remained wary of Calles. Their continued suspicions were confirmed in May, 1926, with the promulgation of the "Law of Mineral Industries."

The mining community believed itself to be in a precarious state despite ARARCO, American Metal, and USSR&M deriving "more of their extensive profits from Mexican operations than from those of any other country."[6] They were aware that, having shelved the projected Mine Law 1918, Mexico had not solved the problem of reconciling the existing mining law with the new Constitution. It had modified the Mine Law of 1910 in practice by ignoring the provisions in direct conflict with the Constitution. A change was bound to come whenever conditions were stable enough to permit government action.

Mexico's difficulty in dealing with American and British mineowners was rooted in a difference in legal concepts. "Natural law guarantees" of security of property stemming from constitutional limitations upon the State's inherent irresponsibility were foreign to Mexican law. English and American law, following Liberal traditions, regarded the subsoil as essentially similar to any other property. Mexico had a tradition of minute control of the propiedad minera in which the State had a special abiding interest. Díaz's Mining Law of 1892 led foreign investors to believe that Mexico would conform to Liberal ideals. But the framers of the new Constitution said in the introduction to Article 27: "It is clear that the exercise of the right to property is not absolute, and inasmuch as it has undergone changes in meaning in the past, it is susceptible to admitting others in the future."[7] The Constitution of 1917 vested in the nation "direct ownership of all the minerals," with the proviso that "the ownership of the Nation is inalienable and may not be lost by prescription." Therefore, minerals could be worked only under concessions severely limiting the conditions of holding and working propiedad minera.

Mineowners believed that the loose government control during the years following 1884 would be recognized and safeguarded by the constitutional provisions forbidding *ex post facto* and retroactive rulings. They were mistaken. Government apologists began a campaign in the

1920's to establish the fact that the traditional concept of a concession was really in force during the entire Díaz period. They compared a concession to a franchise. As a sympathetic American phrased it: "The man who buys a mine receives not a deed, but a permit. He owns the product of the mine, but not the subterranean area itself."[8] The Department of Mines contended that:

> . . . the mining concession which is granted to an individual or enterprise, is only a contract in which the concessionaire is given authorization in order to work this or that mining property, with the condition that he pay the tax and establish regular workings for his exploitation, in such a manner that if he does not do it, the property is declared caducated and remains at the disposition of a new solicitant.[9]

During the early 1920's, Manuel de la Peña and Fernando González Roa worked untiringly to demonstrate that the government's rights over the subsoil were derived from the concept of eminent domain.[10] By this tack they hoped to answer those who argued from the standpoint of English law. At the conclusion of a study made in 1922, González Roa stated that property rights were not immutable but ought to be subject to the customs which the progress and well-being of society demand. He held that the dominio directo of the State over the subsoil is a manifestation of its right of eminent domain and that it was advantageous to both society and industry.[11] To undermine the privileges granted during the Liberal period (1884–1914), González Roa referred to the Ordenanzas of 1783, the Siete Partidas of Alfonso X, feudal usages, and Roman law. To destroy the concept envisaged in the Liberal Constitution of 1857—of a Mexican State represented as a servant and agent of society—it became necessary to deny the concepts which had evolved in Mexico during the preceding thirty years and emphasize the State's ancient prerogatives now clothed in the cloak of "eminent domain" with the cap of "public utility."[12]

Whereas Mexicans had always accepted the State's rights of eminent domain and public utility, their exercise was confined to cases of public emergency and then only with adequate compensation. During the 1920's the government constantly advanced the excuse of eminent domain to justify broadening the sphere of State action. Hence, the State could supervise the working of the subsoil in a minute manner and excuse expropriation by any reason it wished to give. In reality, the government usually acted in a prudent manner toward mining and only demanded a "positive act of exploitation" and the maintenance of minimum workings to insure retention of a concession.

After expropriating oil company properties in 1938, the Mexican government expounded a new view that subsoil concessions were "tenancies at will"—mere "expectancies" with no value beyond the cost of obtaining them and the tangible physical improvements made upon the property.[13] A concession was held to be similar to the medieval *precarium*, a "property" held at the pleasure of the lord who was bound only by his feudal honor to respect it.[14] From the official Mexican viewpoint, therefore, a concession is not an inalienable property right (*derecho real*) since the nation cannot alienate the subsoil in the first place. Rather, it is a personal right (*derecho personal*) which can only be used, not owned, by the concessionaire.[15] In view of these divergent viewpoints, the difficulties experienced in reaching an understanding between the Mexican government and the mineowners concerning mine laws can be appreciated.

Not until 1926 did Calles feel secure enough to issue a mine code based on Article 27 of the Constitution. Even so, he stressed the point that so far as property rights were concerned, the law pertained only to new concessions. An advisory commission had worked on the revision for some time and had issued a preliminary report as early as 1924.[16] While the government improved statistical methods to make tax collections more efficient, it issued statements complaining of the small percentage of properties actually worked. No less than 6,735 mine titles were caducated by the government in 1925.[17] With the industry's stabilization in the summer of 1925, Calles inaugurated a new policy when he demanded that mine companies register their basic business documents and also issued the new law regulating property holdings by foreigners in border regions. Finally in November, 1925, came the announcement that the mine law commission was ready to report.[18]

Calles had congressional authorization to issue a mine law by decree any time before May 4, 1926. Despite miners' pleas, copies of the proposed law were not released until April 28th; the National Mining Chamber had two evenings in which to discuss it. Believing that any commentary might imply concurrence, Chamber officials informally "exchanged impressions" with the Minister of Industry, Commerce, and Labor who informed them that the law would be signed as it stood on May 3rd.[19] They also failed to influence the framing of the bylaws. Notified well in advance, they had prepared suggestions and arguments against the "nationalistic and anti-economic" aspects of the bylaws. All of their objections were quashed; spokesmen explained the government's position and interpretations; and the bylaws were signed with no changes whatsoever.[20]

Government spokesmen claimed that the new law was basically the Law of 1910 except for changes necessitated by the Constitution; the mineowners were certain they knew a radical change when they saw one.[21] A legalistic work designed to cover all loopholes, the law contained 182 articles with an additional 245 articles in the bylaws![22] It was explicit in emphasizing the following points: the divisions among the mining, petroleum, and "diverse minerals" industries; federalizing the mining industry; requiring a great number of "guarantee deposits"; dividing concessions into "exploration," "exploitation," "plant," and "road" concessions; requiring proof of the discovery of ore before the granting of an exploitation concession (a revival of provisions in the laws of 1783 and 1884) and proof of "minimum workings" to retain title; protecting the rights of labor; setting up rules for inspection; outlining the procedures for obtaining easements; requiring notification of the government before the sale of a concession; obliging the mines to accept apprentice engineers; and, finally, fixing the proportion of Mexican to foreign workers and salaried employees. Officially, its object was to favor efficient work, hinder speculation, encourage small miners, augment production by liberalizing the conditions for exploitation and requiring continuous operation, and, finally, to conserve Mexico's resources.[23]

In conformity with the Constitution, foreigners could participate in mining only under a number of restrictions; Mexicans were given preference in equal circumstances. The newly conceived exploration permits were to be good for 2 years, and renewable up to 5 years, but to cover only the proving of a deposit. The law limited exploitation concessions to 30 years with renewal privileges dependent upon government consent.[24] To retain his holding a concessionaire had to maintain a certain amount of work fixed by a formula based upon the area of the holding, the substance exploited, and the various economic factors involved including the distance from transportation. This formula, which was difficult to apply, had as its major object the elimination of unworked speculative holdings and the curbing of land-hogging.[25] Concession areas could not exceed 100 hectares, but no limit was set on the number of concessions that might be held. Ore deposits—such as a caducated mine—could be exploited only after arranging for a special concession. Cash deposits had to be made to insure compliance with many of the law's provisions. It federalized all mine tax laws and required all companies to inscribe their important documents in a "Public Register of Mineral Industries." It also integrated into the mine code previously enacted provisions covering inspection, easements, imposition of fines, use of apprentices, and the employment of 90 per cent Mexicans on the work force. To scotch attempts to call the law retroactive, the property rights of old concessions were continued within the provisions of the laws under which they were granted.

Protests were not long in coming. An "influential source" in Washington was quoted as saying that while the law would stimulate output at present, forcing holdings into Mexican hands and restricting the size of properties would eventually work to the detriment of the industry.[26] Genaro P. García, President of the National Mining Chamber, wished to refute the charge that the law was drawn up by the large miners to burden the small operators. He insisted that the law was equally harsh for both. García challenged the power the law gave the Ministry of Industry, Commerce, and Labor on constitutional grounds; he charged that the thirty-year concession renewable at a government official's discretion was fraught with danger; and the same was true of the need to receive special permission to abandon a mine or mill. Since inspectors were far from irreproachable, the many actions dependent upon their reports would open a potential source of extortion and bribery. García also deplored the law's failure to link regular workings and minimum production to market prices. Conceding that the basic minimum workings standards were reasonable, he contended that the increments in output demanded from the larger holdings, which included reserves necessitated by modern mass production methods, were impossible. He denounced the nationalistic demands for the employment of Mexicans when there were not enough trained natives available. On behalf of the small miners, García denounced the excessive number of guarantee deposits and the prohibition of the sale of ore under an exploration deposit until enough of an ore body had been exposed to justify an exploitation permit. Small operators dependent upon the sale of ore encountered while doing development work would be seriously handicapped. The Chamber also denounced the bylaws for the red tape and legal difficulties which small miners could ill afford to meet.[27] Underlying the specific objections was the industry's distrust of the government's intentions and the arbitrary power placed in the hands of the Ministry of Industry, Commerce, and Labor. The miners insisted that the government issue a circular calling the local mine agents' attention to the fact that the property provisions of the new law did not apply to existing concessions.[28]

Two subsequent government actions disturbed the miners. First, the Ministry of Industry, Commerce, and Labor ordered the mining companies to inform the government of any change in their legal or economic status *before* the act was completed. Miners complained this amounted to premature revelation of business secrets. Only after a long exchange of notes did the Ministry rescind the order.[29] Another action involved guarantee deposits on exploration claims. Under the law these deposits were to guarantee exploration and would be refunded upon the issuance of an exploitation concession. However, the law did not specifically authorize a refund if adequate explorations did not indicate sufficient ore to justify an exploitation concession. While the National Mining Chamber insisted that the deposit was only to insure compliance and good faith in performance, the Ministry, maintaining a strict interpretation of the law, would not refund the deposit unless an exploitation concession was obtained.[30]

Reconciling the small miners to the new law was the government's toughest problem. Small operators had been reduced to marginal producers, working high-grade pockets on the proverbial shoestring. Even the Department of Mines believed that they were doomed to eventual absorption by the larger companies. Hence, the Department wrote the regulations of the new law with the large operators in mind. It required the services of a lawyer, bookkeeper, accountant, and capitalist to comply with demands for the annual reports, minute safety regulations, and annual production quotas. The law made several concessions to the small operator—progressive claim taxes, lower annual production quotas and guarantee deposits, and exemption from employing a safety engineer— but they did not significantly reduce his burden no matter how vehemently the government might call complainants speculators.[31] A travelling mining engineer wrote from Chihuahua that the howl over "exploration permits, production permits, legal difficulties with old titles on new denouncements, cash bonds . . . , the cockiness of labor . . . , renouncement of citizenship, bookkeeping, taxes, and other troubles," by the "scout-prospector, shoestring-miner-promoter," was "deep and sustained" and that new enterprises could not carry the additional cost.[32]

The Mexican government became an increasingly active participant in labor relations. Article 123 of the Constitution virtually made the government a party in labor negotiations. A federal labor code, authorized in Article 123, was not passed until 1931. But government intervention in labor disputes became more marked as the decade of the 1920's advanced. During the early period only local Boards of Arbitration and Conciliation functioned; federal boards were not set up until the late 1920's. Luis Morones, the head of the powerful national labor union, Regional Confederation of Mexican Labor (*Confederación Regional Obrera Mexicana*, CROM), became Minister of Industry, Commerce, and Labor in 1925. Morones' four-year tenure was marked by rigid enforcement of the safety requirements and a growing labor nationalism.

Morones vigorously attacked the problem of mine safety. He refused to accept the employers' argument that workers' negligence was the prime cause of accidents. He insisted that the employers' responsibilities included the provision of safety devices, the constant promotion of safety campaigns and safety-first training, and the maintenance of rescue squads and medical facilities.[33] Inducing a spirit of competition among the workers, with rewards for proficiency in watching out for themselves and their companions, proved to be highly effective. The worker was not permitted to let his guard down or to become indifferent toward familiar dangers. By reversing the older legal interpretations and placing the blame for virtually any accident upon the employer, it became the company's responsibility to organize such campaigns. Mine operators found it cheaper to preach and practice safety than to pay indemnifications.

Morones based his safety camapign on Madero's *Reglamento de Policia Minera,* which was strengthened by a series of penalties in the "Regulations of the Law of Mineral Taxes" of July 31, 1926.[34] A circular of July 12, 1927, in order to insure the workers' compliance, allowed employers to discharge without indemnification men who violated the Work Security Regulations of the mine.[35] The Department collected accident data in detailed form and issued special circulars setting forth extra regulations for particularly dangerous phases of mining. On December 20, 1928, it required all companies to equip their air drills with a water-spray attachment to prevent dust from being shot into the air where it might be inhaled and cause silicosis. Mine operators accepted the reform since indemnification payments for silicosis were so onerous.[36] The Department of Mines ordered mine inspectors to keep close check on preparations for safety and health campaigns and organized "safety competitions" in Mexico City among teams from various companies. Phelps Dodge's Moctezuma Copper subsidiary at Nacozari, Sonora, was by far the most active proponent of safety measures and the leader in the team competitions. Accident frequency throughout the industry showed a drastic decline after 1925.[37] In 1925 there were 27,163 accidents resulting in 378 deaths; in 1931 there were 10,315 accidents and 125 deaths.[38]

Morones struck a blow for nationalism by responding to the Mexicans' grievance that they were barred from executive and technical posts. On January 14, 1925, the Department of Mines ordered mine operators to employ "qualified engineers" to supervise all safety regulations and devices. "Qualified engineers" were those with degrees from Mexican schools or whose degrees had been validated by the National University. This directive admittedly was to force the employment of Mexican mining engineers, only 11 of whom, out of 218, had been able to secure mine employment.[39] Stiff fines brought compliance by the larger companies, but Mexicans were still restricted to their safety departments.[40] A sardonic American reporter pointed out that in the United States engineering societies had long labored to restrict certain jobs to "licensed engineers" and that the shoe hurt only when put on the other foot.[41] On November 28, 1925, mines were ordered to employ certified "physician-surgeons." As in the case of engineers, the initial outcry soon subsided, and by the end of the decade inspectors' reports attested to the growing employment of Mexican professionals.[42]

Mineworkers' unions were weak in the 1920's. Some mines had strong organizations, but no national union existed.[43] The CROM did little to change the picture. In Pachuca, in 1927, only 29 per cent of the workers were organized. The local CROM official remarked: "The company has satisfied all the demands of the CROM, and as long as this is the case we are not trying to extend our organization."[44]

Despite a constitutional mandate, Mexico dawdled in passing a national labor code. Although employers commonly took a highhanded attitude toward hiring and firing and did not pay the constitutionally guaranteed, three months' discharge indemnification, a labor code was not passed until 1931. Guanajuato mineowners, for example, did not pay indemnifications until forced to by the state government in 1927.[45]

Mexico was chary of enacting a national labor code because of delicate financial and international relations, but state governments were not hampered by such considerations. Empowered by Article 123 to pass labor codes, many state governments availed themselves of the privilege. Their main emphasis was upon compensation for death, professional illness, or injury on the job.[46] In Guanajuato State the mineowners were dubious of the intentions of the Boards of Conciliation and Arbitration, but they believed that the Governor would keep them within bounds. From the first the Boards were buried with claims for indemnification by men laid off by depleted mines or injured at work. They rendered their first decisions six months later. Mineowners opposed them so vigorously that the Governor asked for a law permitting expropriation of properties closed by the owners during a conflict with the Boards. The dispute became so bitter in 1924 that the federal government intervened on the grounds that the state had overstepped its authority. Much to the relief of the industry, the national government settled the disputes in favor of the companies. After 1926, when silver prices fell below 60 cents, Guanajuato allowed the operators to cut wages 10 per cent and remove men from "over-manned positions" in an economy drive to keep the mines open.[47]

In some instances employers found the local boards useful since many local officials were not paragons of integrity. When the local "municipal president" appointed the government member of the board, the president could often be bribed.[48] (Even today workers often prefer to bargain directly with their employers and receive a partial settlement rather than take a chance with a board.) When a presidential decree in 1927 took the management of labor disputes out of the hands of the states, the action was opposed "by mining chambers throughout the republic and individual groups."[49]

As early as 1917 Carranza had set up Boards of Conciliation and Arbitration for the Federal District and national territories to settle, on an unofficial basis, strikes involving railroads, mines, and oil and textile companies. Their decisions were not binding.[50] After an extremely bitter railroad strike in 1926, Calles drafted a law on October 20, 1926, recommending the creation of federal boards to cover industries working under federal concessions, or contracts whose workings affected interstate interests, and to adjudicate cases when the contracts in dispute had regular workings clauses.[51] Disputes in major industries were taken out of the hands of state boards in March, 1927, and placed under federal jurisdiction, with each board given "the power necessary to enforce compliance with its decisions." By April, 1928, regional boards covered the entire republic.[52]

Early decisions of the boards were far from fair; nor were their procedures commendable. Employers won few cases and those reluctant to accept board decisions were threatened with jail or even locked up in the offices of the boarrd![53] Recognizing that one-sided operation had become detrimental, the government by the early 1930's changed the boards' membership considerably and thereafter it dispensed something more closely approximating justice.[54]

A constitutional amendment passed on August 31, 1929, deprived the state legislatures of the right to legislate on labor matters, and the passage of a comprehensive labor code was only a matter of time.[55] With the passage of a labor code almost certain, mineowners complained that the rise in labor costs would destroy their profit margins. A slump in new construction and investment coupled with a vigorous pruning of the labor force again blocked passage of the code.[56] But in 1931, government leaders decided that currying favor with labor was more important than appeasing industry. As published, the code was a document of 80 double-column pages containing no less than 685 separate articles. Embodying ideas drawn from the codes of advanced countries, it could only be put into effect piecemeal to fit Mexican conditions.[57]

Mexican railroads recovered slowly from the ravages of the Revolution and could not catch up with the needed repairs and replacements. Deep in debt and operating at a loss, the government did not service their bonds.[58] Railroads became both the national whipping boy and wailing wall. Mining analysts grieved over the plight of the system and deplored its failure to penetrate new districts and to adequately serve old ones.[59] Miners could but suffer and hope for better times.

Actually the railroads had made great progress in rehabilitation, a great achievement in itself. Demands for better and expanded service were fully justified, but, as the 1920's advanced, reports of ore pileups and car shortages became less frequent. Mine companies started taking their private cars out of service as the railroad's own rolling stock became available. Mexican freight rates, even after several increases, were not high compared to United States rates.[60] But criticisms of railroad labor and management for ineptitude were justified. The more prevalent use of motor trucks made plans and demands for railroad expansion into remote areas unnecessary.[61] Still, some expansion did take place. The Southern Pacific finally connected its lines with the Central Plateau; a new line was built eastward out of Sierra Mojada to Cuatro Cienegas and thence to Monterrey; the Guggenheims extended their system in San Luis Potosí to integrate their holdings; and a 25-kilometer spur was built from Jiménez, Chihuahua, to the Ardagas mine. Two other proposals died in the planning stage: a line from the Arizona copper mines southwest across Sonora to the Gulf of California—to permit shipments of Arizona copper by sea—and a unified system to cover southern Chihuahua and northern Durango and Zacatecas.[62]

Wharf facilities at Tampico, the port for most northern base-metal shipments to Europe and the east coast of the United States, were entirely inadequate. The International Ore Company handled its own zinc shipments but was of no help to other shippers.[63] American Metal and ASARCO, complaining that Tampico was "the most expensive port in the world for the handling of minerals," finally forced the port loading monopoly to reduce charges. They began sending their overseas shipments by rail—from Monterrey to Laredo, and thence to Corpus Christi and Galveston for loading on ships. In June, 1928, the loading monopoly reduced its charges 25 per cent, and the National Railways began to enlarge and modernize the Tampico ore wharf.[64]

Motor trucks, coupled with a government-sponsored road building program, appeared as a godsend, particularly on the rugged west coast. Despite labor costs of 37.5 to 75 cents (U.S.) per day, one company reported paying $450 a mile for a 10-mile unpaved road.[65] While most road building was done by the federal and state governments, mining companies did their share of the work. Some companies received tax rebates, a practice favored by the industry but frowned upon by the national government. Roads were not a universal panacea, for in remote districts the cost of gasoline, maintenance, and competent drivers—together with bad weather for several months of the year—made mules and wagons more economical.[66]

Electric power output expanded in Mexico during the 1920's, and the industry's dependence upon the mining industry as its major consumer continued into the 1930's. José Herrera y Lasso observed, in 1927, that the mining industry consumed 166,000 horsepower, or 26 per cent of the national production. Mining establishments consumed 36 per cent of all hydroelectric power.[67] Five years later, Herrera y Lasso raised his estimate of mine consumption to 30 per cent. Privately owned plants alone generated 230,000,000 kilowatt-hours (kw-h.) for the industry.[68] Ernesto Galarza concluded that the economic health of the Mexican electrical power industry depended upon the state of foreign metal markets![69] Mexican Light and Power sold 48 per cent of its 496,000,000-kw-h. output to mining companies; the Guanajuato and Michoacan Power Company sold them 27 per cent of its 85,000,000 kw-h.; and the Chapala Electric Company sold 30 per cent of its 88,000,000 kw-h. to mines. When mines in the Guanajuato and Tlalpujahua-El Oro districts closed in the late 1920's the entire electric power industry of central Mexico virtually starved. Larger companies annually consumed impressive amounts of power. In 1925 Cananea Consolidated consumed 21,093,630 kw-h.; Moctezuma Copper (Nacozari), 20,535,440 kw-h.; San Francisco del Oro, 10,456,300 kw-h.; Mazapil Copper, 7,985,388 kw-h.; and El Potosí Mining, 5,370,590 kw-h.[70]

Southern Mexico with more rainfall developed many hydroelectric sites, but in the arid north thermal plants were used as primary power sources or as standbys. During the drought of 1927–29 the Mexican Northern Power Company curtailed the output of the giant Boquilla Dam from 25 to 40 per cent and rationed its customers. ASARCO closed its central Mexican smelters when drought threatened. A drop in prices alleviated the situation for a while by curtailing some production. Still, El Potosí cut daily production from 1,500 to 800 tons per day; ASARCO closed the Veta Grande mine and San Francisco del Oro, expanding its annual power requirements from 10,000,000 to 19,000,000 kw-h. and curtailing its monthly milling tonnage from 27,950 to 22,220.[71]

American and Foreign Power, an Electric Bond and Share subsidiary, opened a new thermal generating plant in 1930 at Torreón to act as a standby for the Boquilla Dam. It made up the power shortage, but the decline of metal prices and mineral production in the following years lowered its value to the mining industry.[72]

CHAPTER 15

Production, Prices, and Taxes, 1920–1932

MEXICAN metal output did not follow the trend of world prices during the 1920's.[1] Gold production remained constant despite a rising price level since increased by-product output from flotation plants balanced depletion of the gold fields. Silver prices fell in 1920–21 and levelled off in the middle years of the decade, but output from the new and more economical cyanide and flotation mills continued to climb. Lead and zinc production grew rapidly under the stimuli of flotation and increased smelter capacity. Falling costs and new extraction processes drastically affected the production of copper. But integration of the largest Mexican copper producers with the American producers tied Mexico's output to American policies. Hence the restrictive policies of the Copper Export Association and Copper Exporters, Inc. affected United States and Mexican producers alike.

Marketing gold posed no problem at all; the Mexican government stood ready to purchase all gold produced in the country. Silver miners, on the other hand, faced with falling prices found marketing their product abroad increasingly difficult, while domestically silver threatened the stability of Mexico's currency. Silver coinage met the demands of the common people for "hard money"—over 100,000,000 silver pesos were struck between 1922 and 1924 when the Mexican government became the world's largest purchaser[2]—but the coins soon became undesirable to the business and financial community. Silver pesos were quoted at discounts despite the operations of the Monetary Commission. Mexico abruptly curtailed silver coinage and then completely discontinued it.[2]

Mexico's new policy, begun in 1926, marked the end of hopes that it might attempt to stabilize the silver market. Great Britain's announcement of its intention to place India on a gold standard finally frightened off the Mexican government.[4] Silver prices which fell from 80 cents an ounce in 1920 to 66 cents in 1925, reached 53 cents in early 1926, and the Mexican government began to listen to pleas for a tax cut.[5] Silver now fell below 50 cents, and Guanajuato's mines started to close. Only a series of cost-cutting agreements among the companies, the union, and the government halted their abandonment. And in November, 1926, Calles reduced silver taxes.[6] ASARCO started to restrict output, but total production remained high. For some companies dividends became less frequent. The Mexican Corporation, which had just begun to see its way clear financially, announced that its calculated profit of £105,000 with silver at 70 cents had now dwindled to almost nothing.[7] Plants with high fixed overhead charges and by-product problems plagued the Mexican silver industry in the late 1920's, almost causing its collapse in 1932 when prices dropped to 25 cents an ounce. Only the United States silver purchase policy saved the Mexican industry.

Mexican lead production expanded phenomenally in the 1920's due to the higher extraction rate, economic operation of the flotation mills, enlargement of the Chihuahua smelter, and a price inflated by demands of manufacturers of storage batteries and cable sheathing. Mexican lead was so cheap to produce that even slight price advances brought a marked reaction.[8]

Mexican lead served as a balance weight between the New York and London markets as well as between the markets of New York and St. Louis. Despite a protective tariff the United States had to import lead because it could not produce enough to meet its needs. Smelters and refiners imported Mexican lead ore and bullion under bond. During the 1920's, the tariff, in addition to production and shipping costs, kept New York and London ore prices within 1.35 cents of each other and bullion prices within 1.875 cents. If the New York price exceeded the London price by more than those margins, Mexican lead would immediately flow out of bond from United States smelters and refiners and into the market. The price difference for refined lead was 2.125 cents. This figure was important when ASARCO fixed lead prices. Since Peñoles operated a lead refinery in Mexico, ASARCO cut prices from time to time to forestall the entrance of Peñoles' Mexican-refined lead into the United States market. When ASARCO opened its Monterrey lead refinery in April, 1929, bullion exports to the United States fell 47 per cent, and refined lead was shipped directly to Europe. Within the United States, Mexican lead would either flow to New York or up the Mississippi to St. Louis in response to price differentials, thus minimizing the price spread between these two markets.[9]

Irregular Mexican lead supplies could wreak havoc in the market. During the abortive Escobar Rebellion in 1929 American traders believed Mexican production would be cut. Prices rose from 7 to 7.8 cents, and American marginal producers started up. But when the short-lived revolt was crushed, a tremendous quantity of Mexican lead delayed in transit was dumped on the market. Between April and September lead stocks doubled, reaching 70,000 tons in the United States and Mexico. Financing this stockpile became prohibitive; the general collapse of prices in October, 1929, completed the debacle. By the end of the year lead was 6.25 cents per pound.[10]

Major lead producers during the 1920's displayed remarkable forbearance in maintaining relatively stable prices despite stupendous growth in demand. However, by the end of the decade secondary lead and new suppliers threatened the old order, and the International Association of Lead Producers was formed to control the lead market. At first its activities were confined to exchanging statistical data. But in 1929 Mexican and British lead interests entered into a sales agreement to control prices. For a short while the Mexican forced-work regulations and the depreciation of the peso kept production high, but when, in the spring of 1931, the price fell to a third less than the already low prices of 1930, the Association imposed production cuts of 15 and 20 per cent on its members. This move saved the industry from collapsing, but otherwise did not prove too effective. Pressures of British Empire preference and sterling depreciation policies dissolved the cartel in 1932. Mexican production fell drastically in the next two years. Only the indirect support given lead by the curtailment policies of the International Zinc Syndicate avoided complete chaos. Until well into the mid-1930's lead was a "sick metal."[11]

American tariffs determined the trend of market movements in Mexican zinc as well as lead. The Tariff of 1909 effectively shut out Mexican zinc, but the reductions of the Underwood Tariff of 1913 allowed a revival of the industry. Zinc rates in the Fordney-McCumber Tariff of 1922 were specifically aimed at handicapping competitive zinc from northern Mexico; the American Zinc Institute was quite proud of its activities in support of that measure. Rates prescribed by the Smoot-Hawley Tariff of 1930 were even higher.[12] But American overcapacity in zinc would have effectively excluded much of Mexico's production.

Mexico's shortage of zinc-smelting capacity was a cornerstone of the industry's marketing structure in that it made available large quantities of ore and concentrates for export. Aside from the rather small amount of concentrates smelted by ASARCO at Nueva Rosita, Coahuila, the main outlets for Mexican zinc were the ASARCO plant at Amarillo, Texas, and the American Metal plant at Blackwell, Oklahoma; it was exported to Belgium and Germany either directly or after calcination at the IO&S plant in Saltillo. Since zinc moved freely in all world markets except in the United States, its price was set by London quotations.[13]

With the important exceptions of ASARCO, San Francisco del Oro, and American Metal, IO&S—the Mexican subsidiaries of the Société de la Vielle Montagne—controlled Mexican zinc exports. This Belgian firm purchased mines throughout northern and central Mexico and equipped them with the latest machinery, remodeled the Tampico ore docks, and even built a 100-ton lead smelter at Mazatlán. During the late 1920's many companies vainly attempted to offset declining price levels by increasing volume. Hence zinc output in Mexico continued to climb until it reached a peak of 174,050 tons in 1930; by 1932 it had fallen to 57,000 tons.[14]

Marketing Mexico's copper was simpler than selling its lead and zinc. Absence of an American copper tariff allowed free entrance into that market. Furthermore, fully half of Mexico's production (from Cananea and Nacozari) was integrated into the American industry and its marketing apparatus. Only four other significant sources of copper existed: the El Boleo, Mazapil, and Teziutlán mines, and by-product copper.[15] El Boleo shipped to France; the other two companies sold their output on the London Metals Exchange; the custom smelters sold by-product copper according to market conditions.

Events during the period 1926–30 well illustrated the disadvantages to Mexico of the tight control exercised by American copper companies which attempted to control prices through Copper Exporters, Inc., an association organized under the Webb-Pomerene Act. Copper Exporters planned to withhold United States supplies, the bulk of the world's copper output, until the world markets were drained of reserves and it could set higher prices. Once in effect, its scheme hinged upon financing the initial stock-piling operations and of being certain that the demand for copper would remain great enough to absorb the American stock pile. Cananea was in the midst of opening the fabulous La Colorada Pipe, and after an initial jump in production it had to cut its output while copper prices climbed. At El Boleo the French turned out copper at an accelerated rate and installed converters to increase their capacity and to be independent of American smelters. The British plants at Mazapil and Teziutlán had reached capacity by 1926 and stayed there. Marginal producers, lured by higher prices, also entered the market. After rising to 18.107 cents in 1929, the depression dropped copper prices to 5.555 cents in 1932. Huge flotation plants, such as those owned by ASARCO, Fresnillo, and San Francisco del Oro, robbed the Mexican industry of its flexibility to cut production when prices declined. Passage of an American copper tariff in 1932—in the form of a 2-cent excise tax on imported copper—changed the entire Mexican picture. Producers sent copper to the United States only for refining under bond, and Europe became Mexico's largest copper market.[16]

Unstable metal markets after the mid-1920's caused grave difficulties in establishing Mexican legislative and tax policy. The effects of the Law of Mineral Industries of 1926 were lost among the changes occasioned by the variable markets. Mineowners pointed out that in 1926 Mexico issued 1,702 mining titles covering 19,752 hectares, but in 1927 the number dropped to 819 exploitation concessions on 7,772 hectares due to the miners' apprehension over the new law's requirements.[17] Reports of lapsed titles for that reason became more frequent, and the National Mining Chamber warned that the decline of silver prices following India's adoption of the gold standard necessitated a change in government policy.[18] Luis Morones, Minister of Industry, Commerce, and Labor, replied that mineral production had increased in value from 210,000,000 pesos in 1910 to 319,000,000 pesos in 1926 and rejected the allegation that taxes were too high.[19] A Department of Mines spokesman in October, 1927, claimed that the miners' difficulties were attributable to world conditions, not to Mexican mine legislation. Another official summed up the government's position by stating that despite the miners' "constant clamor for help" and allegations that the industry was falling into "decadence," the Department would like to ask: "When haven't the miners complained?"[20]

Production in 1927 and 1928 was kept up by highly profitable expansions of the foreign-owned properties which replaced the production of marginal operators—many of whom were Mexicans—who were forced to close. Many districts were abandoned as companies concentrated capital and operations in their more profitable units. During 1928 demands for changes in the mine law of 1926 were heard from small Mexican capitalists, a political force to be reckoned with.[21] A continuing dearth of new discoveries and the plight of the prospector helped force the government's hand. It announced in February, 1929, the appointment of a commission to study revisions of the 1926 law. The commission reported the completion of its task in November, 1929, and in August, 1930, the Law of Mineral Industries of 1926 was repealed.[22]

Condemnations of Mexico's mine tax policy were even louder than complaints against the mine laws. Limantour's policy under Díaz had been to keep mining taxes low to encourage the industry and permit the government to benefit from the generally increased business activity. Stable taxes allowed industry to plan ahead. The Revolution radically changed Mexican tax policy; Obregón's get-tough policy set the tone for the rest of the 1920's. Mexican mine taxes were set by metal prices, technological advancement, and political relations between the miners and the government. These factors were in constant flux; so were the mine tax laws.

Carranza's ordinance of June 27, 1919, was in effect until Obregón introduced a new measure on March 4, 1924.[23] The new law did not change the tax categories or raise pertenencia taxes. Changes in the production tax were small. But a number of significant innovations included the separation of gold and silver for tax purposes, to allow the tax on each to be revised independently, and the taxing of cruder forms of exported minerals—ores and concentrates—at substantially higher rates. The law set tax exemption limits of 250 grams per ton for silver and 30 per cent metal content for zinc, to encourage the working of low-grade ores, particularly zinc. It assigned a portion of the pertenencia tax to the municipality in which the mine was located, to be used for public improvements.[24]

On June 26, 1924, to support the sagging silver peso, Obregón reaffirmed the embargo on gold exports and required the reimportation of an amount of gold equal to 25 per cent of the value of exported silver.[25] On July 2nd the newly organized National Mining Chamber[26] met to discuss the decree. Real del Monte calculated the obligation would amount to a surtax of 1.313 per cent. A committee from the Chamber visited Minister of Finance Alberto Pani on August 5th. Pani was willing to grant their request to repeal the law for a *quid pro quo:* aid in a 1,250,000-peso harvest loan being negotiated by the Monetary Commission for the cotton planters of La Laguna. Agreeing to finance the loan, the Chamber divided it among its members with ASARCO, Real del Monte, Peñoles, Santa Gertrudis, and the Mexican Corporation taking the major portions. Pani had the unpopular reimport provisions repealed retroactively to July 1, 1924, and reduced the tax on mixed gold-silver bars. Mexico repaid the loan, and the gold reimport requirement on silver exports was not re-enacted.[27]

Calles' revision of the tax law in June, 1925, concerned only a few items, but they were of great importance.[28] It drastically reduced the exemption levels for low-grade ores because of the growing use of flotation. Exempt silver, for example, was lowered from 250 to 100 grams per ton. To save formerly exempted enterprises working on a narrow margin, the new law introduced an alternative method of obtaining an exemption. Ore valued at less than 12 pesos per ton was allowed a 10 per cent tax discount. Miners claimed that the added costs of assays to check the narrow exemption margin brought the new rate up beyond the old one.[29] In the same year the Ministry of Finance issued the important "Bylaws for the Law of Mining Taxes" which governed the mode of tax collection until well into the 1930's.[30]

Calles issued a new stiff tax law on July 28, 1926, to supplement the general mine law of that year.[31] It included a number of increases which were even more unbearable after the few changes made in 1925. Coupled with the new mine law, it appeared to epitomize the miners' contention that Calles wished to milk or ruin the mining industry.

Falling silver prices in 1926 made retention of the new tax law impossible. In October the National Mining Chamber recommended a series of exemptions and discounts which Calles accepted the next month, allowing a reduction in silver taxes if the price fell below 57 cents.[32] In February, 1927, Calles announced the absolute suspension of silver coinage.[33] To relieve the silver industry, now plagued by a price below 60 cents, Calles decreed a new tax law on April 29, 1927, which repeated the basic provisions of the tax law of July, 1926, with the exception of setting progressively lower tax rates for silver below 57 cents. It also allowed miners to present drafts on New York banks when exporting gold instead of having to reimport the metal.[34]

The steadily worsening position of the mineral industries forced a drastic change in tax policy in the new law of December 24, 1929.[35] It combined state and federal taxes into one lump payment, to save book-keeping costs, and substantially lowered the combined rates. Peculiarly it gave silver no relief beyond the 1927 tax reduction. The law extended concessions to newly opened or rehabilitated mines by reducing their taxes for 3 years from 10 to 50 per cent,[36] and it increased the number of mines eligible for the discount extended to low-valued ores. A new provision required all ores containing over 250 grams of gold per ton to be beneficiated and refined in Mexico and the gold sent to the mint.[37]

Several broad trends may be discerned in the changing tax laws of the 1920's. Most important was the influence of the flotation process in lowering the old tax exemption limits: silver from 250 grams per ton to 100 grams, lead from 8 to 4 per cent, and zinc from 30 to 15 per cent. To encourage cleaner workings and support low-grade enterprises, the government introduced exemptions based upon ore value, allowing a 50 per cent discount when the ore's value was less than 8 pesos per ton. Flotation economies and good markets permitted rather large increases in the lead and zinc tax rates. Discrimination to force beneficiation and refining to be done in Mexico became a cornerstone of tax policy. Silver miners were given two forms of relief: general exemptions for low-value ores (later extended to all metals) and a progressively lower tax rate when the price of silver fell below 57 cents. The same general arrangement was in effect for copper. These laws included, for the first time, specific taxes for the states to levy and provided for the remission of portions of the general revenue to the municipalities.[38] Some states now enacted rather elaborate tax laws.[39] To insure better collections, after January, 1925, the tax was levied on direct production, not when the metal was exported or presented for coinage.[40]

Mining companies did not pay only direct mining taxes. Alejandro Carrillo indignantly wrote in 1929 that out of a product valued at 373,-342,398 pesos, mining companies paid wages and salaries of 58,455,908 pesos and taxes of only 10,900,000 pesos.[41] Carrillo simply omitted any allowance for the costs of mining, milling, transporting, smelting, and marketing the ore; for the interest on the investment; or for legitimate profits. He also missed two vital points, the first being that taxes varied greatly from metal to metal. In 1929, lead and copper paid only one-seventieth of their sale value in direct taxes, while 55,043,382 pesos' worth of zinc paid only 568,300 pesos. But 27,032,400 pesos' worth of gold paid 2,105,700 pesos in taxes, and 121,598,834 pesos in silver paid 5,915,600 pesos.[42] Direct taxes on base metals which occurred in low-grade ores had to be low or else the industry could not exist. Carrillo also overlooked the amount paid in indirect taxes, ranging from the omnipresent stamp tax and the surtax on the freight bill, to water taxes, local property taxes, and custom duties. After 1924 Mexico imposed an income tax on company profits.[43]

In 1924 United States Commercial Attaché Dye in Mexico City estimated the miners' total tax bill to be the equivalent of 65 per cent of the industry's net profits, or from 10 to 12 per cent of the gross value of the ores produced, not considering the income tax.[44] Some of the sting is taken out of Attaché Dye's estimates by the observations of A. B. Parsons. In British Columbia, where physical difficulties were as great as in Mexico, taxes—including the income tax—took 20 per cent of the gross value. Parsons believed that while silver and gold producers probably paid more in taxes in Mexico than they would have paid in the United States, producers of base metals appeared to have an advantage.[45]

As the Depression closed in another advantage of Mexico's tax laws was noted. Silver and copper taxes automatically fell, and when the value of the ore itself dropped, mine operators received further discounts if it fell below 12 pesos per ton. Miners also negotiated special exemptions and wage agreements when shutdowns appeared inevitable.[46] Finally, Mexico's devaluation of the peso, when it went off the gold standard, changed the exchange rate from 2 to 3.60 pesos to the dollar. Mining companies selling abroad for dollars benefited accordingly.[47]

PART V

THE GREAT DEPRESSION AND NATIONALISM

CHAPTER **16**

Depression Problems
and Some Remedies

DURING the late 1920's the Mexican mining industry faced two major problems: an increasing number of mine depletions and falling metal prices. Modern mass mining exhausted many venerable districts, and after 1926 reports of depletions became distressingly frequent.[1] In 1929 Genaro García, one of Mexico's most astute commentators on mining, pointed out that the government's gross production figures were misleading since they obscured the lack of new discoveries. While established mining companies exploited older districts intensely with better equipment, they passed up good opportunities elsewhere. Depletion would inevitably result, and many segments of the economy would suffer. García estimated, for example, that mine products made up one-third of the tonnage of railroad freight.[2] The industry's pleas for lower taxes and a mine law based upon incentives resulted in concessions in the Mine Tax Law of December, 1929, and the Mine Law of August 1930. But by that time the Great Depression was under way and disaster could not be averted.

Guanajuato was one of the districts hardest hit. The companies used shutdowns and production cutbacks as a lever to obtain tax and wage concessions. The Peregrina, Guanajuato Reduction and Mines, Guanajuato Consolidated, Angustias, and El Cubo companies either closed their workings or confined development work to the amounts actually mined. A short period of hope was kindled when a "lost" section of the mother vein was found, but diamond-drilling proved its exploitation would be unprofitable.[3]

El Oro's depletion appeared to come in one fell swoop. Although the district's bonanza days were over, during the early 1920's the mines still declared fairly substantial dividends. Efforts to work lower grade ores by increasing milling capacity did not work out well. Esperanza invested over $500,000 dollars in mill expansion. However, the engineers had miscalculated, and the first year showed a £13,000 loss. Esperanza dissolved in January, 1932.[4] Mexico Mines of El Oro paid 110 per cent in 1917 and

171

started the 1920's with dividends as high as 35 per cent. It closed in 1929. A final accounting showed that it had paid a total dividend rate of 11,713 per cent since 1904![5] El Oro Mining and Railway paid over £114,000 in dividends in 1920 and had a treasury balance of £131,906. In 1923–24 it overhauled its entire plant for a final cleanup campaign. In September 1926 the company laid off 1,000 men and transferred all the workable machinery to its properties at La Noria, Zacatecas.[6] Borda Antigua closed in 1928.[7] Even fabulous Dos Estrellas was on the wane. Its milling capacity increased from 1,400 to 2,000 tons a day but reserves fell to 500,000 tons of low-grade ore, and it even milled the pillars and mine fill. Its mill's efficiency made possible working the Esperanza dumps too, but the loss of Borda Antigua ore forced Dos Estrellas to apply for permission to shut down in 1930. Its 3,000 employees were too potent a political force to allow the government to accede to the request. Dos Estrellas remained open, although ore ran only 112 grams of silver and 3 grams of gold to the ton. Finally, in 1938, the enterprise drifted into the hands of a producers' cooperative organized by its workers.[8]

In Jalisco, Cinco Minas and Piedra Bola shut down between 1928 and 1930. Protests and hunger strikes by the men were futile; the courts ruled that payment of an indemnity and recognition of seniority in discharge were the companies' only obligations.[9] The Amparo and Mazata mines forestalled closing when they struck new ore bodies.[10] In Zacatecas, the La Fé mines and Peñoles' Veta Grande holdings suspended operations as the ore became too lean, and the Exploration Company of London closed its Santa Rosa property at Concepción del Oro. Peñoles also closed its Cerralvo unit in Nuevo León.[11] In Guerrero, Chontalpán finally gave out,[12] while in Sonora, the Lucky Tiger Mining Company turned its workings over to small lessees in return for a share of their pickings.[13]

Even Pachuca's legendary mines were being bottomed. The Santa Gertrudis company closed the Santa Gertrudis mine in 1926 and the El Bordo and Santo Tomás in 1930–31. Only the new Mariposa vein kept the company's Dos Carlos mine working.[14] Manuel Santillan of the Geological Institute of Mexico examined Pachuca in 1930. He concluded that large scale exploitation had worked out the virgin deposits and that the only future lay in "out-crops of scanty potentiality" and "blind veins"— two poor ore sources.

> The life of the Pachuca zone depends more upon the intensity with which the already known deposits are exploited, than upon the number of new veins that it is possible to discover.[15]

Physical depletions accompanied numerous closings as metal prices declined after 1926. The economics of the complex ore producers and huge capitalizations kept many workings busy to avoid the total losses occasioned by a shutdown.[16] Falling silver and lead prices led to the discharge of over 5,000 men and a rash of closings from Hidalgo to Chihuahua. One estimate stated that if all the petitions for permission to close were granted, over 15,000 men would be laid off. Miners universally blamed low prices, high taxes, and freight rates. High cost producers dropped out as early as the spring of 1928. Prices stabilized at new low levels and the industry readjusted itself.[17] Total production remained fairly high until 1930, despite the Escobar Revolt of 1929, threatened labor legislation, the Chihuahua power shortage, and the declining price of silver.[18] Government reluctance to permit closings, the mining of high-grade pockets, and the profits made possible by the favorable exchange rate sustained mineral output during 1930.[19] A study by the United States Tariff Commission indicated that the decline in Mexican exports was due more to a fall in prices than in volume and that the subsequent recovery resulted from a rise in prices with volume remaining stable.[20]

After 1930, the Mexican government permitted cuts in production, wages, and employment in lieu of absolute closings. It sanctioned wage reductions arrived at through bargaining without government permission as well as job rotations to spread the work. State tax reductions also aided mining. But in June, 1931, an estimated 28,000 miners out of a total force of about 107,000 were unemployed.[21] And closings still took place: Asientos, Aguascalientes; Mazapil and Fresnillo, Zacatecas; Santa María de la Paz, San Luis Potosí; San Francisco del Oro, Chihuahua; and Nacozari, Sonora. Nacozari alone let out over 1,000 men. Peñoles shut its Torreón smelter in November, 1932; El Boleo dismissed 40 per cent of its labor force and ASARCO petitioned to close its Santa Eulalia workings. In southern Chihuahua, workers petitioned for permission to reopen some mines on a cooperative basis. Mines whose ores contained cheaply worked gold remained open to take advantage of the peso's devaluation.[22]

The resumption of silver coinage afforded a measure of relief. In 1932, Mexico agreed to buy 23,000,000 ounces of silver from the Real del Monte company and the next year signed the International Silver Agreement, pledging the purchase of 29,000,000 ounces during the coming year.[23] Declining lead, copper, and zinc prices closed some complex ore mines removing by-product silver and thereby slightly eased the silver market. The Ministry of Industry, Commerce, and Labor claimed that Mexico's depreciated currency made it possible for some producers to make a profit with silver at 24 cents and lead at 3 cents, but the mineowners were of a different opinion.[24]

In 1932 and 1933 the Mexican mining industry hit bottom. Only one ray of hope lingered: despite the fall in output, the expansion of the 1920's had established Mexico as a world leader in both base- and precious-metal production; her output of silver and base metals in the early 1930's still equalled or exceeded production during the profitable year of 1910.

Mexico, in common with other nations, adopted a policy of nationalism to combat the strains induced by the Great Depression. Already committed by the Constitution of 1917, the government's hand was forced by the Depression. However, the international nature of the mineral economy meant that Mexico would have to give exemptions from certain nationalistic policies. These concessions were not given at the expense of nationals, for the government still reserved a special place for the small Mexican operator. Calles' mining law of 1926 became one of the first casualties of the Depression. It had encouraged the maintenance of production despite declining prices, but a steady fall in the number of new concessions granted in the late 1920's indicated a dark future. A new mine law, promulgated on August 2, 1930,[25] attempted to reconcile the miners' objections with the responsibilities placed upon the government by the Constitution. The commission appointed to draw up the new code listed the miners' major objections as: (1) the obligation of minimum production as proof of regular workings, (2) the thirty-year limit on concessions, and (3) the regulations surrounding the exploratory concessions, particularly those requirements relating to guarantee deposits and the prohibition of the sale of ore until an exploitation concession had been granted.[26]

The commission's reforms were quite impressive. It erased the old law's functional division of the mining industry as being unrealistic and substituted a new division of metallics, nonmetallics, and hydrocarbons; enacted wholesale simplifications of office procedures and mine-working rules; and abolished the exploratory concession and its system of guarantee deposits. Articles 20 through 24 set up a *concesión de cateo* (testing concession) designed for the small prospector. It required no deposit, was valid for two years, allowed the sale of ore and the erection of a small plant, limited a man to one concession at a time, and permitted free conversion into an exploitation concession at any time.[27] The law made exploitation concessions unlimited in time and area and included the rights of easement for the construction of all auxiliary equipment.

Whereas the old law required a minimum production of ore as proof of minimum workings, the new law set up a formula defining regular workings by relating the payment of wages to the size of the holding. This new system was in answer to the criticisms that periods of heavy investment and development were not also necessarily periods of ore production and that times of depression, which should be utilized for development work in preparation for better prices, had become periods of overproduction.[28]

In furtherance of the new regular-workings standards, the reasons for forfeiture were restricted to nonpayment of the surface tax and to noncompliance with the minimum-work clauses. Fines were lowered; the power of inspectors to close mines they judged dangerous was strengthened; the Minister of Industry, Commerce, and Labor was empowered to examine a company's books when it was deemed necessary—since mine products were part of the nation's domain; and the requirements for registry of titles and commercial transactions were tightened. While giving the miners greater freedom, the Mexican government did not abridge its right to oversee the disposal and working of the national domain.

The Labor Code of 1931 did not prove to be the burden that the miners had anticipated. Luis Morones' zeal while Minister of Industry, Commerce, and Labor, in supervising matters relating to safety and hygiene and forcing the employment of Mexican engineers and doctors, had prepared mining for many of the law's provisions. The miners' chief resentment centered on the antiforeign phase of the law which set close limits on the employment of foreigners; the burden of these restrictions was borne by foreign-owned industrial enterprises, since agricultural and domestic workers were exempted. Labor legislation was also resented by foreign investors as an attempt to control industrial development and to keep the national wealth from being exported. New capital export taxes were taken to be a vindication of the industrialists' fears, although Mexico was only following the pattern set by many other nations in a similar position.[29]

Between 1930 and 1934 the basic mine law underwent few amendments.[30] Towards the end of 1933, however, public pressure forced the government to reinvigorate its nationalistic policy. Congress empowered President Abelardo Rodríguez to decree new petroleum and mining laws before August 31, 1934. He issued these amendments on August 28th and published them in the *Diario oficial* on August 31st, to meet the congressional deadline.[31]

These articles intensified the nationalistic controls of the law. Article 8 made the recovery of caducated mine property easier, but Article 25 limited single concessions to 100 hectares. All new private mills and smelters were required to set aside 20 per cent of their capacity for custom work. Article 57 gave cooperative mining associations preference over individuals or companies in case of simultaneous registry of mining claims. Chapter IX tightened the rules governing registration of business documents. Chapter XIII set up a system of National Mineral Reserves, not for conservation but for exploitation by favored groups on conditions set by the President. Chapter XIV established the Commission for Mining Development to act as financer and advisor for Mexican companies and cooperatives and to work special concessions in the National Reserves. The National Mining Chamber did not like the new regulations but had no opportunity to protest, since its copy of the proposed changes arrived just before they were promulgated.[32]

A new Depression-dictated tax law of April 27, 1932, completely replaced the mine tax law of December 1929.[33] Surface-area taxes remained unchanged except for reductions for coal and nonmetallic mineral lands.[34]

New mines were given area-tax reductions for five years. It taxed silver on the more realistic base of 40 cents while recalculating copper taxes on a base of 10 instead of 18 cents. Neither case included marked reductions, only simpler bookkeeping. It gave new mines and mines that reopened in isolated regions graduated reductions on their production taxes for five years. Cateo concessions were completely exempt. Municipalities received 40 per cent of the surface tax; the states were permitted to tax the real property of the mines up to five mills and were to receive a portion of the production tax. The National Mining Chamber claimed the most glaring hardship to be the taxation of mines secured since 1926 at the same rate as mines which did not have the handicap of obligatory minimum workings. While the Chamber believed that some taxes were still too high, the exemptions given to cateo concessions and the method of fixing the states' share of the tax were warmly approved.[35]

The 1932 tax law lasted two years. Changes were held in abeyance while a new tax law was prepared for promulgation with the Mine Law of 1934. The mine tax law of August 28, 1934, differed little from its predecessor, with one important exception.[36] It changed surface-area taxes so that instead of the progressive increments being charged only to the excess over the base, it taxed the entire holding at the rate set for the last unit. For example, an individual holding six hectares—one over the base unit of five—would have to pay the higher rate on all six instead of only the last one. Paradoxically, this change fell heaviest on small miners; large holdings not only had their top rate reduced, but they were better able to pay the increase on the first hectares taxed.

All told, the major trend in Mexican mining law during the early 1930's was an intensification of the nationalist spirit of 1917.

CHAPTER 17

Silver, Government Policies
and Industrial Organization

FOUR important events affecting Mexican mining occurred in 1934. In August a revision of the mine law was issued followed shortly by a revised mine tax law. In the same year, the official party, *El Partido Nacional Revolucionario*, nominated Lázaro Cárdenas for President with a *Plan Sexenal* (Six-Year Plan) as his platform. Finally, the United States embarked upon a policy of purchasing silver up to 25 per cent of the value of its gold reserves. The next four years were kaleidoscopic ones with far-reaching changes in tax laws and nationalization policies; the formation of mining cooperatives; and a fluctuating, politically controlled price for silver. This combination made stability and planning impossible.

Mexico's Six-Year Plan contained a full section on mining based on the ideology that foreign monopolization of the nation's resources was the root of all the evils confronting the industry. It recommended tightening the nationalistic sections of the Mine Law, and also setting aside and exploring extensively the National Mineral Reserve lands for exploitation by cooperative societies or small companies (*minería en pequeño*). It pledged that the government would take a positive role in aiding certain favored types of enterprises. Suggestions included: severely limiting the size of concessions to control monopolization; withholding concessions not deemed in the nation's best interest; forcing the construction of central beneficiation and smelting plants to work under government set rates; revising tax rates to discourage the export of metallic concentrates; studying and organizing cooperative mining and ore-buying societies; and initiating a systematic study of the nation's unexploited mineral reserves and of the metallurgical problems of small enterprises. The Plan placed a major emphasis upon encouraging the formation of cooperatives and National Mineral Reserves.[1] President Cárdenas foretold even more stringent measures in his inaugural address by flatly declaring that mining had left no permanent benefits for Mexico, "because the exploitation of the mining industry has always been in the hands of a privileged few who have had the opportunity of amassing great fortunes and building monopolies."[2]

Mineowners were placed in a dilemma. While the government was blatantly antagonistic, the silver market entered a period of sharp price rises. The question was: where to strike a balance between accepting the government's attitude and making the necessary investments, and resisting the demands of the government and the labor unions by an unprofitable slowdown? The latter policy is alleged to have been seriously considered by some mineowners until ASARCO concluded that its plants could operate profitably under Cárdenas and made its peace with the government and the unions.[3]

The silver boom of 1934–36 owed its origin to the London World Economic Conference of 1933, at which a number of nations, including Mexico, pledged themselves to do something for silver. On December 21, 1933, the United States Treasury began to purchase domestically mined silver at a price 50 per cent above the world level.[4] On June 16, 1934, Congress passed the Silver Purchase Act empowering the United States Treasury to buy silver on the open market, in addition to newly mined domestic silver, until it had accumulated an amount equal to 25 per cent of the United States gold reserves. When the Treasury embarked on an all-out purchasing campaign it pushed silver from 45.17 cents an ounce in July, 1934, to 54.82 cents in January, 1935, and to a peak of 81 cents in late April. It stabilized the price between 65 and 68 cents until December, 1935, then allowed it to settle at 44.75 cents where it remained until the outbreak of World War II. This policy shook the world's silver economy and gave the United States a new weapon for carrying out its foreign policy.[5]

The silver boom caught the Mexican producers unprepared, for they had curtailed development work while the market was slack and now found they were not ready to take full advantage of rapidly rising prices.[6] Political conditions and the exhaustion of the straight silver producers— despite the augmented output of complex ore mines—kept Mexican silver production lower throughout the 1930's than during the late 1920's.[7] Mexican exports to the United States came out of reserves since exports exceeded production by large margins.

Rising silver prices had a telling effect on the Mexican government when they reached the silver peso's bullion point of 71.9 cents. Above a price of 72 cents it became profitable to melt pesos and sell them as silver. Henry Morgenthau, the United States Secretary of the Treasury, repeatedly warned Mexican officials of the danger and suggested that instead of hoarding silver speculatively the Bank of Mexico ought to sell it on the London exchange to keep the price down. A direct gold-for-silver sale was arranged between the United States and Mexico early in 1935, but Mexico held on to its major hoard. Political pressure forced President

Roosevelt on April 24th to approve the purchase of silver at over 72 cents an ounce. A severe shake-up in the administration of the Bank of Mexico followed, and a Mexican Treasury delegation arrived in the United States. They arranged a plan whereby the United States would hold the price at 74 cents for a month if Mexico would: (1) remain in the dollar bloc by supporting the exchange rate of 3.60 pesos to the dollar, (2) recast its currency system, and (3) issue more silver pesos instead of paper ones to encourage the use of silver.[8] Mexico called in all its old pesos and with the aid of American facilities minted a new series of pesos with a smaller silver content. The Bank of Mexico kept 200,000,000 of the old pesos as its seigniorage.[9]

By December, 1935, the continued dumping of Far Eastern silver into the London market satiated the United States Treasury which changed its buying tactics by entering its order for silver after, instead of before, the daily price was set. Silver prices broke sharply. Mexico City again asked for a direct silver-for-gold exchange. Under President Roosevelt's prodding, the Treasury prepared to pay a premium price for Mexican silver "as a gesture of friendship." When Morgenthau learned that the Mexican gold reserves were not threatened and that Mexico was preparing to dump all her silver into the United States Treasury, he refused to make the purchase. He lectured the Mexican Minister of Finance on Mexico's duty to help support the price of silver and agreed to purchase 5,000,000 ounces of silver a month through the Bank of Mexico if Mexico would use more silver. This agreement became part of a peso-dollar stabilization scheme. The bank bought all silver mined in Mexico, which it sold to the United States at the market price, receiving one-half cent per ounce as a handling fee. These dollars were to be used to stabilize the exchange rate. By paying the mine companies in paper pesos, the bank kept the dollars, and the volume of silver sold earned the bank a monthly commission of $25,000. When Mexico started issuing silver pesos in August, 1936, Morgenthau felt the time was propitious to discuss plans to buy the Mexican silver reserve.[10]

Meanwhile, the exchange rate attracted a large number of Yankee tourists who brought in dollars. Desiring to obtain yet more gold, the Mexican government had to recognize that gold smuggling could not be controlled. Hence it offered to exempt from the production tax (9.5 to 10 per cent) all gold presented to the Treasury. This action made smuggling much less profitable. The high price of dollars in Mexico discouraged imports by the individual businessmen and freed the government to use its dollars for purchases of equipment for public works and farm improvement programs.[11]

Owners of Mexican mines had enjoyed a windfall after the devaluation of the peso in 1931. When it became apparent that the silver market was steadily rising and that the peso might weaken, the Mexican government decided to cut itself into any new profits. Up to this time, the progressive tax brackets of the Mexican production tax had been set in New York prices in dollars and cents. Therefore, when the tax was translated into pesos for collection, the amount to be paid jumped every time the peso's exchange rate fell. A new tax law, passed on January 1, 1935, fixed the progressive tax rate brackets in pesos, which meant that a change in the exchange rate would change the percentage to be paid as tax instead of only the amount to be paid in pesos.[12] Since any change in the exchange rate might jump metals into a higher progressive tax bracket set in pesos, the tax rise could be very abrupt. A stable New York price was no guarantee, for a fall in the exchange rate could drastically raise the tax rate even though the mineowner did not collect a cent more at the market. But since he could pay his Mexican expenses in the further depreciated pesos, some of the sting would be taken out. If worked correctly, the two factors might be made to balance out: the miner netting as much as before and the government harvesting the "unearned increment" of the exchange windfall. Miners complained that the progressive brackets had become so steep that a fall in the value of the peso would mean a disastrous loss to them.[13]

The law of January 1, 1935, provided for a graduated silver tax, varying from 6 per cent on silver ore to 3 per cent on refined silver, on a base of silver at 1.20 pesos (33.3 cents, U.S.) per ounce. It rose 1 per cent for each 15-centavo rise in price. The copper tax had similar provisions. When the silver boom hit its stride three months later, an amendment to the tax schedule was issued on April 11, 1935. It provided that the 1 per cent tax rise for each 15-centavo price rise for silver should apply only when the price was between 1.20 pesos and 2.40 pesos (66.6 cents, U.S.). Further rises brought startlingly large increases which captured up to 75 per cent of the excess for the government and gave the states an increase too. Mexico justified the increase by asserting that since mining was again profitable and the subsoil belonged to the nation, the nation had the right to share in the industry's prosperity. No mention was made of the nation's share in losses.[14]

Tax policy became the major bone of contention between the mineowners and the Mexican government. The owners complained that the government virtually confiscated the silver price rises. In defense of the Mexican government it ought to be pointed out that political considerations played a large part in the American silver purchase program, and if Mexico was not aided the policy of purchasing Mexican silver on special contracts would have been fruitless and curtailed. Mexico received its share of Washington's bounty through its high tax. Silver purchases nurtured a mutual dependence between the two nations. But the United States had a tiger by the tail; it could not change its policy without endangering the Good Neighbor Policy, wrecking the Mexican economy, and bringing recriminations upon its head. An estimated 60 per cent of the proceeds of the silver sale, or about $20,000,000, remained in Mexico. Cárdenas' government came to rely upon the American purchases to balance its international payments, stabilize the peso, and finance large-scale purchases of American machinery. Also, American-owned companies produced over 80 per cent of Mexico's silver, and a blow at Mexican silver purchases would hurt them also. Furthermore, Mexico was the United States' sixth largest customer in a world threatened by bilateralism and Nazi trade drives. Therefore, it was quite impolitic to make the dollar too dear and thereby alienate the Mexican market, even though Cárdenas' program of inflation was depressing private trade. Even when United States-Mexican relations worsened after the petroleum expropriation of 1938, silver purchases continued on an "irregular" basis to safeguard American economic and political interests.[15]

Mexican mining had started to recover from the Depression by the beginning of 1934. Peso devaluation and the increased price of gold gave mining a lead in Mexican recovery.[16] In 1932, ASARCO announced the reopening of its units in Santa Eulalia, Chihuahua, and Bonanza, Zacatecas, as well as the addition of equipment to the Monterrey lead refinery. Fresnillo restored the workers' wage cuts, and El Potosí Mining at Santa Eulalia increased operations. Peñoles and Real del Monte hired more men, while Greene-Cananea resumed more extensive operations. At the end of the year, ASARCO increased operations at Charcas and asked its old employees to reapply. The next spring, the San Francisco del Oro mines and the Matehuala smelter reopened, while others announced larger operations. By the summer of 1934, the National Railways reported that 40 to 50 carloads of lead a day were moving to border export points. With the rising price of silver many more mines returned to full-scale activity. Peñoles expanded operations at Monterrey in 1934, and ASARCO reported that its San Luis Potosí smelter was operating at full capacity.[17]

CHAPTER 18

The Cárdenas Era: Aggressive Nationalism and International Difficulties

THE recovery of the Mexican mining industry up to 1936 was paralleled by the rapid growth of Mexican nationalism after the inauguration of President Cárdenas in 1935. Cárdenas disavowed any intention of closing Mexico to foreign investors; however, he emphasized that those investing in Mexican natural resources should be prepared to establish their homes in Mexico and to reinvest their profits there. In that way raw materials sent abroad at the expense of cheap Mexican labor would not leave behind only "exhausted lands, a depleted subsoil, starvation wages, and unrest foreboding disturbance of order." In addition, he announced that the schools were to train Mexican children to think in terms of seeking their fortunes in the minerals of the subsoil "that also belongs to them and which it is their duty to bring out to the light of day."[1] Xenophobia became part of Mexican thought, and antiforeign actions were hailed as a crusade against modern conquistadores. Even naturalized Mexican citizens found it more difficult to obtain mining concessions.[2]

Alberto Terrones Benítez summed up the main points in the government's program to aid workers and small miners as: (1) to create National Mineral Reserves with cooperatives having preference in exploitation; (2) to facilitate the working of placer sites by single miners; (3) to enforce strictly both the sanitary and the safety-first provisions, while overseeing the payment of compensation to workers suffering from professional diseases; (4) to set up beneficiation plants for small miners; (5) to extend financial aid to small miners, especially by tax reductions and exemptions; and (6) to rationalize the tax structure in order to distribute the burden of taxation in a manner proportional to the taxpayers' earning capacity.[3]

Cárdenas' new policy first benefitted labor. Native businessmen were virtually unaffected; benefits came at the expense of foreign-owned industry.[4] Foreign employees—especially professionals—were particular targets for discrimination. A foreign engineer, for example, had to prove that a Mexican was not available before he could obtain a six-month work passport which limited his stay and obliged him to train a Mexican to take his place. New companies found these requirements onerous.[5] The Department of Labor candidly defined the administration's policy in labor matters as "eminently protectionist for our nationals. . . ."[6] But once forced to hire Mexicans, mining companies found that they had neglected an excellent labor source. Given an opportunity, Mexicans could assume positions of responsibility. Heath Steele of Peñoles remarked:

> Experience has shown that despite the general lack of commercial and technical experience among Mexicans, it is possible to select Mexicans just as well qualified by intelligence and aptitude as foreigners to be trained for the filling of various positions.[7]

The Ministry of the National Economy (*Secretaría de la Economía Nacional,* SEN) applied a clever goad to the mineowners in late 1936. Article 18 of the Mining Law stated that all titles were under the jurisdiction of the mine code under which they were issued, which was interpreted as protecting pre-1926 titles from forced workings. A new interpretation advanced by the SEN was that all titles issued before 1892— when the traditional forced-working clauses were repealed—and after Carranza's forced-work decrees of September, 1916, should be subject to forced workings. The Supreme Court not only upheld the SEN but ruled that, since mining was a public utility, abandonment of workings no matter what the origin of the title constituted grounds for caducation.[8] On December 31, 1943, the government amended Article 18 so that all titles, even if granted between 1892 and 1916, were made subject to the forced-work provisions.[9]

To codify the new legal developments, the Department of Mines drafted a new mine law in September, 1936, embodying numerous significant changes. All concessions, no matter when granted, were required to perform regular work "in order to uphold the true character of concessions" and to pay a royalty (tentatively fixed at 5 per cent) which would eventually replace all other mining taxes. It required concession holders to invest 20 per cent of their profits in Mexico. The SEN was empowered to "rectify" claims, "sometimes without application from individuals." It also gave the SEN more power to Mexicanize mining by easing the legal requirements for special concessions in order to encourage exploitation by cooperatives, small miners, and national corporations. A company could not move plant equipment without permission, and it might be expropriated when the public interest required it. The government also was to set aside 500,000 pesos in the national budget for the formation of a Commission for Mining Development which had been authorized in 1934 but never set up. A SEN spokesman tersely stated the aim of the proposed law: ". . . to give the Executive a more effective control over those matters that are of its exclusive jurisdiction."[10]

Congress empowered the President to draft a new mining law in December, 1936, but the final draft was not sent to Congress until July, 1937. Considerably less belligerent than the original, it still contained many clauses highly objectionable to the mineowners, including those placing all concessions under forced workings and ordering the investment of a portion of the profit in Mexico. It now set profit reinvestment at 25 per cent with the money to be used to set up a Banco Minero.[11] However, Mexico was now in the midst of programs to reorganize the railroads under workers' management and to distribute land among the peasants, in addition to the great struggle with the oil companies. When the proposed mine law occasioned furious protests it was withdrawn. A month later the SEN proposed a new version without forced workings, royalty, and reinvestment clauses,[12] but the industry refused to accept even this emasculated version during the national crisis. Finally, the SEN abandoned the bill "because of circumstances."[13]

While the abortive mining legislation was under consideration, the government changed the mine law by two decrees, issued on March 2 and March 20, 1937, which raised the copper-production tax and empowered the Treasury to ask for payment in specie.[14] Mexico also placed lead- and zinc-production taxes on a progressive scale keyed to New York prices. A number of small indirect taxes, which could not be estimated directly, further helped raise the total tax figure.[15] Miners asserted that taxes now were as large as the perfidious and inequitable King's Fifth and cited figures compiled by Alberto Terrones Benítez to back their claim.[16] A. H. Hubbell compiled a list of taxes which comprised the production tax, claim-area tax, mill and treatment-plant tax, income tax, stamp tax, railroad gross-earnings tax, general real-property taxes, absenteeism (or capital-export) tax, and municipal taxes.[17] While not rendering mining unprofitable, they added a heavy burden to operating costs.

In the winter of 1937 the struggle between the oil industry and the Mexican government began to reach its peak on a wave of hysterical xenophobia. The mine workers' union presented a list of drastic demands to the mining companies with the avowed purpose of driving them into a position similar to that of the oil companies to prepare them for expropriation.[18] Mexicans staged riotous celebrations on March 18, 1938. when the government expropriated the oil companies' property. Mining awaited the next blow. But the crisis occasioned by the oil expropriation forced the Cárdenas administration to order the mineworkers' union to make peace.[19] Francis Brownell of ASARCO said on April 5th that the government had assured his company that it did not contemplate expropriating mine properties, and ASARCO shortly afterward settled labor disputes at its Parral, Monterrey, and San Pedro units.[20] Other firms still did not trust the government. They believed that labor would soon force their expropriation too. Although the scare passed and companies reached agreements with the union, on the basis of considerably smaller demands, their fear never quite passed. When Mexico entered World War II, the established concerns, who "confined their operations to salvaging whatever they could," failed to provide new venture capital and exploration programs despite excellent markets. Mexican precious and nonferrous metal production never again exceeded the highs of 1928 and 1929.[21]

United States government reaction to the petroleum expropriation was tempered by the Good Neighbor Policy and Ambassador Josephus Daniels' conciliatory pleas. In late 1937, Secretary Morgenthau became convinced that Mexico's economy was in a precarious state and needed rebuilding, rather than repatching, if that nation were not to become the Western Hemisphere scene of a Spanish Civil War.[22] Eduardo Suárez, the Mexican Minister of Finance, arrived in Washington in December, 1937, to discuss the sale of Mexico's silver reserve of 35,000,000 ounces. The State Department wanted to tie the silver purchase to the land and oil problems since sales of silver were now the largest single item of revenue for the Mexican government. Morgenthau rejected their advice and forced Sumner Welles, the Under Secretary of State in charge of Latin American affairs, to agree to the silver purchase as a short term policy with further sales contingent upon the settlement of the oil question. On December 29, 1937, the purchase agreement was signed.

No sooner was the oil expropriation announced by Mexico than the State Department asked the Treasury to bring pressure to bear by threatening "reconsideration" of the silver agreement, one of Mexico's most vulnerable spots. But Morgenthau believed that many members of the State Department would rather see a Fascist revolution than permit the oil companies to lose their money. In any event, Mexico could sell silver in the free London market for transshipment to the United States. In response to a plea for a united get-tough policy, Morgenthau agreed on March 25th to abrogate monthly purchases but not the reserve purchase agreement. Morgenthau discovered, to his amazement and chagrin, that the official announcement placed the onus for this action on him. Mexico's press loudly denounced Morgenthau despite a later State Department explanation that the policy was a joint responsibility.

Ambassador Daniels in Mexico City complained bitterly that Mexico and the silver miners were "suffering for the sins of the oilmen." Eduardo Suárez claimed that the monthly purchases were part of the reserves agreement, but the Treasury pointed out his error.[23] Purchase of the reserve silver at 45 cents an ounce netted Mexico $15,750,000 at just the time it needed money to ride out the shock. It also gave assurance that the United States did not intend to intervene. Abrogation of the monthly purchases forced the silver price down two cents, and the Treasury began supporting it at the new level. Morgenthau announced on April 14th that the United States would buy all spot silver offered on the open market without questioning its origin. On the same day Mexico released the silver miners from their obligation to sell to the Bank of Mexico. These new arrangements weighed upon the miners who now had to pay invoice and casting charges, but the two-cent price decline was their major burden.[24]

President Roosevelt and Secretary Morgenthau continued to believe that, in the long run, the United States had the most to gain by helping Mexico. The State Department continued to demand without avail that the Treasury further depress the price of silver, and it did stop a scheme by Morgenthau to advance a silver-secured loan to Mexico to aid in reaching a settlement in the oil dispute. While the American boycott of Mexican oil forced Cárdenas into dealings with the Axis, without Morgenthau's support the situation would have been worse.

From its relatively strong position in 1934 and 1935, Mexico's peso rapidly lost strength. Cárdenas' land and labor policies caused capital to flee the country, and the continually unfavorable balance of payments, brought about by the government's public works and agrarian aid programs, ate into the Bank of Mexico's exchange reserves. The shock of oil expropriation and the abrogation of the silver purchase agreement finally broke the Mexican peso. Capital left Mexico in large quantities, while the government printed more paper money. The peso-dollar exchange rate rapidly fell to over five to one and American trade with Mexico fell off drastically.[25]

Mexico took immediate measures to revise the tax laws to keep exporters from deriving all the benefit of the new low exchange rate. On August 4, 1938, President Cárdenas signed a bill providing for a general 12 per cent export tax.[26] Reasons advanced to justify the tax were: the necessity to make up for the lost tariff revenues since Mexican imports had fallen off so drastically; to make up for the loss of petroleum revenue; and to equalize a situation in which one economic group would obtain a socially undesirable gain—that is, to balance the exporters' (miners') gains against the importers' losses.[27] The law itself simply stated its object was to capture part of the exporters' gains while "still leaving them an important percentage of the profits derived from the aforesaid circumstances."[28] Enrique Ortiz of the Department of Mines estimated the tax would yield 30,096,985 pesos on the basis of 1936 production and values.[29]

The figure of 12 per cent was arrived at after a study of the mining industry to determine expenses paid in dollars and those paid in pesos. A Committee on Tariffs and Subsidies to Foreign Commerce (*Comité de Aforos y Subsidios al Comercio Exterior*) was set up on August 9th to supervise the enforcement of the law and oversee the disposition of the proceeds.[30] Since application of the tax in a blanket fashion would ruin marginal interests, the Committee recognized four factors which would determine the exact levy: (1) the automatic rise in taxes because of the fall of the peso—for example, production, sales, and income taxes; (2) circumstances where payment must be made in dollars; (3) the fall of foreign prices whose competition threatened Mexican production; and (4) aid to Mexican dumping operations to rid the domestic market of surpluses or production carried out to keep workers busy. Generally speaking, of the 1.40 peso rise in the exchange rate (from 3.60 to 5.00 to the dollar), the Committee attempted to retrieve 60 centavos for the government and leave 80 centavos for the exporter. It fixed the tax every month; by the end of 1938, the actual tax on gold was 9.1 per cent and on silver 5.7 per cent.[31]

The recession of 1938 and declining silver prices in 1939 made the new tax an onerous one. Mineowners pleaded for the repeal of the export levy and a general reduction in their taxes. They urged the government to encourage the workers to collaborate and to make an effort toward giving the industry greater security by an impartial enforcement of the labor laws; by halting and prosecuting thievery; and by stopping arbitrary caducations.[32] Reviewing its Mexican operations in 1940, ASARCO officials reported that during the administration of President Cárdenas profits had almost ceased because of rising labor costs and the fall in labor efficiency.[33] Changes in the export tax law came not as a result of these protests but because of adverse actions by the United States Congress and the outbreak of World War II.

Many American legislators, thinking the Treasury's silver purchase program economically unsound, were barely tolerant of purchases of American-mined silver; purchases of foreign-mined silver was beyond their understanding. They refused to recognize silver purchases as an integral part of American foreign policy. An attempt in July, 1939, to repeal the Silver Purchase Act eventually failed, but under the threat silver declined from 43 to 35 cents and the Mexican peso fell from 5 to almost 6 to the dollar.[34] The outbreak of war in September, 1939, contributed further to dislocations, and despite government concessions silver and lead production declined. As the volume of exports dropped, government revenue and company income decreased; Mexico had even less dollar exchange available.[35] Another attempt in 1940 to repeal the Silver Purchase Act failed by dint of great pressure from the White House and the plea that the United States could not afford to antagonize Mexico in a time of world crisis.[36]

As a first concession, Mexico exempted silver from the export tax but substantially raised the tax on gold, copper, lead, and zinc to make up the difference. Production and export tax cost an estimated $13,500,000, but silver producers complained they would still suffer a $5,000,000 loss.[37]

In an effort to attract "refugee capital" fleeing war-torn Europe, Mexico repealed its capital export tax and replaced it with a retroactive excess profits tax which weighed heavily on established enterprises.[38] Miners obtained some relief on May 21, 1940, when the government placed silver and lead on the export tax exemption list, followed on October 21st by a decree which halved the export tax on copper, lead, and zinc.[39]

Mexico's reluctance to reduce the tax rate on mining is understandable in the light of the nation's fiscal problems. Mining, receiving from 0.5 to 0.33 per cent of the Federal Budget appropriations, between the years 1935 and 1944, paid taxes which constituted (except for one year) from 28 to 35 per cent of the Federal Budget. The industry's tax burden came to between one-fifth and one-third of the value of mineral production. In the absence of income taxes or other taxable heavy industry, mining taxes and import duties contributed the bulk of the federal government's income. During the period 1935–44, the industry produced a gross value of 5.706 billion pesos of minerals and paid 1.425 billion pesos in taxes for an average of 24.9 per cent. Federal budgets during these years totalled 5.080 billion pesos; so that the mining industry paid 28.0 per cent of the total.[40]

Under the impact of rampant nationalism, foreign investments in Mexican mining steadily declined although the changing exchange rate makes a comparison of statistics difficult. In general, small and medium-sized mining companies were the worst hit groups and many abandoned their workings or turned them over to cooperatives. Small Mexican-owned mines appeared to have a better chance of survival. Alberto Terrones Benítez claimed that out of 879 mining companies operating in 1934 (620 Mexican owned, 207 United States owned, and 52 owned by other nationalities), 559 of them were closed by 1940. His analysis of the remaining 320 mines pointed out that 225 of them produced less than 100 metric tons a month, 60 produced between 100 and 1,000 metric tons, 19 produced 1,000 to 10,000 metric tons, and only 16 produced above 10,000 metric tons per month. The sixteen largest mines, he stated, were all American owned; nearly all the small and medium-sized mines were Mexican owned.[41]

Rising labor costs during the Cárdenas administration had introduced a new problem. Labor-saving machinery was still neglected in Mexico because it required greater investments than mining companies cared to venture. Mexico's nationalization policy and the limited experience of many Mexican miners with complex machinery made investors wary. Investment was for re-equipment rather than for new development.[42] After the inauguration of Cárdenas and the end of the silver boom, even that trend disappeared. After Avila Camacho's inauguration in 1941 the *Engineering and Mining Journal* still reported great hesitancy.[43]

During the Cárdenas administration, foreign companies were accused of manipulating Mexican production to suit their global policies and neglecting Mexican social and national aims in placing their investments. Explaining why the policies of large corporations did not harmonize with Mexican national interests and might even impede them, two engineers—one the future head of the Commission for Mining Development—wrote:

> . . . the politics of exploitation which the large foreign corporations agree among themselves to follow, in accordance with their position as global exploiters, and according to the role which, for their interests, the individual countries ought to play, [they consider] some [nations] as essentially producers of raw materials, and others principally as industrialized and exporters of manufactured products, a goodly portion of which the first group ought to consume.[44]

Foreigners could only reply that they had invested in Mexico to make a profit, a legitimate objective formerly approved of by Mexican governments. Questions of national and social interest were not raised when the concessions were given—some as long as 60 or 70 years before under Díaz. Therefore, why condemn foreign investors for not pursuing for years policies which the Mexican government itself had adopted only recently? Now the pattern was set. Without government understanding, foreigners might lose their profits but the Mexican government would lose its income and Mexicans would be unemployed.[45]

Under government pressure mineowners made concessions to the demand that capital be socially conscious. A convention of small mining companies in 1936 passed a series of the usual resolutions pleading for government aid and understanding. However, discussing "The Nationality of Mining Capital," the convention passed a resolution that "investments [already] made or [to be] made in the future" should not be judged by their size "but on [their] quality and tendency." Investments by Mexicans or foreigners, they declared, ought to be judged by whether they derived their return from "technical exploitation" or from "the exploitation of the working class." Furthermore, the convention denounced Mexican-owned capital sent abroad for safekeeping as being less "Mexican" than foreign capital which remained subject to Mexican law and produced economic benefits. The latter deserved the people's respect and merited the protection of the government.[46]

The nationality of the capital controlling Mexican mining during the 1930's was almost of the same composition as during the 1920's. Large companies with huge investments remained in foreign hands; only smaller, poorer enterprises became Mexican. William P. Rawles estimated in 1933 that Mexican control of Mexican mine production ranged from almost 5 per cent in the case of copper, to 2.5 per cent in the case of zinc.[47] Emilio Alinas Patiño in 1935 set over-all Mexican ownership at 2 per cent. Out of a total mining investment of 198,740,000 pesos in that year, he estimated that Americans held 161,000,000 pesos; French, 5,600,000; and others (mostly British), 31,800,000.[48] United States government studies of American foreign investments showed that mining investments were the largest single block of American money in Mexico. Out of a total of $682,000,000 invested in Mexico in 1929, $230,000,000 was in mining. In 1936, out of $479,000,000 invested in Mexico, $213,-000,000 was in mining.[49] A large drop occurred between 1936 and 1940. Investments of the 36 United States-controlled mining companies in Mexico fell to $168,312,000, a decline of $45,000,000 in four years.[50] Officially, on the basis of the Second Industrial Census of 1935, the SEN declared that some 323,000,000 pesos were invested in the mining industry: 286,330,000 in mines and 36,700,000 in metallurgical plants. American capital came to 223,000,000 pesos in mines and 26,500,000 pesos in plants; British capital amounted to 43,000,000 pesos; and French capital totalled 5,000,000 pesos. The Mexican figure was 7,500,000 pesos in mines and 7,200,000 pesos in plants.[51] Italian interests in 1939 numbered four enterprises with a combined capital of 195,585 pesos; three German firms had invested a mere 18,697 pesos. The small totals for these countries, as well as the lack of any figures for the Japanese, might indicate that their interests were registered in the names of Mexican citizens.[52]

In 1938 the Bank of Mexico began to keep check upon the trend of investments and profits in Mexico.[53] According to the bank's estimates, foreign investments in mining came to 1,001 million pesos in 1938; the total foreign investment was 2,526 million pesos. Mining investments fell to 996 million pesos in 1939, climbed to 1,082 million in 1943 and then declined to 1,025 million in 1945. Total foreign investment steadily increased to 2,900 million. In the matter of profits, the index for all foreign-owned investments climbed from the base of 100 in 1938, to 132 in 1941, and to 185.4 in 1945; the index for foreign-owned mining companies rose only to a peak of 124.1 in 1941, then fell off to 84.5 in 1944, and recovered to 107.8 the next year. Mining was the lowest profit-earner in the Mexican economy.

Declining investments and profits can be attributed in part to continued mine depletion. Guanajuato contracted operations yet further; ASARCO closed its Taviche, Oaxaca, unit and offered to transport the men to other units; and the Amparo and Piedra Bola mines in Jalisco finally gave up the ghost amidst a bitter lawsuit between the company and the workers.[53] At Pachuca, the seemingly inexhaustible mines were playing out, and even the larger companies kept their milling tonnages up by running leaner ore which averaged from 60 to over 100 grams of silver less per ton than ores milled at the beginning of the decade.[55] Mine depletion was not the result of descending ore grades alone. Market prices, equipment and operating costs, rising wages, and social benefit payments also contributed to ore dropping below the margin of profitability. One of the prime causes was the tax rate; special tax reductions often saved a failing enterprise.

Guanajuato is a classic illustration of the decline. As the old operators closed down, small companies, cooperative societies, and single workers moved in. With government approval and support they started to pick over the remains. In 1939, the government opened a 100-ton mill to beneficiate the output of seven mines. Formerly, any one of the seven would have supported a mill several times that size.[56]

In 1946, Raúl Madero, head of the Commission for Mining Development, compiled a list of over 35 depleted mines which had been either abandoned or turned over to cooperatives for a final scraping. Madero then commented:

> . . . it is years since a mine of importance has been opened, since the works which for the past few years have been pursued on a large scale have been in mines already worked, and in them exploration is almost paralyzed, and they necessarily have a short future life.[57]

CHAPTER 19

Labor Relations
during the 1930's

THE keynote of labor relations during the 1930's was the growing belligerency of the *Sindicato Industrial de Trabajadores Mineros, Metalúrgicos y Similares* (Syndicate of Mining, Metallurgical, and Allied Workers of the Mexican Republic). Organized in 1934, it expanded with the Cárdenas' administration's tacit approval to combat the remnants of the old CROM and unite the mine labor movement.[1] The union's attitude kept alive the fear of expropriation in the mineowners' minds.[2] In 1935 and 1936 a wave of strikes hit the mining industry as the union determined to make up the Depression wage losses. When they were over, wages had risen an average of 40 per cent, and the principle of fringe benefits had been set. The union's success was due in large part to the benevolent attitude of the administration and the courts.

Under Cárdenas, Mexican labor law and union contracts came to govern the most minute details of employer-employee relations, but it was still necessary for a foreign employer to use a great amount of tact if he wished to get along with his workers and avoid conflicts.[3] When a worker was hired, a detailed written contract was signed and a copy sent to the union. After a one-month probationary period, a worker could be discharged only for bad conduct, lack of discipline, or for breaking the contract—but not for incompetence. At the time of hiring, the employer must provide an immediate physical examination, including an X ray for silicosis. After a man was accepted, all injuries, deficiencies, and shortcomings became the employer's responsibility. In 1936 the Federal Board of Conciliation and Arbitration held San Rafael of Pachuca responsible for the compensation of the family of a worker who died of silicosis after only 18 months of employment. The Board reasoned that "when a company accepts a worker, it likewise accepts the occupational disease risk even though the worker may have contracted the disease elsewhere."[4] At first the men resented the examination, and the union complained that it was being used to reject men sent from union hiring halls.[5] The government supported the companies in their rejection of men who were unhealthy, alcoholic, chronically sick, generally unreliable, or had a venereal disease; but standards had to be reasonable. San Francisco del Oro found only one man in twenty fit for underground work.[6] Whether this rejection rate reflected the poor state of the Mexican workers' health and the high level of indemnification for which the company was liable, or indicated that company standards were too high, is a moot question.

Generally companies hired through union hiring halls, although a nonunion worker could be employed if a qualified union man were not available. Nonunion workers had to join the syndicate within a month. The labor law allowed 10 per cent of the personnel to consist of foreigners, but union contracts usually placed them at a small number limited to "confidential posts." The traditional attitude of foreign employees undoubtedly had much to do with this limitation.[7] Shifts were limited to eight hours, with an evening shift of seven and one-half hours and a night shift of seven hours, the latter drawing pay for eight. The Federal Labor Law was amended in 1936 to include a day of rest at full wages for each six days' work. When the worker might not be active six days, for reasons beyond his volition or control, the Department of Labor held the employer responsible for one-sixth extra pay for each day actually worked. Five paid holidays were provided in addition to vacations, of from five days to two weeks, depending upon length of service.[8]

Wages could be paid only in legal tender. Wage rates, which varied from region to region, and depended upon individual skills, and were often tied to metal prices, automatically changing as prices rose or fell.[9] This latter practice was started to allow for the profit-sharing provisions of Article 123 of the Constitution. Companies withheld union dues through a mandatory checkoff. All promotions outside the office staff could only be made under a rigid system of seniority called *escalafón* which discounted competence and necessitated keeping voluminous work records.[10] Grievance committees tried to settle complaints, and the companies were often hard pressed in practicing tact, patience, restraint, and understanding. Disciplinary action, aside from discharge, was confined to a suspension of from five to eight days, but was rare owing to union hostility.

Larger mining companies were required to maintain a hospital and first-aid stations, and instruct their employees on industrial and personal hygiene.[11] They had to pay a worker who was ill with an occupational disease 75 per cent of his wage during the illness; for natural illness the company paid 50 per cent of the wage for two months. Venereal diseases, alcoholism, injuries from fights, and chronic illness cost the worker his disability pay rights.[12] Lists of occupational diseases were quite long and determining the causes of various respiratory diseases

—whether they were attributable to mining or to poor living conditions —led to acrimonious debates. When fibricosis was judged an occupational ailment which disqualified mine applicants for employment, the union accused the companies of hiring only young men who would be more obedient instead of the older and more experienced miners—who presumably would be stauncher union men. Finding jobs for miners suffering from lung diseases was a difficult problem. Many became prospectors, members of producers' cooperative mining ventures, or buscones living by high grading or acting as scavengers. A few attempts were made to settle these men on small farm plots.[13]

The campaign against accidents continued and cut the accident rate even further. To a certain extent the accident rolls were inflated, since

> ... the labor tribunals always find a way to show relationship between the accidents and the activities of the company, and it is almost impossible to demonstrate that the accident took place through the fault of the worker, or from causes beyond control, such as fights or drunkenness.[14]

The head of the Department of Labor stated in 1936 that over half the accidents reported in Mexican industry were in mining, and of the national total of 90 fatal accidents, 72 were in mining. However, the mining figures were doubtless more complete than those from other industries—not to mention agriculture—where official vigilance was less alert. Accident victims received some 1,600,000 pesos in settlement of claims, and sick miners were paid some 1,780,000 pesos.[15] Under continuing pressure, the Real del Monte company reported reducing fatal accidents per 100,000 shifts from 1.0197 in 1934 to 0.8938 in 1938.[16]

In fatal accidents the employer was required to pay 612 days' wages plus 30 days' pay for funeral expenses. (When ASARCO challenged the latter provision on the grounds that having paid the indemnity they did not see why they had to bury the man as well, the courts decided that the company should furnish the victim with a coffin.) At Nueva Rosita, Coahuila, in 1936, ASARCO agreed to 712 days' pay as accidental death compensation, and in cases of death for any reason whatsoever, it agreed to pay 45 days' wages, the cost of the coffin, and 500 pesos to the widow. In Sonora, where state laws granted widows a pension, Phelps Dodge's Moctezuma Copper Company at Nacozari operated a marriage bureau in order to find new husbands for them.[17] In cases of injury, the laws had lengthy lists of possible accidents and the resulting indemnities, ranging up to 918 days' wages. Union contracts usually supplemented these payments with demands for artificial limbs and higher compensation.[18]

Mexican law attempted to make all jobs permanent. Union contracts and legal provisions minutely circumscribed the discharge of workers. By constitutional provision an "unjustified" discharge cost the employer three month's pay. Union contracts could add up to another 20 days' pay for each year of service. Even when discharging an employee for a legitimate cause, the employer had to submit legal proof. If a mine had to be closed down, the company would either have to reach an agreement with the union or to apply to a Federal Board of Conciliation and Arbitration for permission to suspend operations. If the Board granted the petition, it provided for promising the men that their seniority would be honored when work was resumed. Companies had to pay the three-month indemnity to workers displaced by new machines, and in cases of closure because of force majeure the Board considered each case on its merits but employers could still be held liable.[19] The Department of Labor endeavored to discourage the employment of buscones, who worked on a share basis, by declaring their contracts to be under the jurisdiction of the Federal Labor Law, only to be overruled in 1947 by the Supreme Court which held the contracts must be made with the proprietors as owners, not as employers.[20]

If an enterprise employing over 100 men was more than a "reasonable" distance from a population center (later defined as 3 kilometers), the company had to provide housing and community services for its workers and a suitable office for the union at a reasonable rent.[21] The law forbade company stores, saloons, charges for hiring workers, and *"coyotes"* (loan sharks) around the payroll office. Antiunion propaganda could not be circulated or a black list kept. If 20 children of school age lived in the community, the company had to set up an *"Escuela Artículo 123,"* as provided for in that constitutional article. The Federal Department of Education provided teachers and plans; the company, following government specifications, supplied the building, furniture, salaries, supplies, and books.[22]

Government enforcement of provisions for decent housing and social benefits could redound to a company's benefit.[23] Commenting on ASARCO's own plans during the 1920's, William Loeb remarked that the decrease in time off for sickness, the decline in the accident rate, and especially the lower turnover rate made the program financially justifiable.[24]

For years the national miners' union had worked for a "standard contract" which would place miners throughout the country on the same wage scale, thus raising wages in the backward and remote areas to the level prevailing in the northern cities. Mining companies vigorously opposed the contract contending that it ignored regional variations in costs and labor efficiency. Peñoles, the first large company approached, finally agreed in the summer of 1937 to pay equal wages to all its workers performing similar tasks throughout Mexico. After negotiating the Peñoles contract, the union called a partial convention to draft a similar contract for presentation to ASARCO and to inform President Cárdenas of its plans. These maneuvers disturbed small miners who believed that they might have to pay equal wages while the custom smelters would pass on their raises in the form of higher treatment charges.

When the union presented its demands to ASARCO, the government also brought official pressure to bear. At a demonstration, the Governor of Chihuahua promised unstinting aid to the miners of his state. Addressing the same rally, Senator Ezequiel Padilla declared that the senators and the governors of Chihuahua, Coahuila, and Nuevo León backed the workers' movement. Under Antonio Villalobos, the Department of Labor officially sponsored the union's demands after ASARCO rejected them. Villalobos suggested on October 4, 1937, that a worker-employer convention of the mining industry be called to discuss a labor contract which would be made a "Law Contract," and hence obligatory throughout the country. A number of other industries had similar agreements. ASARCO rejected the requests of the Labor Department, and the union began punitive one-hour strikes during each work shift. ASARCO also refused to open its books to government inspection and insisted that it could not bargain for a new contract since the general manager, J. R. Woodul, was absent in New York. Surprisingly, on December 1st, the Department of Labor informed the workers that their tactics were illegal and asked them to return to work and permit the Department to look after their affairs. Villalobos telegraphed New York requesting Woodul's return. Rumors spread that ASARCO was stalling until the United States decided on its future silver purchase policy. A preliminary agreement was reached between ASARCO and the union in January, 1938; they agreed upon a two-month period in which to reach a final agreement. Armed with ASARCO's concession, the union made similar demands upon Real del Monte, San Francisco Mines, Cananea Copper, and Fresnillo. If these companies could be induced to sign standard contracts, the way would be open for a Law Contract. But conversations between the union and ASARCO ran into difficulties. National union leaders pressured Cárdenas, but ASARCO stiffened its attitude. At the end of two months ASARCO refused to concede the standard contract, much to the relief of the Small Miners' Council. Mexico had a difficult time in March, 1938, with the expropriation of the property of the oil companies and the United States' suspension of direct silver purchases. Woodul had several conversations with Cárdenas. In an interview with mine union leaders, Cárdenas made it clear to the workers that the crisis following the oil expropriation necessitated a settlement in the national interest. They dropped their demand for a standard wage contract; ASARCO reinstated the workers discharged for taking part in the one-hour strikes and reopened the Chihuahua smelter which had been closed for 22 days.[25]

Generally, the attitude of the Cárdenas administration toward strikes encouraged labor disturbances. Mineowners complained that the new laws invariably supported the workers, while the courts awarded them more than they asked for—an amount usually in keeping with the company's ability to pay.[26] In 1935 alone there were 36 strikes involving 18,329 mineworkers. By the late 1930's strikes became so numerous that it was virtually impossible to keep a record of them.[27] In December, 1938, Section XVIII of Article 123 of the Constitution was rewritten to enlarge the scope of licit strikes. Under the new interpretation, any strike having the objective of obtaining an equilibrium between labor and capital was legal. Only public utilities had to be given ten days' notice. Strikes were illicit only when a majority of the workers on strike practiced violence (!) or when the strike involved government agencies or services in wartime.[28] Before a strike could be called the union had to draw up a list of demands, present it to a federal labor inspector, fix a date for the walkout, and ascertain whether the strike was approved by the majority of the members. Once these rules were complied with the strike was legal, and the company was forced to suspend operations and became responsible for the men's wages.[29]

Unions could call strikes on slight provocations and keep the men out during interminable negotiations, secure in the knowledge that their pay was guaranteed. Some employers accused unions of using the strike period as a paid vacation. In practice, the wages due the men was paid by a lump-sum settlement. During the strike only essential operations— such as pumping—were allowed. Because of severe federal penalties, the company could not bring in scabs. Official bodies needed indeterminable lengths of time to reach decisions. With the possibility of unshakeable bias and corruption on the part of Federal Board members, unions and employers generally preferred to negotiate between themselves. If no acceptable settlement could be worked out and the case eventually reached the Supreme Court, the company either had to accept the Court's decision or face expropriation.[30]

As might be expected, wages increased as strikes became more frequent. The first wave of strikes in 1935 raised wages about 40 per cent, but the average Mexican wage was still between 1,200 and 1,350 pesos ($333 to $375, U.S.) a year, or about 25 pesos ($7, U.S.) for a 6-day week. As the average included supervisory and skilled workers, the ordinary miner and peon received far less. In 1936, wages jumped over 35 per cent to almost 1,800 pesos. Of this increase 16⅔ per cent was attributable to government-ordered provisions for paid Sundays for those who had worked a full 6-day week. Wages rose to an average of 2,100 pesos ($583, U.S.) in 1937. By 1938, the daily wage was 6.54 pesos, and it had risen to 8 pesos by 1939.[31] The rapid rise in the latter years is accountable in great part to the depreciation of the peso, price inflation, and government pressure after the expropriation of oil properties.

A study made in 1938 indicated that the wages in mining were generally double the legal minimum in agriculture and 50 per cent above the minimum industrial wage.[32]

Mining wages had reached their practical limit in the Mexican economy by 1940–41. Unions then aimed at obtaining greater social benefits. Mining companies took a dim view of Avila Camacho's ability to curb union demands.[33] As wages started to rise again after 1942, the percentage of mine workers paying income tax rose from 20 per cent in 1937 to 70 per cent in 1943, indicating that most miners were earning over 5.75 pesos a day—a high wage for Mexico. In 1943, in return for a no-strike pledge, the workers were given another 10 per cent raise.[34]

For social or "fringe" benefits, strikers in the early 1930's demanded free lamps, free safety hats, and more money allocated to medical services. A drive for greater injury and death indemnifications characterized the middle of the decade. During the late 1930's and early 1940's the union asked for lump sums to be paid into its treasury for social benefits and aid in setting up consumers' cooperatives. ASARCO's settlement at Santa Eulalia in 1941, for example, provided for 1,000 days' pay for permanent incapacity, 365 days' pay for nonprofessional illnesses, 500 pesos life insurance, longer vacations, free electric lights in some houses, a number of technical scholarships and correspondence courses, plus 5,500 pesos for social services.[35]

Consumers' cooperatives became quite popular among mineworkers. To start them off, Fresnillo donated 60,000 pesos; San Francisco del Oro, 100,000 pesos; and ASARCO amounts which varied from 10,000 pesos at Charcas to 107,000 pesos at Santa Barbara.[36] A survey made by the University of Mexico in 1944 covered 11 mineworkers' consumer cooperatives. Most commonly they were founded in an attempt to raise real wages. Cananea's unit had 1,147 members and a capital of 67,814 pesos to start; in 1943 it had 3,120 members and 606,814 pesos in capital. ASARCO's Rosita unit grew from 326 to 4,500 members and the Nacozari unit of Phelps Dodge from 435 to 1,254. Although not as large as some others, the El Boleo unit had a capital of 167,121 pesos, and Nacozari had 137,498. Rosita and Cananea reported profits in 1943 of over 100,000 pesos and distributed from 5,000 to 6,000 pesos annually among their members.[37]

These cooperatives were a most encouraging development, and both companies and unions supported them. Innumerable pleasurable distractions in mining towns makes the problem of getting the mineworker to provide proper diets for himself and his family a difficult one. Consumers' cooperatives take an assigned portion of the workers' wages for food and provide better quality at lower prices. In this way they compensate for inadequate wages in relation to the size of families and discourage spending on vices. (Still, some workers sell the cooperatives' food to have cash to squander!) Consumers' cooperatives are helped by the employers who realize that they represent a practical way of providing the worker with an adequate and balanced diet to overcome physical weakness and inefficiency. By eliminating loan sharks and venal merchants, who raise prices to match wage raises, cooperatives help the worker to realize a better life. With a diet traditionally poor in green vegetables and meat, coupled with an overindulgence in liquor and vice, the mineworker sickens and dies too easily. Adequate instruction propagated by the unions in nutrition and how to make money go further with consumers' cooperatives can help the mineworker greatly. Fortunately, the cooperatives are succeeding.[38]

During the 1930's the mineworkers improved their economic status significantly. Although they still did not earn wages equal in cash or purchasing power to those of miners in the United States, in relation to other Mexican workers their wages and social benefits were quite high.

CHAPTER 20

The Producers'
Cooperatives Movement

PRESIDENT Lázaro Cárdenas' promise in the Plan Sexenal of 1934 to aid mineworkers and small national mining enterprises led to a significant innovation: Mexico began to sponsor producers' cooperatives in the mining industry. Cooperatives seemed to offer the best way to free the Mexican miner from his dependence upon foreign capital and to develop in him a sense of managerial responsibility. Quite soon the cooperative program became one of the most controversial subjects in the Mexican mining economy.

As early as 1928 and 1929 some workers had demanded that the government aid them by taking over mining properties to be given to them to work as cooperatives.[1] But nothing was done. On March 10, 1934, Osvaldo Gurría Urgell of the Department of Mines signalled a change in the government's attitude in an address to the *Convención Nacional de Ingenieros*.[2] Commenting upon the Mexican mining economy, he noted its importance to the national economy, its high technical proficiency in working low-grade ores economically, and the superior economic position of the mineworkers among the Mexican proletariat. From the standpoint of the nation, however, he deplored the concentration of the industry in a few places and its control by foreign capitalists, who took over 30 per cent of the value of the extracted minerals out of the country. He theorized that the necessities of large-scale economical workings of lean ores tended to make the industry cluster around existing transportation facilities, thus ignoring undeveloped regions. Small enterprises in these areas were left with development projects too large for their capital resources. Gurría Urgell predicted that the Mexican earth would be gutted of its mineral wealth without compensatory discoveries and that government intervention would be imperative. By subsidizing small operators, the government would encourage exploitation without abusing the older and larger companies which could continue to deplete their known deposits. Mexico's future lay in backing the small mine operators who traditionally had been forced to sell their discoveries to the large enterprises for exploitation. Latent resources now would be developed, more workers would be employed, and statistics would show both a larger and a more widely distributed production of minerals.[3]

In the government's estimation, Gurría Urgell stated, the program's success depended upon the availability of: (1) provisioners and ore buyers, (2) capital, (3) transportation, (4) cheap power, (5) nearby milling plants, and (6) metallurgical plants (smelters and refineries) to handle the small output of these companies. Capitalists, engineers, and metallurgists were scarce in Mexico, and even the first step in building a small concentrating plant required capital and specialized knowledge. Since success could not be achieved in one stroke, the government had decided first to create reserved mineral zones to keep untapped resources out of the hands of foreigners; second, to help the gambusinos and small operators with special plans; and third, to demonstrate to Mexican capitalists that they could obtain profitable results. Gurría Urgell then read a long and detailed policy statement which anticipated the amendment of the Mining Law in August, 1934, creating the National Mineral Reserves and the Commission for Mining Development, and which ordered all mills and smelters to reserve 20 per cent of their capacity for public ores. He urged Mexico to follow the example of Chile and set up cooperatives with various government aids such as selling provisions at cost price, renting drills and pumps, building beneficiation plants, marketing the minerals, and furnishing advice on technical and legal problems. As in the case of Chile, gold placers were among the first areas to be incorporated into the mineral reserves for exploitation by Mexican miners, either alone or organized into producers' cooperatives.[4]

A. Glyka of the *Mineral Survey* in January, 1935 wrote a trenchant critique of the cooperative scheme.[5] He noted the major arguments advanced in favor of cooperative mining societies were that (1) they would reduce Mexico's dependence upon foreign capital and prevent the flight of national wealth abroad; (2) they would employ jobless miners and those in poor health (especially men suffering from silicosis) whom the regular companies would not hire; (3) they would offer excellent opportunities for training Mexicans to become better miners, engineers, administrators, and financial men—if they would study and if the lack of a trained engineer for safety and efficiency work could be overlooked; and (4) prospectors would be encouraged by the knowledge that even remote claims could be exploited by a cooperative and that they would not have to sell out to a large company, which meant a boost in morale as well as increased economic independence. However, the necessary capital would have to be found to keep new cooperatives going during the expensive and critical developmental phase. Before these advantages could be gained, Glyka went on, a number of handicaps would have to be overcome. To judge by experience, he contended, the odds would be against the survival of any given mining enterprise. Therefore, the State must subject cooperatives to a strict vigilance by setting up financing agencies and rigid inspection systems, and demanding a modicum of capital, talent, and a chance of success before agreeing to assist a cooperative enterprise. Cooperatives which fail must not be permitted to drag others under. It would appear, Glyka remarked, that given the financial status of most cooperatives, they would need either to strike a bonanza within a short time or receive substantial aid. Insufficient working capital would plague those cooperatives whose members could put up only a few hundred pesos and had to agree to accept subsistence wages. Adequate State support might eventually engender enough confidence to attract private capital and safeguard the men's savings. But because of the high rate of expected failures, a State agency could not collect interest alone, since the unsuccessful enterprises would outnumber the successful, but would have to become an actual partner—a development which would defeat much of the reasoning behind the cooperative plan. (In actuality, the Mexican government avoided the last contingency only by extending direct subsidies to foundering cooperatives.)

Demands for the opening of mining cooperatives steadily increased after 1932. There was talk in 1933 of plans for the construction of metal treatment plants to process the ores of small producers. In 1935 the Confederation of Workers and Peasants petitioned President Cárdenas to make available to unemployed miners the facilities to exploit a long list of abandoned properties. In the same year the Ministry of the National Economy organized cooperatives in several states.[6] However, the movement was still mainly in a talking stage. Cooperatives had not yet taken over any significant working properties. Their operations were confined to reopening abandoned mines; mines with marginal ore made profitable by the silver price boom of 1935; and mines turned over to the workers to be operated as cooperatives by companies in lieu of the required three months' severance pay if the mine shut down.[7]

As union wage demands became heavier and the cost of paying strike wages became greater, many mineowners found it expedient to turn their properties over to their workers in return for a promise of a portion of the profits plus payment for the property in installments. This procedure became quite common by 1937 and the miners' union asked for legislation to compel companies suspending operations without official sanction to turn the mines over to their employees, at no cost to the men.[8] Coupled with the oil crisis, many mineowners interpreted this "labor squeeze" as an attempt to expropriate the mines by a legal subterfuge.

As time advanced, many workers found the following method, soon reduced to a system, to be the most expedient way of getting control:

> Excessive demands on the part of the laborers lead to difficulties in draw-ing up the collective contract and then to a strike. . . . a company is forced to accept the intervention of the Labor Department to conciliate the differ-ences with the workmen and, whenever conciliation is impossible, to sub-mit to what is referred to as an "economic judgment" whereby the Labor Board determines whether the company is or is not in a position to accede to the laborers' demands. The determination of this economic judgment entails an investigation of the books of the company, its management, and in general of the way it handles its business. From the results of the inves-tigation the Labor Board renders a decision. One can readily perceive the dangers involved in such an investigation. . . . Denied permission to shut down [the company] continues to operate until its resources are exhausted and they are forced to stop, though now legally liable to their employees in various ways. Thereupon the employees, organized into a so-called cooperative society take control. . . .[9]

Assumption of control was preceded by a bargaining session in which the workers' claims were matched against the company's assets under the surveillance of a government inspector. A price would be fixed for the properties, and the company would take the cooperative's notes with the mine as security. Sometimes when a cooperative would fail and market conditions became favorable, the company would recover its property.

This procedure at first forced only small mines to the wall, but soon even large enterprises—such as Guadalupe de los Reyes and El Tajo in Sinaloa and La Naica and Cusi-Mexicana in Chihuahua—fell into the hands of cooperatives. By 1940, important but depleted mines such as Dos Carlos and San Rafael in Pachuca; La Noria and El Bote in Zacatecas; Dos Estrellas in Michoacan; Lane-Rincón in Mexico State; and Amparo in Jalisco were transformed into cooperatives.[10]

Cooperatives held a favored legal position to the chagrin of private entrepreneurs. They had been first authorized in 1927, but little was done until the General Law of Cooperative Societies was passed on May 12, 1933.[11] This law allowed some tax exemptions, but only six mining cooperatives with 291 members were formed under its pro-visions.[12] Despite the protests of private miners and Article 28 of the Constitution, which forbade tax exemptions to mercantile enterprises,[13] a decree of August 31, 1933, exempted authorized cooperatives from a number of taxes for five years.[14] A government declaration later held that cooperatives were not mercantile enterprises.[15]

The General Law of Cooperative Societies was completely revised on January 11, 1938, and became the Magna Charta of producers' coopera-tives. Under its provisions the SEN authorized, by 1946, 75 producers' cooperatives with 19,055 associates to exploit metallic minerals. Of the total, 49 were organized between 1938 and 1940—many as a result of cases brought before the Labor Tribunals.[16] Because of their precarious beginnings, the government extended a number of fiscal aids to the cooperatives. Many marginal cooperatives were hard hit by the 12 per cent export tax imposed upon mining when the peso was devalued following the expropriation of the oil industry. They protested that they would have to cut wages and reduce the work week to four days. As a special favor, the government gave them complete exemption from export taxes for their silver, a 50 per cent rebate on their gold exports, and refunded 150,000 pesos to a number of cooperatives—including Dos Carlos, San Rafael, Dos Estrellas and Lane-Rincón.[17] On December 27, 1938, it rewrote the law exempting cooperatives from paying taxes for five years after their establishment to apply specifically to mine cooperatives and to include the metal-production tax, the claim-area tax, water and electricity taxes, the stamp tax, and the income tax[18]—the last being made permanent.[19] However, the 1941 President Avila Camacho ordered production cooperatives to pay income taxes, and his decree was upheld by the Federal Supreme Court in 1948.[20]

Cooperatives needed aid other than tax exemption. Government-built ore-treatment plants were but the first step; outright cash subsidies, donations of supplies, equipment, and even the capital necessary to start a cooperative were the other aids.[21] For example, in 1938, 45,000 pesos were lent to three cooperatives in Hidalgo; 1,000 pesos and 8,000 meters of pipe were given to a new cooperative near Hermosillo, Sonora; a 350-kilowatt power plant was donated to the cooperatives which took over the El Bote unit of the Pittsburgh-Veta Grande Company at Zacatecas City; and 220,000 pesos were given to the Palau, Coahuila, miners to start the exploitation of the coal mines there.[22] In 1940, the federal government advanced an estimated 1,000,000 pesos a year in such subsidies.[23]

When continual and increasing economic difficulties beset the cooperatives, Mexico's government, itself in difficult financial straits, became disabused of the idea that the nation's future lay with such "self-supporting" enterprises. Every dip in the price of metals meant pleas for help under the threat of an increased number of unemployed miners.[24] Finding scapegoats in the cooperatives was politically inexpedient. Even the miners' union, which had supported the movement, found its relations with the cooperatives' workers not altogether to its liking. When the official party drew up the second Six-Year Plan in late 1939, it modified the cooperative policy to include only those groups able to demonstrate that their workings would be successful.[25] But the movement already was full blown.

The Mexican government directly intervened in cooperative affairs in many ways. When the SEN formed the Federation of Cooperative Societies of the Mining and Metallurgical Industry in 1941, all cooperatives were forced to join or face drastic penalties.[26] This Federation comprised 33 societies, with a claimed membership of 25,000 men, and had as its objective the coordination and improvement of working and economic conditions of cooperative miners. The next year it reported a membership of 42 cooperatives, with a claimed membership of 35,000 men and announced the hiring of a corps of technical consultants consisting of a mining engineer, a metallurgist, a practical miner, an accountant, and an assayer. One major problem was engendered by the change in status of miners, who had to learn how to work independently and not depend upon wages. It was expected that there would be a lack of capital and a need for new equipment, as well as pleas for government control of custom treatment plant charges. But the help needed to pay compensation for injuries was an unanticipated charge.[27] One token of government aid was the formation of a Banco Nacional de Fomento Cooperativo in 1944 to replace the old Banco Nacional Obrero de Fomento Industrial. One of the bank's objects was to aid producers' cooperatives suffering from chronic shortages of capital.[28] However, it offered little to mining cooperatives.

The history of some individual cooperatives is instructive. Some cooperatives—such as those at Promontorio, in Durango State, and Guanajuato—developed normally enough, with the typical squeezing of the company between falling ore grades and rising union demands.[29] The conversion of the Amparo mine in Jalisco was not as smooth. When the negotiations over the percentage of the gross proceeds to be paid to the company collapsed, the company representatives walked out and the cooperative worked the mine without a legal title.[30]

The two largest single cooperatives in Mexico were founded on the remains of the famous Dos Carlos at Pachuca, Hidalgo, and the Dos Estrellas at Tlalpujahua, Michoacan. Cooperatives had started in Hidalgo as early as 1934, with the "La Evoluta" composed of 14 men with a paid-in capital of 49 pesos.[31] On June 19, 1937, the British-owned Santa Gertrudis company decided its Dos Carlos mine, employing 1,500 men, was unprofitable and turned it over to a cooperative on a six-month agreement, with the company giving technical aid and marketing advice.[32] Santa Gertrudis claimed that despite a wage reduction of 30 per cent, it had lost 800,000 pesos in the preceding three years and owed the workers some 1,000,000 pesos, or a sum equalling the value of the machinery. Believing the venture sound, the Cárdenas administration arranged a 20,000-peso loan through a government bank, while the federal and state government, and the miners' union, advanced cash. To cut costs, the cooperative laid off all nonunion men, increased the workday one hour, and abolished extra pay for extra work and Sundays. Despite some preliminary difficulties, including a 150,000-peso electric bill and a SEN squabble with the union over the extent of union control, the cooperative was set up on December 7, 1937, with an initial membership of 1,197 and a paid-in capital of 21,120 pesos. The weekly payroll came to some 35,000 pesos.[33] In January, 1938, the federal government pledged 300,000 pesos for machinery and equipment, while the cooperative, in an outburst of patriotic fervor, pledged 100,000 pesos to help pay for the oil expropriations. By January, 1940, the cooperative proudly claimed the extraction of 15,000,000 pesos (about $3,000,000) in silver. Despite several serious accidents, which forced the Department of Labor to warn the cooperative to observe the safety regulations,[34] Dos Carlos' prestige was the highest in Mexico. Its membership in 1940 was 3,500 men and its payroll 91,000 pesos a week. Dos Carlos leased a number of other properties in the district, including the Barron mine of the Real del Monte y Pachuca company. It engaged in extensive diamond drilling explorations, increased its mill capacity to 1,250 tons per day, helped the San Rafael cooperative,[35] and even aided in the organization of cooperatives in Zacatecas and San Luis Potosí. However, by the fall of 1943 the picture started to change. Workers complained that they received only 1.25 pesos a day, operations were curtailed and men laid off. The inevitable exhaustion squeezed Dos Carlos.[36] To charges made in 1945 that Dos Carlos paid peons only 2.90 pesos (59 cents, U.S.) a day and that silicosis was rampant, the society's representatives sanguinely replied that some 3,000 workers depended upon the cooperative and that the presence of silicosis was not alarming since the disease was rather common among miners! A state loan of 340,000 pesos in mid-1945 was followed by a large federal loan, but the enterprise continued to fail. In 1946 the Labor Department undertook the supervision of Dos Carlos after the management confessed its inability to pay 150,000 pesos in wages. It had received an estimated 2,000,000 pesos in aid.[37]

Daniel Olguín Díaz discussed Dos Carlos' status before the National Mining Congress in 1948.[38] Sr. Olguín Díaz was quite proud of the cooperative's past achievements, for by 1947 it had produced some 76,000,000 pesos in silver; employed an average of 2,500 men to whom it had paid 52,000,000 pesos in wages; turned over 5,000,000 pesos in taxes to the government; spent 3,650,000 pesos in mine pumping costs; and consumed 85,000 pesos in electricity a month—all without the help of one foreign engineer. Yet, despite reserves of 100,000 metric tons of ore blocked out, it milled only 300 tons a day in a mill with a capacity of 1,000 tons. Declining ore grades—400 grams of silver and 2 grams of gold per ton—plus reserves of even lower grade, prevented the profitable milling of more mineral. Costs had advanced 80 per cent since the cooperative was formed, despite wages being only 40 per cent of those paid at the neighboring, privately owned Real del Monte y Pachuca

Company! Sr. Olguín Díaz's exposition of the cooperative's success and achievements was only the springboard for his demands that the Mexican government ask the United States to raise the price of silver to 90 cents an ounce, concede a total exemption from taxes, reduce electric power costs, and provide sundry other aids. In turn, the cooperative would insure the continued employment of its members.

Dos Carlos' end came in 1953 when the Paricutín vein played out. As early as 1950 electric bills were in arrears, and workers had rioted in Pachuca when they were not paid. Finally, the government decided that the weekly deficit of 12,000 pesos ($1,380), despite federal and state aid, was no longer tolerable. It closed the mine in the summer of 1953 and placed the 243 members left on other jobs. Contractors took over the mine for a final picking. Pumps had to be maintained to prevent flooding of the neighboring Real del Monte mines.[39]

As in the case of Dos Carlos, the Dos Estrellas cooperative owed its origin to a company-proposed wage cut in February, 1937. When the union demanded a government examination of the company's books, the analysts found the company capable of maintaining wages. As a last straw, the company's 500,000-peso dam burst killing 100 people and making it liable for over 2,500,000 pesos in compensation and damage suits.[40] On December 16, 1937, the mineowners and the union signed an agreement to turn the workings over to a cooperative on January 1, 1938, for an eight-month trial. Predicting an output of 1,000,000 ounces of silver a month, the workers fell to their task with enthusiasm. Output soared and dislocation of the exchange rate in 1936 made for high profits. The cooperative announced a net profit of 600,000 pesos—after repaying a 200,000-peso government loan—and finally bought the property in 1940. It set the property's gross value at 4,886,491 pesos, but various deductions, including monthly payments already made, brought the price down to 1,279,771 pesos ($204,000, U.S.). But the purchase was made at an inopportune time, for war in Europe and American congressional action weakened the silver market while the peso was stabilized, cutting the profits made on exchange. As enthusiasm waned output fell, and the operating capital, after paying the purchase installments, was not large enough to finance necessary purchases of machinery. The enterprise also lacked trained technicians and planning. In 1942 the cooperative petitioned the government for a subsidy of 30,000 pesos a month in addition to a suspension of any tax collections. It contended that if the mine were closed, 4,000 men would be out of work and that the entire region would starve. From 1941 to 1944 production fell from 1,038,953 to 618,905 fine ounces of silver. Rehabilitation of the enterprise could only come at a high price. The cooperative petitioned the government in 1944 for an emergency relief fund of 500,000 pesos to pay for steel and machinery ordered in the United States but requiring cash for delivery.[41] By 1946 the cooperative had reached a crisis: production was down to 800 tons of lean ore a day and it lost 335,246 pesos in that year alone. Indebtedness and obligations totalled 3,500,000 pesos. In an inadequate effort to combat the warborn inflation, wages had only been raised from 1.80 pesos a day to 2.60 pesos by cutting the working force from over 2,700 to 1,100 men. Still, the directors called for a 15 per cent wage cut and harder work.

On March 3, 1947, the cooperative turned its administration over to the Commission for Mining Development (CFM) which assumed the burden of keeping the mine open because it was the sole economic support of 35,000 people in the cities of El Oro, Mexico State, and Tlalpujahua, Michoacan. The CFM hoped to find enough ore to put the enterprise on a paying basis and continue to augment the national gold reserve.[42] Conditions bettered at Dos Estrellas, despite protests by the workers at having to take orders from the government and demands for more "autonomy."[43] Since World War II silver output has been set at the following figures:

TABLE 8

SILVER PRODUCTION AT DOS ESTRELLAS: 1945–58

(*In Fine Ounces of Silver*)

Year	Production	Year	Production	Year	Production
1945	419,793	1950	404,260	1955	525,134
1946	271,486	1951	461,445	1956	508,837
1947	297,229	1952	376,570	1957	481,546
1948	387,071	1953	493,382	1958	425,082
1949	371,796	1954	593,269		

SOURCE: American Bureau of Metal Statistics, *Yearbook, 1949*, p. 80; *1958*, p. 102.

A most vexing problem for the cooperatives was the conduct of the buscones, or gambusinos, who singly or in groups forced their way into mine workings to practice their *forte* of stealing ore. Many of these men were old miners with occupational illnesses which prevented their regular employment. Sometimes they worked placers or picked over old mine workings on a share basis with the owner; often they stole into mines to work ore "pips." Their lax methods sometimes damaged the mine's structure and made scientific exploitation impossible. They possessed no group strength, and ore buyers regularly cheated them. As a whole, their production was of some importance; in a local situation they could be very important.[44] Attempts by mineowners to halt their depredations had been unavailing, since local authorities usually took an indulgent view. The Guanajuato cooperatives, however, took their grievances to President Cárdenas after the state authorities had done nothing. They threatened to close entirely unless the depredations stopped, and Cárdenas ordered federal troops to guard the mines.

An extremely difficult situation arose in Mapimí, Durango, when Peñoles leased the Ojuela mine to a cooperative. Large numbers of buscones, financed by illegal ore buyers, moved into the district. They worked remote parts of the mine in which there were 250 miles of underground workings. Relations were tense until Peñoles authorized the cooperative to organize an ore-buying agency to purchase the buscones' ore and prevailed upon the cooperative to accept them into membership. Still the buscones complained that the cooperative agency cheated them. This cooperative worked for over 20 years cleaning out a 400-year-old mine that could no longer be mined by a corporation with even moderate-sized production.[45]

Any evaluation of the cooperative program must balance a number of socially desirable goals with a rather dismal achievement. Cooperatives have not been free of corrupt administrators, nor of meddling politicians and labor leaders.[46] At times the workers were high-pressured into forming cooperatives in mines which could not be made to pay. These cooperatives were forced to cut wages and social benefits in a manner which would not be tolerated by a union in bargaining with a private employer.[47] They blatantly ignored safety regulations and incurred official reprimands.[48] Equipment in the mines they acquired was usually antiquated, and the cooperatives had little capital with which to replace it. Also, during the 1940's heavy equipment became virtually unobtainable.[49] Despite subsidies and tax exemptions, the slightest variations in metal prices, the foreign exchange rate, or even the need for small amounts of new equipment would bring the precarious finances of many a cooperative to a point of crisis.[50] Either through lack of foresight or money, cooperatives neglected to develop ore and plan for future production, confining their efforts to buscón-type work, working narrow extensions of ore bodies, and robbing pillars. The proceeds earned were divided immediately without thought of the future when metal prices might drop or the ore give out.[51] After the initial enthusiasm abated, operating efficiency fell. Many cooperatives were eventually abandoned or returned to private ownership.[52]

As might be expected, the operating efficiency of the cooperative miners was generally low. A survey made by the Armour Research Foundation of the Illinois Institute of Technology brought out the fact that the Cloete coal mines, under cooperative management, never did better than 2.5 tons per man-day; but when they were turned over to the Monterrey and Monclova steel companies for joint operation, improvements raised the mining yield to 4.0 tons per man-day.[53] Cooperative workings in the Palau district on the old Mexican Coal and Coke Company's Esperanza basin holdings came in for a trenchant critique:

. . . the operations of the Mexican Coal and Coke Company included a washery, 200 beehive coke ovens, and a battery of more modern coke ovens. . . . The property was taken over by a cooperative formed by the miners who had worked for the Company. . . . Thereafter, the operations followed a somewhat different pattern. The cooperative contented itself with working the coal blocks originally left in place by the Mexican Coal and Coke Company. The washery no longer exists. The newer coke ovens, shut down preceding the operating change, have been allowed to fall into disrepair, as have also the 200 beehive ovens. Perhaps 70 of the beehives, at all odds the most archaic equipment on the property, have been put into serviceable condition. Meanwhile, the great portion of the mine shaft and tunnels have been allowed to become flooded. With this accomplished, the miners are beginning to work on a new mine in the Sabinas basin, leaving an estimated 80 million metric tons of coal in the Esperanzas basin.[54]

Preparing workers for the responsibilities of management of cooperatives has been quite difficult. Totally lacking technical or administrative preparation, executives impeded the cooperatives at every step. Executive turnover was high because cooperative organization made decisive administration almost impossible, and the State constantly intervened. An oft-repeated demand in cooperative society petitions was to keep politics out of production.[55]

The cooperatives' value and function is not to be found in the field of profit. By keeping old mines alive, they kept a number of men employed at useful tasks and some discovered new veins and were profitable for a while. Cooperatives, despite drawbacks, still afforded the Mexican miners an opportunity to take over executive positions and to acquire administrative experience in the mining industry. And the movement built up a Mexican segment in an essentially foreign-owned industry. In doing that, however, the cooperatives undermined an ancient part of the Mexican socioeconomic scheme by which workers from a depleted mine returned to the land instead of applying for government subsidies.[56]

An essential weakness of the movement stems from its having lost sight of its primary goal: the opening and development of new or neglected fields. Instead, it fed on the carcasses of dying firms or those weak enough to be done to death by labor unions and government officials. By not opening new areas, the movement remained sterile.[57] The type of enterprises that were transformed into cooperatives made it impossible to improve the workers' economic and social status, and welfare work often was curtailed. Paying little taxes, they narrowed the base of taxation, throwing a greater burden on existing private enterprises, and they represented a fiscal burden to the government which constantly had to extend credits and grants. Most cooperatives had only a relatively short and indefinite potential life. It would have been better in the long run if the Mexican government had faced the problem of re-educating, retraining, or resettling the potentially unemployed miners when their source of livelihood fell below the marginal level. It had to be recognized that despite some successes the development of cooperatives *per se* was not the hoped for universal panacea.[58]

CHAPTER 21

Private Enterprise
and Government Policy

MEXICO'S attempt to Mexicanize mining included not only aid to cooperatives but a program for helping the individual gambusino or buscón. The government concentrated on aiding enterprises in which the workers were the entrepreneurs, apparently distrusting all sorts of capitalistic enterprises, even companies with a small capital—the so-called minería en pequeña. Large enterprises shied away from Mexican ventures, contending that labor costs and government intervention had robbed them of profit. Mounting wage and social welfare demands of the unions and government interference also shut out smaller enterprises.[1] While a few workers could find new veins and make superficial explorations, smaller concerns traditionally supplied the capital for the initial development. If the venture appeared good, they sold out to a larger company.[2]

Small Mexican entrepreneurs still remained an element second in importance only to the large foreign corporations. They sold ore and concentrates to the large enterprises for milling or smelting. As a group they produced a large volume of metal and were dependable taxpayers to federal, state, and municipal governments. These firms exploited not only silver, gold, lead, and zinc, but also manganese, mercury, and tin. Their precarious finances often led to bankruptcy. Some undertook fairly extensive operations, others could only scratch the surface. As the backbone of exploitation of the Sierra Madre and isolated regions, they merited government support.[3]

Complaints voiced by the small miners at conventions in 1936 and 1940 pointed up three problems: taxes, labor difficulties, and finances. They argued that the tax system was illogical; the imposition of both a high surface tax and obligatory workings was a duplicate impost; and that some sort of reconciliation was needed between the export tax on metals and the progressive feature of the production tax, which became effective not only when the actual market price of a metal rose but also when the peso's exchange rate declined. Against labor, they complained of the burdens of meeting minute requirements and keeping voluminous records which taxed their resources. Finally, they wanted a government mining bank to meet their peculiar finance needs. Minor complaints concerned transportation—particularly the need to build roads and to improve the service on the government-owned railway. Concerning smelters, they contended that they were dependent upon the large plants which controlled the market and punitive action by the government against those enterprises would affect small mining adversely. Throughout their meetings ran the thread of belief in the government's ability to give them decisive aid.[4]

The Mexican government would not face the fact that without medium and large-scale concerns willing to push new investments, the government itself would have to fill the gap. As with the colonial government, which declared the subsoil to be the patrimony of the king, the implications of participation in mining in terms of money, time, technical personnel, and a bureaucracy was a greater burden than the Mexican government was ready to assume. Not until the late 1930's did the government recognize the problem when it formed the Commission for Mining Development to perform some of these functions.

President Abelardo Rodríguez, Cárdenas' predecessor, started setting up the National Mineral Reserves. The first haphazard measures indicated the lack of a definite objective. A presidential *acuerdo* (resolution) on October 8, 1932, authorized two reserves of gold and silver ores in Oaxaca under Section I, Article 8 of the Mining Law.[5] This procedure was regularized on November 2, 1932 by another acuerdo authorizing the SEN to declare as national reserves all free land wherein the commercial exploitation of any one of 26 minerals was possible.[6] A stream of orders soon set up reserves throughout Mexico.[7] Article 123 of the Mining Law was amended on December 29, 1932 to empower the President to promulgate the bylaws necessary to the National Mineral Reserves and to set the rules for the exploitation of gold placers declared part of the reserves.[8] Throughout 1933 and 1934 many reserves were set up—mainly in the states of Oaxaca, Nayarit, and Mexico—thus avoiding the big mining states. An *Oficina de Exploraciones* (Exploration Office) was also established to explore, classify, and arrange for the exploitation of the reserves, but it accomplished nothing.

During this period, the government employed two methods of setting up reserves. One method declared claims, singly or in groups, simultaneously in caduca, free and incorporated into the reserves. The other outlined a block of territory and declared that all free land in that area or all free land containing specified minerals to be a part of the reserves.[9] Except for an acuerdo of August 15, 1933, placing all coastal lands in the national salt reserves, the minerals most usually named were gold, silver, and sodium nitrate.[10]

Osvaldo Gurría Urgell in his address in March, 1934, to the National

Convention of Engineers had stressed the need to utilize the reserves constructively.[11] But the program remained dormant until the Mining Law was amended again on August 31, 1934, to authorize the creation of reserves on the basis of either substances, deposits, or zones. It also abjured the SEN to get mineros en pequeño and cooperatives to exploit those reserves.[12] Bylaws, issued on March 19, 1935, provided that: (1) concessions be granted only to Mexicans or Mexican companies with the proper background and economic resources; (2) the grant be for a lot of 9 hectares; (3) it be for an indefinite time, subject to the minimum workings rules, and must be started within 30 days; and (4) the concessionaire must pay a royalty on the gross production—averaging about five per cent—to be fixed individually by inspectors.[13] On May 14, 1935, newly inaugurated President Cárdenas authorized the SEN to make contracts exclusively with cooperatives for the exploitation of the coastal salt reserves.[14] Noting that the reserves were set aside in order to aid certain classes of miners as well as for conservation, an important presidential acuerdo on August 18, 1936, empowered the SEN to make any contracts which in its judgment furthered that object. The next year, Cárdenas stated that he was quite satisfied with the progress of the program for getting Mexicans to exploit the reserves.[15]

During its first three years the Cárdenas administration set up reserves with great, though uneven, vigor. By the spring of 1936, 109 titles covering 35,554 hectares were caducated and placed in the reserves.[16] A series of decrees put much of the free coal- and iron-bearing lands under government control; in 1943, under Avila Camacho, all free bituminous and anthracite coal lands were incorporated.[17] In November, 1935, a decree incorporated placer deposits of all metals in the reserves. Later decrees added all deposits of radioactive substances and then free deposits of tin, alunite, and native sulphur. The SEN also incorporated all free gold and guano deposits into the reserves in December of that year. A lull then descended until after November, 1937, when some specified iron, coal, and manganese deposits were added. Blanket incorporation orders in 1938 covered phosphates, potassium salts, fluorite, tungsten, molybdenum, manganese, cromite, nickel, platinum, aluminum, magnesium, and antimony ores with cobalt and mercury being added in March, 1939, following the incorporation of all free gold bearing deposits in five western states.[18]

By this time the National Mineral Reserves were quite extensive, and the problem was to get them properly exploited. In fact, the SEN revoked 15 reserve zones out of the 45 set up between 1935 and 1940. On July 31, 1941, the reserves totaled 151,080 hectares or about 10 per cent of the area under mine titles.[19] After his inauguration, President Avila Camacho's policy was to release great amounts of land since the number of concessions granted had been so amazingly small.[20]

To speed up the granting of concessions, the regulations of March 19, 1935, and August 18, 1936, were set aside by a new series on April 4, 1939.[21] These new regulations divided concessions into cateo (testing) and exploitation concessions; the former was granted for 2 years and covered 9 hectares while the exploitation concession had no fixed area but required an investment of 200 pesos a year for each hectare and a minimum of 8 workers, and more for more land. It also required guarantee deposits, detailed plans, and a demonstration of financial ability. Obviously, the law designed this concession with the small mining company in mind. Unlike the previous policy, cooperatives were not given preference. Gold and tin placers were specifically reserved for individual workers, and except for those placers, the SEN was to fix a royalty of up to 6 per cent in addition to all taxes. If the concession lapsed for any reason, the physical improvements became the property of the nation. Governmental power over the National Reserves was affirmed by the Supreme Court on August 23, 1940, which ruled that concessions on the reserves were not subject to the Mining Law and could be issued under rules laid down by an administrative agency.[22]

Avila Camacho's administration issued a new series of regulations on December 23, 1941, which represented a compromise among the earlier acts.[23] They kept the form of the 1939 act while reviving the looseness of the previous laws. Concessions were renamed "Zone exploitation concessions" and "Pertenencia exploitation concessions." But the former title applied only to gold and tin placers; the latter title allowed the same terms as in the 1939 law. Actual terms of a concession were left to the discretion of the SEN. To insure that only individuals worked the placers, exploitation terms specified the use of only the hand tools indispensable "for each individual and his physical effort." The law made concessions of unlimited life, required that workings be brought to full scale within 2 years, and spelled out the method of granting concessions in painfully complete detail. Avila Camacho again liberalized the law in the spring of 1944 by allowing the SEN yet greater discretion in granting reserves concessions needing large investments.[24]

Of most importance was President Avila Camacho's revocation of a great number of reserve orders. He released all antimony deposits in the state of San Luis Potosí on January 27, 1940, explaining that putting mineral deposits in zones placed the exploiter of those deposits under greater handicaps than under the general Mining Law and, therefore, exploration had been discouraged.[25] On February 10th, 14 minerals were released *in toto* from the reserves with the explanation that since the size of the mineralized areas and their localization were unknown at the time of incorporation, prospecting and exploitation were discouraged. Avila Camacho declared again in 1941 that the reserves regulations raised impossible obstacles and hindered any development.[26]

During World War II Mexico completely relaxed its reserves policy. No new reserves were formed until August 22, 1945, when the SEN reincorporated all radioactive ores and elements. Shortly before, potassium salts and guano reserves were released to encourage the manufacture of fertilizer.[27]

Begun to aid small miners, the mineral reserves program never lived up to its initiators' expectations. Overly ambitious plans did not take into account the Mexicans' lack of financial and technical resources which hindered development of the reserves and led to eventual stagnation. Since Mexico lacked capital, and since modern mining needs large amounts of capital equipment to produce economically, the original hopes had little chance of fulfillment. Reserves never included silver, silver-lead, or copper ore which were being badly depleted. Instead, the program restricted exploitation of still abundant minerals so that the conservation effect of the plan was small. Only an intelligent and active implementation of the policy could have made the program a success. But such implementation required greater foresight, sharper planning, and more money than Mexico was willing or able to give. In effect, the reserves policy degenerated into a negative policy of denying certain lands to foreigners under the guise of "saving" them for Mexicans, who were totally unprepared to undertake their development. Mexico's attitude completely ignored the fact that a reserve should be available at an opportune moment and not merely an indication that an area may contain certain minerals in uncertain quantities. Unless the industrial capacity, skills, and knowledge necessary to exploit a given mineral become available, it will continue to remain "stuff" in the ground. A. Glyka wrote a succinct critique of the reserves philosophy as early as 1935:

> The very nature of the mining industry, which for so many years has shown itself susceptible to cycles of prosperity, demands that the reserves be converted into resources or available ore at the earliest possible moment so that the fullest possible advantage might be taken of the periods of prosperity.
>
> The only way in which the mineral reserves of a nation may be built up is by means of development work which reveals certain quantities of ore of a profitable nature, and unless such development work is carried on constantly, the reserves of the country commence to dwindle until no reserves exist. The only thing remaining is the unknown contained in vast tracts of land believed to contain metals in paying quantities.[28]

Several government aid programs did develop during the late 1930's to help small enterprises which had gotten under way themselves. In answer to the need for local beneficiation plants, the old idea of local smelters was abandoned in favor of small mills from which concentrates could be shipped to the large central smelters.[29] This new idea motivated the clause in the Mining Law amendments of August, 1934, requiring all new private mills and smelters to reserve 20 per cent of their capacity for the treatment of custom ores. A later amendment extended it to all mills. Small miners also needed aid in exploring new territory, cheap and efficient assay services, and advice and direction in setting up new mining units. To meet their needs, the SEN established an Exploration Department and a Laboratory Department.[30] In his New Year's Message for 1937, President Cárdenas promised to set up seven ore-treatment plants.[31] During that summer the SEN built two small but complete experimental and assaying laboratories in Michoacan, and the Exploration Department announced that it had constructed a 50-ton plant costing 70,000 pesos at Tlalpujahua, Michoacan, to serve that district and neighboring El Oro. It also projected a 100-ton plant at Guanajuato and a 50-ton plant at Huautla, Morelos, to aid local cooperatives.[32]

The Commission for Mining Development (CFM) shouldered the major burden of aiding small mining enterprises. Authorized in August, 1934, the CFM was not finally established until December 31, 1938.[33] The Commission's two major purposes were to provide an experimental laboratory to aid small companies which could not afford their own facilities and to operate a chain of small beneficiation plants. To finance this work the CFM was to derive resources from five sources: (1) government lands destined for investment in mining, (2) mineral reserve lands given to it by the SEN, (3) donations of funds by federal or local governments, (4) funds from the Federal Budget, and (5) profits from its own operations. President Cárdenas charged the Commission members in 1940 with the prime duty of setting up metallurgical plants for small miners in the four major mining districts of Mexico in order to free them from dependence on foreign-owned plants.[34] The CFM declared that it wished to give Mexicans a greater hand in the exploitation of their own resources, but it would supplement rather than supplant existing enterprises since there was room enough for all.[35] Granted a budget of 1,000,000 pesos, the government ceded to the Commission "the properties which the Federal Government has acquired for that object."[36]

Immediately the CFM started work on six projects. By June, 1940, it had received 1,583,333 pesos of which 70 per cent had gone into the metallurgical plant-building program. By starting ore-buying agencies, it attempted to take the place of the vanished private buyers who used to assemble independent lots of ore for sale to central smelters.[37] Twelve offices were opened, but the plan did not succeed, and the CFM closed them in 1943. It placed its losses at 64,929 pesos. A venture intended to aid coal mining cooperatives was partially successful. While the San Felipe mine cooperative kept the Torreón thermal electric plant supplied with fuel and showed small profits, the rising costs of transport, social benefits, and extraction cut the net return.[38] In 1944, the federal government bought over 85,600 hectares of coal land in Muzquiz and Sabinas, Coahuila, for the Commission to develop. All told, the Commission held the largest coal deposits in Mexico. By 1948 the CFM had leased these coal lands to the Compañía Carbonífera Unida de Palau, S.A. to test their profitability, and negotiations were being carried on with the Monterrey Iron and Steel Company to work another 3,000 hectares of coal land.[39]

A most important unit run by the CFM was the experimental plant at Tecamachalco in the Federal District. Built in 1934, at a cost close to 500,000 pesos, the government turned it over to the Commission in 1941. Its facilities were large enough to do extensive experiments and to even set up small pilot plants for flotation, mechanical concentration, amalgamation, cyanidation, magnetic concentration, and smelting. Tecamachalco not only gave advice to small miners but trained technical personnel and worked on problems for larger concerns. Its equipment, comparable with the finest in Mexico, was further improved by an SEN investment of 250,000 pesos.[40]

At Guanajuato, the CFM spent over 1,100,000 pesos building a 100-ton cyanide plant for 735,000 pesos, purchasing several old mines for 375,000 pesos, and drawing up plans for two more 100-ton mills. Low ore grades and the activities of buscones unsuited many of the mines for scientific exploitation, thus casting doubt on their ability to supply enough ore to keep the mill running. Even with a large investment there was no assurance that the plant would show a profit.[41] In Tlalpujahua, Michoacan, the CFM took over a 53-ton mill from a bankrupt cooperative as part of its plan to exploit mines in that district and in El Oro. While yielding only a small profit, its future appeared assured.[42] Three plants erected in Sonora failed because inadequate study led to overcapacity and the wrong beneficiation method for the ores of the district.[43] A 100-ton combination flotation-cyanide plant, near Ocotlán, Oaxaca—to aid the Taviche district—failed when the available ores turned out to be good only for cyanidation. The CFM rebuilt the entire mill which then proved too large for the district's production; a 1,500,000-peso exploration program failed to turn up any commercially exploitable ore bodies. Another plant projected at Mazatlán was abandoned when the terms demanded for a loan by the government agency, *Nacional Financiera*, were too high.[44]

Studying the reasons for its program's failures, the Commission concluded that five factors were necessary for success: (1) a dependable ore supply, (2) a study of the beneficiation method needed, (3) sufficient economic means, (4) secure water rights and assurances of supplies, and (5) adequate transportation. It also had the major problem of locating successful plants in socially or politically desirable areas. Because of previous mistakes, the CFM placed its operating loss from 1939 to 1945 at 5,287,295 pesos. In 1944, its yearly loss was 971,000 pesos; it received no royalties from any lands except those exploited by the San Felipe coal mine. Lax accounting methods instituted by the Commission's original executives and niggardly government grants made the economical erection of many plants impossible.[45]

In actuality the CFM's work in developing a broad nationally owned segment of the industry has been too much dependent upon government policy with regard to mineral reserves and mining cooperatives. Mexico is the home of some of the major private mining operations in the world. Hence, only drastic intervention or a very strong government policy akin to petroleum expropriation could affect the basic ownership pattern of the Mexican mineral economy. At present the mining cooperative, the gambusino, the buscón, and the unemployed miner do not constitute a cause for revolutionizing Mexican mining. The future of the CFM and the Mexican mineral reserves policy hinges on the discovery of enough ore and the availability of sufficient capital. In this way, small entrepreneurs can be attracted and given confidence to exercise the aggression, enterprise, and technical ability necessary to build a viable Mexican segment within the industry.

CHAPTER 22

The Mining Industry
in the Second World War

MEXICO was caught in a trough of the financial difficulties and trade disruptions of the early years of World War II. But the United States rearmament program soon brought on a boom in mining. Production and profits climbed, labor prospered, and the railroads staggered under the increased freight. Inflation struck as imports lagged far behind exports and an investment spree and industrial boom swept the country. Since the wartime prosperity depended upon the United States' need for raw materials, the last years of the war were apprehensive ones. When the war contracts tapered off, taxes, high wage scales, and strikes conspired to force production down. The war's end found Mexico with several hundred million dollars in gold and foreign exchange representing her favorable balance of payments. But labor unrest, inflation, and taxes gave Mexico uneasy feelings concerning postwar adjustments.

The outbreak of war found Mexico adjusting her economy to the petroleum expropriation, beset by labor problems and complaints about taxes, a fluctuating exchange rate, and a declining price for silver.[1] War in Europe dealt Mexican mining a hard blow in 1939. Although the United States bought 90 per cent of the country's output of silver, gold, and copper, the principal lead and zinc markets were in western Europe. Lead shipments in 1938 came to 23 per cent of production to the United Kingdom, 22 per cent to Belgium, 19 per cent to Germany, 10 per cent to France, and 6 per cent to the Netherlands. In the case of zinc, the percentages were 30 per cent to Belgium, 26 per cent to Germany, and 13 per cent to France. In late 1938, Peñoles reported shipping 5,000 tons of lead to Germany and Czechoslovakia in one month. Italy took about 2,000 tons of lead a month in 1939 and early 1940.[2]

By the late fall of 1939, the spectre of depression began to haunt Mexican mining. Britain's blockade cut off Mexican exports to the Axis powers, and the disruption of world shipping led to fewer shipments to the Allies as well. Government controlled markets hampered metal sales. Germany, the largest single purchaser of base metals, was lost as a market.

Britain and France, determined not to drive up prices through scare purchases, bought only what they needed during the "Sitzkrieg" days of 1939–40, feeling assured of supplies of British Empire and Mexican lead. An oversupply of Mexican lead broke the market, for stocks accumulated in warehouses and producers cut their work week or shut down entirely. In London the Lead Producers Association (including ASARCO's Mexican units), organized in 1938 to curtail lead production and improve prices, came to an abrupt end.[3] With the fall of France, in the summer of 1940, Mexican mining was in desperate straits.

The recession hit lead and zinc producers particularly hard. These metals continued to pile up in Mexican warehouses despite increased business with the United States and the British Empire. Chihuahua reported in 1939 the smallest ore output since 1935. By the fall of 1940, ASARCO, Peñoles, the San Francisco Mines of Mexico, and El Potosí had either shortened the work week, reduced wages, or cut production by 25 to 35 per cent.[4] This general depressed state of lead and zinc producers lasted until 1942. Gold, silver, and copper still sold well in the unimpaired United States market. Copper output actually increased, although congressional politics caused the price of silver to decline about ten cents an ounce.

With political stability, the peso now showed signs of strength and rose from six to five to the dollar which cut profits made on cheap exchange (although taxes fell also). Mining cooperatives, which needed the extra pesos to make their workings profitable, particularly felt the loss of the exchange premium.

Wages in mining did not decline during the economic setbacks of 1940 and 1941. Despite the difficult conditions, a strike still threatened ASARCO. ASARCO resisted, estimating the cost of the demanded wage increases and fringe benefits at some 14,000,000 pesos a year. The strike closed the Mexican Zinc Company and the Cia. Carbonífera de Sabinas from October, 1940, to February, 1941. Avila Camacho, newly inaugurated as President of Mexico, acted as arbitrator. His final decision was to cost ASARCO about 500,000 pesos a year.[5]

Of little immediate comfort to Mexican mining in late 1940, but portending well for the future, were President Roosevelt's re-election, which assured the continuance of the silver purchase program, and Manuel Avila Camacho's election as President on a platform pledging relaxation of Cárdenas' vigorous social program and nationalistic policies. For his inauguration Avila Camacho invited "various American officials and members of Congress in a position of influence with reference to the silver program."[6] His platform included a Second Six-Year Plan with an extensive section on mining, pledging that the new administration would extend all possible government assistance to mining, especially Mexican-owned companies. State aid would be advanced to intensify the exploitation of industrial metals and assist gambusinos and small-scale miners in explorations. It promised more government-sponsored metal-treatment plants as well as stricter regulation of mill and smelter charges (declared to be public utilities) and ore marketing. Exploitation of the National Mineral Reserves and placers were also to be encouraged with special privileges for mining cooperatives. It pledged to enforce the forced-work provisions and to draw up plans to compel exploitation of the low-grade ore in concessions.[7]

In his address to the opening of Congress on September 1, 1941, President Avila Camacho intimated that for the immediate future the peso's exchange rate would be stabilized. Miners were reassured by the news of the continuing cheap peso since it was a prime export industry.[8] Businessmen, however, morbidly declared that President Avila Camacho was continuing Cárdenas' attitude toward labor, and there was little improvement in labor-capital relations; production costs were still rising and the cost of living was very high. Mexico's international economic position would continue to deteriorate unless mining costs were lowered to allow Mexican metals to compete in the world market. They cited as evidence a contract by the Defense Metals Corporation of the United States to purchase 190,000 tons of Chilean copper and only 10,000 tons from Mexico. Steady work, they claimed, could only be obtained with reasonable salaries and reasonable profits.[9]

As early as January, 1941, the United States proposed that Americans alone be allowed to buy Mexican mining products. Mexican mine operators were unreceptive to this proposition despite the industry's precarious position because, they contended, the United States would be able to fix prices with the knowledge that all other offers would be rejected. Japanese buyers, for example, paid Mexican producers up to $96 for a flask of mercury while the United States paid only $70. Mexican miners wished to deal with the United States but at the going world price.[10] Finally, an 18-month agreement announced on July 15, 1941, between Mexico and the United States Federal Loan Agency, representing the Metals Reserve and Defense Supplies Corporation, provided that all antimony, arsenic, bismuth, cadmium, cobalt, copper, fluorides, lead, manganese, mercury, molybdenum, tin, tungsten, vanadium, zinc, and graphite, in any form, not consumed in Mexico or exported to other countries in the Western Hemisphere, would be sold to the United States at the current market price. President Avila Camacho then issued a decree implementing the agreement.[11]

Unfortunately, the July agreement was too vague and the immediate effects were disappointing. A correspondent described late 1941 as "a tough winter for mining in Mexico. Production has dropped sharply and exports are at a new low, with the United States almost the only buyer. . . . buying less in number and quantity of mining products than in the recent past."[12] He wrote this gloomy report despite the signing, on November 19, 1941, of a far-reaching agreement between the United States and Mexico aimed at settling a number of old disputes.[13] Following these rules, commissioners from both nations met, and on April 17, 1942, they announced an acceptable settlement of the agrarian and oil expropriation claims.[14] A reciprocal trade treaty, also authorized in November, 1941, was signed during the summer of 1942. It stabilized the Mexican peso with United States backing, by setting a fixed ratio to the dollar. The United States also agreed to purchase 6,000,000 ounces of silver a month from the Bank of Mexico under the pre-1938 conditions. Cut off from silver from the Eastern Hemisphere, and with its domestic production being sold to the Treasury at a high fixed price, the United States welcomed an assured supply for its domestic industrial silver market.[15]

Pearl Harbor led to the activation of Mexican-American cooperation. In January, 1942, the United States government gave Dr. Alan Bateman the task of negotiating a new agreement for the purchase of Mexican minerals. Looking back, Dr. Bateman has written that few men realized the extent to which the United States had become dependent upon foreign sources. Vast quantities of such a variety of minerals were needed that many whose supply seemed abundant in relation to demands during the Great Depression turned out woefully inadequate.[16] Bateman was assigned to negotiate an agreement whereby the hazards of the industry would be diminished, metal prices increased and stabilized, taxes and railroad rates frozen, and labor conditions adjusted to permit wartime expansion and postwar curtailment. The so-called Bateman-Suarez-Tellez Agreement committed the United States to buy at least $100,000,000 worth of Mexican metals at rather high fixed prices and to aid Mexico in obtaining vitally necessary machinery, manufactured goods, and raw materials. Purchases were to include at least 75,000 tons of copper, 250,000 tons of lead, and 200,000 tons of zinc. In response to the generous price, Mexico promised to stabilize its economy and cooperate to facilitate increased mine output. Both government and labor leaders assured the United States that they would take a liberal and cooperative attitude toward the application of labor laws and regulations.[17]

To facilitate the import of these metals, the United States in May, 1942, suspended duties on all imports controlled by government agencies. On December 23, 1942, the United States signed a reciprocal trade pact with Mexico which reduced the duty on lead metal and ores 50 per cent and provided for it to remain at that level until after the war when duty on both would be permanently lowered 20 per cent. This policy was quite successful. Mexico supplied the following percentages of United States imports in 1944: antimony, 66.8 per cent; cadmium, 96 per cent; copper, 5.8 per cent; lead, 54.2 per cent; zinc, 44.6 per cent; silver, 29 per cent; fluorspar, 68.7 per cent; and graphite, 66 per cent.[18]

War now stimulated mining activity. Operations which required little capital investment, equipment, and labor expanded the most. Investors favored operations with a short time lag between the start of exploitation and the appearance of profits. They eagerly sought mercury, antimony, manganese, fluorite, mica, and graphite and reopened old silver workings for the lead-zinc content.[19] ASARCO pushed work in Tepic State and the old Xichu and San Luis de la Paz sections of Guanajuato. The Eagle-Picher Mining and Smelting Company of Oklahoma erected a 700-ton concentrator at Taxco to work zinc ores. After 35 years, ASARCO finally opened an electrolytic zinc smelter at Corpus Christi, Texas, to treat Mexican zinc ores.[20] Many mining investments earned handsome profits. An unlimited market permitted capacity production cutting overhead costs per unit. The Public Mining Registry in 1944 topped all records for the registration of claims, concessions, and contracts. It inscribed 108 new mining and allied societies with a combined capital of 42,928,106 pesos—some 15,500,000 pesos more than in 1943.[21]

But the war-born boom had its share of difficulties. Machinery shortages were chronic; some mines started rehabilitation programs, but this phase soon passed. During the expansion of 1942–43, only high-priced secondhand machinery was available. Producers of precious metals suffered, particularly the silver-mining cooperatives. A few mines, notably copper producers, were able to obtain financial assistance and priority ratings from the United States government. Cananea Copper, for example, received a large loan from the Metals Reserve Corporation to develop an open-pit mine and build a flotation plant.[22]

The railroads proved incapable of meeting the new burden. When German submarines in the Caribbean Sea forced deliveries from Mexico to the United States by railroad, it appeared that they would collapse entirely, and mining supplied one-third of the railway's freight. A new ore pier at Tampico remained idle while stocks of ores piled up at railroad sidings due to the shortage of freight cars. There were fears that the fruits of the trade agreement could not be harvested if the railways could not make deliveries. Poor maintenance, coupled with a high accident rate, disabled a great number of irreplaceable locomotives. Lack of responsibility and discipline among the workers and administration amounted to a national scandal. Mexican railroads rented some 7,000 freight cars from American railroads, but the real shortage in 1943 was in engines, not in cars. A Mexican-American Railway Mission sent to help was hamstrung at every turn. By 1944 it had only begun to supervise the introduction of better operations, maintenance and rehabilitation practices, and the rebuilding of long stretches of the roadbeds. At best its wartime achievements prepared the way for a postwar rehabilitation.

Many mines reported shortages of fuel oil, gasoline and other supplies, and late deliveries. The Kildún mine in San Luis Potosí—employing 1,000 men, to cite only one example—twice narrowly averted closure with the timely delivery of long delayed supplies and fuel oil. A war-induced mining revival in the marginal Monterrey area was nipped by a combination of poor railway transportation and a shortage of gasoline and tires for trucks. On December 2, 1944, the Mexican government allowed the railroads a 15 to 20 per cent freight increase, effective January 1, 1945, which affected mine supplies but not minerals. Railroad transportation remained critical during the entire war.[23]

Trained and dependable mine labor also became scarce. At the beginning of the war the United States planned to recruit Mexican mineworkers to replace Americans serving in the Armed Forces, or who had left the mines for more pleasant and better paying jobs elsewhere. The Mexican government soon vetoed these plans, claiming that the employment of Mexicans in American mines would play havoc with the wage structure in Mexican mines and, by depriving them of labor, would reduce shipments of war materials to the United States. In the spring of 1944, 600 Mexican miners were sent north for a six-month period of intensive training in American methods.[24]

Mexico's declaration of war against Germany on May 28, 1942, brought partial peace to the labor scene. The failure to control inflation was a major cause of labor unrest. A number of strike threats and a few actual strikes marked the summer and fall of 1942. Most labor contracts ran out in late 1942. Since the high prices paid for minerals allowed wage increases, the strikes were quickly settled or averted.[25] A Mine Workers' Convention met in November, 1942, in an ugly mood. President Avila Camacho prevailed upon the leaders to recess the convention to allow the delegates to return to their locals; he assured them that he was personally considering their case and appealed to them to remain on the job. When the convention reconvened in December, Avila Camacho persuaded the union leaders to accept a raise of only 10 per cent instead of the 25 per cent they were demanding. He thus headed off a strike scheduled for the end of January, 1943. Miners were now among the highest paid of all Mexican workers. Most of them earned more than 5.76 pesos a day. Whereas only 20 per cent of mineworkers earned over 167 pesos a month in 1937–38, by 1942–43, 70 per cent earned that much and paid an income tax.[26]

Mining companies accepted these raises and averted strikes in 1943, a year remarkably free of labor controversy. Lic. Euqeiro Guerrero, President of the Federal Board of Conciliation and Arbitration, stated that during that year 768 formal notices of intention to strike had been filed with the Board but that only 5 strikes had gone into effect.[27] The government did its best to keep labor demands reasonable since the agreements with the United States had been based upon the understanding that labor troubles would be controlled to assure deliveries.[28] President Avila Camacho, on September 23, 1943, supplemented the national Minimum Wage Law of 1942 with a decree effective October 1st, granting all workers raises of from 5 to 50 per cent, depending upon their daily income. Mineworkers found the decree tempered for them by the provision that workers who had received pay increases in 1943 would benefit only to the extent of the difference. Most mining companies accepted the decree as a wartime measure; they could meet the new pay scale because of better business conditions. The government exempted some companies when they proved that compliance was economically impossible. Other companies fought the measure in the courts with varying success. An element in preserving labor peace was that 1943 was an "off year" in the prevalent biennial labor contracts. Also, the men had overtime work with extra pay.[29]

The year 1943 marked the pinnacle of Mexican mineral output during the war, an achievement undoubtedly based on the stability that pervaded the entire economy. One report stated:

> Currently, there is no threat of a strike anywhere in the industry, and many mines are now on a 24-hour, 7-day a week working schedule. Miners seem to be satisfied with pay hikes of 10 to 15 per cent, generally, which were granted recently. Some companies have provided cash liberally, to enable their employees to establish consumer-cooperative societies.[30]

Labor peace was shattered on April 3, 1944, when the miners' union notified the Board of Conciliation and Arbitration of its desire to strike on May 4th. It demanded wage increases of up to 50 per cent from 140 mining companies. The union based its demands on the cost of living which had risen 90 per cent from 1939 to mid-1944. To the union's contention that the companies could well afford the raise, the operators maintained that the money would have to come out of reserves since current profits were not sufficient to pay higher wages. In addition, it would disrupt the economy and make postwar operations impossible. Upon the urging of President Avila Camacho, the union postponed the strike to confer further with the employers. The strike leaders also wished to reopen discussion of a uniform industry-wide contract. When the conferences failed, between 50,000 and 60,000 workers struck against 105 mining companies on June 8, 1944. Threats of a suspension of lead deliveries caused some apprehension, but the United States government would not raise the price of lead. Many settlements were effected during the first month since the largest companies were eager to resume operations. Opposition of the employers collapsed and all major companies were back at work by the end of July, although another month elapsed before full production was achieved. Cananea Copper, closed from June 8th to July 13th, estimated its loss at over $166,000. Settlement terms varied from company to company with a general pattern of increases of from 10 to 12.5 per cent with some fringe benefits plus varying strike wage payments. Wage increases ranged from 25 to 75 centavos (5 to 15 cents, U.S.) a day; the uniform labor contract was abandoned.[31]

During the war Mexico undertook two indirect actions which affected mining. To meet a growing power shortage, it cracked down on the wholesale stealing of power by illegal taps. The result was more power for industry, more taxes collected on electric bills, and new investments for the expansion of power production. The government froze freight rates during most of the war to stabilize rising costs. When the railroads announced higher rates they exempted strategic metals and minerals, as well as coke destined for the mining-metallurgical industries.[32]

Mexico took advantage of the mining companies' better financial position to push through legislation which would have met more determined opposition in less opulent days. A decree of December 31, 1943, modified several articles in the Mining Law. It amended Article 18 to make titles granted before 1926 subject to the same forced-work provisions as the titles granted after that year.[33] This change affected an estimated 6,000 mining claims out of some 15,500. When the Mining Chamber of Mexico complained, the President delayed enforcement at first until February 11, 1947, and later for an additional year.[34] Another major change amended Article 19 to require all metal-treatment plants (instead of only those built after 1926) to apply for government concessions to bring these plants under direct supervision of the SEN. On August 1, 1944, the SEN gave the mining companies six months to obtain the franchises. The owners immediately protested the law as being retroactive. Peñoles received an *amparo* (injunction) from the courts against its enforcement as did other companies, including ASARCO and El Potosí mining. President Avila Camacho repealed the law on December 31, 1945.[35] On August 1, 1944, a presidential decree suspended the law of December 31, 1943, requiring metal-treatment plants to reserve 20 per cent of their capacity for custom ore. The decree cited a rise in idle mill capacity to justify the change.[36]

The tax burden of the Mexican miners changed very little in 1941; a cut in the excess profits tax was matched by an increase in the income tax.[37] The next year certain controls over mining enterprises were relaxed and some tax relief given. Mexico, on July 8, 1942, suspended taxes on returns from capital invested in mining during the war.[38] The Ministry of Finance (*Secretaría de Hacienda y Crédito Público*), in the spring of 1943, agreed to allow a long list of ores and minerals destined for the United States to be exported without a permit.[39] Answering protests by the Executive Committee of the Confederation of Industrial Chambers in the fall of 1943, the Ministry of Finance categorically stated that, despite rumors, mining taxes would not be raised. It explained that the tax return from mining was satisfactory and that increases were not contemplated in either the general tax rate or the export tax.[40] In fact, in

December, 1944, it drastically revised downward the onerous export tax on silver.

Ing. Jenaro González Reyna severely criticized the wartime tax burden in an address to the First National Mining Congress. Using a chart compiled by Alberto Terrones Benítez, he noted that of each 100 pesos' worth of metal extracted by the miners in 1935, the government took 24 pesos in taxes; in 1943 that proportion had risen to 33 pesos. Furthermore, of each 100 pesos in the Federal Budget almost 30 were supplied by mining.[41] While González Reyna's exposition may be criticized for oversimplification, the mineowners were unanimous in condemning the oppressive nature of the tax levy and its inhibiting effect upon the industry.

As the war progressed silver became increasingly scarce. Handy and Harman reported in July, 1942, that no newly mined silver would be available in the United States for industrial and art uses since Allied coinage and war use consumed the available output.[42] Silver rose in Mexico in 1942 from 34 to 60 cents an ounce, and buyers offered long-term contracts at the latter price. To prevent a silver boom as in 1919–20, the United States and Mexico agreed in the summer of 1942 on a pegged price of 44¾ cents per ounce which would bring an estimated $8,000,000 more a year into Mexico. A convention of cooperatives insisted that Mexico work for price parity—71.11 cents an ounce—with the United States silver producers who sold directly to the United States Treasury. They wished to take full advantage of a strong silver market which would make their marginal and submarginal workings profitable.[43]

Silver rose in price as a reflection of the general world inflation. With the curtailment of jewelry manufacture, the United States imported large amounts of Mexican silver jewelry. Silver consumption in making jewelry and household ornaments in Mexico jumped in 1943 from less than 3,000,000 ounces a year to 6,000,000 ounces. Also at this time the Mexican public began hoarding silver coins as a hedge against inflation. To restore confidence the government coined all the silver it could acquire— a policy which ran counter to interests of the silversmiths who made large profits on all they could produce and export. Mexico was caught in the dilemma of 1917–20: with the world market for silver booming, internal monetary demands interdicted its export. With the conclusion of the silver price agreement with the United States, Mexico on August 26, 1942 embargoed the export of silver coin and bullion to force their diversion into domestic monetary uses. The Bank of Mexico was to buy all industrial silver at 70.17 pesos per kilogram minus insurance, freight, and a 40-centavo commission. It suspended all silver taxes and replaced them with a 10.95-peso-per-kilogram "emergency impost"—an estimated increase of 65 per cent. Cooperatives were to receive a 5.79-peso rebate.[44] When silversmiths disguised bullion as crude silverware to circumvent the order, Mexico raised taxes on jewelry and licensed its export.

The silver shortage forced Mexico to issue 1-peso banknotes and bronze 20-centavo coins while silver coins disappeared from circulation. Mexico asked the United States in 1943 to suspend temporarily the Silver Purchase Agreement to enable her to restore some order. A presidential decree then empowered the Bank of Mexico to buy all new silver and coin enough to satisfy the increased demands.[45]

Mexico partly repealed the hated export, or Aforo, tax on December 30, 1944, to help the gold and silver miners.[46] As in all periods of rising costs, precious-metal producers suffered because they had to sell at fixed prices while the government attempted to increase its bullion stocks as an anti-inflation measure. The decree established a subsidy amounting to the original Aforo tax for gold and 3.18 pesos per kilogram of silver for mines producing ore whose value was at least 80 per cent gold or silver.[47] It indirectly aided the ailing cooperative mines. Miners still complained that the red tape involved in applying for the subsidy was worse than the original tax and that, for one reason or another, practically none of the promised subsidies had been paid.[48]

Early in 1945 it became apparent that there existed an acute world shortage of silver.[49] Mexican producers—particularly cooperatives—clamored for parity with American silver miners. Mexico still permitted the lucrative export of silverware despite war needs for silver, although at a reduced rate which amounted to less than 2,000,000 pesos in 1944. Bullion exports declined from about 2,000,000 kilograms a year to 325,000 by 1944 because of the government purchase program.

Since the amount of silver coined in two years came to less than a normal year's export, the Confederation of Chambers of Commerce concluded that the government held some 1,000,000 kilograms of silver in the national monetary stock and "evidently adopted this policy of devoting much silver to minting and building up the metallic monetary reserve of the white metal with the expectation that the price of silver will increase in the United States."[50] Mexico's hopes were realized on September 20, 1945, when the American government set the open market price of silver at 71.11 cents.[51] Silver pesos now passed their bullion point with their silver content being worth 1.33196 pesos. Mexico repealed the Monetary Law of July 25, 1931, and demonetized its silver coins. The Canadian Consul estimated the government made a $20,000,000 profit on its reserves.[52] Since the public had been hoarding silver coins and few were in daily use, there was no shortage of a circulating medium. An offer by the Bank of Mexico to pay a 20-per-cent premium on the face value of old coins returned for reminting met with little success.[53] Wartime regulations forbidding the export of silver eventually were repealed, but little went directly abroad. Silver continued to flow into the Bank of Mexico at the market price.[54]

Silver miners reaped only a small benefit from the new high prices.

Mexico abolished the silver subsidy of December, 1944, and re-established the tax rates set by the Law of 1935 which took 65 per cent of the increase—some 17 of the 26 cents.[55] Finance Minister Eduardo Suárez was reported to have said that the government was entitled to this share of the price rise because natural resources were part of the nation's patrimony.[56] Then, on January 1, 1946, some 40,000 workers struck against all enterprises producing silver and demanded a 40 per cent pay raise based on the better price of silver. Their action also affected most lead and zinc producers. Final settlements were not reached until March and averaged one peso a day retroactive to the beginning of the strike plus lost wages. Marginal mines suffered the most.[57]

Early in 1944 rising American stockpiles of base metals threatened the contracts between the United States and Mexico. In fact, the United States abolished bonus payments for some foreign minerals at the time Eduardo Suárez was negotiating an extension of Mexican contracts. Only lead seemed to have an assured future. Reports from Mexico stated that some 60,000 tons of minerals had accumulated in mine yards awaiting railroad transportation. Output during 1944 was 20 to 25 per cent lower than the record-breaking levels of 1943.[58] By the beginning of 1945 Mexico reacted strongly to peace rumors. With the collapse of Germany in April, 1945, mine operators began to fear for their future and even labor unions became less belligerent, settling their disputes amicably. Although the Metal Reserves Corporation raised the price of Mexican lead from 5.45 cents per pound to 5.85 cents, rising costs were a worry. By spring the United States was cancelling and curtailing contracts, and Mexican mine productivity dropped. By May, the Mexican Mining Association estimated that some 10,000 employees would have to be dismissed the next month unless the government extended large-scale aid, for the indirect subsidy allowed gold and silver producers was not large enough and would have to be increased.[59]

As 1945 progressed, American cutbacks bit deeply into Mexican production. In April the price of zinc declined 5 per cent. On September 1st, the United States withdrew subsidies to copper and lead producers. Estimated at 3 centavos a pound, its loss affected Cananea, El Boleo, and Nacozari, causing the copper producers to appeal in alarm to the Mexican government. Also, the United States restored the zinc tariff which had been lowered 50 per cent. On November 1st, the United States cancelled all its war contracts; zinc and copper sales fell some 80 per cent by the end of the year. The American Embassy reported the closing of marginal mines and rising unemployment.[60] Still, there were two bright spots: the demand for lead continued strong, and silver had experienced a sharp rise of 26 cents which brought its price to 71 cents an ounce. During the war Mexico accumulated gold and American exchange because imports had not been available to match her exports to the United States. Mexico had had an estimated $53,000,000 in gold and exchange on December 31, 1941. By the end of 1945 she held $376,000,000.[61]

Increased costs incurred during the war placed mining in a poor position relative to other segments of the Mexican economy. With the insatiable war market disappearing, mining—a heavily taxed industry without the benefit of government aids in marketing—suffered from inflated costs at home and fixed prices on sales abroad. It lost an estimated 10,000,000 pesos ($2,150,000) from the strike of the summer of 1944. In addition, since October, 1944, the cost of fuel had risen 52 per cent and wages 15 per cent. Although its output had been exempted from increased freight rates, the industry had to pay higher rates on supplies of machinery, coke, timber, cyanide, chemical products, and clay. One estimate was that between 1937 and 1945 the industry's costs had risen 148 per cent. Wages and salaries alone had increased some 40,000,000 pesos annually despite the fact that employment decreased from 40,000 men in 1937 to 31,000 in 1944–45.[62] Much of the rise in costs was due to Mexico's failure to control inflation despite attempts to check it by monetary means. A government agency called *Nacional Distribuidora y Reguladora* (National Distributing and Regulating Agency) offered groceries and prime necessity items at popular prices. With the help of the mining unions (often with company money) it opened stores in mining centers.[63] On the whole, these efforts were quite unavailing. Between 1939 and 1945 the cost of living in Mexico more than doubled.[64]

CHAPTER 23

The Changing Status of the Mining Industry

THE difficulties of the Mexican mining industry since the war have spawned numerous diagnoses, prognoses, and calls for radical changes. Decadence, depletion, lack of investment, and market diversification are terms used constantly.[1] To appreciate these terms, we must examine the drawbacks to expansion and the fears and complaints of the mine operators.

Throughout Latin America since 1945, a rash of mineral discoveries has been brought about by new exploration methods, the desire of American industrial interests to expand reserves, and encouragement by local governments. But in Mexico mineral output stagnated after 1943; in the case of precious metals, it declined tremendously. The only significant postwar discoveries have been the sulphur deposits of Tehuantepec and the El Carmen copper mine. Large companies have developed only prospects brought to their attention or older marginal mines. Exploring parties and expensive modern geophysical and geochemical methods have been little used. Efforts of the Mexican government have been small and not in keeping with its general interest and activities in fomenting other industrial developments. Government assistance to mining has been sporadic and usually aimed at remedying specific social and political problems. One result of neglect is the absence of a complete geological map of Mexico.[2]

As operators of "an industry depleting the nation's wealth for export and the benefit of foreign investors," miners find themselves the center of a public surveillance from which manufacturers are exempted. They are the focus of a widespread xenophobia. Ardent nationalists proclaim the small Mexican-owned companies as the nation's salvation and therefore deserving of special privileges. Popular ideologies regard mining as ripe for national control.[3] Complaints by the miners that their interests are neglected fall into the maelstrom of politics where votes and nationalism outweigh the need to protect and stimulate the industry.[4] Although not a totalitarian country, the influence of the Mexican government is paramount as far as mining is concerned.

Mexico was in an ideological transition at the end of the war. Politicians spoke as if the attitudes of the thirties still dominated the economic and political life; yet the war had transformed Mexico.[5] A new bourgeoisie worked with foreign capital and Mexican inflation-born credit to stimulate a tremendous expansion in industry, trade, and construction. Slogans of the Cárdenas era appeared shabby and faded in the midst of a capitalist boom.

Mexico's leaders faced a threefold task: (1) manipulating the potent political elements calling for more socialization and a strong antiforeign policy; (2) encouraging further activity by the aggressive bourgeoisie, many of whom were foreigners; and (3) raising the standard of living and maintaining economic growth.[6] Juggling these policies was no mean feat, for the bourgeoisie and foreigners complained of the taxes and socialistic policies in national developments[7] while the leftists complained of the low living scales and dependence upon foreign capital. Rampant inflation and peso devaluation accompanied Mexico's economic growth; hardship was widespread. Cárdenas' radicalism and land distribution policies ultimately slid into limbo, and private enterprise found a more congenial atmosphere. Mexico manipulated the economic structure as it deemed necessary, fostering public works and government corporations, granting special privileges for favored enterprises and exemptions for new business and foreign investments in desired industries.[8]

Despite the government's growing business-mindedness, the after-effects of Cárdenas' presidency hung over Mexican mining for years. Mine operators believed that a continued depressed outlook for the industry stemmed from unsympathetic government policies, and the low priority mining held in development policies contributed to this attitude. Only when prices rose tremendously, as during the Korean War, did mining do well. Not until the mid-1950's did the government recognize the precarious state of the industry.

During Miguel Alemán's campaign for the presidency in 1946, his published platform exhibited a moderate tone concerning mining, although as President he did little. He promised to (1) encourage prospecting; (2) work toward the maintenance of the price of silver to stimulate mining, induce new investments, and offset the decline in base metal workings; and (3) promote the export of refined metals. His platform promised to promote the social welfare of mineworkers, particularly those afflicted with lung ailments. Instead of tirades against "foreign monopolies" and "exploiters," it declared: "Government, mine owners and mine workers must all enthusiastically lend a hand in the development of our mining industry." It extended the usual pledges to augment the mineral reserves, protect small miners and prospectors and lower the prices of materials needed by the industry. Its promise to the cooperatives was hedged: ". . . to furnish technical and economic aid to miners' cooperatives, bearing in mind all other legitimate interests." A most important omission was a pledge to re-examine the mine tax structure.[9]

During the campaign Alemán organized a series of round-table conferences to acquaint himself with national problems. Mineowners candidly criticized the tax structure and transportation difficulties, asked for union responsibility and recognition of managerial rights, and took the government to task for permitting inflation to continue. They criticized the mining laws for demanding large investments and yet failing to extend sufficient guarantees for the owners' equity. They viewed as a particularly grave threat the order that all mines be under regular work regulations, and they feared interference by the Commission for Mining Development. Surprisingly, the exposition of the miner's union declared that whatever benefited the industry was good for the workers in the long run. They particularly criticized high operating costs owing to government interference and freight rates. Government regulations respecting the mineral reserves, they declared, raised production costs and reduced much ore to "non-ore" by making it economically unexploitable. Inflation, too, was berated. The union also requested production bonuses and a policy of forced reinvestment.[10]

Despite the friendlier attitudes of Presidents Miguel Alemán and Adolfo Ruíz Cortines, for a long time the mining industry did not receive its awaited aid. In fact, the National Institute for the Investigation of Mineral Resources, an official body set up in 1949,[11] recommended to presidential candidate Ruíz Cortines that he set up a semiofficial body to oversee the mining industry and give technological aid.[12] It proposed a plan to remedy all the ills and complaints of the industry and the unions—at the price of government controls. The plan was never carried out.

During the presidency of Ruíz Cortines, the government's attitude changed. Its influence practically eliminated strikes in the industry, and in 1953 it decreed the first law giving tax reductions to small mines and new enterprises. But the changes were rather insignificant, and on January 1, 1956, a completely rewritten mine tax law was issued. Although confining its reductions to new or small enterprises, it did permit special tax concessions to be negotiated at the discretion of the Ministry of Finance which changed little, but was evidence of a thaw. After the inauguration of President López Mateos in 1958, an unidentified "industry spokesman" told an *Engineering and Mining Journal* reporter that the government would have to rewrite the production and export tax laws in addition to extending other incentives before a favorable response could be elicited. A mining executive added the information that his company had a number of "pretty big projects in the drawer" waiting for tax reductions and incentives.[13] Future expansion depended on future policy.

While other industrial segments of Mexico's economy boomed, the relative output of metals declined. Frequently repeated, but now quite questionable, was the cliché that mining was the backbone of the economy. The general index of volume of industrial production climbed from 100 in 1945 to 130.1 in 1951, but the index for mining and metallurgy varied from 73.8 to 94.2. During those years the output of gold and silver never exceeded 85.8 per cent of 1945, and often it was under 75 per cent. Output of industrial metals in 1950 did reach 4.2 per cent over 1945 owing to high lead and zinc production. In all cases the indices of production for metals lagged behind the marks set by all other industries. A report by the International Bank notes that in a "factor cost" analysis, before the war "mining" contributed as much as 10 per cent of the value of the national product of Mexico. This portion fell off rapidly to 3 per cent in 1939–45, 2.6 per cent in 1946–50, and 2.5 per cent in 1951–54.[14] Still, mining yielded from 5 to 10 per cent of the nation's tax receipts.[15]

Mine products changed their position in Mexico's foreign trade pattern after 1945. While the value of agricultural exports increased 150 per cent between 1939 and 1950, mineral exports rose only 17 per cent.[16] Mining's portion of the value of Mexican exports—*excluding* gold and silver—fell from 36 per cent in 1938 to 28 per cent in 1948 and to 23 per cent in 1953, despite rising prices.[17] These shifts reflected the diversification of the Mexican economy which caused mining to lose its traditional predominance. Mining received little government aid while active programs were pursued to stimulate agricultural production and exports.

Increased foreign investments offset Mexico's need to export precious metals to settle her balance of payments. Instead, silver and gold were used to augment the monetary reserve and aid the policy of fighting inflation by issuing coins high in silver to encourage hoarding. This policy could not always be carried out. The Bank of Mexico noted in 1947:

> The unfavorable balance of trade was not compensated [in 1946] with invisible exports [foreign investments] as occurred in 1944 and 1945, but rather it was necessary to send abroad part of the accumulated reserves of [precious] metals and exchange.[18]

Still, precious metals figured less prominently as exports and became of greater importance in Mexico's internal monetary arrangements.

Postwar metal prices reflected the world-wide inflation and the continued high demand for metals. In spite of wide fluctuations in prices, short periods of oversupply, and several "crises," metal producers did not face the hardships and uncertainties of the pre-World War II years. Good prices tended to drive world output steadily upward and increase competition for the free markets.

Mexico's production of metals, however, cannot react directly to changes in world prices for its mineral economy is marked by great inflexibility. Economists working for the International Bank were of the opinion that Mexico's 1950 nonferrous and precious metal output—equal to the 1927–30 figures, except for zinc—was about as high as possible. They believed that the railroad block alone accounted for a diminution of between 5 and 10 per cent; the lack of electric power and investments were further limitations. Smelter capacity was not always adequate to meet sudden increases in low-grade ore shipments, and for several years after the war there was a coke shortage.[19] The power and centralization of the miners' union can drastically affect national output by paralyzing the entire mining economy in one stroke. For example, high prices in early 1946 coincided with an industry-wide strike and hence volume declined more than value.

Labor contracts run for two years, but a rise in prices or a fall in peso exchange can lead to immediate demands for wage adjustments.[20] Mexican law also affects production since the labor force cannot be reduced for any reason without severance payments—to which union contracts often add extra indemnities. Therefore, Mexican production tends to remain high even when markets weaken.[21] Finally, continued depletion adds its weight. Some old works have been reopened or expanded (Naica, Esmeraldas, Nuestra Señora) and some new discoveries made (El Carmen), but depletions outrun exploration. Unless new deposits are developed, nonferrous metal production will decline as has the output of precious metals.[22]

Mexican mining is caught in a vicious circle. Inflexibility in organization inevitably leads to a decline which makes the system yet more inflexible.

Postwar Markets
and Production Trends

MARKETS for Mexican minerals narrowed considerably with the end of the war. Orders for war industries ceased and normal world-wide industrial and trade relations were disrupted. Germany and Japan disappeared as consumers of raw materials; Western Europe depended on United States aid; Central European markets were behind the Iron Curtain; and Far Eastern markets were lost in civil wars and colonial revolts. Most nations suffered from exchange shortages and inflation, and metal markets operated under government control. But Mexico had an "ace in the hole," for the United States now emerged as her major customer for all export metals, and the American economy was functioning at a high level.

Mexico's readjustment was aided by the United States becoming a "have-not" nation in minerals. To maintain a fully employed economy the United States would now have to import metals formerly exported. Fabricators and consumers fought the high prices demanded by domestic metal producers. A new foreign economic policy was forged in struggles over tariffs and import quotas. For the American miner the days of laissez faire were over.[1] The question now was whether the government should support sagging prices and production by import quotas and stock-piling or indirectly by tariffs.[2] These new developments tied Mexico to the industrial tempo of the United States since that country bought the lion's share of her mineral exports. Mexico needed a diversity of markets, but currency blocs and "lines of empire" barred her metals from many European markets.[3]

Marketing problems weigh heavily upon Mexican mining since domestic industry absorbs only a small portion of the mines' output, and national economic policies cannot stimulate demand. After 1940, Mexico became largely dependent upon the United States metal market.[4] Variations in United States economic activity have immediate effects upon Mexican mining, and American import and tariff policy is of paramount importance in setting prices. And that policy is determined primarily by domestic politics, not by analyses of the international economic scene or considerations of foreign policy. In the case of silver, the United States policy made possible market manipulation by the Bank of Mexico. Mexican mining is at the mercy of forces which neither the Mexican government nor the producers can influence or counteract.

World copper production has shown huge postwar gains in output in response to high demand and prices. World output rose from some 2,500,000 to 3,000,000 tons between 1945 and 1952, while the price went from below 12 cents a pound to over 24 cents. Despite the traditional fear that a high copper price promotes the use of substitutes and permanently damages the copper market, the postwar expansion in consumption absorbed the price rise. But Mexico's copper output did not increase after World War II; in fact, it barely held its own. While the El Carmen mine in Chihuahua was a significant discovery, and there has been a greater output of by-product copper, these gains serve only to make up for the decline of El Boleo and Nacozari. General increases in production are attributable to the new Cananea low-grade ore plant.[5] In late 1949 the copper producers issued a plea for reductions in the production and export taxes claiming that while 0.7 per cent copper ore could be profitably worked in the United States, Nacozari had to close down because 2.7 per cent ore could not be exploited under existing conditions in Mexico.[6]

An economic analyst in Mexico has observed that copper prices during the last century "have had a negligible effect on tonnage production" and that an increase of only 200 to 300 metric tons a year could be expected in the near future.[7] An examination of the historical relation between discoveries and technological advances and Mexican production tends to bear out his claim. Prices and cost factors have been marginal to new ore strikes and new processes. This "stickiness" in Mexican copper production has been of great importance during the years of high postwar prices.[8]

A minor aid to Mexican copper was the suspension in April, 1947, of the American excise tax on the imported metal. It was reimposed for 10 months in 1950–51 and then suspended again.[9] Copper import policies are a bone of contention between copper fabricators and American companies with foreign mines, and domestic copper producers. As long as copper prices are high for a long period, the protectionist arguments of the domestic producers are not too successful.

After the war, lead and zinc underwent various turns of fortune. It became apparent that the United States now had a permanent production shortage of these metals at world prices. Prewar production and trade patterns now changed.[10] With prices well over prewar levels, world lead production rose some 40 per cent, but American output barely maintained 1945 levels. Before the war the United States had imported 6 per cent of its lead supply; postwar imports ran between 27 and 32 per cent, or well over 300,000 tons per year.[11] Mexico, consuming only about 5 per cent of her production, contributed large amounts.[12] Zinc production in the United States also just about managed to maintain wartime levels. However, the mines no longer could supply the smelters with sufficient ore. As a result, the United States began to import ores and concentrates. Mexico, with a smelter capacity well below mine output, in 1949, supplied 59 per cent of the United States' import of 241,000 tons of ores and concentrates.[13] American construction of zinc smelters since 1940, for reasons of international politics and locational economics, has been predicated on the importation of Mexican zinc concentrates.

Lead prices increased from the war-controlled 6.5 cents a pound in 1945 to an all-time high of 21.5 cents on January 1, 1949. Only the unavailability of greater supplies put a ceiling on industrial consumption and government stock-piling. To encourage lead imports, Congress suspended the lead tariff from June 20, 1948 to June 30, 1949.[14] Since then lead has sold at more moderate prices. Zinc prices paralleled lead, rising from a war-fixed price of 8.25 cents to an average of 12 to 13 cents in 1948–49. It maintained this level despite a growth in world production of almost 43 per cent between 1945 and 1950.

Rising lead and zinc prices stimulated Mexico's output. Older enterprises worked at capacity, many marginal enterprises appeared, deposits formerly abandoned or worked only on a small scale were reopened or expanded, and dumps were reworked. This expansion was not based on any major new discovery, and, as prices became more stable after 1952, production leveled off.[15]

After dropping sharply in 1946 due to strikes, lead and zinc production began to climb as prices rose. By 1949 zinc reached an average output of slightly less than 180,000 metric tons per year; lead averaged about 10 per cent higher. The industry adjusted wages upward some $7,500,000 in the summer of 1948 following devaluation of the peso. When business conditions in the United States turned downward in 1949, Mexico exerted pressure on the miners' union not to strike that year since the industry could not bear another pay raise.[16] When lead prices began to decline in early 1949, one estimate was that a 3.5-cent drop in the price of lead alone would occasion a loss of over $15,000,000 in foreign exchange income. The Mexican Mining Chamber claimed that by the spring of 1949 some 280,000,000 pesos ($40,000,000) had been lost by the decline in lead, zinc, and copper prices. Production still continued high during 1949. An absence of strikes, the devaluation of the peso (legally fixed in June, 1949, at 8.65 to the dollar from its old level of 4.85), and good prices for the precious metals in complex ores (due to the Bank of Mexico's policy of supporting silver) offset the price declines.[17] Furthermore, since Mexican labor laws made curtailing operations difficult only marginal operations shut down.

During the first half of 1950, zinc prices rose, while lead continued to fall. But Mexican production of both metals increased because of the nature of its complex ores. ASARCO's subsidiary, the Mexican Zinc Company, operating the only zinc smelter in Mexico, worked around the clock. Mexican lead producers complained about the dropping price, but their own output was a major cause of the decline. In May, ASARCO announced a 12 per cent cut in lead production.[18]

The outbreak of the Korean War in June, 1950, jarred metal prices. Lead and zinc quotations quickly shot up 50 per cent. The United States imposed controls on nonferrous metals on January 21, 1951, and set ceiling prices.

Following World War II, the importation of lead and zinc was governed by the 1942 United States–Mexican agreement, which had been extended to other countries by the "most-favored nation" clause. The zinc tariff was set at 40 per cent of the duties prescribed by the Tariff Act of 1930; the lead tariff was halved. These rates were reaffirmed in the Geneva Trade Conference of 1947. With war in Korea, Mexico abrogated her Reciprocal Trade Agreement with the United States as of January 1, 1951, in order to adjust her booming, inflation-ridden economy. Lead duties reverted to their full level although zinc duties remained the same because they were covered by other agreements. In late 1950, exports of lead to the United States jumped as American consumers bought before the higher duty became effective. Since prices continued to rise in the European market, there was no crisis. In any event, the United States reduced its duties on lead in June, 1951, to the 1942 level under the Torquay Tariff Agreements of 1950.[19]

Mexican lead and zinc properties expanded operations and marginal mines opened again. The "endemic difficulties"—poor transportation, high taxes, labor demands, and a shortage of coke—soon pressed the industry. Mexico took the opportunity of raising freight rates 10 per cent on July 16, 1950. By late 1950, the mining industry produced at full capacity, and continued to operate at that level through the first half of 1952.[20] The two years following the Korean War were excellent ones for Mexican lead and zinc producers as production and prices pushed on to new highs.

American price controls led to the establishment of two metal markets: an American market at controlled prices and a European market. In turn, the American market was a double one with certain metal producers accorded "premium prices." Mexican lead, for example, sold at 18.5 cents, a premium of 1.5 cents over the fixed price. Government-controlled London prices stood some 5 cents a pound higher; the free European price was still higher. As a result, Mexican lead and zinc left Gulf ports for Europe at prices of 22 and 31 cents respectively.[21] It was reported that ASARCO, heading a "lead cartel," was holding lead shipments back to maintain the European price, and the Chamber of Mines "announced that lead prices would be fixed by a board of companies, mines and government officials. . . ."[22] American imports fell some 60 per cent.

War prices induced metal production to increase throughout the world. By December, 1951, metal markets became uneasy because of the pressure of excessive inventories, money rates, and declining American imports.[23] Mexican prices broke in January, 1952. Lead fell to the United States ceiling price that month, and zinc followed in April. On February 12, 1952, the United States Congress permitted lead and zinc to enter duty free until prices fell below 18 cents for a calendar month. Large amounts of Mexican lead and zinc were imported duty free, and these metals were even withdrawn from bonded customs warehouses. The suspension was lifted on June 26, 1952, for lead, and on July 24, 1952, for zinc. Hundreds of thousands of tons of duty-free lead had entered the United States—about 100,000 tons from Mexico alone. An essentially parallel development took place in zinc.[24] For the next 18 months prices hovered just below 18 cents, giving domestic producers tariff protection.

ASARCO, Fresnillo, and Peñoles maintained high production levels until late 1952 but were pessimistic about the future because of higher wages, labor regulations, a 20 per cent raise in the railroad rates, and Mexico's unchanging attitude toward taxes.[25] In time, lead production fell off, never to reach the uncommon high of 1951–52. Zinc, however, has steadily gone on to new highs.

Mexico was still left with one nagging problem: the extent to which zinc and lead producers have become dependent upon the United States since 1942 and the importance of that market to maintaining its balance of trade. Changes in American tariffs affected 70 per cent of Mexico's mine output. In 1954 only 76 per cent of Mexico's mineral exports went to the United States compared with 85 per cent the preceding year. This shift, attributed to a tariff scare in 1953, could not be called more than a straw in the wind.[26]

After 1940 silver, surpassed by lead and zinc, lost its position as Mexico's major mine product and declined in value from 25 to 20 per cent of the total mineral output. However, its problems are still given a high priority. Silver mining is of great importance in several localities, serving as a monetary reserve and a source of dollars for the Bank of Mexico, and yielding important revenues. In any event, the International Bank characterized the role of precious metals in Mexico's future as a by-product, no longer a prime product.[27]

Several interacting factors have characterized postwar silver marketing: (1) the United States Treasury purchases of all newly mined American silver at premium prices effectively keeps it off the market; (2) with the continuing absence of American silver, the world demand presses close upon a limited supply; (3) industrial and art uses of silver have exceeded all expectations; (4) while there has been a general flight from silver coinage, several nations coined enough silver to make up the loss of the other governments; and (5) with the growing demand, Mexico's silver supply determines the open market price level.[28] Discovering that it held the balance of power in the world silver market, Mexico stopped passively supplying American industrial demand and began to manipulate the open market price and to keep supplies thin.[29] Advantages have accrued to the Mexican economy, the Treasury, and silver miners—both natives and foreigners.

Mexican mining prospered for only a short time following the price rise of 1945 as higher taxes and wages nullified most of the gains. On August 1, 1946, the Silver Bloc in the United States Congress forced an upward revision of the price for newly mined American silver to 90.5 cents an ounce.[30] President Avila Camacho immediately proposed splitting the 21-cent increase equally between labor, management, and the government. The miners' union approved the plan, and the companies—perhaps still smarting from a strike in January and February, 1946—quickly settled for pay raises dependent upon the silver content of the ore. Raises ranged from 1.60 pesos a day at Peñoles to 3.50 pesos at the Real del Monte company. Mexican silver on the industrial market rose in price to 86 cents as a reflection of general business conditions. Cooperatives benefited tremendously.[31]

In the spring of 1947, the price of silver fell sharply, going to 59¾ cents in June, 1947. Real del Monte protested it could no longer pay the wage raise based on the President's "three-way split" formula.[32] Mexico decided to support the market by coining 40 millions in 1- and 5-peso pieces to fight inflation by encouraging hoarding. One-peso pieces had a higher silver content than the 5-peso coins. The Bank of Mexico then set a price of 70 cents (U.S.) for all newly mined Mexican silver.[33] But, when Mexico devalued the peso during the summer of 1948, the bullion points of the 1- and 5-peso pieces became 64 and 83 cents respectively and the 1-peso coins disappeared.[34] An increase in mid-1948 of the output of 5-peso coins by 50 per cent as a postdevaluation anti-inflation measure removed virtually all Mexican silver from the world market.[35]

As a bolster to her currency, to increase government revenues, and to offset the effects of devaluation, Mexico embarked upon a policy of influencing the price level of the silver market. During 1948 the Bank of Mexico bought some 28,400,000 ounces of silver—about one-half of the year's production—and on October 21, 1948, all silver exports were made subject to the Bank of Mexico.[36] In January, 1949, the bank announced its intention to absorb all of Mexico's silver for coinage. The success of this policy was soon evident. During the entire year of 1949, silver fluctuated 3.25 cents—the smallest change recorded since the days of the United States Treasury pegging in the 1930's and the OPA.[37]

The Bank of Mexico then sought ways to stabilize the price of silver at between 70 and 75 cents.[38] One method was a new "coin" of one ounce of silver 0.925 pure for the Chinese trade and for jewelers to use as a convenient source of small amounts of sterling silver.[39] Most important was the coinage of pesos and coins for foreign governments. In 1949 alone, some 31,000,000 ounces in coin were sold to Nationalist China and 14,000,000 more to Saudi Arabia.[40] During the next two years between 600,000 and 700,000 coins a day were being struck. Mexican silver disappeared from the open market. Lic. Carlos Novoa, Director General of the Bank, affirmed at the end of 1950 that Mexico had the right to pursue policies which would "stabilize"—not raise—the price of silver, since, as the world's largest producer, she was entitled to protect her interests. Bank officials denied hoarding and asserted that its stock of silver was only sufficient to cover minting demands. Lic. Carlos Sánchez Mejorada, President of the Mining Chamber, "praised the Bank for its recent stand on silver, and expressed the gratitude of the mining industry for the Bank's silver management policy," which had raised the price from the former "stable" level of 73 cents to over 80 cents in 1950.[41]

The strength of the Bank of Mexico's silver policy can be observed in the sale of Cuba's silver reserve. In July, 1950, the Cuban government decided to sell 80,000,000 silver pesos—some 62,000,000 fine ounces. Cuba and Mexico cooperated in timing the offering to such good advantage that not only was the market maintained, but it rose from 72.75 cents in May to 80 cents in October—with many accompanying denunciations of the Bank of Mexico.[42] The Rotterdamsche Bank defended Mexico with the remark that it had removed much of the speculation from the silver market and that the price fluctuation during the Korean War was considerably smaller than in other metals.[43]

During the following years the Bank of Mexico continued to absorb virtually all of Mexico's output. The open market price for silver reached 90.16 cents between February and June, 1951—a record unequalled since 1919—which was about as high as it could go without the United States Treasury selling from its Free Silver Fund stocks. Mexican strategy was to withhold offerings by the bank which would leave a gap in the supply-demand balance of the market. To attract silver to the New York market the price went up to equal the United States Treasury purchase price.[44]

Late in 1951, Mexico struck 1,000,000 5-peso coins containing 72 per cent silver (about 20 grams) and worth 56.61 cents (U.S.), each with silver at 88 cents. Since the value of the peso was only 11.58 cents (U.S.), the coins had a cash value of 57.90 cents, a very small margin in the event of a rise in the price of silver and most encouraging for hoarding. With the devaluation of the peso in 1954, these coins disappeared from circulation.[45]

Silver's postwar behavior, as during the 1930's, was the product of government policy with Mexico now joining the United States in price manipulation. Attempts by American administrative officials to have the Silver Purchase Act repealed were unavailing.[46] Since one object of subsidiary coinage is to make a seigniorage profit, the rising price of silver drove governments to use cheaper metals. Hence, despite Mexico's success in selling coinage silver, there was a flight from silver to cupronickel coinage in many traditional quarters including the United Kingdom, India, and Pakistan. Circulation of silver coin increased between 1939 and 1947, due to inflation and prosperity, but it was based on expanded use by the United States, Mexico, Saudi Arabia, West Germany, and, for a while, the British Commonwealth. India, however, withdrew 256,000,000 ounces from circulation to offset the greater American use of 454,000,000 ounces. When the United States insisted that Lend-Lease Act silver be repaid in silver metal, the United Kingdom and India began to retire their coinage to recover the silver content which nullified the expanded British use of 88,000,000 ounces between 1939 and 1947.[47] On the other hand, the increasing demand in industry and the arts kept consumption high and even led to the comment that with silver's demonetization in so many places it had become "a common commodity."[48]

Burton Crane of the *New York Times* succinctly analyzed Mexico's policy in a report on Saudi Arabian coinage.[49] He noted that the new Saudi Arabian coins were already being melted down by private speculators because the coins contained so much silver that even when issued, they were only a hairsbreadth under the bullion point. Ironically, it was the Saudi Arabian coinage that exhausted Mexico's silver reserve and forced the Bank of Mexico to withdraw from the silver market, thus driving up the price of silver and pushing the Saudi Arabian coins over the bullion point. Crane's description of Mexican policy was quite apt:

> Mexico for years has made a practice of minting coins for hoarders. It has done this by putting into each coin just enough silver to match the purchasing power of the corresponding paper note. Then, when the paper money depreciated, the silver coins went into holes in the ground. Mexico figured this was as good a way to sell silver as any other.[50]

And the portion of silver which finds its way from the melting pot back to market is usually too small to break a healthy market.

Mexico's silver policy must be recognized as successful and necessary. Open to condemnation from the theoretical viewpoint of free-market economics, its policy is justified by social and political necessities as well as by economic realities. In many ways, the supply of silver is uncontrollable; it is produced as by-product silver, or in communities whose existence depends on the continued production of silver, or by the melting of old coins and plate. Still, the postwar supply is smaller than the prewar output. American silver policy—which Mexico applauds, but certainly did not initiate—removes a large fraction of the world's silver from the market; Mexico's exercise of control is only marginal. Growing postwar industrial demand further firms the market. Mexican government revenues and the prosperity of a large segment of her mining industry and its workers depend upon a high price for silver. In fact, Mexico has made the sale of silver coins to her own people a part of her anti-inflation program. Also, it should be remembered that, unlike the American program, Mexico's support is flexible and takes much of the speculation out of the silver market. Her support of the market during the demonetization programs of Cuba, Spain, and Japan maintained an orderly market. Finally, Mexico's aggressive campaign to encourage the use of silver coinage—and her own example—is an important factor in raising the price. Since much of the world's commerce and production already exists under the umbrella of protectionism, Mexico feels completely justified in her course of action in regard to silver. The very success of the government's policy justifies its pursuit, for only on the basis of a high and relatively stable price for silver could the metal be used for coins and as an anti-inflation measure. Perhaps the most insistent problem is the continued cry of the silver buyers and fabricators against "market manipulation."[51] But given political and economic realities, and present monetary policy, their cry will continue to be heard only in the wilderness.

Although never counted as a gold producing country, Mexico's gold production is important to its domestic economy.[52] In 1940 and 1941, its gold output had a higher value than silver, which was selling in a depressed market. After the conclusion of a silver purchase agreement with the United States in 1942, gold's relative importance declined appreciably. Since 1949, because of the devaluation of the peso, gold production has matched prewar values of over 100,000,000 pesos per year, reaching 171,000,000 pesos in 1955.

After the decline of the famous Golden Mile of Mexico in the 1920's, the increase of by-product gold from the complex ore mines using the flotation process sustained the gold output. With the continued decline of the precious metals mines, Mexican gold production has tended to become a function of complex-ore production. The general economic principle governing gold mining is for output to rise during depressions—with a fixed price for gold, profitability increases with the fall in the price level—and to fall during prosperity. But a study by the International Monetary Fund indicated that there was no identifiable relationship between production and profitability in Mexico because of the proportion of by-product gold.[53]

Mexico's output of gold fell below 20,000 kilograms in 1943, and it has not exceeded 16,000 kilograms since then. Ofttimes it is around 12,000 kilograms or less. In order to encourage the mining of gold as well as silver during the war, President Avila Camacho decreed a subsidy for high grade gold and silver ores, but this subsidy failed to increase the output of gold.[54]

Gold's monetary importance provided Mexico with a police problem. Anxious to preserve its gold for its monetary reserves and to meet its international balance of payments, Mexico has had to face the problem of gold being smuggled out of the country for sale abroad at premium prices. Gold prices in Europe and the Orient have been abnormally high because of the demand for the yellow metal as a hedge against unsettled political conditions. With black-market prices at times more than double the legal price, gold smuggling offered high returns. In the summer of 1946, the Mexican government raised the official purchase price of gold to discourage smuggling, but without notable success.[55] Actually, the Mexican government itself was deriving benefits from the gold situation. Although the sale and export of gold bullion was prohibited, the Bank of Mexico sold 50-peso gold coins at $39.53 an ounce. At the behest of the International Monetary Fund, this practice, "which afforded considerable profit," was suspended on June 25, 1947.[56] The Bank of Mexico justified its action on the grounds that gold coin sales to the public tended to stop speculators who were smuggling out gold. As during past decades, the 1940's and 1950's saw a series of government orders designed to channel gold into the Treasury, control exports, and discourage smuggling. The very number of these orders attests to their lack of success.[57]

CHAPTER **25**

Government Policy
and Mining Problems

IN 1951–52 the International Bank for Reconstruction and Development
subsidized a thorough study of the Mexican economy by a joint committee
of Mexican and American economists.[1] These economists pointed out
that government policy was the key to the economic position of mining
and, obliquely, justified the critical bills of particulars put forth by the
miners and their organizations at congresses and meetings. They observed that the government's prime economic objective was to indus-
trialize Mexico and expand agricultural production. To secure immediate
returns, Mexico had been taking advantage of the reserves and surplus
capacity in older segments of the economy, such as railroads, by deliberately overworking them and neglecting their maintenance—a policy of
"milking" the economy or "converting capital equipment into current income to be used for other purposes." Mexico subjected mining to similar
pressures. To stimulate high immediate returns from mining which would
"not be limited by inadequate public facilities [i.e., railroads and power
lines] . . . [the exploitation of] existing ore reserves in developed mining
areas enabled production to rise with only small expenditures."[2] The
bank's report charged the Mexican government with neglecting the
nation's ore reserves, as well as its transportation and power networks.[3]
While it is doubtful that these developments were conscious objectives of
Mexican public policy, they were consequences of that policy. In the
words of the bank's investigators:

> Whatever the aim of official policy, its chief effect has been to discourage
> new investment in the industry. The negative results of this policy are
> now apparent in the creeping stagnation overtaking the Mexican mining
> industry. The tax system and inadequate transportation difficulties, as well
> as lack of power facilities in some areas, have kept investments at low
> levels. As known high-grade ore reserves are depleted, the effects of this
> state of affairs upon production are becoming apparent.[4]

The government's attitude manifested itself in a number of ways. In framing programs to meet the industry's problems, there were many elaborations of the difficulties of the smaller enterprises. Apparently it is considered impolitic to point out in public that larger enterprises have difficulties too, and their output constitutes the bulk of Mexico's production. A study by the Economic Committee for Latin America of the United Nations estimates that from 80 to 90 per cent of Mexican mineworkers are employed by large or medium-scale enterprises. Another estimate placed only 20,000 workers—about 25 per cent of the mining labor force—in the employ of 800 smaller companies, 98 per cent of which were Mexican owned.[5] In contrast, the lion's share of the value of Mexico's mine output and the jobs in the industry comes from less than a dozen enterprises. The *Grandes Compañías* (Large Companies) are characterized by large capital investments, ownership of the largest deposits of industrial and precious metals in the best districts; ownership of extensive reserve areas and large mills; and the domination of the economic life of their districts. Small mining can be divided into four types: *Pequeñas Compañías* (Small Companies) which work on a small scale, may have a mill, and sell ore or concentrates to the large companies. In toto, they provide a significant portion of Mexico's output and are the backbone of the industry in the Sierra Madre and isolated regions. In addition to industrial and precious metals, they also produce minor metals such as manganese, mercury, and antimony. *Pequeños Mineros* (Small Miners) is a term used to describe unorganized groups of miners working together on their own account. Found in great numbers, they struggle along, scratching the surface without the resources to develop their discoveries. They sell their output to larger companies, particularly to smelters. These enterprises are easily wiped out, and once closed are gone for good. Gambusinos are single men, out on their own, looking for anything their labor might turn into cash. Many of them are old miners who cannot get work or who are ill, often with respiratory diseases. Their workings are small, often gold or tin placers. They are considered nuisances in many districts because they steal into mines looking for ore pips or to pick over old workings. They are often cheated by ore buyers. Mining cooperatives are the fourth type of small enterprise. Taking over older, depleted workings, they generally achieve a high production and good dividends for a period. But for many, a lack of technical direction and discipline leads to early failure.[6]

The plight of the pequeñas compañías is of most interest to the Mexican nation since most are national companies. In the National Mining Congress of 1948 a great number of papers were addressed to their major problems: taxes, labor difficulties, and finances.[7] These enterprises suffer from shortcomings inherent in their size; they lack the proper equipment for exploring and hence planning is difficult. Their power machinery is inadequate—usually secondhand. Owing to their lack of capital and equipment, the length of time allowed them for exploratory concessions is not sufficient for the development of their prospects to the point of meeting the "regular work" laws. The various government reports that are required tax their small administrative overhead. They must have government help from technical offices in order to assay their ores and give advice on beneficiation. Taxes take a large part of their income. One group of small miners in 1948 claimed that of the gross value of their ore, 37.06 per cent went for taxes, 25.56 per cent went for freight and treatment, leaving 37.38 per cent to cover production costs. They claimed the highest rate of bankruptcies of any industry in Mexico.[8] (An estimate for an "average base metal mine" in *Mining Engineering* in 1954 placed the figures at 37 per cent for taxes, 20 per cent for freight and treatment, 41 per cent for operating costs, and 2 per cent net profit.)[9] Enforcing the labor laws with their numerous social and fringe benefits, as well as the burdens imposed by the labor contracts, was more than these enterprises could bear. Consequently full compliance with the labor laws was not expected of them.

As a factor in the mining economy, the small companies represented, above all else, a national stake in the mining industry. Yet, despite many assurances of government favor, it was the less important pequeños mineros and the cooperatives who received government attention. Perhaps a lingering socialist feeling concerning "capitalistic enterprises" was more powerful than nationalism.

Mine operators of all types vigorously attacked government attitudes which they believed contributed to the poor status of mining, particularly the mining law and taxes. Changes in the Mining Law enacted following World War II were few. Until the 1960's Mexico used the Mining Law of 1930 with the revisions of 1934 and 1943.[10] However, these revisions did not alleviate the mineowners' frequently reiterated complaints, particularly those concerning the high annual investments required to satisfy the law's regular work provisions.[11] The trend of the revisions, in fact, was toward stiffening the conditions under which mineowners might hold their concessions.

As already noted in Chapter 22, the 1943 requirement that all beneficiation plants secure new concession papers, to place them under the provisions of the current mine law, was rescinded on December 31, 1945. However, while new papers were not necessary, these plants still were to operate under the provisions of the current mining law rather than the one under which the concession was issued. Cries of "*ex post facto,*" "retroactive ruling," and even "bad faith" were of no avail. Owners had to comply with new directives even if they were in contravention of the law in force when the original grant was made.[12] In the matter of forced workings the government took a similar stand, insisting (under the reforms of 1943) that all mining concessions would be subject to regular workings provisions even if they predated the 1926 law which first required them. At the end of 1947 the period of grace ended; reregistry of the concession in order to secure new papers was not demanded.[13]

Mexico's Supreme Court backed the new policy, upholding in 1947 the cancellation of two concessions despite pleas that market conditions made workings unprofitable. When several mining companies filed for an amparo (injunction) against the new regular work regulations, the Court ruled against them.[14] Meanwhile, on October 15, 1946, the Ministry of the National Economy (SEN) amended the bylaws of the Mining Law to require all companies to file a statement of their previous year's workings and investments 60 days after the anniversary of their concession. Excess investments during one year could not be carried over as a credit to the next year. However, the claims held by one company could be lumped together if the investment in any given year, in one or more claims, was large enough to cover the total required for all claims.[15] An attempt in 1951 to reform the regular work provisions, by expressing the work required not in investment terms but in actual drilling and excavation norms in relation to the type of deposit, came to naught despite the SEN's admission that the current rules "have not given the results in practice which were hoped for. . . ." Basing its opinion on 21 years' experience, the Ministry admitted the law's "notorious contradictions" and the "disagreements," as well as the "manifest illegality" of some sections of the bylaws. It further condemned the old law because despite its provisions "the majority of mining claims are not worked as was desired," and the data accumulated were "sterile, and mostly false."[16]

Government control of foreign investments is also of great importance to the mining industry. During the war, the inflow of foreign capital led to fears that Mexicans would be frozen out of the new enterprises, and nationalist elements wished to assure the reinvestment of a significant portion of profits made in Mexico. Therefore, in June, 1944, all investments or purchases of property by foreigners were made subject to permits granted only if the foreigners involved were permanent residents, or if a majority of the stockholders were Mexican citizens. A presidential decree of June 23, 1947, required foreigners to obtain a permit before investing any capital in Mexico, and limited foreign participation to 49 per cent ownership of any Mexican corporation, unless special permission were given to own more. An Interdepartmental Commission to Coordinate Control of Foreign Investment set up the next month began to undercut the law at once, declaring publicly that 51 per cent Mexican ownership is not necessarily required since the Ministry of Foreign Relations could waive that requirement and fix another proportion. The Mexican government, well aware of the prevalence of nationalistic prejudices, was quite willing to be lenient in issuing permits and even winked at the use of Mexican citizens as dummy stockholders.[17]

Mine operators contended that their worst problem was the tax situation which discouraged investment by making Mexican mines poor risks in ordinary circumstances. They asked for fewer and lower levies to permit them to produce at lower costs. Stagnation was universally blamed on the tax rate. One study pointed out that among the leading lead producing nations, Mexico ranked fourth in operating costs before taxes, and seventh afterward.[18] R. A. Beals, writing in *Mining Engineering,* has detailed this figure in a study of lead-zinc mines operating under American and Mexican conditions.[19]

TABLE 9

COMPARISON OF COSTS IN OPERATING A LEAD-ZINC MINE IN THE UNITED STATES AND MEXICO

(*In U.S. Dollars*)

(*Hypothetical: Based on a Survey of Tax Schedules and Company Reports*)

Item	United States	Mexico
Gross Value.....................................	$800,000	$800,000
Treatment.......................................	200,000	200,000
Production and Export Tax[1]...................	none	280,000
Net Smelter Value.............................	600,000	320,000
Mining Cost[2]..................................	500,000	300,000
Operating Profit...............................	100,000	20,000
Depletion......................................	50,000	none
Net Taxable Income............................	50,000	20,000
Tax (approximate).............................	25,000	10,000
Net Income....................................	25,000	10,000
Dividend Tax..................................	none	1,500
Net Cash Gain (Net Income plus Depletion)....	75,000	8,500
Government Cash Gain..........................	25,000	298,000
Ratio: Company to Government Gain.............	1:0.33	1:35
Summary:		
Net Profit.............................	12%	2%
Operating Costs........................	56	41
Taxes.................................	12	37
Freight and Treatment..................	20	20

[1]Basis, average 35 per cent over-all tax.
[2]Base, 50,000 tons (U.S.) at $10 per ton; Mexico at $6 per ton. Difference in costs may be less.
SOURCE: R. A. Beals, "Will Taxation Destroy the Mining Industry in Mexico?" *Mining Engineering,* VII (Feb. 1955), 127.

The International Bank study estimated that taxes took between 50 and 60 per cent of the profits in mining, while industry and commerce paid only between 30 and 40 per cent. This policy, the bank economists continued, discouraged Mexican and foreign investors. Mining companies invested their Mexican profits abroad, and new investment was generally reinvestment of a portion of the profits.[20]

Evaluating the papers presented before the First National Mining Congress in 1948, the *Comisión Dictaminadora* ("Judgement-Rendering" Commission) reported that small and large companies as well as producers' cooperatives asked for the production tax to be eliminated or reduced, and incentives for low-grade ore producers. It pointed out that since high-grade ores were disappearing, and that technical improvements had failed to stem the tide of bankruptcies, the only course open was to reduce costs—salaries, materials, or taxes. Of these, in actuality, only taxes could be reduced.[21]

Mexico's government appeared to be indifferent to this situation. A new mine tax law—not enacted until 1955—did not reduce the tax rates but provided special treatment for new, marginal, and small-scale enterprises. Nationalistic politicians believed this attitude to be morally justified since mining exhausts the nation's wealth, and the State had to take what it could while it could.[22]

Mexico levies a number of taxes which affect the mining industry. After the major production, export, and claim-area taxes, there is an income tax, an excess profits tax, and dividend and undistributed profits taxes. Thirty per cent of the latter tax may be deferred by investments in Mexico, and provisions are made for depletion and depreciation allowances. As a final filip there is a federal "10 per cent additional" surtax on the amount due under any federal tax law.[23]

Mexico's basic impost on mining has remained the production (or severance) tax. Miners criticize it as an absolute tax which takes a percentage of the value of the metal in the ore and is payable whether the company makes a profit or not.[24] Only extremely low-grade ore producers, mines in remote areas, and small mines with a gross ore production valued at less than $16,000 a year have been given exemptions or lower rates.[25] Rates vary with the level of processing before export, are set on a progressive base dependent upon the metal's market price, and are subject to violent and unreasonable fluctuation when the peso-dollar exchange rate changes.[26] The tax favored low-cost producers and therefore might be said to encourage modernization except that it discriminated effectively against small producers of low-grade ore who could not afford much capital equipment. Since large producers generally worked lower grade ores, they felt the tax to be an intolerable burden. Furthermore, it directed exploitation to the higher grade ore by rendering the exploitation of lower grades unprofitable.[27] Of course this development was not in conflict with Mexico's real but unavowed policy of encouraging the exploitation of resources which provided quick returns and high tax payments while neglecting long-range planning. From the miners' standpoint, one of the most troublesome effects of the tax was the readjustments occasioned by currency revaluations. As a more equitable substitute for the production tax, the miners advocated an income tax which would tax actual profits.[28]

In turn, the Mexican government defended the production tax on the basis of practicality; it was easy to assess and collect, while an income tax was difficult to determine, hard to collect, and the yield varied. Because of traditional Latin business practices, the government regarded the income tax as a supplement to other imposts, not as the base of the system, although the changing structure of the Mexican economy made income taxes of greater importance.[29] Concerning the effects of the progressive rates following devaluation, the government contended that the miners were benefiting by an unearned increment of windfall profits based on the weakness of the Mexican economy. Furthermore, despite the progressive production tax, profits were still large enough to necessitate an export tax to recoup most of the remaining benefits for the government. (Figures collected for the International Bank study indicated that profit margins in mining rose between 1939 and 1949 from 5 per cent to 28 per cent. These returns were considered low for Mexico and not higher than those obtained in other countries on the same level of economic development.)[30] Finally, Mexico contended, as a severance tax it recovered in the national interest a portion of the value of the minerals exploited by private producers.[31]

Objections were also entered against the pertenencia tax, a progressive claim-area levy based on the number of units held by one company in one mining district. It was originally designed to force exploitation and forestall preemption since the tax was due whether the mine were worked or not. However, the requirement for exploitation to retain mine title, first inserted in the Law of Mineral Industries of 1926, achieved the same objective directly and imposed a double burden. When mines with concessions antedating 1926 were placed under the regular work provisions, the justification that the tax was necessary to force those mines into production was rendered obsolete.[32] In practice, the progressive features of the tax, instead of forcing preemptors and speculators to disgorge, placed a burden on companies which made large investments to exploit low-grade ores and needed large areas to insure sufficient reserves to safeguard their money. In the Mine Tax Law of 1955 the progressive feature was finally removed.

Rates for Mexico's mine tax law remained basically unchanged from 1940 to 1955, although the export tax was altered to fit changing conditions. The only new tax was that levied upon gold on August 26, 1943.[33] In other cases, such as the changes in the tax on silver during the war, certain exemptions and deductions were allowed, or the export tax was changed, but the production tax rate remained substantially the same.

After World War II, Mexico instituted a policy of subsidies by permitting various deductions from taxes. Miners believed the term "subsidies" to be false, since they were really tax reductions.[34] And the size of an enterprise's tax bill was not the key to its financial stability. The first "reduction subsidy" was granted on November 11, 1948, to relieve only very small workings producing from 50 to 250 tons of ore a month.

Tax reductions ranged from 30 to 80 per cent of the production tax. New or reopened mines were accorded production tax reductions for 5 years of from 5 to 50 per cent after negotiations with the Ministry of Finance. On June 20, 1950, reductions of from 50 to 80 per cent for three years were given to companies opening small treatment plants of less than 50 tons capacity per day.[35]

President Adolfo Ruíz Cortines issued an all-inclusive decree covering deductions on July 28, 1953.[36] After detailing his interest in small national enterprises and their attempts to compete with large-scale foreign operators in developing new deposits with national capital, Ruíz Cortines went on to spell out a reduction in the combined production and export taxes, and the supplementary tax on gold. Only enterprises paying less than 200,000 pesos in taxes were eligible for reductions. Those with small tax bills might get reductions of up to 75 per cent at the discretion of the Minister of Finance. Previous laws on the subject were derogated. Foreign-owned enterprises were not discriminated against in this nor in subsequent laws; but almost all of the enterprises small enough to be eligible were Mexican.[37] It was claimed that the first two months following saw an increase of 2,000 tons in the output of lead, zinc, and copper which was directly attributable to the tax reduction. One estimate placed savings for the small miners at some 24,000,000 pesos annually and an increased production of 10,000 tons of zinc a year worth $1,150,000.[38] Yet, in the winter of 1954, a convention of miners addressed by officials of the SEN and the Ministry of Finance was told that the government agreed with them that the changes in the tax structure were really insignificant.[39] Not until January 1, 1956, did Mexico enact a new mine tax law entitled "Law of Taxes and Promotion of Mining."[40]

Second to the production tax as a center of the mine operator's ire was the *Impuesto de Aforo*, or export tax, enacted after the devaluation of the peso in 1938 to forestall windfall profits. Unlike other imposts, the export tax was under a special commission which changed the assessed valuation of the commodity, or the tax rate itself, in accord with market conditions and readjustments in the economy. In theory the tax would be done away with when the economy had adjusted itself to the new price level. But it was kept and changes were used to help cooperatives, silver miners (during the latter part of the war), and to offset the long-term fixed costs payable in pesos upon which mine operators could otherwise make savings due to devaluation.

In the postwar years, the export tax was subjected to numerous changes. President Avila Camacho completely exempted silver on April 4, 1946, because of the readjustments necessitated by the strike of that year.[41] The general tariff law issued on November 18, 1947, made export taxes permanent and incorporated them along with a 2 per cent surtax on the total export duty. Despite many exemptions, mine operators complained that export taxes paid by the industry were higher under the revised law.[42]

When the peso was devalued on July 22, 1948, a 15 per cent ad valorem surtax was decreed on August 24th. Both the mine operators' association and the miners' union protested the surtax. It was immediately noted that mine production did not fall off in the period following the imposition of the surtax, but exports did decline. Later, shipments were resumed with the hope of retroactive relief. Relief came on October 22, 1948, retroactive to August 24th. A new decree allowed exporters to recoup their payments by deductions from future taxes. In addition, gold was exempted from the export tax. The deduction was estimated to be equivalent to four-fifth's of the 15 per cent surtax.

At the beginning of 1949, the basic export duties on mine products were scaled down so that most paid between 1.7 and 5 per cent. Metal exports, however, were not included in another reduction on June 30, 1949, since the government apparently believed that the plan of October 22, 1948, afforded sufficient relief. In late 1952, and again in early 1953, the surtax on exported electrolytic copper was lowered to aid the new refinery near Mexico City. For a short while this reduction was rescinded, but it was extended again when electrolytic copper exports ceased. As late as January 1954, business groups protested the surtax as a barrier to development, only to be told by government spokesmen that the duties were being constantly reviewed and revised as the market situation of a given commodity required.[43]

In recent years, the Mexican personal and business income tax has increased in fiscal importance and the rates have risen.[44] Income taxes are progressive and are calculated on net income after certain deductions. In addition, mining companies which set up reserves (by investing in securities approved by the National Securities Commission) to cover the severance pay of their employees, to be paid when the deposit is exhausted, may also deduct that amount. As of 1954, rates on business income started at 3.8 per cent for $160 annual taxable income and went up by brackets to 33 per cent on the portion over $80,000. The latter group paid a minimum of $20,000. In the case of employees, taxes started on net taxable incomes of $24 a month which paid 1.5 per cent. Personal taxable incomes of $4,000 a month and over reached the final 46 per cent bracket, with a minimum in that bracket of $1,086. While these rates were not oppressive, there still was the burden of double taxation for foreigners.

After taxes, mine operators contended that the poor state of public facilities contributed most to the industry's depressed state. Lack of adequate railroad service, the need for roads in remote areas and new regions, and the general shortage of electric power facilities all imposed burdens on the industry.[45]

Mexico's railroads owe much to the mining industry; traditionally, mine expansion went hand in hand with railroad expansion. Older mine areas are therefore well served. But as the Mexican economy diversified and mining lost its dynamic role, railroads did not respond to mining needs. Two problems resulted: newer districts do not have sufficient transportation connections, and older districts do not receive sufficient rolling stock. Mines are forced to operate below capacity and to build up stock piles at the railroad sidings.[46] The International Bank team reported that the great demand for metals in 1950–51 had caused a pile up of some 190,000 metric tons at railroad sidings (worth about 400,000,000 pesos, or 20 per cent of the total mineral production of 1950), and that in general the railroad block reduced the potential capacity of Mexico's mines from 5 to 10 per cent.[47]

Hardly recovered from the damage of the Revolution, railroads plunged into a period of neglect caused by the Depression, and there occurred political fights over labor and administration. Deliberately neglected by Cárdenas, in his efforts to build up other portions of the economy, the railroads entered World War II in a dilapidated condition.[48] An American railroad mission, working with a United States government grant of $6,600,000, managed to establish the rudiments of order out of the chaos.[49] In June, 1947, the Mexican government took over the Southern Pacific with 1,400 miles of track.[50] Administrative inefficiency, corruption, and labor attitudes were as important as physical neglect in effecting the deterioration. With no policy for subsidizing railroad deficits as an aid to the rest of the economy, the railroad deficit continued to grow and service deteriorated despite continued rate increases.[51] Railroads became an impediment to Mexico's development, and the International Bank report recommended a complete overhaul of the system as a key project.

Railroad improvements before 1951 consisted mainly of setting up systems to expedite handling and the rearranging of schedules.[52] Freight rates were raised on the demands of railroad workers for higher wages, to pay for improvements, and to get mining to pay its "fair share." The purchase of gondola cars for ore shipments, with an Export-Import Bank credit, was cited as necessitating rate increases. Some companies used private cars but paid the National Railways full rate for hauling them! Even the mineworkers' union protested that rising rates threatened small marginal mines with extinction.[53] Korean War demands swamped the railroads; purchases of new stock filled only a small fraction of the needs. Finally, loans from the Export-Import Bank, which came to over $56,-000,000, in addition to the recommendations of the International Bank, began to take effect. By 1952, under President Ruíz Cortines, conditions began to improve.[54]

While Mexico's railway system stagnates, highways expand at an ever increasing rate.[55] The modern road program, started in 1925, continued unabated even during the war years. Today, highways link the most important regions of the nation. In spite of high building costs they are the only practicable way of incorporating small remote communities into the national economy. Also, they are indispensable as feeder lines to the railways. Despite continual reports of expansion, the newer mining districts and the promising, remoter areas complained that they were not provided roads in return for their tax money. Given the over-all needs of the republic, the limited funds available, and the cost of building roads into sparsely populated mountain districts, there existed a reasonable basis for government "neglect." In any event, with government policy emphasizing agricultural development, agricultural communities could be expected to receive preference.[56] Despite government pronouncements, roads into isolated mining districts are pushed only when they fit into national plans. After the war, the International Bank report noted a new outlook: Mexico was attempting to offset the miners' difficulties by a program of road building to mine centers and by making special tax adjustments for companies building their own roads.[57] Under a special policy promulgated in 1952 to increase road construction in mining districts, the government vigorously pushed construction of hitherto neglected feeder roads to the main highways and railroads.[58]

These developments, along with the section of the Mine Tax Law of 1955 permitting mining companies to negotiate tax concessions in return for building their own feeder roads, promise rapid improvements in the matter of highway transportation. Trucks, once legally barred as ore carriers, have now become a threat to the railways. And in remote areas the airplane also has a role.[59]

After World War II a complete rebuilding of the Tampico Ore Pier was necessary. Handling costs had become high, and it paid to ship by rail to Galveston or Corpus Christi, Texas, and then load the mineral into ships. The new pier, to cost an estimated $1,500,000, was started in late 1952. Before it was completed, however, increased shipments via Tampico necessitated lengthening it to some 300 meters.[60]

Relations between the electric power system and mining resembled relations between mining and the railways. Many of the basic power systems had been installed to service mines, and for many years the mining industry was the largest single purchaser of electric power. By the late 1930's power shortages began to plague the industry since neither miners nor the power companies wished to expand electric output under the prevailing political conditions. Shortages and failures necessitated stand-by plants. After the war, when the power industry again began to expand, new developments were designed either for growing industries in larger cities or as multipurpose hydroelectric projects to aid agriculture. Transmission lines were not extended to newly opened mining areas or to aid the expansion of older ones. Many mines, having to depend solely upon their own power plants, were unable to expand operations.[61] Having lost its dynamic position, mining now depended upon other sectors of the economy to spark the expansion of the power network.

Not until the 1950's did the Federal Power Commission finally push plans for line expansion into the more remote mining areas.[62]

A lack of sources for loans, credits, and investment capital for mining is another weak point. Between 1942 and 1956, mining received less than one per cent of the loans extended by the Mexican banking system.[63] Most of these loans financed metal sales and were secured by existing stocks of ores or metals.[64] The Mexican public, too, is no longer disposed to play the "mining lottery," since modern methods call for large investments with a long-time lapse before dividends. Meanwhile, Mexico abounds in quick return opportunities in other industries. And government policy no longer favors mining nor encourages mine investments by either Mexicans or foreigners.

Miners—particularly small operators—complain bitterly about the banks which, they say, collect high interest rates and yet demand a great deal of security. Marginal enterprises can secure no help at all. Stock, freely offered by the miners to spread the risk, does not interest bankers who want mortgages on the real property owned by the miners. So-called "mining banks" are either metal brokers or extend aid to enterprises backed by Nacional Financiera, the government finance agency. The government-owned Bank for Cooperative Development lends money only to some cooperatives and works with the Commission for Mining Development.[65]

Miners themselves are often not too clear about whether they want capital or bank credits. Commercial bank loans are generally advanced for specific projects or needs on a relatively short-term basis. It is quite possible that the small amount lent by banks to mining enterprises is as much as sound commercial banking practices will allow, considering the small miners' lack of security and low credit rating. Investment banking in Mexico is still an underdeveloped activity. The only other alternative would be a government development bank. But this arrangement would mean risking public moneys and entering into a partnership with the government, which would probably enforce a strict supervision to safeguard its loan.

Bankers defended their actions by noting that risks in mining were great while interest rates were fixed by law. It was a gamble they could not afford to finance since the risks were greater than the interest charged. Banks would have to absorb the weight of many failures, with no share in the profits of the few successful mines since they could take only notes, not stock. Gambusinos and many small companies simply had no credit standing. No sure method existed of assessing the value of a mining property, and since the subsoil was the nation's inalienable property, the mine itself was not mortgageable. Mining presented too many intangibles and risks for any but secured, short-term loans.[66]

Many mine operators demanded a true mining bank.[67] At the National Mining Congress of 1948, the head of the Commission for Mining Development (CFM) recommended that the Mexican government empower the CFM to extend loans to "duly selected" small miners at long terms with low interest rates, "accepting beforehand that these investments are quite risky and that no one will be able to answer for their commercial success."[68] When the Judgement–Rendering Commission of the Congress presented its conclusions, it suggested, first, that if the general crisis affecting the industry would be resolved, the credit problem would be automatically remedied. Then it recommended that a portion of the taxes on mining be set aside annually to aid small enterprises through official and private institutions. It did not recommend the establishment of an official mine bank. Finally, it appended the entire proposal of the CFM for Assembly approval.[69] However, the Assembly did not look kindly upon the CFM and insisted upon adding a significant clause to the Commission's recommendation:

> In view of the fact that the official and semi-official institutions have sickened, because of their very nature, from defects inherent to institutions of their nature, it is desirable that credit to small mining enterprises, with all its adjunctive services, should be imparted by a private bank with capital drawn from those miners in proportion to the importance of their businesses. In the event that that bank comes into being, the help of the Federal Government to extend credit to small mining enterprises ought to be imparted through the agency of that bank.[70]

This proposal might be interpreted as a bid by the small miners to force the large mining concerns to finance a bank for their aid. If politics and personal influence could be kept out, there would remain the administration problem of financing enterprises as risky as mining.

The exact capital structure of the Mexican mining industry cannot be determined, and even the International Bank report did not estimate the total investment. It noted that the foreign investment in mining did not indicate a total investment since there were a number of transfers of ownership to Mexicans and Mexican ownership of small smelters and mines. However, it continued: "As all the big mining companies in Mexico are foreign-owned, it is likely, in spite of these qualifications that the figures [of direct foreign investment in mining] represent the major part of investment in mining."[71]

Estimates have placed the American investment at more than 70 per cent of the total, even after the sale of Real del Monte by USSR&M. Mexican holdings may come to 10 per cent, with the British accounting for most of the difference. In numbers, some 70 per cent of properties are Mexican owned.[72]

A study of the information published by the International Bank, the Bank of Mexico, and the United States government concerning mining investment in Mexico discloses that between 1938 and 1953 the peso value of foreign investment rose every year with but two exceptions. From some 578,237,000 pesos in 1938, mine investment increased to

792,258,000 pesos in 1945, 967,387,000 pesos in 1950 and 1,423,345,000 pesos in 1953. But its portion of the total foreign investment in Mexico fell from 29 per cent to 21 per cent.[73] This decline is attributed to the fact that mining comprised 25 per cent of foreign direct investment in 1939–44 and only 9 per cent in 1945–49.[74] Mining money was entering Mexico, but at nowhere near the rate of money directed toward other activities. In relation to Mexico's annual gross domestic investments, mining between 1939 and 1950 comprised from 0.2 to 1.5 per cent of the total, reaching the higher marks only during wartime.[75] Net earnings climbed from a prewar total of about $8,000,000 to a wartime high of $14,000,000 in 1943, then fell off until 1947 when they rose to $24,600,000. They reached a Korean War peak of $37,900,000 in 1951 and $29,400,000 in 1952 to be succeeded by lows of $10,100,000 in 1954 and $10,700,000 in 1955. By 1956 an upswing was in evidence, and earnings went up to $19,800,000.[76] United States direct investments in Mexican mining and smelting fell steadily in value from $230,000,000 in 1929, to $168,000,000 in 1940, and to a nadir of $108,000,000 in 1943. They started to rise in 1946 from $111,000,000 to $120,500,000 in 1950, $131,000,000 in 1952, and $144,000,000 in 1953. Although the 1956 figure of $165,000,000 just about equalled the 1940 figure, it did not match the $213,000,000 for 1936 or the $230,000,000 for 1929.[77] One might well draw the conclusion that while not comparable to former days, the industry was not quite moribund yet.

An important facet of United States investments is the reinvestment of earnings. The International Bank report stated that during the period 1939–50, mining investments were limited almost entirely to reinvested earnings of existing companies.[78] While this statement might be true for the industry as a whole, it may not hold for every company, and it gives no idea of the total reinvestment. Reinvestment in the form of undistributed subsidiary earnings in Mexican mining were set by the United States Department of Commerce at $4,000,000 in 1953 and at *minus* $20,000,000 in 1954.[79] Data on American capital movements are presented in the following table:

TABLE 10

United States Direct Investment Capital Movements
in Mexican Mining and Smelting: 1945–54

(*In Millions of Dollars*)

1945–47	−4[1]	1952	−4
1950	−8.1	1953	8
1951	−5	1954	18

[1]Negative indicates inflow of capital to the United States.

Source: M. Abelson, "Private United States Direct Investments Abroad," *Survey of Current Business*, XXIX (Nov. 1949), 22, Table 6; S. Pizer and F. Cutler, "Growth in Private Foreign Investments," *ibid.*, XXXIV (Jan. 1954), 8, Table 3; Pizer and Cutler, "International Investment and Earnings," *ibid.*, XXXV (Aug. 1955), 18, Table 5.

Hence, it can be seen that in 1953 and 1954, funds did move from the United States into Mexican mining offset in the latter year by withdrawals from subsidiaries. Complete figures on reinvestment are lacking. But since there usually were earnings, and the industry did expand, the role of reinvestment must have been of basic importance.[80]

The effect of United States mining investments on the Mexican economy in 1955 was summed up by data gathered from companies holding 86 per cent of the United States-owned investments in Mexican mining. Out of $212,000,000 in sales, they sold $133,000,000 in the United States; $33,000,000 to other countries; $46,000,000 in Mexico; and produced $166,000,000 in foreign exchange. Some $198,000,000 were paid out locally: $31,000,000 for wages; $73,000,000 for materials and supplies; $13,000,000 in income taxes; $43,000,000 in other taxes; and $38,000,-000 in "other and unspecified" payments. Imports by this group of companies came to only $16,000,000, $4,000,000 of which was of capital equipment. They employed about 27,000 men with 2,000 employees classified as "supervisory, professional and technical." Although the exact number of employees brought from the United States is unknown, in all Latin America they totalled 1,230 people. Given the size of American-owned operations in Peru, Chile, and Mexico, probably between one-quarter and one-third were in Mexico. Finally, company remittances came to some $9,000,000, of which $8,000,000 was for dividends and branch profits, with $1,000,000 for interest, royalties, and fees.[81]

A note must be added concerning the rate of return. Earning rates in Mexico are high by American standards: government securities pay 9 and 10 per cent and 20 to 40 per cent is regarded as a fair business return.[82] Although from 1948 to 1951 the rates of return in Latin America were 4 to 9 percentage points higher than returns on investments in the United States, a UN study remarked that "the spread between the rates of return may be regarded as narrow in view of the current risks attaching to investment abroad. . . ."[83] The International Bank report concluded that postwar returns from mining of 14 to 28 per cent "compares unfavorably with other economic activities in Mexico and with mining in other countries."[84] Hence, given the attitude of the Mexican public and government toward mining, plus the general risk in investing in mining as well as investing abroad, return rates considered high in other circumstances are in reality moderate. And, if the Mexican mining industry is to continue as a field of exploitation for private capital—most of it foreign since Mexican capital is not interested—fair returns must be substantial returns.

Double taxation has had its effect on the structure of mining investments in Mexico. American tax law—as well as Mexican policy and law —induces investors to set up subsidiaries in Mexico instead of corporate branches.[85] As pointed out by the United States Department of Commerce, probably the principal reason for setting up subsidiaries "is that the earnings of a foreign corporation are not ordinarily taxable in the United States unless paid out as dividends to the United States owners of the stock. This enables an investment to be built up through the retention of profits more rapidly than under the branch form of organization in any country where the income tax rates are lower than in the United States."[86] In actuality the net tax liability of United States firms investing in Latin America is small. Lack of an agreement on double taxation between Mexico and the United States means that a reduction in Mexican income taxes would not benefit or encourage United States investment, since the corporation would still have to pay taxes equal to the higher American rate; only the division of the payment would change with Mexico receiving less.

Mine labor in Mexico constituted only 1.2 per cent of the labor force in 1950. However, for a country where a large portion of the population exists on the level of subsistence, the high productivity of each miner, his relatively good income, and the position of the industry as a center of work skills, gives mining an importance beyond that indicated by mere employment figures. In an index in which the average gross productivity of all gainfully employed people in Mexico is set at 100, mining has been estimated at 409, compared to 167 in manufacturing, 76 in construction, and 36 in agriculture. From 80 to 90 per cent of the men were employed by either medium or large scale enterprises, which increased their productivity. The gross value produced per employee has been estimated at $3,785. In Latin America as a whole, the gross production per worker in mining is higher than in any other economic activity, in both absolute and relative terms.[87]

The general status of mine labor and the protection afforded it by law and the union in the early 1950's did not differ markedly from the late 1930's.[88] In fact, the Federal Labor Law of 1931 continued in effect, though amended. Social insurance represented the major addition, covering: (1) compensation for industrial accidents and occupational illnesses paid for by the employer alone; (2) insurance against nonoccupational illnesses and maternity paid for by the employer and employee; and (3) insurance covering disability, old age, death, and involuntary unemployment at an advanced age also paid for by the employer and employee. In many labor contracts the employer undertook to pay the employee's contribution.[89] Safety measures never slacked off. Mining accidents between 1945 and 1950 were 48.8 per cent fewer than between 1939 and 1944. In metallurgical establishments the number was down 14.2 per cent.[90]

The provisions of Mexican law concerning maintenance of employment levels have been a great burden to mining. Ever mindful of the instability of metal markets, managers were wary of increasing their work force to exploit lower grade ores during good times, because laying off the new men during a downturn would mean paying at least three months' wages as severance pay. Since Mexican mines are under pressure to work during poor times, their output weakens metal prices even more. At other times, under the stimulus of rising prices, production and employment are slow to expand and large amounts of lower grade ore are left behind. Mexican labor probably has made immediate gains in its economic position, but at the expense of wasted national resources and lower investment in the industry.[91]

Appraising whether or not the Mexican mineworker is efficient poses a hard problem. His talents and capabilities are undeniable, but at the same time he labors under handicaps which interdict their full use and development. Mineowners are reluctant to invest in improvements so that workings are often undermechanized. Unionization has further undermined efficiency: poor workers cannot be discharged, discipline cannot be maintained, the labor force is kept overly large by legal and union requirements, and the rigid system of escafalón—promotion based solely on seniority—deprives able men of a chance while saddling the enterprise with foremen marked chiefly by age and perseverance in attendance. Finally, the poor state of auxiliary services, such as the railways, not only curtails mine output but also leads to the inefficient use of capital. The gap between the potential and the actuality of labor's performance is dismaying to many observers.[92]

While the power of labor constantly vexes the industry and sympathetic labor boards reinforce union tactics favored by the Constitution, its actual scope of action is limited by the current administration's policy. The President's approval or disapproval of a threatened strike is of key importance to both labor and management. When industry's economic position changes for the better, labor depends upon the President's help to secure wage adjustments. On the other hand, the mining companies look to the President for support against labor demands during difficult times. Although during the presidency of Cárdenas labor seemingly could do no wrong, in the 1940's and 1950's the President intervened several times to restrain the unions.

Mineowners have had certain specific requests to make of their workers. To aid planning, they have asked unions to live up to their contracts and permit the administration to keep a sufficient number of "confidential posts" exempt from unionization. Pay raises should be matched by rises in productivity. And employers should have the freedom to reduce the number of workers and the scale of operations when necessary.[93]

In addition to schemes for adjusting their earnings by tying wages to metal prices and adding production bonuses, the workers also wished an extension of consumers' cooperatives. They also made known their desire that the government ease taxes and the restrictions against mining in order to create more jobs (since what was good for the industry would be good for the workers as well), and they advocated a number of policies including forced reinvestment and all-out aid to small operators.[94]

Mine labor is still bedeviled with social problems neglected by both the union and the government. Workers need more education to help them raise their productivity and make better use of their leisure time. Although safety is stressed in the larger mines, smaller enterprises and cooperatives lack the necessary devices. Occupational illnesses—silicosis, tuberculosis, hookworm, and anemia—are endemic; too often the terms "gambusino" and "incapacitated" are synonymous. Falling ill of tuberculosis or silicosis, a miner will turn to scraping out a marginal living alone or with a few companions. Needing social and vocational rehabilitation, these individuals are constantly victimized.

In many mining communities vice abounds in its traditional manner, and workers will steal food from their families to pay for their pleasures. Cooperative stores perform a useful function in collecting the family food bill directly from the employer, but instances are recorded in which the men sell this food for cash to buy liquor. The usual diet is low in calories with too few greens and too little meat. There exists an unrelieved ignorance concerning elementary nutrition. As a result the men tend to be weak and are poor workers who sicken easily and die young. Finally, the cost of living in mining camps is high; merchants raise prices to match wage increases; and the men easily become dependent upon loan sharks. These problems are far from solved. Only the cooperative store and close work between employers and the union may control it.[95]

Continuous union pressure for wage raises has to be seen against the background of peso devaluation and inflation. Prices rose 500 per cent between 1939 and 1956, tripling since 1945 alone.[96] Union demands, based upon the contention that the industry could pay, had to be high to enable their members to keep up with living costs. Employers sympathized with this problem and criticized the government as the prime mover by failing to halt inflation.[97]

The key to most Mexican labor problems is the inflation which has been deliberately stimulated by the government. To accelerate industrialization and economic expansion, Mexico has pursued an inflationary policy which encourages investment. Since investments come from a small group of wealthy property holders who can afford to save, an inflation of real property values and business incomes places in their hands large sums of currency for greater savings and further investment. Meanwhile, wage earners struggle to maintain themselves. The result has been a high rate of savings and investment for the economy as a whole at the expense of the lower income groups. This trend was expressed in economic jargon by the International Bank report:

> The unparalleled development in 1939–50 was only made possible, on the one hand, by forcing savings up and by curtailing consumption and on the other hand, on concentrating on investment opportunities which offered quick and substantial returns. . . . [A] new phase has already been foreshadowed by a tapering off of the rate of increase or real income per capita

in 1945–50, due partly to a more rapid growth of population, but mostly to a slower increase in total output.[98]

James E. Maddox expressed it in plainer terms:

> The principal method for encouraging private investments has been a deliberate policy of inflation which has squeezed the real incomes of the lower income classes while it raised the income of the rich and relatively well-to-do groups. . . .
> This policy of squeezing the poor and enriching the rich in order to encourage savings and investments on the part of the latter doesn't sound much like the revolutionary cries of two and three decades ago, when The Revolution was breaking up large haciendas and giving the land to the peons and nationalizing the oil industry.[99]

After the bitter strikes of 1946 brought on by the rise in silver prices, the nonsilver producers were also forced to grant raises equal to those given by the silver mines.[100] Through 1947 mine labor was quiet, but a new wave of strikes broke out in the spring of 1948. Significantly, the union did not shut down the entire industry, but labor stoppages sporadically affected mining from March until the end of May. Several large units were shut down—Fresnillo for as long as two months—but most others settled with the union within a short time. By midsummer, production was back to normal. Wage increases ran from 18 to 20 per cent and cost the companies, according to the union, some 60,000,000 pesos (about $10,000,000) in addition to other benefits. ASARCO at Monterrey, for example, promised to build 480 model houses for its workers to rent for one day's wages a week. Attempts by workers in the Pachuca area to strike against nationalized mines, or mines in which government agencies had a financial interest, were declared illegal by the Ministry of Labor and the men returned to work within 24 hours.[101]

The new strike pattern set in 1948 apparently resulted from the damage wrought by the general closedown in 1946. The industry lost production during a good market, and the government lost tax revenue as well as silver for its anti-inflation program. This situation did not reoccur. A few key units would be struck in a staggered timetable or the government called in as mediator. But the industry was too important to permit it to be crippled or to have investors scared off.

Mexican mining experienced hard times during 1949 as the United States entered its first postwar recession. The continued drop in metal prices robbed the union of any argument to justify a strike. Production did go up as the government's silver policy partially offset nonferrous metal losses. During the summer, plans for a walkout were called off.[102] As the Mexican economy regained stability in 1950 and the two-year labor contracts expired, the union again asked for a raise. Cautioned by President Alemán not to paralyze the industry, union officials pressed the companies separately, even unit by unit. Fresnillo became the center of a protracted walkout. After a 72-day strike (perhaps the longest ever held against a major company) the union and management settled on a pattern of about 14 per cent. The conflicts were short, and *The Mining World* remarked that the industry was pleased by the quick settlements. When strikes hit ASARCO's coal and zinc units in Coahuila during the summer, the Ministry of Labor declared them illegal: the threat to steel production was too great. Unrest continued in the coal fields, complicated by a squabble in the union about alleged communist leadership and government opposition. Government action broke the strike against ASARCO's units, but strikers in the Palau coal fields held out from September, 1950, until the following spring. "Hunger marchers" elicited no help in Mexico City, and the movement collapsed when the courts ruled against them.[103]

As the government was winning over the communist elements in the miners' union in 1951, the union again began demanding wage hikes of from 25 to 30 per cent based on the "fabulous profits" earned during the Korean War. It allowed Fresnillo again to set a pattern with a 14 per cent raise in early April. A presidential committee then released a report favoring a formula for raises based on rising metal prices with allowances for increased costs and taxes. Above all, the committee asked for no work stoppages. Final settlements of from 10 to 14 per cent plus fringe benefits cost the companies, according to the union's Secretary General, around 150,000,000 pesos ($17,300,000) a year, a figure probably inflated to impress his membership.[104]

Wage increases now were granted each year despite the biennial feature of the labor contracts. Strikes were infrequent; most disputes were settled by negotiation. The Bank of Mexico reported that in 1952 wages and salaries rose 9.7 per cent over the previous year, and from 10 to 15 per cent the following year, despite a fall in company income. Strikes in 1953 started with demands for a 60 per cent increase. An American consular report placed settlements at from 10 to 14 per cent because of low lead and zinc prices and declining output. Devaluation in 1954 led to demands for a 45 per cent increase and resulted in settlements of 12 per cent, despite President Ruíz Cortines suggesting only 10 per cent. The rapid settlement of this dispute was attributed to the Ministry of Labor's policy of studying the situation and "suggesting" reasonable increases as a pattern for each industry. In 1955, for the fifth consecutive year, labor contracts were raised on an average basis of 10 per cent plus fringe benefits.[105]

It must be emphasized again, however, that the status of the mineworker did not materially improve a great deal. Price rises, abetted by peso devaluation and the government's inflationary price policy for encouraging investments, prevented the men from more than barely keeping up with the cost of living. Even when the annual 10 to 15 per cent increases grew like compound interest, the 300 per cent rise in prices nullified them. In 1951 and 1952 the Bank of Mexico estimated the annual per capita income in mining at 6,700 pesos and 7,150 pesos respectively— less than $1,000. In any event, miners were among the lucky 10 per cent of the active labor force able to negotiate increases. For the mass of the Mexican workers there was a decline in real income.[106]

Mining cooperatives have declined in importance since World War II. They never achieved their original objective of opening new fields for exploitation and utilizing Mexican talent in training a national managerial and entrepreneurial group. Cooperatives came to be recognized as a repository for played-out workings and miners who otherwise would be a social problem. They used their political influence to secure government aid and delay the economic readjustments necessitated by the depletion of old districts. Aid to cooperatives only prolonged the agony of mine exhaustion by taxing the rest of the economy. Workers were not retrained, and capital was not redirected. A delegation representing the state of Hidalgo, for example, in addressing the National Mining Congress in 1948, stressed the need to reduce the cooperatives' tax burden since they were keeping unemployed workers off the government's hands.[107] While the cooperatives could make themselves heard— at the National Mining Congress, for example[108]—they no longer enjoyed government support and their economic role was recognized as marginal. Calls for new cooperatives are still heard, but they are sporadic and do not threaten any mine of consequence. Older cooperatives continue to call for assistance, some—notably Dos Carlos and San Rafael in Pachuca —have closed for good, while others have managed to scrape along by virtue of CFM aid—as in Guanajuato. Dos Estrellas, continuing under strict government control, has been able to recover sufficiently to turn out 400,000 to 500,000 ounces of silver a year.[109]

According to the data furnished by the SEN, as of March, 1948, there were 75 cooperatives functioning with some 19,000 members. Between 1934 and 1939, 52 cooperatives were established, but only 23 since 1939. The four largest were Santa Fé at Guanajuato with 1,300 members; Dos Carlos at Pachuca with 2,000; Dos Estrellas in El Oro, Mexico, and Tlalpujahua, Michoacan, with 2,300; the Mineros de Rosario in Sinaloa (the old El Tajo workings) with 1,023. Between 1939 and 1946, they had been given subsidies by tax rebates equal to about 2,000,000 pesos a year.[110] Any future growth is highly doubtful. In fact, if the acquisition of the Real del Monte mines by the Mexican government in 1947 is any criterion, future nationalization of declining mines will only take place under strict government control to ensure the necessary discipline and honesty.

Evans Just put the situation in a nutshell:

Typically, the history of these cooperatives has been a succession of difficulties. Theoretically, they should be able to go forward, for a while at least, with fair success, as they are relieved of the heavy taxes which burden other producers. However, between occasional corruption and their inability to develop efficient managements, the workmen usually earn far less than before they displaced the previous owners. Also, safety and medical services lag, and operations are subject to frequent interruptions for lack of maintenance and good equipment. Most of the cooperatives are in debt up to the limit of their credit and are obliged to call on the Government from time to time for financial assistance. Thus a former source of tax revenues frequently becomes a drain on the public treasury. Today the cooperatives are on the decline and complete lack of development work is shortening their lives.[111]

Mexico's policy of direct government aid and intervention in mining through the National Mineral Reserve program and the CFM continued after the war. The results, however, have been far from spectacular. The National Mineral Reserves program, a product of the economic nationalism and socialist thought of the 1930's, attempted to deny large areas to "unplanned exploitation by undesirable elements" by placing them under special concessions. Consequently the Mineral Reserves became practically closed tracts. The favored small Mexican operators could neither use modern exploration methods to discover deposits nor could they start exploitation on the necessary scale. Mexican and foreign capitalists stayed away because of what they called "unrealistic" concession terms. While known reserves were being depleted, large areas were virtually excluded from exploration.

Extensions of the Mineral Reserves since 1946 have been few. The incorporation of the mineral resources of the continental shelf into the national mineral holdings was really but an extension of constitutional Article 27.[112] However, the years 1955–57 did witness some renewed activity. In June, 1955, a number of areas near El Bote, Zacatecas, were incorporated into the Reserves and added to the patrimony of the CFM. At the same time, 47 lots were released from the CFM's patrimony and opened to the public under the same conditions as other Reserve holdings. A large manganese reserve in Lower California was removed from the Reserves in May, 1958. In March, 1956, all titanium deposits in Mexico were made part of the Reserves, followed in November, 1957, by a large area in Urupán, Michoacan—upon recommendation of the Council on Non-Renewable Natural Resources; in May, 1958, a zone near Durango City, Durango, was included. Other additions in 1957 reflected the desire to develop a national fertilizer industry.[113] In May, 1957, and March, 1958, radioactive minerals in Oaxaca were transferred from the patrimony of the CFM to the *Comisión Nacional de Energía Nuclear*. Finally, a series of famous sites in Guanajuato incorporated into the Reserves and the patrimony of the CFM between 1940 and 1945, were placed directly in the Reserves again in 1955. Two years later three of these lots were placed in the CFM's patrimony again.[113]

Attempts by Mexico to aid or resuscitate mining have been fitful, uncoordinated, and underfinanced. For example, a report in 1946 by American government experts led to a flurry of plans under which a portion of the taxes on mining was to be used to subsidize prospecting.[114] Nothing came of them. In 1950 the National Institute for the Investigation of Mineral Resources replaced the Directive Committee for the Investigation of Mineral Resources which had sponsored the publication of a series of studies on geology and mining possibilities.[115] Five years later the Non-Renewable National Resources Council was set up to coordinate and direct geologic, technologic, and mining investigations by no less than eight government agencies working on different aspects of "the mining problem." All of these agencies have carried out investigations of mining, although in many cases the results have been of minor significance and many were simply additions to unused files.[116]

CFM activities since the war have been wide ranging but have produced little of major importance. Perhaps, in carrying out the official policy of helping only small enterprises and attempting to keep decaying areas open for a while longer, it has sunk its money into a morass. Exploring in Oaxaca—without results—reopening abandoned mines in San Luis Potosí, and trying to keep El Boleo afloat a while longer, dissipated much of its inadequate funds.[117] Its attempts in the Guanajuato area to survey "secondary" gold and silver deposits, dewater old shafts to search for lead-zinc veins, and diamond-drill for unsuspected silver veins, probably served as a greater social stimulus to the district than as an aid to the Mexican economy.[118] Perhaps of greater importance is the CFM's establishment of a number of field offices in various parts of the republic to provide a full metallurgical laboratory and advisors for small operators. These units would supplement the work of the central laboratory at Tecamachalco.[119] In 1951 Sonora opened an office called "Department of Mining Development of the State" to provide similar services.[120]

The United States has extended aid to Mexican mining under various programs. During World War II the United States Geological Survey studied Mexico's mineral resources extensively, working on over a dozen metals. This program, in cooperation with Mexican personnel, has continued, concentrating mainly on copper, lead, and zinc deposits. Their study of the El Boleo district, for example, is a definitive one. In general, it has been confined to field and laboratory work, training Mexicans in the United States and Mexico, and issuing publications and reports. Later, the United States Bureau of Mines entered the scene with two technicians, one of whom was assigned to Tecamachalco to better the laboratory techniques. In 1952 the United States staff numbered four men. The major part of this venture, which became part of the general Point IV program, was with CFM. A general Point IV agreement was not signed until June, 1957, and Mexico has continued to insist "on the national character of the program and the right to ask for what she wants rather than what the United States thinks Mexico needs." As a result, the United States' role has been principally to appraise the feasibility of the Mexican program and to supply limited numbers of personnel.[121]

Securing sufficiently trained Mexican personnel has not been easy for the mining industry. While quite proud of its mining school, which dates back to the eighteenth century, Mexico did little to modernize the dilapidated building in central Mexico City. Pride in the date on the cornerstone was not matched by pride in the laboratories. Classes at times fell to four students, and promising youths studied abroad. It is now hoped that with the facilities at the new University City, just outside Mexico City, the training of mining engineers will be revived.

Few Mexicans hold top positions in the leading mining companies. While the employment of Mexican professionals by foreign companies has increased tremendously since the Morones campaign of 1928, foreign companies do not plan to use Mexicans to head their Mexican subsidiaries. With job opportunities few, bright young men prefer to study in other, more promising, fields of engineering, start their own businesses, or become doctors or lawyers. Meanwhile, Mexicans still look to the foreign-owned mining companies to cooperate in training a cadre of Mexican engineers and offer them experience and practical instruction. Peñoles, for example, offered one scholarship for a student studying toward a specialty in mining engineering in an American school and two scholarships for study in Mexican schools. Labor contracts in 1948 contained clauses obligating the mining companies to send one hundred miners' sons to the National Polytechnic Institute with monthly support and travel money. The government itself announced the opening of a series of courses in Pachuca to train some one hundred men a year in practical mining and safety programs.[122]

The position of foreign technicians and engineers did not improve. A strongly nationalistic decree issued in 1945 granted full license rights only to foreigners resident at least five years in Mexico. Others could be employed only as professors of engineering sciences, consultants or technical instructors, or directors. These "three exceptions . . . are made in deference to international reciprocity."[123]

Mexican mining has a future, but its future depends heavily upon the government's policy toward the industry. Certainly an understanding and helpful attitude on the part of the government is essential in helping the mining industry overcome its problems. Taxes must be reduced, prudent conservation and orderly extraction must be practiced, discoverers must be given adequate incentives and rewards while investors are protected, and a more just balance must be struck between capital and labor, nationals and foreigners. In the long run, it is in the field of exploration in which Mexico's weakness lies—particularly in comparison with countries such as Peru, Venezuela, and Canada. Unless there are changes in the basic attitude (which stems from strong nationalist feelings), the government's indifference toward the value of exploration will continue. The result will be a decadence due to a narrowing base of exploitation, which perhaps will end with the nationalists cutting off their nation's nose to spite the foreign and native capitalists' faces.[124]

But at the same time the problems are not as overwhelming as they are often made out—nor is the future as bleak. In fact, it may be worthwhile to reflect that the health of the United States economy and American tariff policy can be as important to the Mexican mining industry as Mexican tax policy, geological exploration, or union aggressiveness. The future of Mexican mining in the long run is much brighter today than it was during the period between World War II and the Korean War. A few new operations, the growing output of nonmetallics,[125] and continued high levels of lead and zinc output are straws in the wind. Mining, it appears, will never again dominate the Mexican economy; nor will it rest upon a base of silver and silver-lead workings. But in its new orientation it has both a future and a definite place in the Mexican economy.

PART VII

A SUMMATION

Mexico's Experience

FOR ages Mexico has been a tragic land. Since the days of the first Indian invaders it has known little peace. Mexican blood has flowed copiously in internecine conflicts. An oppressive social and economic system squeezed out more blood as part of the price of peonage. Observers of the Mexican common people have repeatedly told of their friendliness, their shyness, and of their desire to live a happy life as best they can materially within a small insulated sphere in which, God willing, they will die. The Mexicans have had their full share of exploiters, corrupt politicians, bandits, and merciless soldiery. However, the traditional attitude has been that God is great, God is good, and God will provide. Materialistic aggression and initiative, the spirit of Western European and United States capitalism, have affected only a portion of the Mexican population, and even those possessing the capitalistic spirit are hampered by the mass fatalism and indifference. They are made cautious by the tradition of violence and arbitrary government, and they are hobbled by their nation's technological backwardness.

During the past thirty years, Mexico has enjoyed a kind of "Peace Through Revolution." Industrialization has begun, aided by governmental solicitude and the importation of foreign production techniques. But industrializing a nation with the inhibiting presence of old ideas, old predilections, and old vested interests is more difficult than starting from scratch. Undoing the mistakes and shortcomings of the past is the job the Mexican government has undertaken. The success or failure of the present program of the revolutionary party in Mexico will determine the future of over thirty-five million people.

For four centuries Mexico has been one of the world's great mineral producing countries. Her wealth of silver attracted Spanish prospectors and miners who explored the most remote districts, and hardly a mining area today does not have a tradition of Spanish workings. The Spanish workings were advanced for their time. Later they were replaced by English steam engines and mining methods, which in turn gave way to modern mass techniques. Nonferrous metals, iron, coal, and oil, which were added to the list of exploitable minerals during the nineteenth and twentieth centuries, necessitated large workings. As a result of the expanded scale of workings, a number of fabulously wealthy areas have been literally gutted, while many other areas are working on shrinking reserves. New discoveries are few; the list of depleted districts is long; and phophecies of a bleak future are heard in increasing number and volume. But, because of its cost and Mexico's geological structure, there has been little geophysical exploration to supplement prospecting and geological examination.

Must Mexico's future in mining remain dismal? Can her difficulties be surmounted? How is she to derive full benefit from her mineral resources? The answers to these questions are not encouraging. The burden of cost which the government can afford to bear is limited. With foreign investors branded as undesirables, Mexico must attempt to interest more native capital in an industry which is a gamble. While gambling in mining has been popular in Mexico, today it requires large sums of money, driving initiative, ingenious intelligence, and managerial skill to develop a successful paying enterprise. And there are many safer alternatives which pay just as well. For the government to assume the role of developer in a sort of Five-Year Plan, would require a great social sacrifice. And the notion of voluntary social sacrifice for national progress does not rest lightly upon any people. In social terms alone, a directed aggressive economic policy in the field of mining by the government would run into enormous difficulties.

But mine products carry a great weight in the Mexican economy. The bulk of Mexicans gainfully employed are engaged in marginal or subsistence farming with a low per capita income and productivity. They are economic zeroes, backward elements in the national political, social, and economic life. Mineworkers enjoy a high per capita income and productivity. Mine products provide a metallic base for Mexico's currency and bring in foreign exchange when sold abroad. They are an important source of government revenue—which can be used to support a variety of programs—as well as consumers of power, transportation, supplies, and job seekers. Without mines many of the remoter sections of Mexico would be completely desolate, and ranches and farms would be without markets. Finally, as industrialism begins in Mexico, the mining industry provides the needed raw materials.

However, for Mexican nationalists, mining has its negative aspects. As an extractive industry it guts Mexico's soil of raw materials to be fabricated and consumed abroad. Foreign ownership means that profits are sent abroad. Because of Mexico's economic weakness, she cannot control or change the direction of the international economy, or even the international market for a commodity, without substantial foreign cooperation as in the case of silver. This means that the fluctuations of the world business cycle strike Mexico with particular severity. Since the incentive for expanding the industry lies abroad, any exercise of national control makes for retaliation in the form of declining investments. Some analysts regard mining as a factor making for instability in the Mexican economy. The present Mexican mining industry is not an unmitigated blessing; understanding its faults from the Mexican viewpoint and arriving at possible solutions are not simple tasks.

Throughout history, mining has been a political football with the State attempting in many ways to encourage the working of the subsoil with the greatest possible efficiency, productivity, and return for itself. State regulations have varied with economic and social conditions, the psychological outlook of the people, the internal political situation, foreign and domestic capital available, the type of labor, international markets, and numerous other considerations. A change in any of these factors necessitates a change in relations between the government and industry. In any country, mining may experience several types of control as a more desirable and profitable relationship between the miner and the government is sought.

Mexico's mining industry has gone through six distinct stages in its history and is now in a seventh. In the first, the Spaniards scoured the country and spread their workings from Pachuca, Real del Monte, and Tlalpujahua, near Mexico City, to Oaxaca in the south, Jalisco in the west, and from Guanajuato to Sonora, in the north. They did not consider any site which could be reached by burro as too remote. They brought European methods, and from time to time the Spanish Crown sent expeditions of European scientists to improve techniques. Forced labor gave way in time to a wage-earning group of professional miners. The Crown treated mineowners as agents of the royal fisc and considered the industry to be the most important in the New World. While bound by many restrictions stemming from the Crown's legal ownership of the subsoil, as codified in the Ordenanzas of 1783, the miners enjoyed a number of favors. Their privileges ranged from aid in securing labor to subsidization of prices on supplies and special credit facilities. Yet, despite the wealth of individuals—such as de la Borda and the Conde de Regla— the Mexican mineowner was not content with his lot, for he regarded mining as a steppingstone toward ownership of a hacienda. Only a small group stuck to prospecting and mining as a permanent way of life. The professional mine laborers' ranks had to be replenished constantly with new recruits willing to give up tilling the soil for a few years and to labor in the mines for cash wages.

The War of Independence brought mining into its second stage. At the end of the fighting the industry was devastated, the Spanish mineowners were driven from the country, and the republic did not possess the financial resources necessary to render the services formerly offered by the Spanish Crown. Consequently, the mining laws had to be amended to permit alien mining interests to enter Mexico. English investors in particular descended upon Mexico, leasing mines wholesale and bringing in the latest steam engines and pumps. However, the cost of rehabilitating and working the deep levels made for heavier charges than the low-grade ore could pay. Poor administration, coupled with high maintenance costs for the machinery, completed the financial debacle. The government's inability to contain banditry or to suppress revolutions finally drove the optimistic British investors out of Mexico. In many cases, the mines reverted to Mexicans and to primitive means of exploitation. This second stage of mine exploitation ended in failure. The British were willing to accept the restrictions of the Ordenanzas of 1783, but their own mistakes, linked with the instability of the government and government policy, doomed their enterprises. The English opened no new districts; they simply worked the lodes uncovered by the Spaniards. The first experiment in encouraging mining by relaxing the bans against foreigners proved a failure.

Porfirio Díaz's encouragement of economic liberalism in Mexico ushered in the third stage of the mining industry's progress. A liberal mine law was passed in 1892 in order to "rationalize" government control over the mines and to attract foreign investors again. The foreigners came, lured by special contracts, the freedom granted by the government's philosophy of laissez faire, Díaz's preservation of law and order, and the lowering of taxes. Miners from the United States crossed the border, bringing with them the techniques of stamp-milling, pan-amalgamation of silver ores, and blast-furnace smelters. The neglected complex ore and base metal mines came at last into their own. New districts were opened in El Boleo, Sierra Mojada, and throughout northern and western Mexico. Mexico's Golden Mile was uncovered. A period of ore export to smelters in the United States was shortly followed by those same companies building smelters in Mexico. The expansion of railroads and an electric power industry aided the boom. Soon the cyanide process brought new life to the old silver districts. Díaz succeeded only too well in revitalizing the Mexican mining industry and making it a leading member of the world's mining community.

Díaz's success, however, had a price tag attached to it. Capitalists are willing to invest money and to bring the fruits of the industrial revolution to backward areas, but in their relations with governments in lands in which their home nation cannot act as "protector" they demand concessions, guarantees of economic freedom, and security of property. Since the Mexican government had been captured by the current philosophy of economic liberalism, it cooperated by relaxing the regulations restraining property holders. New political pressures entered the scene, brought by the foreigners investing in Mexico and expecting extranational protection.

Díaz's military strength and political sagacity were sufficient to force Mexico to accept the new era of prosperity. After 1905, latent Mexican nationalism and the traditional opposition to any entrenched Mexican ruler appeared on the political scene. These forces crystallized in 1910; a political revolution broke out which unleashed a complete social and economic revolution. Widespread discontent with mining was one of the causes of the Revolution, since the industry had been built up by legal and economic concessions to foreigners. Díaz had managed to start the exploitation of Mexico's subsoil on a large scale, but the Mexican people now deemed the price excessive. In fact, much of the turmoil which characterizes Mexican political and social life today is due to the patterns imposed upon Mexico by the Díaz dictatorship of 1876–1911.

In this stage of its development the mining industry was torn by a long and vicious civil war in which the rights of human beings and property—particularly if they were foreign—were violated wholesale. Revolutionaries labored long and hard to undo the work of the Díaz regime, attempting to replace laissez faire with a nationalistic policy of property control tempered with a desire for social reform. New principles of taxation were introduced, and the Spanish colonial requirement to work mines continuously was reintroduced. But the pressure of the foreign interests was strong, and the revolutionaries were forced to hedge their proposals with pledges disallowing retroactivity.

Despite the booming metal markets of World War I, Mexico could not bring her minerals into the world markets in quantities approaching those shipped before 1912. Still, several copper companies and the Pachuca silver miners did rather well for themselves. Despite the threat of new stringent laws and the fluctuation of political tides, the confidence of the large companies in the eventual return of stability to Mexico was reflected in their policy of picking up desirable properties.

The fifth stage in the history of Mexican mining began with Alvaro Obregón's ascension to power in 1920. While he did not relinquish any of the revolutionary nationalistic prerogatives, Obregón took a more lenient attitude toward foreigners to curry favor with the United States and strengthen his position at home. Fortunately, Obregón's term of office coincided with a general rise in prices, an expansion of mine workings, the introduction of the flotation process to Mexico, and the achievement of stability by the revolutionary regime. Obregón's successor, Calles, riding this crest of political strength and economic prosperity, reinstituted many of the Revolution's more stringent regulations in the Law of Mineral Industries of 1926. His nationalism was directed mainly toward the oil companies, but foreign-owned mining companies suffered as well. However, in 1927–28 the silver market sagged dangerously and then collapsed. Other metals soon followed. The nationalistic mine laws and high taxes caused a further deterioration in the industry's position as the Great Depression gathered force. Many of the older mine districts had been almost gutted, and reports of depletions and requests for permission to suspend work appeared in great numbers. The industry finally collapsed during the period 1931–33. Ironically, the inflexible regular work laws made it easier to shut down completely than to reduce operations. In 1930, Calles' mine law was repealed and replaced with a new, more lenient law as well as with a lower tax schedule.

The 1920's had had a profound effect on Mexico. Government policy had brought an end to the era of ever-increasing foreign participation in the exploitation of Mexico's mineral wealth. New operations were carried out on a larger scale and were more centralized; but new discoveries were minor and the number of depleted districts became larger. The mineral industry's structure and organization were frozen. Disputes over the constitutional clauses governing property rights and labor frightened away potential foreign investors. New companies did not enter Mexico, and established concerns only increased their pace of operations at the deposits they already held. Under this stimulus mineral production reached new peaks. The moot question was whether the rigidity of the industry's technoeconomic structure and its lack of initiative were due to a lack of new exploitable areas or to the nationalistic policy of the government. Were the policies of the Mexican government with regard to foreign investors impeding further growth? That question has never been answered. In the next decade the Mexican government turned toward an all-out policy of encouraging native participation in the national mineral industry.

With the Depression of the 1930's, Mexican mining entered its sixth stage. A resurgence of nationalism fostered the belief that the hardships of the Depression were foreign born, as were the exploiters of Mexico. Presidents Rodríguez and Cárdenas devoted themselves to nationalistic objectives. The Mexican government dedicated itself to opposing foreign interests in favor of Mexicans, but the implementation of that policy left no doubt that the government was favoring only small miners or mineworkers organized in "approved organizations." Only the independent buscones, the mine cooperatives, and the very small mining companies received government assistance.

Manuel Avila Camacho's election as President, followed by Mexico's entrance into World War II, marked the beginning of the seventh stage of Mexican mining history. The hysterical xenophobia, with its tinge of socialism, began to fade. Working to stabilize Mexico after the turbulent Cárdenas era, Avila Camacho was aided by assurances that American silver purchases would continue. Furthermore, after a period of panic following the loss of European markets, the United States negotiated a series of international agreements with Mexico, including one for the purchase of Mexican metals at good prices. Production climbed; strikes, now officially frowned upon, became infrequent and short; railroads almost collapsed under the burden of increased shipments. The mining industry's prosperity was great enough for Avila Camacho to decree the extension of the regular work laws to all mines. By the end of the war, Mexican mining was again in difficult straits. Nonferrous metal markets were disrupted, and labor again became aggressive. A strike during the first two months of 1946 prostrated the industry; production for the year plunged to new lows. Rising silver prices only partially benefited the industry since increased taxes and labor costs bit into the gains.

Not until the outbreak of the Korean War did the industry recover. It has been in the production of lead and zinc, the minor metals, and industrial minerals—particularly sulphur—that the industry has retained its importance. Precious metals never regained their old position. Copper output is supported by the expanded workings of low-grade deposits at Cananea and the increase in by-product copper. Government intervention is now a distant threat. The institutions founded during Cárdenas' presidency have not fulfilled their promise to dominate mining. But the tax structure needs to be reformed. And there is the overriding, stubborn fact that the industry's inflexibility is due to the large companies' empirical knowledge that Mexico has been rather well surface-prospected and that the major mineral zones are well known. Expansion has been in older districts or in workings made profitable by either high prices or more efficient exploitation. Some smaller operations have been expanded. While new mineral deposits no doubt exist, and can be uncovered by extensive and expensive geophysical searches, the shortcomings of the transportation and power network—as far as mining is concerned—plus present tax policy, render many likely sites economically unexploitable.

The hostility of the Mexican government to further foreign investment keeps out the technical knowledge and the large sums of capital which are necessary to develop remote ore bodies. As a group, capitalists tend to be reluctant to pioneer until a bold spirit blazes a trail. They remain even more reluctant if it appears likely that their pioneering will become the object of denunciations by public officials.

Is the Mexican government's initiative and energy great enough to overcome the obstacles which deter private investors? As yet, the answer must be in the negative. The Commission for Mining Development has not revitalized the industry. The same must be said of the various exploration commissions and programs. Government initiative and money have either been lacking or forthcoming only in niggardly quantities. Social and political considerations have led to the inefficient use of much of the money which has been appropriated. The miners' cooperative program did not open a new era of mine ownership; cooperatives, instead of pioneering, have been confined to picking over the bones of old mines.

Mexico's mining program now faces a great challenge; the bonanza days are over; low-grade outcrops and workings which have been known for centuries, or were located in easily exploitable locations, are being rapidly depleted. Future growth depends upon geophysical exploration, an extension of transportation, and tax reforms. Today mining needs large-scale risk and expenditures. Foreign capitalists are not particularly welcome, and Mexican capitalists are shy of mining propositions involving large outlays. To follow a nationalistic program, the Mexican people must sacrifice to obtain money for exploration and equipment. Sacrifice is one of the prices of nationalism, and it includes governmental austerity and shifts in the socioeconomic outlook of the people. Whether Mexico is prepared to pay this price for a nationalized mineral industry is doubtful. Can mining be allowed to expire if the new industrialism is to thrive? Can the Mexican economy support programs for the promotion of both mining and industry until their interdependence permits self-support? Constructive nationalistic alternatives lead to unpleasantness and sacrifice or to inflation. An openhanded encouragement of private foreign capital in mining is politically unpalatable. Mexico's leaders face a formidable task.

APPENDICES

Article 27 of
the Mexican Constitution of 1917*

ART. 27. The ownership of lands and waters comprised within the limits of the national territory is vested originally in the Nation, which has had, and has, the right to transmit title thereof to private persons, thereby constituting private property.

Private property shall not be *expropriated* except for reasons of public utility and *by means of* indemnification.

The Nation shall have at all times the right to impose on private property such limitations as the public interest may demand as well as the right to regulate the development of natural resources, which are susceptible of appropriation, in order to conserve them and equitably to distribute the public wealth. For this purpose necessary measures shall be taken to divide large landed estates; to develop small landed holdings; to establish new centers of rural population with such lands and waters as may be indispensable to them; to encourage agriculture and to prevent the destruction of natural resources, and to protect property from damage detrimental to society. Settlements, hamlets situated on private property and communes which lack lands or water, or do not possess them in sufficient quantities for their needs, shall have the right to be provided with them from the adjoining properties, always having due regard for small landed holdings. Wherefore, all grants of lands made up to the present time under the decree of January 6, 1915, are confirmed. Private property acquired for the said purposes shall be considered as taken for public utility.

In the Nation is vested direct ownership of all minerals or substances which in veins, layers, masses, or beds constitute deposits whose nature is different from the components of the land, such as minerals from which metals and metaloids used for industrial purposes are extracted; beds of precious stones, rock salt and salt lakes formed directly by marine waters, products derived from the decomposition of rocks, when their exploitation requires underground work; phosphates which may be used for fertilizers; solid mineral fuels; petroleum and all hydro-carbons—solid, liquid or gaseous.

In the Nation is likewise vested the ownership of the waters of territorial

*Only those sections of Article 27 which are pertinent to the mining industry and this study are reprinted.

seas to the extent and in the terms fixed by the law of nations; those of lakes and inlets of bays; those of interior lakes of natural formation which are directly connected with flowing waters; those of principal rivers or tributaries from the points at which there is a permanent current of water in their beds to their mouths, whether they flow to the sea or cross two or more States; those of intermittent streams which traverse two or more States in their main body; the waters of rivers, streams, or ravines, when they bound the national territory or that of the States; waters extracted from mines; and the beds and banks of the lakes and streams hereinbefore mentioned, to the extent fixed by law. Any other stream of water not comprised within the foregoing enumeration shall be considered as an integral part of the private property through which it flows; but the development of the waters when they pass from one landed property to another shall be considered of public utility and shall be subject to the provisions prescribed by the States.

In the cases to which the two foregoing paragraphs refer, the ownership of the Nation is inalienable and may not be lost by prescription; concessions shall be granted by the Federal Government to private parties or civil or commercial corporations organized under the laws of Mexico, only on condition that said resources be regularly developed, and on the further condition that the legal provisions be observed.

Legal capacity to acquire ownership of lands and waters of the nation shall be governed by the following provisions:

I.

Only Mexicans by birth or naturalization and Mexican companies have the right to acquire ownership in lands, waters and their appurtenances, or to obtain concessions to develop mines, waters or mineral fuels in the Republic of Mexico. The Nation may grant the same right to foreigners, provided they agree before the Department of Foreign Affairs to be considered Mexicans in respect to such property, and accordingly not to invoke the protection of their Governments in respect to the same, under penalty, in case of breach, of forfeiture to the Nation of property so acquired. Within a zone of 100 kilometers from the frontiers, and of 50 kilometers from the sea coast, no foreigner shall under any conditions acquire direct ownership of lands and waters.

· · ·

VII.

The Federal and State laws shall determine within their respective jurisdictions those cases in which the occupation of private property shall be considered of public utility; and in accordance with the said laws the administrative authorities shall make the corresponding declaration. The amount fixed as compensation for the expropriated property shall be based on the sum at which the said property shall be valued for fiscal purposes in the catastral or revenue offices, whether this value be that manifested by the owner or merely impliedly accepted by reason of the payment of his taxes on such a basis, to which there shall be added ten per cent. The increased value which the property in question may have acquired through improvements made subsequent to the date of the fixing of the fiscal value shall be the only matter subject to expert opinion and to judicial determination. The same procedure shall be observed in respect to objects whose value is not recorded in the revenue offices.

.   .   .

United States Tariff Rates on Imports of Zinc and Lead, 1897–1930

(Duties in Cents per Pound)

	Tariff Act				
	1897	1909	1913[1]	1922	1930
Zinc:					
Ore, below 10% Zn	Free	Free	10% (1/4¢)	Free	1–1/2
10 to 20%		1/4	10% (1/4¢)	1/2	1–1/2
20 to 25%		1/2	10% (1/4¢)	1	1–1/2
over 25%		1	10% (1/4¢)	1–1/2	1–1/2
Slab zinc		1–3/8	15% (2/3¢)	1–3/4	1–3/4
Zinc dust		1–3/8	15% (1–1/4¢)	1–3/4	1–3/4
Sheets, plain		1–5/8	15% (5/8¢)	2	2
Old and worn-out		1	15% (4/5¢)	1–1/2	1–1/2
Lead:					
Ores	1–1/2	1–1/2	3/4¢	1–1/2	1–1/2
Base bullion	2–1/8	2–1/8	25% (1¢)	2–1/8	2–1/8
Lead pigs, bars, old	2–1/8	2–1/8	25% (1–1/16¢)	2–1/8	2–1/8
Sheets, pipe, shot	2–1/2	2–3/8	25% (2¢)	2–3/8	2–3/8

[1]The Tariff Act of 1913 specified the duties in percentages. (In effect from October 3, 1913 to September 21, 1922.) Items in parentheses indicate average duty collected. The average duty collected on lead by the Tariff Act of 1913 was 1.1¢ per pound.

SOURCE: Morris J. Elsing, "Lead, Zinc, Copper and the Tariff," *Mining & Metallurgy*, XIII (Oct. 1932), 450.

United States Tariff Rates
on Imports of Lead, 1930–58

(Duties in Cents per Pound on Lead Content)

Tariff Paragraph and Description	Tariff Act of 1930		
	Statutory Rate[1]	Trade Agreement Modification	
		Rate	Effective Date and Trade Agreement
Par. 391:			
Lead-bearing ores, flue dust, and mattes of all kinds.	1-1/2¢	3/4¢[2]	Jan. 30, 1943, Mexico[3]
		3/4¢[2]	June 6, 1951, GATT[4]
Par. 392:			
Lead bullion or base bullion, lead in pigs and bars, lead dross, reclaimed lead, scrap lead, antimonial lead, antimonial scrap lead, and type metal.	2-1/8¢	1-1/16¢[2,5]	Jan. 30, 1943, Mexico[3]
		1-1/16¢[2,5]	June 6, 1951, GATT[4]
Alloys or combinations of lead not specially provided for.	2-1/8¢	1-1/16¢	Jan. 30, 1943, Mexico[3]
		1-1/16¢	June 6, 1951, GATT[4]

[1]Currently applicable to the products of Communist-dominated countries or areas designated (during 1951–53) by the President pursuant to Sec. 5 of the Trade Agreements Extension Act of 1951. This rate was applicable to products of all countries, effective Jan. 1, 1951, when the trade agreement with Mexico terminated, until June 6, 1951, when a new rate of duty pursuant to the General Agreement on Tariffs and Trade (GATT) became effective.

[2]Duty suspended from June 20, 1948, to June 30, 1949, inclusive (Public Law 725, 80th Cong.); and again from Feb. 12, 1952, to June 25, 1952, inclusive (Public Law 257, 82d Cong.).

[3]Trade agreement with Mexico terminated effective Jan. 1, 1951.

[4]General Agreement on Tariffs and Trade.

[5]Duty on scrap lead was suspended for practically the entire period from Mar. 14, 1942, to June 30, 1952, and the duty on antimonial scrap lead from Mar. 14, 1942, to June 30, 1956 (Public Law 497, 77th Cong.; Public Law 384, 80th Cong.; Public Law 613, 80th Cong.; Public Law 869, 81st Cong.; Public Law 66, 82d Cong.; Public Law 535, 82d Cong.; Public Law 221, 83d Cong.; Public Law 678, 83d Cong.; and Public Law 66, 84th Cong.).

Source: U.S. Tariff Commission, *Lead and Zinc: A Report to the President* (Washington, D.C., Apr. 1958), p. 123.

United States Tariff Rates on Imports of Zinc, 1930–58

(Duties in Cents per Pound)

Tariff Paragraph and Description	Tariff Act of 1930		
	Statutory Rate[1]	Trade Agreement Modification	
		Rate	Effective Date and Trade Agreement
Par. 393:			
Zinc-bearing ores of all kinds, except pyrites containing not more than 3 per cent zinc. (Duty on zinc content only.)	1-1/2¢	1-1/5¢	Jan. 1, 1939, Canada
		3/4¢	Jan. 30, 1943, Mexico[2]
		3/4¢	Jan. 1, 1948, GATT[3]
		3/5¢	June 6, 1951, GATT[3]
Par. 394:			
Zinc in blocks, pigs, or slabs.	1-3/4¢	1-2/5¢	Jan. 1, 1939, Canada
		7/8¢	Jan. 30, 1943, Mexico[2]
		7/8¢	Jan. 1, 1948, GATT[3]
		7/10¢[4]	June 6, 1951, GATT[3]
Old and worn-out zinc (fit only to be remanufactured), zinc dross, and zinc skimmings.	1-1/2¢[5]	3/4¢[5]	Jan. 30, 1943, Mexico[2]
		3/4¢[5]	Jan. 1, 1948, GATT[3]

[1]Currently applicable to products of Communist-dominated countries or areas designated (during 1951–53) by the President pursuant to Sec. 5 of the Trade Agreements Extension Act of 1951.

[2]Trade agreement with Mexico terminated effective Jan. 1, 1951.

[3]General Agreement on Tariffs and Trade.

[4]Duty suspended from Feb. 12, 1952, to July 23, 1952, inclusive (Public Law 258, 82d Cong.).

[5]Duty on zinc scrap suspended for practically the entire period from Mar. 14, 1942, to June 30, 1953, inclusive (Public Law 497, 77th Cong.; Public Laws 384 and 613, 80th Cong.; Public Law 869, 81st Cong.; and Public Laws 66 and 535, 82d Cong.).

Source: U.S. Tariff Commission, *Lead and Zinc: A Report to the President* (Washington, D.C., Apr. 1958), p. 124.

Value of Net Product Produced in Mexican Territory by Economic Activities

(Amounts in Millions of Pesos at Current Prices)

Activity	7–Year Period 1939–45		5–Year Period 1946–50		4–Year Period 1951–54	
	Annual Av.	Pct.	Annual Av.	Pct.	Annual Av.	Pct.
Commerce	2,994.5	28.0	9,531.6	31.9	16,935.1	29.1
Agriculture	2,126.7	19.9	5,536.2	18.5	11,519.4	19.8
Manufacturing	1,880.4	17.6	5,423.9	18.2	9,360.9	16.1
Mining	322.1	3.0	772.6	2.6	1,438.8	2.5
Construction	207.5	1.9	575.1	1.9	1,040.4	1.8
Petroleum	154.9	1.4	455.4	1.5	826.7	1.4
Elec. Power	54.5	0.5	142.8	0.5	293.4	0.5
All Others	2,967.1	27.7	7,417.1	24.9	16,800.7	28.8
Total	10,707.7		29,854.6		58,215.4	

SOURCE: James G. Maddox, American Universities Field Staff, *Report*, June 14, 1956, p. 11, compiled from figures in International Bank for Reconstruction and Development, *Economic Development of Mexico* (1939–1950) and studies by the Department of Economic Studies of the Bank of Mexico.

Notes

1. For the material and organization of this short survey I am indebted to Professor Charles H. Behre, Jr., who kindly lent me the paper "The Mineralogenic Provinces of Mexico," written by himself and Mr. Armine F. Banfield for presentation to the 20th International Geological Congress meeting at Mexico City in 1956. This account is based, in large part, on the typescript of that address. The completed study will appear in the *Comptes Rendus* of the 20°Congreso Geológico Internacional (1956) under the title "Regional Zoning of the Mineral Deposits of Mexico." An abstract appears in the *Resumenes de los trabajos presentados* (1956), pp. 84–85. The following surveys of the geology of Mexico are recommended: Manuel Santillan, "Synopsis of the Geology of Mexico," *Bulletin of the American Association of Petroleum Geologists,* XX (1936), No. 4 (reprinted in the *Mineral Survey,* III [Nov. 1935], 19–22); Ezequiel Ordóñez, "Principal Physiographic Provinces of Mexico," *ibid.,* 1277–1307; Andrés Villafaña, "La industria minerometalúrgica en México," *Boletín de minas y petroleo* (hereinafter cited as *Bol. de min. y pet.*), XVI (May 1945), 8–14; E. Ordónes, "Las provincias fisiograficas de México," *Revista geográfica* (Mexico), I (1941), 133–181; Jenaro González Reyna, *Riqueza minera y yacimientos minerales de México* (Mexico, 1956), pp. 19–54 (and citations, pp. 53–54); T. P. Clendenin, "Mexico's Metallic Ore Deposits," *Mining Engineering* (hereinafter cited as *Min. Engin.*), III (Oct. 1951), 860–863; Robert T. Hill (U.S. Geological Survey, "The Geographic and Geologic Features of Mexico and Their Relation to the Mineral Products," American Institute of Mining and Metallurgical Engineers *Transactions* (hereinafter cited as AIME *Trans.*), XXXII (1902), pp. 163–178; E. Ordóñez, "Las principales unidades geográficas mexicanas y la distribución de los criaderos minerales," *Mexican Mining Journal* (hereinafter referred to as *Mex. Min. J.*), Feb. and Mar., 1916, 105–106. Also see M. Santillan, "El Cobre en México," in 16th International Geological Congress, *Copper Resources of the World* (Washington, D.C., 1935), I, pp. 379–406; and J. González Reyna, "Geología, paragenesis y reservas de los yacimientos de plomo y zinc de México," in 18th International Geological Congress, *Report Pt. vii: The Geology, Paragenesis and Reserves of Lead and Zinc* (London, 1950), pp. 121–142. An excellent map depicting Mexican ore deposits is the "Carta general minera de la República Mexicana," published by the Secretaría de la Economía Nacional. Also see the "Carta geológica de la República Mexicana," published by the Instituto de Geología under the direction of Ing. Teodoro Flores in 1942.

2. González Reyna, *Riqueza minera,* maps in cover pocket.

3. James E. Harding (Manager, Mina El Arco), "Salvaging a $300,000 invest-

ment in a Lower California Gold Mine," *Mining and Metallurgy* (hereinafter cited as *Min. & Met.*), XVIII (Aug. 1937), 378–379.

4. G. J. Mitchell, "Effect of Erosion on Mineralized Areas in Northern Sonora," *Engineering and Mining Journal* (hereinafter cited as *E&MJ*), CX (Dec. 4, 1920), 1081–82.

5. Quoted in Percy F. Martin, *Mexico's Treasure-House* (New York, 1906), p. 16.

6. R. Gentum, "What Is the Biggest Nugget?" *E&MJ*, CXVII (Apr. 5, 1924), 567. Baron Alexander von Humboldt pointed out that Mexican ores were not high grade but so abundant that efficient exploitation made them profitable. See *Essai politique sur le royaume de la Nouvelle Espagne* (Paris, 1811), II, pp. 510–514, quoted in Clement Motten, *Mexican Silver and the Enlightenment* (Philadelphia, 1950), p. 29.

7. Letter to *E&MJ*, CXVI (Dec. 1, 1923), 949.

8. H. W. Pudan, "What Constitutes Ore in Mexico?" *Mineral Survey* (hereinafter cited as *Min. Sur.*), IV (Nov. 1936), 27–28.

9. *E&MJ*, CXXI (Jan. 2, 1926), 22.

10. Carlos Díaz Dufoo, *México y los capitales extranjeros* (Mexico, 1918), pp. 146–149, 170–171.

CHAPTER 2

1. For general discussions of the art of metal extraction and metal working in pre-Colombian America see S. K. Lothrop and C. W. Root, *Metals from the Cenote of Sacrifice, Chichén Itzá, Yucatan* ("Harvard University, Peabody Museum Memoirs," X:2), Cambridge, Mass., 1952, pp. 7–27 and Paul Rivet and Henri Arsandaux, *La métallurgie en Amérique précolombienne* ("Université de Paris, Travaux et memoires de l'Institut d'Ethnologie," XXXIX), Paris, 1946, pp. 8–33 (esp. pp. 23–24); pp. 121–131 (esp. pp. 123, 126–127); and pp. 173–187. Also worth consulting are the following articles in the Rivet and Arsandaux numbered bibliography: Bergsøe (Nos. 29 and 30), Lothrop (No. 165), and Saville (No. 277). Rather interesting comments are made by A. M. Tozzer in his translation of *Landa's Relación de las cosas de Yucatán* ("Harvard University, Peabody Museum Papers," XVIII), Cambridge, Mass., 1941, No. 951, p. 182. Bernardino Sahagún discusses aboriginal "mining" in his *Historia general de las cosas de Nueva España, libro X, cap. ix.* (In the edition printed in Mexico in 1938, see Vol. III, pp. 284–285.) For evidence of "Indian mines" see Manuel Orozco y Berra, *Historia antigua y de la conquista de México* (Mexico, 1880), II, pp. 303, 313 ff.; and Trinidad García, "Trabajos de las minas de cobre antes de la conquista," *Los mineros mexicanos* (Mexico, 1895), pp. 208–209, 210–211. The basic arguments against believing in the existence of Indian mines were well summed up by Antonio del Castillo as early as 1856. See A. del Castillo, "Minas en México," in M. Orozco y Berra, ed., *Apendice al diccionario universal de historia y geografía* (Mexico, 1856), II ("IX de la obra"), pp. 828–829. T. A. Rickard in his authoritative *Man and Metals* (New York, 1932), II, pp. 682–685, subjects the viewpoint and exposition of those supporting the existence of Indian mining and smelting activities in Mexico to a strong critique. Modesto Bargalló in his *La minería y la metalurgia en la América española durante la época colonial* (Mexico, 1955) discusses the contemporary evidence in detail

(pp. 24–34) but is rather ambiguous in his use of the term "smelting," which ought to be used to describe only the chemical processes of reduction, not merely the melting employed to separate mixed native metals. In discussing the reduction of ores, he reverts to the conditional tense, and his unusually heavily footnoted study lacks citations on this point.

2. Bargalló, *La minería*, pp. 238–239. Also see Rickard, *Man and Metals*, II, pp. 554–556, 805; George C. Greenwell, "Gunpowder in Mines," Manchester Geological Society *Transactions* (May 31, 1870), pp. 1–2; H. C. Chellson, "From Gunpowder to Modern Dynamite," *E&MJ*, CXXXVII (May 1936), 231–234; B. F. Tillson, "Mining—Man's First Useful Art," *Min. Engin.*, I (Feb. 1949), 37. Greenwell places the introduction of gunpowder blasting in England in the 1630's; Rickard places it in the 1680's.

3. Bailey W. Diffie, *Latin American Civilization: Colonial Period* (Harrisburg, Pa., 1945), pp. 106–108. The probable use of Indians as prospectors by the Spaniards is discussed by H. W. Purdan, "Some Aspects of Mexican Mining Geology," *Min. Sur.*, III (Oct. 1935), 22. Bargalló appears to agree. (*La minería*, p. 54.) See the critique of Trinidad García, "El descubrimiento del Mineral de Tasco," *Mineros mexicanos*, pp. 133–135; and Rickard, *Man and Metals*, II, pp. 683–685.

4. Diffie, *Latin American Civilization*, Chap. vi; G. Crespo y Martínez, *México; industria minera; estudio de su evolución* (para la grande obra "México—Su evolución social"), Mexico, 1903, pp. 32–33. Also see Fausto de Elhuyar, *Memoria sobre el influjo de la minería en la agricultura, industria, población y civilización de la Nueva España* (Madrid, 1825); and Gustavo P. Serrano, *Mining and Its Influence on the Progress and Development of Mexico* (Mexico, 1951). In *leyes* 1 and 2, *título* XVIII, *libro* IV, of the *Recopilación de las leyes de las Indias*, the declaration of royal ownership and the necessity for licensing prospectors and declaring their discoveries applied not only to gold and silver mines, but to mines of "other metals." (Henry W. Halleck, *A Collection of Mining Laws of Spain and Mexico* [San Francisco, 1859], pp. 130–131.) Also see Diffie, *Latin American Civilization*, pp. 118–119; and Clarence H. Haring, *The Spanish Empire in America* (New York, 1947), pp. 268–269. For the paucity of workings other than precious metals, see Bargalló, *La minería*, pp. 213, 294–295.

5. García, "El descubrimiento del Mineral de Tasco," *Mineros mexicanos*, pp. 135–139, 143. Bargalló lists much activity but little in the way of notable results. (*La minería*, pp. 55–59, 61.)

6. García, *Mineros mexicanos*, pp. 46–48, 108–110. This and the following accounts of the discovery of other mines in Mexico have been taken from García, *Mineros mexicanos*, pp. 114–116, 121–124, 144–145, 152, 156, 188–190, 191–193. Also see Walter Howe, *The Mining Guild of New Spain and Its Tribunal General* (Cambridge, Mass., 1949), pp. 4–8; H. R. Wagner, "Early Silver Mining in New Spain," *Revista de Historia de América*, No. 14 (June 1942), 49–71; Bargalló, *La minería*, pp. 61–65; and M. O. de Mendízabal, "Los minerales de Pachuca y Real del Monte en la época colonial," *El trimestre económico*, VIII (July–Sept. 1941), 253–309.

7. For a subsequent history of Mexican mining during the colonial period, see Bargalló, *La minería*, Chaps. xviii and xxiii and Clement Motten, *Mexican Silver and the Enlightenment* (Philadelphia, 1950), Chaps. v and vi.

8. By far the best account is in Bargalló, *La minería*, Chaps. vii, xx, and xxvii. Also see Motten, *Mexican Silver*, Chap. ii (esp. pp. 14–15). Scattered throughout Motten's study are numerous observations on the methods used to exploit mines in colonial Mexico.

9. See the accounts of Gen. Lew Wallace in "Mines of Santa Eulalia, Chihuahua," *Harper's Magazine*, XXXV (Nov. 1867), 692; T.A. Rickard, *Journeys of Observation*

(San Francisco, 1907), p. 107; and J. P. Kimball, "On the Silver Mines of Santa Eulalia," *American Journal of Science and Arts*, 2nd Ser., XLIX (Mar. 1870), 167–168. Motten claims that the sacks may have weighed up to 300 lbs! (*Mexican Silver*, p. 18.) Also see Alberto Grothe, "Adelantados de la minería en México durante el siglo del centenario de Independencia," Instituto Mexicano de Minas y Metalurgia, *Informes y Memorias* (hereinafter cited as IMMM, *Informes*), II (1911–12), p. 53; S. B. Newell, "Mexican Methods of Mining," Institution of Mining and Metallurgy (London) (hereinafter cited as Inst. of Min. and Met. [London], *Transactions*, VI (1897–98), pp. 130–137; and Alan Probert, "Early Silver Capitals of Mexico," 3rd Congress of the Pan-American Institute of Mining Engineers and Geologists held jointly with 1st Congress of Mineral Resources of Mexico and the Mid-year meeting #172 of the AIME (Oct. 29–31—Nov. 4, 1951); Robert G. Cleland, "The Mining Industry of Mexico: A Historical Sketch," *Mining and Scientific Press* (hereinafter cited as *Min. & Sci. Press*), CXXIII (Nov. 5, 1921), 18.

10. The most exhaustive survey of this beneficiation process is in Bargalló, *La minería*, Chaps. ix, xvii, xxi, and xxvii. For a general survey of the methods used in the late 18th and early 19th centuries, see Motten, *Mexican Silver*, pp. 21–28 and Chaps. v and vi. For contemporary discussions see Francisco Javier de Gamboa, *Comentarios a las ordenanzas de minas* (Madrid, 1761), Chap. xxii; Alexander von Humboldt, *Ensayo político sobre el reino de la Nueva España* (Spanish trans., Mexico, 1941), III, pp. 273–302. Articles have also appeared in the AIME *Trans.*, XI, pp. 61–78; XXIX, 116–121; XXXII, 276–285, 484–497; Inst. of Min. and Met. (London), *Trans.*, VII, pp. 229–237; XIII, 111–114. On Medina see Motten, *Mexican Silver*, p. 22, and Haring, *Spanish Empire*, pp. 262–263 and citations there.

11. Bargalló, *La minería*, Chap. viii; W. M. Brodie, "Metallurgy of Native-Silver Ores of Southwestern Chihuahua," *E&MJ*, CI (Feb. 12, 1916), 297–300.

12. Gamboa, *Comentarios*, Chap. xxi, Par. 17. (Trans. by Richard Heathfield, *Commentaries on the Mining Ordinances of New Spain* [London, 1830], II, p. 159.)

13. *Ibid.*, Chap. xxi, Pars. 21–30. (Heathfield's trans., pp. 162–167.)

14. Cleland, "The Mining Industry of Mexico," 16. Also see the sketch of mine credit agencies in "Colaboración de la Comisión de Fomento Minero," in Primer Congreso Minero Nacional, *Memoria* (hereinafter cited as PCMN, *Memoria*), Mexico, 1948, pp. 337–338.

15. From excerpt quoted in Luis Chavez Orozco, *Revolución industrial, revolución política* (Mexico, 1937), pp. 14–15. Also see pp. 12–14. For a discussion of the "Representación's" significance in the development of Mexican mining, see Howe, *Mining Guild of New Spain*, pp. 14–15, 40–46.

16. Early Spanish legislation in the matter of mining was rather haphazard, with many decrees issued after 1493 as the Crown groped for a policy. Finally the Spanish mining codes of 1559, 1563, and 1584 were applied to Mexico as well as certain royal orders applicable to the special conditions in America. See Gamboa, *Comentarios, passim,* and Juan de Solórzano Pereira, *Política indiana* (Madrid, 1647), libro VI, cap. i. One student has remarked: ". . . it is clear that for most of the colonial period the Crown issued only stop-gap legislation. It was not interested in long-range planning (except to curb abuse of the Indians) and merely asked that the flow of wealth be maintained and increased. The laws, cedulas, and ordinances designed to accomplish this may have helped in special cases, but by and large they served only to make every concern of New Spain secondary to mining and to establish the mineros (generally speaking, anybody associated with the mining industry) as a highly privileged class." (Motten, *Mexican Silver*, p. 15.) An excellent short survey of the Spanish mining laws preceding 1783 is to be found in M. de la Peña's *El dominio directo del Soberano en las minas de México*, 2 vols. (Mexico, 1928), I, pp. 13–42. The background of the passage of the Ordenanzas

of 1783 is given in Howe, *Mining Guild of New Spain,* Chaps. i and ii, and in Motten, *Mexican Silver,* pp. 40–45. For an excellent short summary of the major provisions of the Ordenanzas, see Howe, *Mining Guild,* pp. 62–77. The Ordenanzas of 1783 was reprinted many times during its one-hundred-year life. A list of editions of the Ordenanzas of 1783 and its many revisions is to be found in John T. Vance and Helen Clagett, *Guide to the Law and Legal Literature of Mexico* (Washington, D.C., 1945), pp. 202–205. In the edition *Ordenanzas de minería y colección de las órdenes y decretos de esta materia,* Nueva edición dispuesta por C. N. (Paris and Mexico, 1881), *leyes* 1 and 2 of *título* V appear on page 68.

17. The idea of the bank was discussed by Gamboa in 1761. (*Comentarios,* Chap. vii, Pars. 48–126.) The matter was pressed again by Velásquez de León and Lassaga in their "Representación" of 1774. Also see Howe, *Mining Guild of New Spain,* pp. 41–43, 70–74, 301–369; and Bargalló, *La minería,* Chap. xxvi.

18. J. L. Tamayo, "La minería de Nueva España en 1794" *Trimestre económico,* X, 287–319. The study of this development is the theme of Motten's book, *Mexican Silver and the Enlightenment.*

19. Motten, *Mexican Silver;* Arthur Whitaker, "The Elhuyar Mining Missions and the Enlightenment," *Hispanic American Historical Review,* XXXI (Nov. 1951), 557–585.

20. Diffie, *Latin American Civilization,* Chap. xviii; Howe, *Mining Guild of New Spain,* pp. 440–449. For an excellent description of a colonial Spanish mining community, see Robert C. West, *The Mining Community in Northern New Spain: the Parral Mining District* (Berkeley, Calif., 1949).

21. For differences in the estimates of gold and silver production in the 16th century, see Diffie, *Latin American Civilization,* p. 114. He also discusses total production and coinage figures in *ibid.,* pp. 113–114, 374, and 380. The 18th- and 19th-century figures are from the estimates of A. Soetbeer reprinted in the *Anuario de estadística minera, 1922* (hereinafter cited as *An. de estad. min.*), pp. 42–43. Also see Howe, *Mining Guild of New Spain,* pp. 453–458, and Diffie, "Estimates of Potosí Mineral Production, 1545–1555," *Hispanic American Historical Review,* XX (May 1940), 275–282.

22. Chavez Orozco, *Revolución industrial,* p. 9.

23. Mariano Galvan Rivera (ed.), *Colección de órdenes y decretos de la soberana junta provisional gubernativa,* 1821–23 (2d ed., Mexico, 1829), II, p. 192.

24. Alfred Tischendorf, *Great Britain and Mexico in the Era of Porfirio Díaz* (hereinafter cited as *Gt. Br. and Mex.*), Durham, N.C., 1961, pp. 23–31; J. Fred Rippy, *British Investments in Latin America, 1822–1949* (Minneapolis, Minn., 1959), pp. 24–25; Cleland, "Mining Industry of Mexico," 638–639; Leland H. Jenks, *The Migration of British Capital to 1875* (New York, 1927), pp. 54–64.

25. Tischendorf, *Gt. Br. and Mex.,* loc. cit.; E. J. Howell, *Mexico: Its Progress and Commercial Possibilities* (London, 1892), pp. 63–64; J. R. Southworth and P. G. Holms, *El directorio oficial minero de México* (hereinafter cited as *El directorio*), Liverpool, 1908, X, pp. 6–7; Alfred James, "British Mining Investments in Mexico," *E&MJ,* XCI (Feb. 25, 1911), 411.

26. H. A. C. Jenison, "The Mining History of Mexico," *E&MJ,* CXV (Feb. 24, 1923), 368.

27. *Colección de los decretos y órdenes de interes común, que dictó el gobierno provisional en virtud de las bases de Tacubaya* (Mexico: Imprenta de J. M. Lara, 1850), I, pp. 374–377; II, pp. 17–18, 221–229, 424–425; III, pp. 19–20, 25, 62–63, 68–69. Production figures are from Soetbeer. (See Note 21 above.)

28. Cleland, "Mining Industry of Mexico," 639. For the workings of the credit system, see Rickard, *Journeys of Observation,* pp. 174–175, 197–198; and Wallace, "Mines of Santa Eulalia," 702.

CHAPTER 3

1. An excellent general survey of the establishment of the Porfirian state is José C. Valadés, *El Porfirismo, Historia de un régimen*, 2 vols. (Mexico, 1941–48). For a detailed survey of the mining industry and government policy during the late 1860's and early 1870's, see Francisco R. Calderon, *La vida económica en la República restaurada* [1867–76] (Vol. II of the *Historia moderna de México*, Daniel Cosío Villegas [ed.]), Mexico, 1955, pp. 115–174. Also see Miguel A. Quintana, *Los ensayos monetarios como consecuencia de la baja de la plata* (Mexico, 1931), pp. 55–59; Walter V. Scholes, *Mexican Politics during the Juárez Regime, 1855–1872* (Columbia, Mo., 1957), pp. 143–148; G. Armando Servin, "Nuestra política tributaria de 1869–1911," *Trimestre económico*, VIII (Oct.–Dec. 1940), 425–440; Secretaría de Estado y del Despacho de Hacienda y Crédito Público, *El erario federal en el último decenio, 1869 a 1879* (Mexico, 1879). For a description of mule trains, guards, and schedules from mining centers to the Mexico City mint see John W. Foster, *Diplomatic Memoirs* (Boston, 1909), I, pp. 71–73.

2. Re-establishing relations with the European nations which had supported Maximilian was difficult. See Tischendorf, *Gt. Br. and Mex.*, Chap. i; A. P. Tischendorf, "The Anglo–Mexican Claims Commission, 1884–95," *Hispanic American Historical Review*, XXXVII (Nov. 1957), 471–479; and Scholes, *Mexican Politics*, pp. 144–145.

3. J. D. Long, "American Investments in Mexico," *American Industries* (Apr. 1911), 12.

4. *Código de minería de la República Mexicana* (Mexico, 1884). In lieu of a more detailed footnoting of the following section, the reader may refer to Eduardo Martínez Baca, "Historical Sketch of Mining Legislation in Mexico," AIME *Trans.*, XXXII (1902), pp. 520–565 (esp. pp. 538–557), also printed as *Reseña historica de la legislación minera en México* (Mexico, 1901). Also see Richard E. Chism, "The New Mining Code of Mexico," AIME *Trans.*, XIV (1885–86), pp. 34–53. For a detailed listing of the drafts and editions of the law of 1884, see Vance and Clagett, *Guide*, pp. 204–205.

5. Pedro Bejarano, et al., *Proyecto del código de minería de la República Mexicana formada por la comisión que nombró la Secretaría de Fomento* (Mexico, 1884); Santiago Ramirez, *Apuntes para un proyecto de código de minería* (Mexico, 1884); Ignacio Vallarta, *Dictamen sobre el proyecto de código de minería* (Culiacan, 1884); M. de la Peña, *El dominio directo*, I, p. 144.

6. *Recopilación de leyes, decretos y providencias de los poderes legislativo y ejecutivo de la Union formada por la redacción del "Diario oficial"* (Mexico, 1888), XLVIII (Jan.–June 1887), pp. 269–275. For an account of the writing of the act, see Herbert A. Crossman, "The Early Career of José Iyes Limantour, 1854–1886" (Unpubl. doctoral diss., Harvard University, 1949), 199–201.

7. See Note 3 above.

8. C. K. Leith, *World Minerals and World Politics* (New York, 1931), p. 98; W. Feuerlein and E. Hannan, *Dólares en la América Latina* (Mexico, 1944), pp. 76–77.

9. Cleland, "The Mining Industry of Mexico," 641; David A. Wells, *A Study of*

Mexico (New York, 1887), p. 161. For an interesting pro and con discussion of the role of American prospectors in Mexico, see the letters of Cyrus Tolman and J. N. Nevius in *E&MJ*, LXXVIII (July 7, 1904), 29; (Aug. 11, 1904), 213.

10. Anon., "Americans Develop Metal Mines After Mexicans Find Them," *E&MJ*, CXV (Mar. 17, 1923), 509; G. Montes de Oca, "Reseña minera del Estado de Jalisco," *Boletín minero* (hereinafter cited as *Bol. min.*), XXII (Oct. 1926), 224; L. de Silva, "El Estado de Sinaloa," *ibid.*, X (July–Aug. 1920), 11–23.

11. R. T. Hill, "Santa Eulalia District, Mexico," *E&MJ*, LXXVI (Aug. 1, 1903), 160.

12. For a description of the methods used in Mexican mines and ore treatment plants toward the end of the 19th century, see J. H. Palmer, "Mining in Mexico: Native Methods of Working," *The Mining Journal*, LXIV (Mar. 24, 1894), 328; C. Launay, "Mines et Industries Minières," in M. M. Bonaparte and L. Bourgeois (eds.), *Le Mexique au Début de XX⁰ Siècle*, 2 vols. (Paris, 1904), I, pp. 299–304; Crespo y Martínez, *México; industria minera*, pp. 133–136, 141–147. J. W. Malcolmson, "Mining in Mexico," *E&MJ*, LXXVII (Jan. 7, 1904), 22; *E&MJ*, LXXVIII (Dec. 8, 1904), 902; J. N. Nevius, "The Mexican Malacate," *E&MJ*, LXXIV (Sept. 27, 1902), 410–411; W. B. Devereux, "A Native Method of Smelting Copper Ores in Jalisco, Mexico," AIME *Trans.*, XI (1882–83), pp. 106–109; W. L. Austin, "Smelting Notes from Chihuahua," *ibid.*, XII (1883–84), pp. 185–192; P. Frazer, "Certain . . . Mines in . . . Nuevo Leon and Coahuila, Mexico," *ibid.*, 542–553, 565–566; W. L. Austin, "A Mexican Cupellation-Hearth," *ibid.*, XIII (1884–85), pp. 41–45; R. E. Chism, "The Vallecillo Mines, Mexico," *ibid.*, pp. 351–369; R. E. Chism, "Sierra Mojada, Mexico," *ibid.*, XV (1886–87), 554–571; Anon., "On Adobe and Other Makeshift Furnaces," *E&MJ*, LXXVI (July 11, 1903), 49–51; (July 18, 1903), 85–86.

13. J. H. Clemes, "The Lixiviation of Silver Ores," Institution of Civil Engineers (London), *Minutes of Proceedings*, CXXV (1896), pp. 88–125; F. W. Clark, "Lixiviation and Amalgamation Tests," AIME *Trans.*, XIV (1885–86), 395–399; Ottokar Hofmann, "Trough Lixiviation," *ibid.*, XVI (1887–88), 662–692; F. H. McDowell, "American Mining Machinery in Mexico and Central America," *ibid.*, XIII (1884–85), pp. 408–417; E. Stein, "Chloridizing Roasting of Silver Ores in Mexico," *E&MJ*, LXXVIII (Sept. 1, 1904), 346–347. For detailed descriptions of the patio process, pan amalgamation, and lixiviation as practiced during the decade 1890–1900 in various parts of Mexico—including the Hacienda San Francisco, Pachuca; El Bote, Zacatecas; Minas Prietas, Sonora; San Francisco del Oro, Chihuahua; and Sombrerete, Zacatecas—see Henry F. Collins, *The Metallurgy of Lead and Silver* (London, 1900), Part II, pp. 29–251.

14. John Hays Hammond, *Autobiography*, 2 vols. (New York, 1935), I, pp. 159–168; J. Baragwanath, *Pay Streak* (New York, 1936), pp. 202–219.

15. W. A. Prichard, "Looking for Mines in Mexico," *Mining Magazine* (hereinafter cited as *Min. Mag.*), I (Nov. 1909), 205–212; D. V. Navarro, "Algunas de los factores económicos que han influído en el desarrollo de la industria minera en México," *Bol. min.*, XXVII (Feb. 1929), 92.

16. Hammond, *Autobiography*, I, pp. 109–143.

17. J. Castanedo, "Manera de resolver las oposiciones conforme a las anteriores legislaciones mineras y a la actual Ley de Industrias," *Bol. min.*, XXIV (Sept. 1927), 143. Sometimes the offer of better wages only served to demoralize the workers who had little experience with excess cash. Letter, J. N. Nevius to *E&MJ*, LXXVIII (Aug. 11, 1904), 213. Also see Walter E. Weyl, "Labor Conditions in Mexico," *Bulletin of the Department of Labor* (Washington, D.C., 1902), No. 38 (Jan. 1902), pp. 1–94 (esp. pp. 27–50, 50–56); A. H. Rogers, "Character and Habits of the Mexican Miner," *E&MJ*, LXXXV (Apr. 4, 1908), 700–701; E. A. H. Tays, "Present Labor Conditions in Mexico," *E&MJ*, LXXXIV (Oct. 5, 1907), 621–624;

Southworth and Holms, *El directorio,* p. 9; *E&MJ,* LXXXIX (Mar. 26, 1910), 679; Anon., "What Mexico Needs," *E&MJ,* CVIII (Oct. 11, 1919), 614; Letters to the Editor by George Laird, *E&MJ,* CIX (Jan. 31, 1920), 303; and R. B. Brinsmade, *E&MJ,* CXIV (Nov. 11, 1922), 842.

18. Santiago Ramirez, *Informe ... de su exploración en la Sierra Mojada, ...* (Mexico, 1880), pp. 5–8, 57–58; Richard E. Chism, "Sierra Mojada, Mexico," *AIME Trans.,* XV (1886–87), pp. 542–588 (by far the best historical and technical work on the district); J. W. Malcolmson, "Sierra Mojada, Coahuila, Mexico, and Its Ore Deposits," *ibid.,* XXXII (1902), pp. 100–104; S. F. Shaw, "Ore Deposits of Sierra Mojada," *ibid.,* LXVIII (1928), p. 571; Ivan Ragaz, "Comments," *ibid.,* 584; S. F. Shaw, "Constancia Mining Properties in Coahuila," *E&MJ,* CXIII (Mar. 29, 1922), 722.

19. Ramirez, *Informe,* pp. 54–57, 62–63; Persifor Frazer, *Geological and Mineral Strikes in Nuevo León and Coahuila, Mexico* (Philadelphia, 1884), p. 6; Shaw, "Constancia Mining Properties," 723; Percy F. Martin, *Mexico of the XXth Century,* 2 vols. (London, 1907), II, pp. 284–285. This plant replaced a most interesting primitive installation described by Chism, "Sierra Mojada," pp. 554–568. Also see J. Fluery, "El Mineral Sierra Mojada" (report of a visit in Jan., 1902), *Boletín de la Secretaría de Fomento* (1905), 6–9; J. Ibarra, "Informe sobre la visita de inspección practicada a las minas de la compañía minera 'La Constancia,' S.A.," *Bol. min.,* VII (May–June 1919), 506–507; O. H. Hahn, "On the Development of Silver Smelting in Mexico," Inst. of Min. and Met. (London), *Trans.* VIII (1899–1900), pp. 233–234; Ragaz, "Comments," *loc. cit.*

20. Ragaz, "Comments," *loc. cit.*

21. Letter from J. W. Neill, who was in charge of construction, to *E&MJ,* CXXVII (Jan. 5, 1929), 18–19; for technical and economic details see H. F. Collins, "Smelting Processes for the Extraction of Silver and Gold from Their Ores," in James Forrest (ed.), *Smelting Processes* (London, 1893), pp. 31–36. (This is a reprint of paper No. 2655 of the Institution of Civil Engineers [London], *Minutes of Proceedings,* CXII [Jan. 31, 1893], pp. 140–146.) Also see R. H. Vail, "El Paso Smelting Works," *E&MJ,* XCVIII (Sept. 12, 1914), 465–468; I. F. Marcosson, *Metal Magic: The Story of the American Smelting and Refining Company* (New York, 1949), pp. 149–150; J. W. Malcolmson, "Mining Development in Mexico during 1902," *E&MJ,* LXXV (Jan. 3, 1903), 36; R. T. Hill, "Notes from a Little Journey to Mexico," *E&MJ,* LXXIV (Aug. 21, 1902), 145.

22. *Anuario de legislación y jurisprudencia, sección de legislación* (Mexico, 1886), Año III (1886), pp. 510–511; *Recopilación de leyes ... formada por la redacción del "Diario oficial,"* LVIII, pp. 157–158, from the *Diario oficial,* XXIV, No. 143 (June 16, 1891); Malcolmson, "Sierra Mojada," p. 102; Malcolmson, "Mining in Mexico," *E&MJ,* LXXVII (Jan. 7, 1904), 21.

23. For an excellent detailed survey of the company and a biography of Gov. Shepherd, see David M. Pletcher, "City Boss: Alexander R. Shepherd," *Rails, Mines and Progress* (Ithaca, N.Y., 1958), Chap. vi. For a short history of the region, see Brodie, "Native Silver in Southwestern Chihuahua," *E&MJ,* LXXXIX (Mar. 26, 1910), 664; González Reyna, *Riqueza minera,* pp. 103–116, 120 (citations); J. González Reyna, *La industria minera en Chihuahua* (Mexico, 1946), pp. 60–61; *Min. Sur.,* X (Dec. 1942), 18–19.

24. Grant Shepherd, *The Silver Magnet* (New York, 1938), pp. 13–28. Grant Shepherd was a son of Gov. Shepherd and wrote a fine account of the working of the mine and of life in the district. Also see G. Law, "Primitive and Modern Mountain Transportation," *Min. Sur.,* II (Feb. 1935), 19.

25. Charles B. Dahlgren, *Historic Mines of Mexico* (New York, 1883), pp. 101, 219–220; *Mexican Year Book for 1909–1910,* p. 493; Southworth and Holms, *El directorio,* p. 34; Cleona Lewis, *America's Stake in International Investments*

(Washington, D.C., 1938), p. 202; Adolfo Dublán and José María Lozano (eds.), *Legislación mexicana, o colección de las disposiciones legislativas expedidas desde la independencia de la República* (Mexico, 1887), XVII, pp. 492–496.

26. Brodie, "Metallurgy of Native-Silver Ores of Southwestern Chihuahua," *E&MJ*, CI (Feb. 12, 1916), 299; J. C. F. Randolph, "The New Mill at Batopilas," AIME *Trans.*, X (1881–82), pp. 293–295, 298–300; M. R. Lamb, "Stories of the Batopilas Mines," *E&MJ*, LXXXV (Apr. 4, 1908), 689–691.

27. Randolph, "The New Mill at Batopilas," pp. 293-302; González Reyna, *Riqueza minera*, pp. 117, 122–124; Shepherd, *Silver Magnet*, pp. 60–63. For a description of the plant which was replaced, see Collins, *Metallurgy of Lead and Silver*, p. 32.

28. Obituary, "Alexander R. Shepherd," *E&MJ*, LXXIV (Sept. 20, 1902), 370 (for a portrait of the Governor, see *ibid.*, LXIX [Apr. 14, 1900], 433); *E&MJ*, LXXIV (Sept. 6, 1902), 313–314; (Dec. 13, 1902), 798; LXXV (Mar. 14, 1903), 420; (June 27, 1903), 979; González Reyna, *loc. cit.*; J. R. Southworth, *Las minas de México* (Mexico, 1905), pp. 77–78; Southworth and Holms, *El directorio*, pp. 34–35; *Mexican Year Book for 1911*, p. 211; *E&MJ*, XC (July 9, 1910), 92; XCI (Mar. 11, 1911), 505; XCV (Mar. 26, 1913), 876; CXV (June 9, 1923), 1031.

29. For an excellent historical survey, see I. F. Wilson and V. S. Rocha, *Geology and Mineral Deposits of the Boleo Copper District, Baja California, Mexico* (hereinafter cited as *Geol. of Boleo*), U.S. Geological Survey, Professional Paper No. 273 (Washington, D.C., 1955), pp. 88–124 (and esp. references, pp. 5–6 and 128–132). Also see G. de la Bouglies and E. Cumenge, *Étude sur le district cupifère du Boleo (Basse-Californie)*, Paris, 1885, pp. 13–15, 19–23; J. B. Huttl, "The Boleo Enterprise," *E&MJ*, CXXXII (Oct. 26, 1931), 346. For notes on the geology of El Boleo, see Edmond Fuchs, "Notes sur le gite de cuivre du Boleo (Basse-Californie mexicane)," Société Géologique de France, *Bulletin*, Ser. 3, No. 14 (1885), pp. 79–92; A. F. Wendt, "The Copper Ores of the Southwest," AIME *Trans.*, XV (1886–87), pp. 75–76 (based on report of D. W. Brunton); and W. H. Weed, *The Principal Copper Mines of the World* (New York, 1908), pp. 245–246; González Reyna, *Riqueza minera*, pp. 79–81; Joaquin M. Ramos, *Informe relativo a los trabajos ejecutados por la comisión exploradora de la Baja California en el año de 1884* (Mexico, 1886), pp. 125–128.

30. Bouglies and Cumenge, *Étude*, pp. 19–23, 25–27, 38–42, 47, 59, 61–65.

31. Carlos Pacheco, *Exposición que hace el Secretario de Fomento sobre la colonización de la Baja California* (Mexico, 1887), pp. 27–29; Dublán and Lozano, *Legislación mexicana*, XVII, pp. 341–342; Anon., "Negociación minera 'El Boleo,'" en Santa Rosalia, Baja California (Septiembre de 1917)," *Bol. min.*, IV (Nov. 1917), 467–471; Anon., "El mineral de 'El Boleo' . . . ," *Bol. min.*, XXIV (Sept. 1927), 147–153; *Mexican Year Book for 1909–1910*, p. 493; H. N. Branch, "Concessions: A Brief Analysis," in R. G. Cleland (ed.), *Mexican Year Book for 1920–1921*, p. 231.

32. Pacheco, *Exposición*, p. 28; Southworth, *Minas de México*, pp. 250–251; L. Duncan, "Copper Operations of Compagnie du Boleo," *E&MJ*, CIV (Sept. 8, 1917), 415–417; L. López and L. C. Espinoza, "El mineral 'El Boleo,'" *Bol. min.*, V (Mar.-Apr. 1918), 306–307; Isidrio Lagunas, "Informe ... sobre ... Cia. del Boleo," *Boletín de industria, comercio y trabajo* (Sección de Trabajo), V (July–Sept. 1920), 1–3; J. B. Huttl, "The Boleo Enterprise," 364; Crespo y Martínez, *México; industria minera*, p. 139.

33. Lagunas, "Informe," 3–4; Duncan, "Copper Operations," 416.

34. Southworth, *Minas de México*, p. 250; H. Lang, "Disposal of Slag from Smelting Works," *E&MJ*, LXXXIII (June 29, 1907), 1240–41; Ernesto Galarza, *La industria eléctrica en México* (Mexico, 1941), p. 9; J. R. Southworth, *El terri-*

torio de la Baja California (San Francisco, 1899), p. 80. Abstracts of the official company reports (containing much interesting data on various aspects of the workings), *E&MJ*, LXXIV (July 12, 1902), 51–52; LXXVIII (Aug. 4, 1904), 190; Weed, *The Principal Copper Mines of the World*, p. 9; Anon., "The Copper Mines of Mexico," *E&MJ*, LXXXIV (Oct. 5, 1907), 626; J. F. Rippy, "French Investments in Latin America," *Inter-American Economic Affairs*, II (Autumn 1948), 64.

35. For excellent descriptions of mining methods, see R. V. Pierce, "Copper from Mexico," *Compressed Air Magazine*, LI (May 1946), 127–129; Wilson and Rocha, *Geol. of Boleo*, pp. 90, 95–124. Also see *Bol. min.*, XXXI (June 1931), 160–173; XXXIII (Mar. 1932), 103–6; *E&MJ*, CVIII (Dec. 6, 1919), 884; CXII (Aug. 6, 1921), 225; (Sept. 24, 1921), 551; CXVII (May 5, 1924), 576; CXVIII (July 19, 1924), 105; (Oct. 25, 1924), 667; CXIX (May 16, 1925), 823; (May 23, 1925), 860; (May 30, 1925), 900; CXX (Sept. 26, 1925), 508; (Oct. 24, 1925), 670; CXXII (July 17, 1926), 106; CXXIV (July 27, 1927), 348; CXXVI (July 21, 1928), 111; (Dec. 22, 1928), 999; CXXVII (May 11, 1929), 775; CXXVIII (Aug. 3, 1929), 190; (Aug. 10, 1929), 228; CXXIX (Feb. 8, 1930), 162; CXXXII (Oct. 26, 1931), 346–348; (Nov. 9, 1931), 394–397; (Nov. 23, 1931), 440–442; *Min. & Met.*, X (June 1929), 286; American Bureau of Metal Statistics, *Yrbk.*, *passim; An. de estad. min., passim.*

36. Wilson and Rocha, *Geol. of Boleo*, pp. 90–91; *Min. Sur.*, III (May 1936), 25; IV (Aug. 1937), 32; (Nov. 1937), 32; (Dec. 1937), 31; V (July 1938), 19; (Aug. 1938), 15; VI (May 1939), 17; VII (May 1940), 16; XI (Sept. 1944), 27–28; *E&MJ*, CXLVI (Jan. 1945), 122; CXLVII (Feb. 1946), 159; CLV (May 1954), 108; (Oct. 1954), 168; CLVI (July 1955), 171, 173; CLVII (Apr. 1956), 196; Pierce, "Copper from Mexico," *loc. cit.*; R. Pérez Siliceo, "Posibilidades y reservas en la zona minera de 'El Boleo,' Santa Rosalia, B.C.," *Bol. de min. y pet.*, XVIII (Apr. 1947), 3–7; U.S. Dept. of Commerce, *Foreign Commerce Weekly* (hereinafter cited as *For. Comm. Wkly.*), LII (Sept. 27, 1954), 7; International Cooperation Administration, *Mexico, Monthly Progress Report* (Sept. 1955), US BuMines files; J. N. Franklin, "Oxidized Copper," *E&MJ*, CLVII (July 1956), 102.

37. Wilson and Rocha, *Geol. of Boleo*, pp. 91–94.

CHAPTER 4

1. Comisión de Código de Minería, José W. de Landa y Escandon, Oficial mayor, *Proyecto de ley minera de las Estados Unidos Mexicanos* (Mexico, 1892), quote from p. 7. Similar statements of the Minister of Development, Manuel Fernandez Leal, are quoted in Martínez Baca, "Historical Sketch," pp. 558–559. Also see José Castanedo, "Conferencia dada ... en la Escuela de Verano," *Bol. min.*, XXVI (Sept. 1928), 175.

2. *Ley minera y ley de impuesto a la minería* (Mexico, 1892). A good general study of Mexican mining law at this time is Richard E. Chism, *Encyclopedia of Mexican Mining Law* (Mexico, 1904). For editions of the law of 1892, see Vance and Clagett, *Guide*, 205–207.

3. For the effect of this error of thought, see the comment of Vice-Consul Coen at Durango City, in U.S. Department of State, *Foreign Relations of the United States, 1917* (hereinafter cited as *For. Rel. of the U.S.*), pp. 1051–52; and R. B.

Brinsmade, "The Subsoil of Mexico and Article 27," *E&MJ*, CXV (Feb. 10, 1923), 279–280.

4. Crespo y Martínez, *México; industria minera*, pp. 117–118.

5. W. H. Trewartha-James, "The Mining Law of the United States of Mexico, July 1st, 1892," Inst. of Min. and Met. (London), *Trans.*, IX (1900–01), pp. 16–23; and remarks by same in *ibid.*, XXV (1915–16), p. 170.

6. *Diario oficial*, XXVI, No. 136 (June 7, 1892). The *Reglamento* (bylaw) of the Mine Law is dated June 30, 1892 (*Diario oficial*, XXVII, No. 4, July 5, 1892).

7. Martínez Baca, "Historical Sketch," pp. 521, 564; *Monthly Bulletin of the International Bureau of the American Republics* (May 1906), p. 1378; *An. de estad. min., 1922*, p. 168; Wilfred H. Callcott, *Liberalism in Mexico, 1857–1929* (Stanford University Press, 1931), pp. 138, 162. Also see González Reyna, *Riqueza minera*, p. 10, for a table of mine concessions in force. His figures do not agree with those quoted in the text.

8. Dublán and Lozano, *Legislación mexicana*, XXVII, pp. 125–127. Some still believed the tax burden to be unduly heavy. See editorials in *E&MJ*, LXXV (Feb. 14, 1903), 249–250; LXXVI (Sept. 12, 1903), 380–381.

9. For a detailed summary of the politics and administration of Mexico's shift to the gold standard, see Edwin W. Kemmerer, *Modern Currency Reforms* (New York, 1916), pp. 467–552 and citations; David M. Pletcher, "The Fall of Silver in Mexico, 1870–1910, and Its Effect on American Investment," *Journal of Economic History*, XVIII:1 (Spring, 1958), pp. 33–55; F. Calderon, *La República restaurada; La vida económica* [1867–1876], pp. 175–185; M. Romero, "The Silver Standard in Mexico," *Mexico and the United States* (New York, 1898), pp. 559–620; M. A. Quintana, *Los ensayos monetarios*, pp. 77–95; Quintana, "El Alza del precio de la plata," *Memoria del Segundo Congreso Mexicano de Ciencias Sociales*, 4 vols. (Mexico, 1946), IV, pp. 386–387; Enrique Martínez Sobral, *La reforma monetaria* (Mexico, 1909), pp. 43–45, 90–91, 92–93; Walter F. McCaleb, *The Public Finances of Mexico* (New York, 1921), pp. 176–177; Dickson H. Leavens, *Silver Money* (Bloomington, Ind., 1939), pp. 113–116; Wagner, *Bullion to Books*, pp. 87–89; N. H. Emmons, "The Value of Ores," AIME *Trans.*, XXXII (1902), pp. 94–95, 99; D. Navarro, "La crisis minera," *Bol. min.*, XXIX (Mar. 1930), 195–196. For examples and analyses of the mine operators' problems under the dual monetary standard, see letters to the *E&MJ*, LXXVI (Oct. 24, 1903), 627–628 (Nov. 14, 1903), 745; LXXVIII (Dec. 15, 1904), 957; and editorial (Dec. 1, 1904), 858. For silver prices see the *An. de estad. min., 1924*, p. 291. The Comisión Monetaria Mexicana estimated that 86.59% of the amounts paid out by the mining companies were paid in silver. (*Actas de las Juntas Generales* [Mexico, 1904], p. 55.)

10. Dublán and Lozano, *Legislación mexicana*, XXXVI (1904), pp. 1355–56; XXXVII (1905), pp. 348–355; Pletcher, *Rails, Mines and Progress*, p. 305n.

11. Dublán and Lozano, *Legislación mexicana*, XXXVII (1905), pp. 355–359.

12. Southworth, *Minas de México*, p. 6.

13. Victor M. Braschi, "The Influence of Smelting, Electricity and the Cyanide Process on Mexican Silver Mining," IMMM, *Informes*, II (1910–11), No. 4, p. 134.

14. Letter, H. M. Cobb, Guanaceví, Durango, to *E&MJ*, LXXIX (Apr. 6, 1905), 664.

15. *Mex. Min. J.* (Apr. 1909), 12.

16. See the report of Vice-Consul-General Albert de Baer, Mexico City, in *E&MJ*, LXXXIV (Aug. 3, 1907), 210. For an interesting discussion of the economics of muleback transportation, see G. Law, "Primitive and Modern Mountain Transportation," *Min. Sur.*, II (June 1935), 21–22.

17. M. R. Lamb, "Tales of Mountain Travel in Mexico," *E&MJ*, XC (Oct. 1,

1910), 676–677; and C. S. Thomas, "Traveling in Mexico," *E&MJ*, XCI (June 17, 1911), 1201–3.

18. H. R. Conklin, "Transporting Heavy Machinery in Mexico," *E&MJ*, XCV (Mar. 8, 1913), 501 ff. Also see Randolph, "Mill at Batopilas," AIME *Trans.*, X (1881–82), pp. 297–298.

19. V. M. Braschi and E. Ordoñez, "The Mexican Railroad System," AIME *Trans.*, XXXII (1902), pp. 259–260; and F. W. Powell, "The Railroads of Mexico," in R. G. Cleland (ed.), *The Mexican Yearbook, 1920–21*, pp. 184-185.

20. Nevin O. Winter, *Mexico and Her People of Today* (Boston, 1910), pp. 291–292; Powell, "Railroads of Mexico," pp. 185–186.

21. J. Y. Limantour to the Mexican Chamber of Deputies, *Boletín de la Secretaría de Fomento*, Segunda Época, Año VI, 1906–07 (Minería y Metalurgia), Jan. 1907, 472; reprinted in translation in U.S. War Dept., Office of the Chief of Staff (War College Division, General Staff, No. 21), *Monograph on Mexico* (Washington, D.C., 1914), pp. 159–161, and pp. 157–171 in general. In rebuttal see Carlos Villafuerte, *Ferrocarriles* (Mexico, 1959), Chap. viii, for considerations often overlooked. For examples of American-baiting on this matter, see Will Davis, *Experiences and Observations of an American Consular Officer During the Recent Mexican Revolution* (Chula Vista, Calif., 1920), pp. 1–7; and Moisés González Navarro, *El Porfiriato: La vida social* in D. Cosío Villegas (ed.), *Historia moderna de México*, IV, pp. 178–180.

22. See the difficulties of the Choix Consolidated Mining Co. of Sinaloa, in Southworth and Holms, *El directorio*, p. 174. The Kansas City, Mexico, and Orient Railroad, planned to run in Mexico from Ojinaga on the Rio Grande to Topolobampo on the Pacific, would cross some of the best and most promising mineral land in Chihuahua and Sonora. Started in 1903, it was finally completed in Nov. 1961. (*New York Times*, Aug. 1, 1961 and Nov. 26, 1961. D. Pletcher, *Rails, Mines and Progress*, Chap. viii, discusses the beginning of the road and the work of Arthur Stilwell.)

23. W. H. Seaman, "Mining Operations in . . . Chihuahua," *E&MJ*, XC (Oct. 1, 1910), 654; editorial, *E&MJ*, XC (Oct. 29, 1910), 877.

24. Montes de Oca, "Las plantas metalúrgicas mexicanas," *Bol. min.*, XIV (Sept. 1922), 308.

25. *Mex. Min. J.* (Oct. 1907), 8–11; Wagner, *Bullion to Books*, pp. 24, 135.

26. Luis Salazar, "Mexican Railroads and the Mining Industry," AIME *Trans.*, XXXII (1902), pp. 303–304, 332–334.

27. *Mexican Year Book for 1908*, pp. 323–403. These figures were obtained by adding the branches noted in the *Year Book* as being principally devoted to mining, to the branches and short systems passing through mining country, and to railroads built by mining companies for use of their property or to tie their holdings together.

28. Salazar, "Mexican Railroads," pp. 314, 318; Launay, "Mines et Industries Minères," p. 303; Wagner, *Bullion to Books*, pp. 25, 27–28; *E&MJ*, LXXVII (May 19, 1904), 817.

29. Collins, "Smelting Processes," p. 20.

30. For a full treatment of this subject and the sources of this section, see Marvin D. Bernstein, "Economic Organization of the Mexican Coal Industry," *Inter-American Economic Affairs*, V (Spring 1952), 73–91. Also see Santiago Ramirez, *Noticia historica de la riqueza minera de México* (Mexico, 1884), pp. 147–184; the series of articles by Jesús Ibarra in the *Bol. min.*, VI (July–Sept. 1918), 1–8, 20–24, 309–320; Depto. de Minas, *El carbon mineral en México* (Mexico, 1921), p. 3; González Reyna, *Riqueza minera*, pp. 445–458.

31. Robert T. Hill, "The Coal Fields of Mexico," 12th International Geologic

Congress, 1913, *The Coal Resources of the World*, II, pp. 553–559; González Reyna, *Riqueza minera*, pp. 443–445, 452–456.

32. Jacobo Küchler, *Los valles de Sabinas y Salinas* (Mexico, 1866). Also see W. H. Adams, "Coals in Mexico—Santa Rosa District," AIME *Trans.*, X (1881–82), pp. 270–273.

33. Ramirez, *Noticia historica*, pp. 185–190.

34. For surveys of the major and minor coal fields, see Santiago Ramirez, *Noticia historica*, pp. 147–192; R. T. Hill, "The Coal Fields of Mexico," pp. 553–559; Depto. de Minas, "El carbon mineral en México," *Bol. min.*, XI (May 1921), 629–649; González Reyna, *Riqueza minera*, pp. 394–409; L. Torón Villegas and A. Esteve Torres, *Estudio de las zonas carboníferas de México, I, La cuenca carbonífera del Yaqui (Estado de Sonora)*, Mexico, Investagaciones industriales del Banco de México, S.A., 1946; L. Torón Villegas and A. Esteve Torres, *Estudio de las zonas carboníferas de México, II, La cuenca carbonífera de Tlacolulan, Ver.* (Mexico, n.d.); L. Torón Villegas, "Los carbones minerales de México y sus posibilidades de utilización," PCMN, *Memoria*, pp. 543–555; M. Riojas V. and C. M. Galindo, "La región carbonífera de Piedras Negras," *ibid.*, pp. 533–537; I. F. Wilson and V. S. Rocha, *Coal Deposits of Santa Clara District near Tonichi, Sonora, Mexico* (U.S. Geological Survey, Bulletin No. 962–A), Washington, D.C., 1949; J. L. W. Birkinbine, "Exploration of Certain Iron-Ore and Coal Deposits in the State of Oaxaca, Mexico," AIME *Trans.*, XLI (1910), pp. 166–188: L. Torón and S. Cortés-Obregón, "Exploration of the Oaxaca Coal Fields in Southern Mexico," AIME *Trans.*, CXCIX (1954), pp. 505–509; Luis Reyes Soto, "El carbon mineral en México," paper presented at July 28–29, 1955, technical session of the first annual meeting of the [Mexican] Institute of Mining, Metallurgy, Petroleum, and Geological Engineers, Chih., Chih. (mineo. copy in files of US BuMines); S. Cortés Obregón, "The Coal Used in the Mexican Iron and Steel Industry," UN, Secretariat of the Economic Commission for Latin America and Technical Assistance Administration, *A Study of the Iron and Steel Industry in Latin America* (New York, 1954), I, p. 25; J. González Reyna, "The Coal Deposits of Coahuila, Mexico," *Economic Geology*, XLV (May 1950), 249–51; E. Cantero y Pérez and G. González Carranza, "Yacimiento carbonífero de Año Nuevo, Municipio de Manuel Benavides, Edo. de Chihuahua," *Bol. de min. y pet.*, XVIII (Mar. 1947), 3–7.

35. Reyes Soto, "El carbon mineral en México," 19–21. Also see the estimates of Gonzáles Reyna, *Riqueza minera*, p. 403. The US Dept. of Com., Bureau of Foreign Commerce, in its study *Investment in Mexico* (Washington, D.C., 1955), p. 56, estimates Mexico's coal reserves at from 2,175 million to 3,260 million tons, of which from 1,250 to 1,800 million tons are of coking grade.

36. For a discussion of sources relating to production figures before 1910, see Bernstein, "Economic Organization," 78 ff. For an early survey of the Coahuila fields, see E. J. Schmitz, "Geology and Mineral Resources of the Rio Grande Region in Texas and Coahuila," AIME *Trans.*, XIII (1884–85), pp. 393–401; O. H. Hahn, "On the Development of Silver Smelting in Mexico," p. 260.

37. Edwin Ludlow, "The Coal Fields of Las Esperanzas, Coahuila, Mexico," AIME *Trans.*, XXXII (1902), pp. 143–144.

38. For other companies operating in Coahuila at the time, see *E&MJ*, LXXIV (Oct. 4, 1902), 463; LXXV (Jan. 3, 1903), 36; LXXVIII (Aug. 11, 1904), 235.

39. Address of E. E. Olcott, President, AIME, in AIME *Trans.*, XXXII (1902), p. cxxiv.

40. Malcomson, "Sierra Mojada," pp. 102–103; J. W. Malcolmson, "Relations of Mining and Smelting between the United States and Mexico," *Mines and Minerals*, XXVI (Mar. 1906), 344; W. R. Ingalls, "The Tariff on Lead," in *Lead and Zinc in the United States* (New York, 1908), pp. 216–219, 225–227; E. May, "Lead Industry in the United States," in W. Y. Elliott et al., *International Control*

in the Non-Ferrous Metals (New York, 1937), p. 667; Marcosson, *Metal Magic,* p. 45.

41. By far the best history of the development of the smelting industry in Mexico at the end of the 19th century is Hahn, "Silver Smelting in Mexico," pp. 231–303 (esp. pp. 231–234, 296–303 for lists and some descriptions of smaller plants). Also see Collins, "Smelting Processes," pp. 37–51, 72–76; and J. W. Malcolmson, "The Erection of Silver-Lead Smelting Works in Mexico," in J. Forrest (ed.), *Smelting Processes.* For short histories of the major smelters, see G. Montes de Oca, "Las plantas metalúrgicas mexicanas," *Bol. min.,* XIV (Sept. 1922), 308–317. For the general development of blast-furnace smelting of nonferrous metals at this time see Collins, *Metallurgy of Lead and Silver;* A. S. Dwight, "A Brief History of Blast Furnace Lead Smelting in America," AIME *Trans.,* CXXI (1936), pp. 9–37; and H. Hixon, *Lead and Copper Smelting* (New York, 1897).

42. Anon., *A Guide to Monterrey* (Monterrey, 1894), pp. 119–121, 125; Hahn, "Silver Smelting in Mexico," p. 234; Sam W. Traylor, *Out of the Southwest* (Allentown, Pa., 1936), pp. 62–66; Harvey O'Connor, *The Guggenheims* (New York, 1937), p. 95.

43. *Guide to Monterrey,* pp. 125–126; *Mexican Year Book for 1908–1909,* p. 501; Hahn, "Silver Smelting in Mexico," pp. 234–236; G. Montes de Oca, "La fundición número 2 en Monterrey," *Bol. min.,* XIV (Aug. 1922), 155; A. B. Parsons, "Monterrey: Smelting and Industrial Capital of Mexico," *E&MJ,* CXXI (June 12, 1926), 963.

44. Launay, "Mines et Industries Minières," p. 309; Gatenby Williams (pseud. of William Guggenheim), *William Guggenheim* (New York, 1934), pp. 69–84; Hahn, "Silver Smelting in Mexico," pp. 238–280; T. A. Rickard, "Interview with E. P. Mathewson," *Interviews with Mining Engineers* (San Francisco, 1921), p. 339; *E&MJ,* LXXVII (May 26, 1904), 856; LXXVIII (Sept. 22, 1904), 483; G. Montes de Oca, "La fundición número 3, en Monterrey, perteneciente a 'The American Smelting and Refining Co.,'" *Bol. min.,* XII (July 1921), 21–33; Marcosson, *Metal Magic,* pp. 46–51; O'Connor, *Guggenheims,* pp. 88–100.

45. Rickard, "Interview with E. P. Mathewson," p. 340; Hahn, "Silver Smelting in Mexico," pp. 280–283; Launay, "Mines et Industries Minières," pp. 311–312; Southworth and Holms, *El directorio,* p. 32; *E&MJ,* LXXVI (July 18, 1903), 100; LXXVIII (Oct. 27, 1904), 684; G. J. Young, "The El Paso Smelter," *E&MJ,* CXIX (June 27, 1925), 1041; Guggenheim, *William Guggenheim,* pp. 123–124; Wagner, *Bullion to Books,* p. 24; Marcosson, *Metal Magic,* p. 52.

46. Marcosson, *Metal Magic,* pp. 52–53, 57–72, 192; O'Connor, *Guggenheims,* pp. 101–125; Hahn, "Silver Smelting in Mexico," pp. 284–287; T. A. Rickard, *The Romance of Mining* (Toronto, 1944), p. 241.

47. Marcosson, *Metal Magic,* pp. 190–191.

48. *E&MJ,* XLIX (May 3, 1890), 489. For a complete description of the San Luis Potosí plant and the processes, see Hahn, "Silver Smelting in Mexico," pp. 288–291.

49. Hahn, pp. 292–294 for more details.

50. *Ibid.,* pp. 295–296 for more details. Data for the foregoing was compiled from Southworth, *Minas de México;* and Southworth and Holms, *El directorio, passim.* For a list of the principal smelters and their exact capacities in 1899, see Launay, "Mines et Industries Minières," p. 310; and M. Romero, *Geographic and Statistical Notes on Mexico,* pp. 28–29.

51. N. H. Emons, "The Value of Ores in Mexico," AIME *Trans.,* XXXII (1902), pp. 96–98; Malcolmson, "Relation of Mines and Smelting," 344; Malcolmson, "Mining in Mexico," *E&MJ,* LXXVII (Jan. 7, 1904), 21–22; Raymond and Ingalls, "Address to the AIME," *Mex. Min. J.* (June 1909), 20.

52. Martin, *Mexico's Treasure-House,* pp. 244–245.

53. Ingalls, *Lead and Zinc in the United States,* pp. 79, 225–226.

54. *E&MJ,* LXXX (Sept. 30, 1905), 608; (Oct. 21, 1905), 756; *Mexican Year*

Book for 1908, p. 508; *Mex. Min. J.* (Feb. 1908), 10; Martin, *Mexico*, II, pp. 316–317.

55. *E&MJ*, XCVII (Jan. 10, 1914), 63, 67. For 1916 figures, see *ibid.*, CIII (Jan. 6, 1917), 9, 18; and Marcosson, *Metal Magic*, pp. 209–210.

56. Victor M. Braschi, "The Influence of Smelting, Electricity, and the Cyanide Process on Mexican Silver Mining," IMMM, *Informes*, II (1910–11), pp. 132–133. J. W. Malcolmson also pointed out the growing dominance of mines by smelters in order to assure balanced charges: "Mining in Mexico, 1902," *E&MJ*, LXXV (Jan. 3, 1903), 35; "Custom Smelting Industry in Mexico," *E&MJ*, LXXVIII (July 7, 1904), 25.

57. Galarza, *La industria eléctrica en México* (hereinafter cited as *Indus. eléc.*), pp. 10–11; Ministerio de Fomento, *Noticia sobre las aplicaciones de la electricidad en la República Mexicana* (Mexico, 1899). For an excellent description of steam pumps in Real del Monte in the late 19th century, see E. Ordoñez and M. Rangel, "El Real del Monte," *Boletín del Instituto Geológico*, No. 12 (1899), pp. 42–63.

58. Galarza, *Indus. eléc.*, p. 9.

59. Traylor, *Out of the Southwest*, pp. 53–54ff; *Guide to Monterrey*, p. 121; Martin, *Mexico*, II, p. 278; Launay, "Mines et Industries Minières," p. 292; G. E. Walsh, "The Electrification of Mexican Mines," *E&MJ*, LXXX (July 6, 1905), 9–10.

60. IMMM, *La industria minera de México; Estado de México*, p. 199.

61. Galarza, *Indus. eléc.*, pp. 181–182.

62. Malcolmson, "Mining in Mexico, 1902," *E&MJ*, LXXV (Jan. 3, 1903), 38; (Feb. 21, 1903), 312; LXXVI (Aug. 15, 1903), 249; R. T. Hill, "The Guanajuato Mining District," *E&MJ*, LXXVII (Apr. 21, 1904), 643–644; *Mexican Year Book for 1908*, pp. 522–523; *Mexican Year Book for 1911*, pp. 174, 180; Hammond, *Autobiography*, I, pp. 479–486; Galarza, *Indus. eléc.*, p. 38; Gustavo P. Serrano, *Mining and Its Influence on the Progress and Development of Mexico* (Mexico, 1951), pp. 57–58.

63. Martin, *Mexico's Treasure-House*, pp. 202–203; *Mexican Year Book for 1911*, p. 180; *E&MJ*, LXXXIX (Jan. 1, 1910), 36; A. S. Brady, "Guanajuato Operations in 1910," *E&MJ*, XCI (Jan. 7, 1911), 73.

64. *E&MJ*, LXXXIX (Mar. 12, 1910), 554; *Min. Mag.*, I (Sept. 1909), 28.

65. *Mexican Year Book for 1911*, p. 173; *E&MJ*, LXXXIX (Jan. 15, 1910), 194; (May 28, 1910), 1135; XC (Nov. 19, 1910), 1033; XCI (Jan. 7, 1911), 72, 73; CXVI (Dec. 1, 1923), 958; Galarza, *Indus. eléc.*, pp. 38–39; J. Herrera y Lasso, "Guanajuato Power and Electric Company, Michoacan Electric Co., y el Central Mexico Light and Power Co.," Secretaría de Industria, Comercio y Trabajo, *Boletín de industria, comercio y trabajo* (Sección de industria), V (July–Sept. 1920), 68–69.

66. Martin, *Mexico*, II, p. 297; E. Villafaña, "Distribución de fuerza eléctrica en el Estado de Guanajuato," *Bol. min.*, XXV (June 1928), 356–359.

67. Tischendorf, *Gt. Br. and Mex.*, pp. 112–115; R. J. MacHugh, *Modern Mexico* (London, 1914), p. 188; Galarza, *Indus. eléc.*, pp. 27–28.

68. *Mexican Year Book for 1911*, p. 176; *Mexican Year Book for 1920–1921*, p. 221; *E&MJ*, LXXVIII (Dec. 29, 1904), 1043; LXXXIX (May 5, 1910), 934; XCII (Nov. 4, 1911), 911; Anon., "The Boquilla Hydro-Electric Power Plant in Mexico," *Engineering* (London), July 26, 1918, 93–94; G. C. Oropresa, "Cia. Agricola y de Fuerza Eléctrica sobre el Río Conchos," Depto. de Industrias, *Boletín de industrias*, 2a. época, I (Apr.–June 1922), 31; Galarza, *Indus. eléc.*, pp. 40–41; John A. Spender, *Weetman Pearson, First Viscount Cowdray* (London, 1930), p. 289.

69. M. Peña, "La negociación minera 'Moctezuma Mining Co.,'" *Bol. min.*, V (Feb. 1918), 181.

70. Anon., "Electric Power Costs at El Tigre," *E&MJ*, XCV (Mar. 8, 1913),

523; *ibid.*, XCI (Feb. 18, 1911), 393; J. W. Malcolmson, "Electric Power Installation at El Tigre, Sonora, Mexico," AIME *Trans.*, XLV (1913), pp. 189–193; Galarza, *Indus. eléc.*, p. 67.

71. J. Klemm, "Steam Turbine Installation in Mexico," *E&MJ*, XCIX (Mar. 3, 1915), 603; H. Rose, "Santa Gertrudis Mill, Pachuca," *E&MJ*, C (Aug. 5, 1916), 252–253 (reprinted in *Bol. min.*, IV [Aug. 1, 1917], 191); Editorial, "Los paros y readjustes en las minas de Chihuahua," and J. Castanedo and J. Horcasitas, "La minería en el Estado de Chihuahua," *Bol. min.*, XXVIII (Dec. 1929), 455–456, 457–460; Galarza, *Indus. eléc.*, pp. 31, 41–42, 64; J. Herrera y Lasso, *La fuerza motriz en México* (Mexico, 1927), pp. 10–11.

72. H. L. Scaife, "El Mineral de Zacualpán," IMMM, *Informes,* II (1910–11), pp. 101–104; *E&MJ*, XCII (Oct. 14, 1911), 774; Galarza, *Indus. eléc.*, p. 111.

73. Galarza, *Indus. eléc.*, pp. 90, 93–98, 180. The peso at this time stood at two to the dollar.

74. For details and examples of the advantages of cyaniding over other methods with cost analyses, see Rickard, *Journeys of Observation*, p. 129; E. Girault, "La Compañía de San Rafael y Anexas de Pachuca," IMMM, *Informes,* I (June 1910), pp. 237–238; J. L. Mennel, "Recent Advance of Cyanidation in Mexico," *Mex. Min. J.* (Mar. 1908), 20; T. A. Rickard, "Old and New Methods in Pachuca," in T. A. Rickard (ed.), *Recent Cyanide Practice* (San Francisco, 1907), pp. 299–301; Southworth and Holms, *El directorio,* pp. 98–99; Malcolmson, "Mining in Mexico, 1902," *E&MJ*, LXXV (Jan. 3, 1903), 38.

75. Burton Hunt, "Cyanidation in Mexico," *Min. & Sci. Press*, XCVII (Aug. 29, 1908), 286; reprinted in H. F. Bain (ed.), *More Recent Cyanide Practice* (San Francisco, 1910), p. 176.

76. E. A. H. Tays and F. A. Schaertz, "The Treatment of Clay Slimes by the Cyanide Process and Agitation," AIME *Trans.*, XXXII (1902), p. 179. Several other early mills are listed by F. J. Hobson, "Cyanidation in Mexico," in *More Recent Cyanide Practice*, pp. 167–169.

77. T. A. Rickard, "Cyanide Practice at El Oro," in *Recent Cyanide Practice*, pp. 114–115; Rickard, *Journeys of Observation*, pp. 54–55; A. W. Allen, "Early History of Cyanide Practice," *E&MJ*, CXXIV (Oct. 8, 1927), 572; Hammond, *Autobiography*, II, pp. 510–515.

78. Rickard, *Journeys of Observation*, pp. 53–78.

79. E. M. Hamilton and C. Butters, "On the Cyaniding of Ore at El Oro, Mexico," Inst. of Min. and Met. (London), *Transactions*, XIV (1904–05), pp. 4–5. Also see G. Coetani and E. Burt, "Fine Grinding of Ore by Tube Mills, and Cyaniding at El Oro, Mexico," AIME *Trans.*, XXXVII (1906), pp. 3–55. For comments on Mexican timidity, see Ferdinand McCann, *Cyanide Practice in Mexico* (San Francisco, 1912), pp. 13–14.

80. Launay, "Mines et Industries Minières," p. 308; C. Butters' interview with Rickard, *Interviews with Mining Engineers*, p. 123; and Butters' remarks in Inst. of Min. and Met. (London), *Trans.*, VII (1899–1900), pp. 236–237. For a description of the Sonora workings at this time, see J. R. Southworth, *El Estado de Sonora* (Nogales, Ariz., 1897), pp. 48–53.

81. Hobson, "Cyanidation in Mexico," pp. 167–169.

82. T. H. Oxnam, "Cyaniding Silver-Gold Ores of the Palmarejo Mine, Chihuahua, Mexico," AIME *Trans.*, XXXVI (1905), pp. 234–287; Allen, "Early History," 572–573; A. W. Allen, "Hydrometallurgy," *E&MJ*, CXXI (Jan. 16, 1926), 114; G. Law, "Primitive and Modern Mountain Transportation," *Min. Sur.*, II (June 1935), 23.

83. John F. Allan, "Notes upon Preliminary Tests and Cyanide Treatment of Silver Ores in Mexico by the MacArthur-Forrest Process," AIME *Trans.*, XXV

(1904), pp. 12–31. This is an excellent discussion of the probable role of cyaniding under Mexican conditions. Allan was quite pessimistic about the future of the process in Mexico because of the large number of refractory and complex ores. He believed that cyanide's major role in treating silver ores would be to supplement older processes.

84. Bernard MacDonald, "How Cyanidation Was First Applied to Silver Ores," *E&MJ*, CXIX (June 20, 1925), 1003–4; Martin, *Mexico's Treasure-House*, pp. 200, 255–256; Hobson, "The Cyanide Process at Guanajuato," in *Recent Cyanide Practice*, pp. 12–15; C. T. Rice, "Guanajuato, The Great Silver Camp of Mexico," *E&MJ*, LXXVI (Oct. 3, 1908), 670; Allen, "Early History," 572.

85. Hobson, "Cyanide Process at Guanajuato," and Rickard, "Old and New Methods in Guanajuato," in *Recent Cyanide Practice*, pp. 13–15, 296, 299; L. de Silva, "La planta metalúrgica Bustos-Flores, de la 'Guanajuato Reduction and Mines Co.,' Gto.," *Bol. min.*, XIV (Oct. 1922), 507 ff. For other experiments, see E. G. Spilsbury, "Improvement in Cyanide Practice [at the San Matias mill, Guanajuato Development Co., 1909]," AIME *Trans.*, XLI (1910), pp. 367–379.

86. H. E. West, "Pachuca," *Mex. Min. J.* (July 1907), 13–15; B. Burwell, "Pachuca, Home of the Patio Process," *E&MJ*, CVIII (Nov. 8, 1924), 726. However, in 1903 cyanide experiments were carried out by the La Luz Company. See *E&MJ*, LXXVI (Nov. 28, 1903), 826.

87. Anon., "Cyanide Replaces Patio at Pachuca," *E&MJ*, LXXXIV (July 27, 1907), 160; McCann, *Cyanide Practice in Mexico*, pp. 67, 81; *Mex. Min. J.* (Jan. 1909), 23; V. B. Sherrod, "Some Features of the Work of the Guerrero Mill, Pachuca," IMMM, *Informes*, I (Dec. 1909), pp. 125–128.

88. J. P. Alcombe, "Notes on the San Francisco Mill, Pachuca, Mexico," Inst. of Min. and Met. (London), *Trans.*, XXII (1912–13), pp. 661–670; IMMM, *La industria minera de México; Estado de Hidalgo* (Mexico, 1912), pp. 55, 104–105; *E&MJ*, XCVIII (Sept. 19, 1914), p. 540; McCann, *Cyanide Practice in Mexico*, pp. 98–100, 136–143. A running rivalry broke out between the defenders of the virtues of the Pachuca tank and the supporters of the Parral tank introduced at the Veta Colorado Mining and Smelting Co. plant at Parral, Chihuahua, in 1905 by Bernard MacDonald. See H. Adams, "The Continuous System of Cyaniding in Pachuca Tanks," AIME *Trans.*, XLII (1911), pp. 595–601; and B. MacDonald, "The Parral Tank System of Slime Agitation," *Ibid.*, pp. 819–837.

89. J. D. Nichol, "Metallurgical Methods at Pachuca, Mexico," *Min. Mag.*, II (Feb. 1910), 126–134.

90. *Mex. Min. J.* (Jan. 1909), 10. For a general description of Mexican methods, see A. F. J. Bordeaux, "The Cyaniding of Silver Ores in Mexico," AIME *Trans.*, XL (1909), pp. 764–775.

91. Anon., "Why Zinc Is Not Desired by Lead and Copper Smelters," *Mex. Min. J.* (Sept. 1912), 18.

92. *E&MJ*, LXXVIII (Aug. 4, 1904), 195; (Sept. 8, 1904), 403.

93. M. Perogordo y Lasso, "La industria del zinc en México," *Bol. min.*, XVIII (Sept. 1924), 96; *E&MJ*, LXVIII (Dec. 29, 1904), 1043.

94. P. C. Hanna, "Zinc Industry in Mexico, Northern District," *Mex. Min. J.* (Nov. 1909), 17–18; T. W. Voetther, "Zinc Industry in Mexico, Central District," *ibid.* (Dec. 1909), 17.

95. US Tariff Comm., *The Zinc Industry* (Washington, 1921), p. 32.

96. Editorial, "The Agitation for a Tariff on Zinc Ore," *Mex. Min. J.* (Jan. 1909), 11.

97. US Tariff Comm., *Zinc Industry*, p. 32; *E&MJ*, XCI (Mar. 18, 1911), 564; (Apr. 22, 1911), 803.

98. J. L. Keena (U.S. Consul, Chihuahua), "Zinc Shipments from Mexico," *E&MJ*,

XC (Aug. 6, 1910), 262; *E&MJ*, LXXXIX (Jan. 15, 1910), 189.

99. *Mex. Min. J.* (Sept. 1910), 15; *E&MJ*, LXXXIX (Jan. 1, 1910), 41; (Sept. 17, 1910), 579.

100. K. Thomas, "Mining in Mexico, 1910," *E&MJ*, XCI (Jan. 7, 1911), 65; *Min. Mag.*, I (Nov. 1909), 203.

101. *E&MJ*, XCI (Jan. 7, 1911), 72; XCII (Aug. 19, 1911), 372; XCIII (Jan. 6, 1912), 78; XCV (Jan. 25, 1913), 254; J. Ibarra, "Informe acerca de la planta calcinadora perteneciente a la 'International Ore Co.,' S.A., Saltillo, Coahuila," *Bol. min.*, VI (Nov.–Dec. 1918), 691–696; US Tariff Comm., *Zinc Industry*, p. 26.

CHAPTER 5

1. T. L. Carter, "Ancient Mine Workings," *Min. Mag.*, VIII (Jan. 1913), 59.

2. Letter, J. N. Nevins to *E&MJ*, LXXVIII (Aug. 11, 1904), 213.

3. Thomas E. Gibbon, *Mexico Under Carranza* (New York, 1919), pp. 122–124; G. O. James, "Through the Sierra Madres in Chihuahua, Mexico," *E&MJ*, LXXIV (Aug. 2, 1902), 141.

4. L. Salazar, "Metal a la vista," *Boletín de la Secretaría de Fomento*, Número de Propaganda (July 1905), 2–3.

5. Tischendorf, *Gt. Br. and Mex.*, pp. 76–77.

6. The Secretary, AIME (R. W. Raymond), *Excursions and Entertainments: Mexican Meeting, November 1901* (Supplement to the official proceedings of the meeting—no date or place of pub.), in AIME *Trans.*, XXXII (1902), p. cxl. (This supplement was both published separately and in the *Transactions*.) Also see Julia B. Thomas, *A Month in Mexico with the AIME* (no place of publication, 1901). A further account of the trip can be found in *E&MJ*, LXXII (Nov.–Dec. 1901), *passim*. The entire Nov. 30th issue of the *E&MJ* is devoted to the trip. For an excellent survey of Mexican mining at this time, with good illustrations, see J. Struthers, "Notes on the Mining and Metallurgical Industries of Mexico," *E&MJ*, LXXII (Oct. 26, 1901), 530–39.

7. Congrès Géologique International, *Compte Rendu de la X⁰ Session, Mexico, 1906* (Mexico, 1907); *Guide des Excursions du X⁰ Congrès Géologique International, Mexico, 1906* (Mexico, 1906).

8. *Commercial and Financial Chronicle* (Mar. 21, 1903), 657; *ibid.* (Apr. 11, 1903), 813; *E&MJ*, LXXIV (Nov. 29, 1902), 726; LXXV (Apr. 4, 1903), 534; (Apr. 11, 1903), 572; (Apr. 25, 1903), 643; Editorial, "Some Aspects of Mining Finance," *E&MJ*, LXXVI (Nov. 28, 1903), 802.

9. Hammond, *Autobiography*, II, pp. 506–510.

10. Marcosson, *Metal Magic*, p. 190. For a series of broad comments on the Guggenheims' activities in the 1890's, see Guggenheim, *William Guggenheim*, pp. 67–138.

11. *Mexican Year Book for 1911*, p. 223; *E&MJ*, LXXV (Feb. 28, 1903), 343; LXXVI (Sept. 5, 1903), 366; LXXVII (May 26, 1904), 856; LXXX (Sept. 23, 1905), 564; (Oct. 21, 1905), 756; Wagner, *Bullion to Books*, p. 163.

12. *E&MJ*, LXXX (Sept. 23, 1905), 564; (Oct. 7, 1905), 658; (Oct. 21, 1905),

756; O'Connor, *Guggenheims,* pp. 328–329. Another version, more interesting than accurate, is told by Edward I. Bell, *The Political Shame of Mexico* (New York, 1914), pp. 130–133.

13. Marcosson, *Metal Magic,* pp. 191–192.

14. Anon., "Relationship between ASARCO and American Smelters Securities Company," *E&MJ,* XC (Aug. 27, 1910), 394; Marcosson, *Metal Magic,* pp. 78–79.

15. O. H. Hahn, "Silver Smelting in Mexico," pp. 294–295.

16. M. Alcalá, "La fundición de Velardeña," *Boletín de la Secretaría de Fomento,* 2a. época, Año VIII (Dec. 1907), 331–342; *E&MJ,* LXXVII (May 19, 1904), 817; XC (Dec. 31, 1910), 1327; C. A. Bohm, "Mexico," *E&MJ,* LXXXIII (Jan. 15, 1907), 44; "Report of ASSCO to New York Stock Exchange" (in applying for a listing), *E&MJ,* LXXXVIII (Dec. 4, 1909), 1128; *Mexican Year Book for 1913,* p. 114; Southworth, *Minas de México,* p. 99; Southworth and Holms, *El directorio,* p. 72; Wagner, *Bullion to Books,* pp. 130–131; Marcosson, *Metal Magic,* p. 210.

17. Wagner, *Bullion to Books,* pp. 124–125.

18. *E&MJ,* LXXV (May 23, 1903), 794; (June 20, 1903), 943; LXXVI (Nov. 7, 1903), 711; (Dec. 10, 1903), 903; LXXVII (Apr. 28, 1904), 696; (May 12, 1904), 776; LXXVIII (July 21, 1904), 115; (Sept. 15, 1904), 442; LXXXV (June 20, 1908), 1267; Wagner, *Bullion to Books,* pp. 124–126, 131; G. Montes de Oca, "La fundición de Avalos, Chihuahua," *Bol. min.,* XIII (May 1922), 599; Southworth and Holms, *El directorio,* p. 33; Martin, *Mexico,* II, p. 316; Marcosson, *Metal Magic,* pp. 200, 208–210. For the Guggenheims' forestalling of smelter competition in Chihuahua in 1898–99, see O. H. Hahn, "On the Development of Silver Smelting in Mexico," pp. 297–298. For a description of an early (c. 1893) small (28 to 40 tons of ore per day) smelter at Terrazas, Chihuahua, see H. F. Collins, *The Metallurgy of Lead and Silver,* Pt. II, pp. 321–326.

19. "Report of ASSCO," *loc. cit.; Mexican Year Book for 1909–10,* p. 501; *Mexican Year Book for 1912,* p. 155; Southworth, *Minas de México,* p. 195; *E&MJ,* LXXV (June 6, 1903), 869; LXXVII (Mar. 17, 1904), 452; LXXVIII (Sept. 15, 1904), 448; LXXXIX (Feb. 12, 1910), 387; (Apr. 9, 1910), 795; XC (Nov. 19, 1910), 1033; (Dec. 10, 1910), 1181; G. Montes de Oca, "La fundición de Matehuala, S.L.P.," *Bol. min.,* XIII (Oct. 1921), 463.

20. *Mexican Year Book for 1908,* p. 508; *E&MJ,* LXXVII (June 9, 1904), 937.

21. J. Horcasitas and C. Bruchhold, "Tratamiento de minerales oxidados plomo-estañíferos [por] la 'American Smelting and Refining Co.,' en Avalos, Chihuahua," *Bol. min.,* XXXI (Feb. 1931), 42. The same comment was made by James Malcolmson in 1903 and 1904: "Mining Development in Mexico During 1902," *E&MJ,* LXXV (Jan. 3, 1903), 35; "Custom Smelting Industry in Mexico," *E&MJ,* LXXVIII (July 7, 1904), 25. For the attitude of the Mexican government toward smelters owning mines during the nationalistic fervor of the Cárdenas administration, see Depto. de Estudios Económicos, Sec. de la Economía Nacional, *Apuntes acerca del porvenir de la minería en México* (Mexico, 1935), p. 33.

22. Statement of Edward Brush, Vice-President of ASARCO, *Mex. Min. J.* (June 1913), 16; *E&MJ,* CXIV (July 22, 1922), 171.

23. T. A. Rickard, *Romance of Mining,* p. 241; O'Connor, *Guggenheims,* p. 100; E. Villafaña, "Las minas tepezelanas de Asientos, Ags.," *Bol. min.,* XV (Feb. 1923), 227; E. Villafaña, "El distrito minero Tepezala-Asientos, Ags.," *ibid.,* XV (Apr. 1923), 465.

24. O'Connor, *Guggenheims,* pp. 133–135.

25. These figures were compiled from those given in *Mexican Year Book for 1909–10,* p. 492; Southworth and Holms, *El directorio,* p. 33; and "ASSCO Report," *loc. cit.;* Malcolmson, "Mining in Mexico, 1902," *E&MJ,* LXXV (Jan. 3, 1903), 35–38; G. A. Burr, "Two Notable Concentrating Plants," *E&MJ,* LXXVI (Sept. 12,

1903), 392–3. For comments on ASARCO's reticence to release data, see *E&MJ*, LXXXVIII (Dec. 11, 1909), 1178; and Southworth, *Minas de México*, pp. 55–56.

26. *E&MJ*, LXXIV (Oct. 18, 1902), 530; (Nov. 1, 1902), 600; LXXV (Apr. 11, 1903), 572; LXXVII (June 23, 1904), 1017.

27. Malcolmson, "Mining Development in Mexico," *E&MJ*, LXXV (Jan. 3, 1903), 39; Southworth and Holms, *El directorio*, p. 138; *Mexican Year Book for 1912*, p. 165; M. López Núñez, "Las minas Carrillos y Dolores, de [ASARCO], Unidad Angangueo, Michoacan," *Bol. min.*, XXVI (Oct. 1928), 234–245; T. Flores, *Geología minera de la región NE del Estado de Michoacan (1935)*, Universidad Nacional Autónoma de México, Instituto de Geología, *Bol. núm.* 52 (Mexico, 1946), pp. 66–69. Argentiferous ore from Angangueo had been smelted in the 1890's at the Las Trojes, Michoacan, smelter—one of the earlier modern smelters built in Mexico—which had a capacity of 90 tons of charge per day. See H. F. Collins, "Smelting Processes for the Extraction of Silver and Gold from their Ores," Institution of Civil Engineers (London), *Minutes of Proceedings*, CXII (1893), pp. 146–147, 161–162; and J. W. Malcolmson, "The Erection of Silver-Lead Smelting Works in Mexico," *ibid.*, pp. 164–171.

28. *E&MJ*, LXXV (Apr. 4, 1903), 534; Southworth, *Minas de México*, pp. 198–199; *Mexican Year Book for 1909–10*, p. 495; *Mex. Min. J.* (Aug. 1911), 42; *E&MJ*, LXXVI (Aug. 22, 1903), 287; (Oct. 31, 1903), 671; XCII (Aug. 26, 1911), 424; XCIII (Jan. 20, 1912), 192; G. Montes de Oca, "La planta de flotación de 'Tiro General' en Charcas, S.L.P.," *Bol. min.*, XXI (Mar. 1926), 105.

29. For details of the financing of the mine and its vicissitudes see A. Tischendorf, *Gt. Br. and Mex.*, pp. 90–91. Also see IMMM, *La industria minera de México; Estado de México* (Mexico, 1912), pp. 207–224; Southworth and Holms, *El directorio*, pp. 130–131; O'Connor, *Guggenheims*, pp. 171–177; Hammond, *Autobiography*, II, pp. 510–515; Anon., "The Esperanza Mine, El Oro, Mexico," *E&MJ*, LXXIV (July 12, 1902), 46; *E&MJ*, LXXVI (July 4, 1903), 27; (Aug. 1, 1903), 173; (Aug. 29, 1903), 325, 330; LXXVII (Jan. 28, 1904), 172; J. H. Curle, "American Gold Mines," *E&MJ*, LXXVI (Sept. 12, 1903), 384; XCIII (Apr. 27, 1912), 862; CXXI (Mar. 27, 1926), 517; Rippy, *British Investments in Latin America*, pp. 100–101.

30. The personal biographical material is based on James H. McClintock, *Arizona*, 3 vols. (Chicago, 1916), II, pp. 603–605; and "William C. Greene," in *Dictionary of American Biography*, VII, pp. 577–578. Ira B. Joralemon's biographical sketch in *Romantic Copper* (New York, 1934), Chap. vi, is wholly from McClintock and often fanciful. For a more complete survey of Greene's life and early history of Cananea with fuller citations, see Marvin D. Bernstein, "Colonel William C. Greene and the Cananea Copper Bubble," *Bulletin of the Business Historical Society*, XXVI (Dec. 1952), 179–198; and David M. Pletcher, "Cowboy: William C. Greene," *Rails, Mines and Progress*, Chap. vii. Also see I. F. Marcosson, *Anaconda* (New York, 1957), pp. 251–259.

31. B. Rubio, "Las minas de 'The Cananea Consolidated Copper Company,' S.A.," *Bol. min.*, XXV (June 1928), 362.

32. Bernstein, "Greene," 181–182; W. H. Weed, "The Cananea Copper Deposits, Mexico," *E&MJ*, LXXIV (Dec. 6, 1902), 745; Chas. F. Shelby, "Growth of the Cananea Copper Smelting Works," *E&MJ*, LXXXVI (Nov. 14, 1908), 954; W. B. Bimson, *Louis D. Ricketts* (New York, 1949), pp. 17–20.

33. *New York Daily Tribune* (Aug. 6, 1911); *Dict. of Amer. Biog.*, *loc. cit.*

34. McClintock, *Arizona*, *loc. cit.*; Bernstein, "Greene," 182–183.

35. Bernstein, "Greene," 183–189. Also see G. Law, "Primitive and Modern Mountain Transport," *Min. Sur.*, II (Apr. 1935), 18–19; and D. M. Pletcher, "The Development of Railroads in Sonora," *Inter-American Economic Affairs*, I (Mar. 1948), 30–31.

36. By far the completest coverage of the Cananea strike is in Manuel González

Ramirez, *La huelga de Cananea* (Vol. III: *Fuentes para la historia de la Revolución Mexicana*), Mexico, 1956. Although the interpretation of León Díaz Cárdenas in *Cananea* ("Biblioteca del Obrero y Campesino," *núm*. 11, Mexico, 1937) is marked by a naïve Marxism, the documents were obtained from Ricardo Flores Magon, one of the strike leaders, and are valuable. Also see Pletcher, "Cowboy," pp. 236–252 (and references therein in lieu of a more detailed listing); Lyle C. Brown, "The Mexican Liberals and Their Struggle against the Díaz Dictatorship," *Anthology MCC* (Mexico City: Mexico City College, 1956), pp. 328–361; M. González Navarro, *El porfiriato*, pp. 316–322; Marjorie R. Clark, *Organized Labor in Mexico* (Chapel Hill, N.C., 1934), pp. 10–11; Bernstein, "Greene," 189–192.

A most interesting, if somewhat romantic, first person account of the strike was recorded by Captain Thomas H. Rynning, who led the U.S. Rangers into Mexico, in his autobiography, *Gun-Notches; the Life Story of a Cowboy-Soldier* (New York, 1931), pp. 290–315.

37. John K. Turner, *Barbarous Mexico* (New York, 1910), pp. 213–219, gives a very competent account of the strike compiled by interviewing eyewitnesses.

38. *Ibid.*, p. 219.

39. Francisco I. Madero, *La sucesión presidencial en 1910* (San Pedro, Coahuila, 1908), pp. 206–208; Brown, "Mexican Liberals," pp. 360–361. See *Min. Sur.*, VIII (June 1941), 30, for a report of the meeting on the 35th anniversary of the strike.

40. Dwight E. Woodbridge, "Labor Data of a Northern Mexico Mine," *Mex. Min. J.* (July 1913), 348–349. (Reprinted from *E&MJ*, XCVI [July 26, 1931], 177 ff.)

41. Bernstein, "Greene," 193–197; First Report, *Cananea Central Copper Co. from Aug. 6, 1906, to Dec. 31, 1907* (Duluth, Minn., 1908).

42. L. D. Ricketts in an interview with T. A. Rickard, *Interviews*, pp. 442–443; L. D. Ricketts, "The Cananea Consolidated Copper Co.," *E&MJ*, LXXXV (Apr. 11, 1908), 754–755; C. F. Shelby, "The Cananea Blast Furnace," *E&MJ*, LXXXV (Apr. 25, 1908), 841–842; Ricketts, "Cananea Consolidated Copper Co.," *E&MJ*, XCI (June 24, 1911), 1246–48; Report of W. D. Thornton, "Greene Cananea," *Mex. Min. J.* (July 1912), 46; *E&MJ*, XCIII (Jan. 27, 1912), 240; (June 15, 1912), 1202; L. D. Ricketts, "Experiments in Reverberatory Practice at Cananea, Mexico," Inst. of Min. and Met. (London), *Trans.*, XIX (1909–10), pp. 147–185.

43. *New York Daily Tribune* (Aug. 6, 1911); *New York Times* (Aug. 6, 1911); *Mex. Min. J.* (Sept. 1911), 35; *E&MJ*, XCII (Aug. 19, 1911).

44. B. Rubio, "La mina denominada Los Pilares," *Bol. min.*, XXVI (Dec. 1928), 461–462. For contemporary accounts of the geology, see S. F. Emons, "Los Pilares Mine," *Economic Geology*, I (July–Aug. 1906), 629–643; and W. H. Weed, *Principal Copper Mines*, pp. 241–242.

45. Rickard, Interview with L. D. Ricketts, *Interviews*, pp. 435–436; 453; Walter Douglas, "The Phelps Dodge Enterprise—Historical Sketch," *E&MJ*, CXXVI (Oct. 27, 1928), 643; Joralemon, *Romantic Copper*, pp. 216–217; Bimson, *Ricketts*, pp. 15–16. For an excellent general history of Phelps Dodge workings at Nacozari, see Robert G. Cleland, *A History of Phelps Dodge* (New York, 1952), pp. 129–138, 143, 197–199, 241–243, 266.

46. H. B. Layton, "The Nacozari Mines, Mexico," *E&MJ*, LXIX (June 9, 1900), 678–679; (June 16, 1900), 707; J. Langton, "The Power Plant of the Moctezuma Copper Co.," *AIME Trans.*, XXXIV (1903), pp. 748–776; Southworth and Holms, *El directorio*, p. 198; Rickard, *Interviews*, pp. 435–438; D. V. Navarro, "La campaña contra accidentes en las minas de Pilares de Nacozari, Sonora." *Bol. min.*, XXIII (Feb. 1927), 96; J. Castanedo, "La negociación minera 'The Moctezuma Copper Co.,'" *Bol. min.*, XXIV (Nov. 1927), 270.

47. M. Peña, "La negociación minera 'The Moctezuma Copper Co.,'" *Bol. min.*,

XIII (June 1921), 807–816; Castanedo, "La neg. min. 'The Moctezuma Copper Co.'"; C. Bruchhold, "La planta de flotación de 'The Moctezuma Copper Co.,'" *Bol. min.*, XXIV (Sept. 1927), 168–169; J. Douglas, "Arizona Copper Mines in 1902," *E&MJ*, LXXV (Jan. 3, 1903), 9; Douglas, "The Phelps Dodge Enterprise," 643; *E&MJ*, LXXXIV (Aug. 17, 1907), 331; B. E. Russell, "Nacozari Mining District," *E&MJ*, LXXXVI (Oct. 3, 1908), 657–659; Anon., "The Pilares Mine at Nacozari," *E&MJ*, XCI (May 20, 1911), 1016; Pletcher, "Development of Railroads in Sonora," 35; Rickard, *Interviews*, pp. 437–438; D. C. Livingston, "Mining Methods at Nacozari, Sonora, Mexico," AIME *Trans.*, XLIII (1912), pp. 662–669.

An attempt to develop copper mines in Sonora near Cananea by Phelps Dodge did not turn out well. See *E&MJ*, LXXIV (Nov. 1, 1902), 600–601; (Dec. 27, 1902), 863; LXXV (May 9, 1903), 722; LXXVIII (Sept. 8, 1904), 409; (Oct. 20, 1904), 643; (Dec. 29, 1904), 1043.

48. For biographical material see *E&MJ*, CII (Aug. 12, 1916), 313; (Oct. 21, 1916), 764; CIV (Dec. 15, 1917), 1056.

49. Southworth and Holms, *El directorio*, p. 63.

50. C. Launay, "Mines et industries minières," p. 313; Southworth, *Minas de México*, p. 195; *Mexican Year Book for 1909–10*, p. 501; *E&MJ*, CXVI (Aug. 23, 1913), 380; S. P. Lindau, "A Wooden Smelter Stack," *E&MJ*, CXII (Aug. 13, 1921), 257; G. Montes de Oca, "La fundición de San Luis Potosí, S.L.P.," *Bol. min.*, XIII (Apr. 1922), 453–454; A. W. Butt, *Where Silver Rules* (n.p., 1896), p. 7. Approximately the same wage rate prevailed at the ASARCO smelter at Aguascalientes.

51. Southworth, *Minas de México*, p. 195; Southworth and Holms, *El directorio*, pp. 53, 63, 158, 164; *Mexican Year Book for 1909–10*, p. 501; *E&MJ*, LXXIV (Nov. 22, 1902), 694; Malcolmson, "Mining in Mexico, 1902," *E&MJ*, LXXV (Jan. 3, 1903), 39; (Mar. 7, 1903), 382; (Apr. 4, 1903), 534; LXXVII (Mar. 31, 1904), 532; H. W. Hixon, "Pyritic Smelting (at Teziutlan)," LXXVII (June 23, 1904), 996; LXXVIII (Sept. 22, 1904), 483; XC (July 9, 1910), 57; (Nov. 19, 1910), 1033; XCI (Jan. 7, 1911), 34; (May 6, 1911), 906; XCV (Feb. 15, 1913), 398; CI (Jan. 8, 1916), 116–117; G. A. Burr, "Two Notable Concentrating Plants," *E&MJ*, LXXVI (Sept. 12, 1903), 392–3; G. Montes de Oca, "La fund. de S.L.P."; R. Fernandez, "La industria minero-metalúrgica en el Estado de San Luis Potosí," *Bol. min.*, XIV (Oct. 1922), 485–489; G. A. Laird, "The Gold Mines of the San Pedro District . . . San Luis Potosí, Mexico," AIME *Trans.*, XXXV (1904), pp. 858–878; F. R. Van Horn, "The Occurrence of Silver-, Copper-, and Lead-Ores at the Veta Rica Mine, Sierra Mojada, Coahuila, Mexico," *ibid.*, XLIII (1912), pp. 219–233.

For a technical description of the Sombrerete plant before Towne's acquisition of the property see H. F. Collins, *Metallurgy of Lead and Silver*, Part II, Chap. ix, and pp. 236–239, 244.

52. For a clear map of property holdings in the district, see Martin, *Mexico's Treasure-House*, pp. 179, 228.

53. J. R. Finlay, *The Cost of Mining* (New York, 1920), p. 515; A. Wandke and J. Martínez, "El distrito minero de Guanajuato," *Bol. min.*, XXIX (Apr. 1930), 279–295; (May 1930), 320–329.

54. Rickard, *Journeys of Observation*, p. 206; Martin, *Mexico's Treasure-House*, pp. 89–92 and *passim*. The dirt under the patio floors was also rich with soaked-up silver amalgam, and the Guanajuato River bed ran from $8 to $14 a ton because of the patio tailings dumped there. See *E&MJ*, LXXV (Apr. 18, 1903), 607; (June 27, 1903), 979.

55. Rickard, *Journeys*, p. 198. For a most excellent geologic and technical survey of the district shortly after 1900, see R. T. Hill, "The Guanajuato Mining District," *E&MJ*, LXXVII (Apr. 14, 1904), 599–601, (Apr. 21, 1904), 642–644.

56. For a complete description of the properties owned and leased by the major companies in Guanajuato with technological details, see L. López, "Informe, Distrito de Guanajuato, Gto.," *Bol. min.*, I (May 15, 1916), 291–293, 321–323.

57. Southworth and Holms, *El directorio*, p. 96; Martin, *Mexico's Treasure-House*, pp. 295–296; *E&MJ*, LXXIV (July 28, 1902), 128; J. W. Malcolmson, "Mining in Mexico, 1902," 38; Hill, "Guanajuato," 644; C. T. Rice, "Guanajuato, The Great Silver Camp of Mexico," *E&MJ*, LXXXVI (Oct. 3, 1908), 670.

58. For details on these holdings, see Southworth and Holms, *El directorio*, pp. 94–106; and Martin, *Mexico's Treasure-House*, pp. 114–117.

59. Rickard, *Journeys*, pp. 174–175, 197–198.

60. *E&MJ*, LXXIV (Nov. 29, 1902), 726; LXXV (Feb. 21, 1903), 312; LXXVI (Sept. 12, 1903), 403; LXXVII (Feb. 18, 1904), 292; (Mar. 10, 1904), 411; LXXVIII (July 14, 1904), 74; (Dec. 22, 1904), 1004 (for an excellent description of the property at the time); Southworth and Holms, *El directorio*, pp. 97–98; López, "Informe," 323–324; L. G. Aguirre, "Informe referente a las negociaciones mineras del Estado de Guanajuato," *Bol. min.*, III (Feb. 15, 1917), 172–173.

61. *E&MJ*, LXXV (June 27, 1903), 979; Southworth and Holms, *El directorio*, pp. 95–96; E. Villafaña, "La mina de 'El Cubo,' Guanajuato," *Bol. min.*, XXVIII (Aug. 1929), 106–107.

62. See the description of the new Cornish pumping engine in AIME *Excursions, Mexico, 1901*, pp. clxxvi–clxxvii; and general description, c. 1890–1900, in H. F. Collins, *Metallurgy of Lead and Silver*, Chap. iii and esp. p. 61.

63. For excellent short histories of these mines with emphasis upon the 19th century, see Instituto Geológico de México, *Boletín*, Nos. 7, 8, and 9, "El Real del Monte," 36–37; and Crespo y Martínez, *México; industria minera*, pp. 141–147.

64. H. E. West, "Pachuca," *Min. & Sci. Press*, XCII (May 26, 1906), 346; L. Salazar, "La excursión de la I.M.M.M. a Pachuca y Real del Monte," IMMM, *Informes*, I, pp. 103–104.

65. Southworth, *Minas de México*, p. 132; United States Smelting, Refining and Mining Co., *Annual Report for 1906*; Anon., "Doing Something for Silver," *Fortune*, XII (July 1935), 80. For a good short sketch of the discovery and working of the mine, particularly under the British leesees, see M. Romero, *Geographical and Statistical Notes on Mexico*, pp. 15–17.

66. Anon., "Historic and Famous Mines of Pachuca Are Being Remade," *Mex. Min. J.* (Aug. 1907), 17. For an interesting but dubiously accurate facet of this transaction, see E. Bell, *The Political Shame of Mexico*, pp. 164–165.

67. USSR&M, *Annual Reports, 1906–11*. Other information on this period, not all of it in agreement with the Annual Reports, can be found in *Mexican Year Book for 1912*, p. 169; F. McCann, *Cyanide Practice In Mexico*, pp. 67, 81; IMMM, *La indus. min.; Edo. de Hidalgo*, p. 55.

68. AIME *Excursions* (Mexico, 1901), pp. clxxviii–clxxix; *E&MJ*, CV (Nov. 3, 1917), 809; Southworth and Holms, *El directorio*, pp. 115–119; *E&MJ*, CII (Aug. 26, 1916), 371.

69. E. E. Chase, letter to *Min. & Met.*, XIII (Aug. 1932), 369.

70. *Min. Mag.*, II (June 1910), 427.

71. For details see *Mex. Min. J.* (Nov. 1909), 15; (Feb. 1910), 15; *E&MJ*, LXXXIX (Jan. 1, 1910), 41; (Jan. 22, 1910), 214–216; (Mar. 12, 1910), 588; (Apr. 23, 1910), 867. John Hays Hammond was criticized for his role as promoter. For details of the deal, see *Min. Mag.*, I (Sept. 1909), 5–6; II (Jan. 1910), 2, 7–8; (Mar. 1910), 187–188; (June 1910), 427. J. F. Rippy sets the paid-in capital at £1,368,000. (*British Investments in Latin America*, p. 52.)

72. *E&MJ*, XC (Oct. 29, 1910), 852; M. G. Matteson, "Mining Problems at Santa Gertrudis," *E&MJ*, XCIV (Sept. 21, 1912), 547; *ibid.* (Nov. 23, 1912), 994; CII (Aug. 5, 1916), 247. For a complete survey of the Pachuca district in 1910,

see J. D. Nichols, "Metallurgical Methods at Pachuca, Mexico," *Min. Mag.,* II (Feb. 1910), 126–134.

73. *E&MJ,* CXXVI (Sept. 22, 1928), 461.

74. IMMM, *La indus. min.; Edo. de Méx.,* pp. 173–174, chart facing p. 186; Rickard, *Journeys,* pp. 35–53; H. D. Crowder, "A Nation's Mineral Resources," *Min. Sur.,* II (Feb. 1935), 15.

75. Tischendorf, *Gt. Br. and Mex.,* pp. 86–90; Rippy, *British Investments in Latin America,* pp. 100–101; Wagner, *Bullion to Books,* pp. 21–22, 30–34; Southworth and Holms, *El directorio,* pp. 129–130, 132, 134; *Mexican Year Book for 1908,* pp. 480, 481, 484; IMMM, *La indus. min.; Edo. de Méx.,* p. 225, chart facing page 174, and *passim; E&MJ,* LXXIV (Aug. 9, 1902), 200; (Nov. 8, 1902), 624–625; LXXV (Jan. 24, 1903), 149; LXXVI (Dec. 5, 1903), 840; LXXVIII (July 7, 1904), 6; (Nov. 10, 1904), 764; (Nov. 17, 1904), 798; XC (Dec. 31, 1910), 1287–88; XCI (May 13, 1911), 944; Hammond, *Autobiography,* II, pp. 510–515.

76. Southworth, *Minas de México,* pp. 163–165.

77. IMMM, *La indus. min.; Edo. de Michoacan,* pp. 53–66, 101; *Mexican Year Book for 1908,* pp. 487–489; Anon., "French Interests in Mexican Mining," *E&MJ,* XC (Sept. 10, 1910), 527; T. S. Saunders, "Las Dos Estrellas Gold Mine," *Min. Mag.,* XXV (Aug. 1921), 89–90; *E&MJ,* LXXVIII (Dec. 1, 1904), 884.

78. *E&MJ,* LXXXIX (Apr. 2, 1910), 738; XC (July 2, 1910), 41; (Aug. 20, 1910), 385; (Sept. 10, 1910), 532; XCI (Apr. 22, 1911), 833; XCII (Nov. 25, 1911), 1060; XCV (Feb. 8, 1913), 350; XCVII (Mar. 28, 1914), 648; *Min. Mag.,* II (Feb. 1910), 112; (Mar. 1910), 188; XXVI (Mar. 1922), 138; XXXVIII (Apr. 1928), 200.

79. Dahlgren, *Historic Mines,* p. 153; Southworth, *Minas de México,* p. 103; *Mexican Year Book for 1908,* p. 489.

80. *E&MJ,* LXXV (Feb. 28, 1903), 343; XCVIII (Sept. 12, 1914), 492.

81. K. B. Heberlein, *Cia. Min. de Peñoles: Report of the General Manager and Balance for the Year 1909* (Mexico, 1910).

82. Launay, "Mines et industries minères," pp. 294, 313–314; J. D. Villarello, "Le Mineral de Mapimí," No. 18 of *Excursion du Nord, Guide des Excursions de Xe Congrès Géologic International, Mexico, 1906,* pp. 2–3. For production details and statistics, see *Mexican Year Book for 1908,* p. 490; J. W. Malcolmson, "Mining in Mexico, 1902," *E&MJ,* LXXV (Jan. 3, 1903), 37; (June 6, 1903), 869; LXXVII (Jan. 21, 1904), 138; (May 12, 1904), 776.

83. Heberlein, *Peñoles: Report, 1910* (for complete production statistics); *Mex. Min. J.* (Nov. 1907), 23; *Mexican Year Book for 1911,* p. 210; *Mexican Year Book for 1912,* pp. 163, 168; *E&MJ,* XC (Nov. 5, 1910), 902; XCIV (Aug. 31, 1912), 424; XCV (Jan. 25, 1913), 254; Cia. Min. de Peñoles, S.A. (Estado de Durango), *Estatutos reformadas aprobadas por la asemblea general de accionistas ... 31 Mayo 1910* (Mexico, 1910).

84. Southworth and Holms, *El directorio,* pp. 68–69, 147; R. T. Hill, "Notes from a Little Journey to Mexico," *E&MJ,* LXXIV (Aug. 2, 1902), 145; LXXIV (Nov. 22, 1902), 694; Malcolmson, "Mining in Mexico, 1902," *E&MJ,* LXXV (Jan. 3, 1903), 35–36; (Feb. 21, 1903), 308; (Mar. 21, 1903), 455; (Mar. 28, 1903), 494; LXXVI (Oct. 17, 1903), 600; (Oct. 24, 1903), 633; (Nov. 7, 1903), 716; LXXVIII (July 7, 1904), 34; (Aug. 4, 1904), 195; XC (Oct. 1, 1910), 657; T. C. Hamm, "Industrial Progress in Durango," *Mex. Min. J.* (Oct. 1912), 27; Wagner, *Bullion to Books,* p. 163; O'Connor, *Guggenheims,* pp. 328–329; J. Ibarra, "El Estado de Coahuila," *Bol. min.,* XI (Jan. 1921), 13–16.

85. J. Ibarra, "Informe general [de municipalidades varios] del Estado de Zacatecas," *Bol. min.,* XXIX (Apr. 1930), 258–259.

86. Southworth, *Minas de México,* p. 240; Anon., "Mazapil Copper Company,"

Mex. Min. J. (Aug. 1907), 15; Martin, *Mexico*, II, 284–285; *E&MJ*, LXXV (Feb. 7, 1903), 240; LXXVII (Apr. 21, 1904), 663; LXXVIII (Nov. 3, 1904), 724; Anon., "Mazapil Copper Co. Operations," *E&MJ*, CX (Sept. 11, 1920), 524; G. Montes de Oca, "La planta de "The Mazapil Copper Co., Ltd.,' Saltillo, Coah.," *Bol. min.*, XII (Aug. 1921), 198; Ibarra, "Informe general"; Rippy, *British Investments in Latin America*, p. 100; Tischendorf, *Gt. Br. and Mex.*, p. 78.

87. Southworth, *Minas de México*, 219–220; J. R. Southworth, *El Estado de Sonora*, pp. 49–50, 52–53.

88. Southworth, *Sonora*, p. 51; Tischendorf, *Gt. Br. and Mex.*, p. 78.

89. *Mexican Year Book for 1911*, pp. 214, 222, 227; *E&MJ*, LXXV (Mar. 7, 1903), 387; (Apr. 11, 1903), 576; LXXVI (Nov. 28, 1903), 826; XC (Aug. 6, 1910), 249; (Oct. 1, 1910), 690; (Dec. 24, 1910), 1279; XCI (Mar. 25, 1911), 637; XCV (Jan. 18, 1913), 206; *Mex. Min. J.* (May 1911), 37; (Aug. 1913), 376; (Jan. 1916), 14.

90. Letter, A. S. Cragoe to *E&MJ*, CXVI (Dec. 1, 1923), 950; R. T. Hill, "Notes from Mexico," *E&MJ*, LXXIV (Aug. 2, 1902), 145; (Oct. 18, 1902), 530.

91. For the Alvarado legends see Hammond's *Autobiography* and Grant Shepherd's *Silver Magnet*, passim. Business details are from Southworth and Holms, *El directorio*, p. 39; *E&MJ*, LXXXIV (Oct. 5, 1907), 656; XCI (Feb. 18, 1911), 393; M. W. v. Bernewitz, *Cyanide Practice, 1910–1913*, pp. 544–545.

92. *Mex. Min. J.* (Apr. 1908), 29; (June 1908), 29; *Mexican Year Book for 1911*, p. 229; Southworth and Holms, *El directorio*, p. 185.

93. Southworth and Holms, *El directorio*, pp. 175–184. For a description of the technical aspects of these workings, see H. Forbes Julian and Edgar Smart, *Cyaniding Gold and Silver Ores* (London, 1907), pp. 47–48, 141–142, 156–158, 246–249.

94. *E&MJ*, LXXX (July 29, 1905), 183; M. B. Parker, "El Tigre, Sonora," *Mex. Min. J.* (July 1908), 19–20; Southworth and Holms, *El directorio*, p. 196; *E&MJ*, XCIII (June 22, 1912), 1212; *Mexican Year Book for 1913*, p. 106; D. L. H. Forbes, "The Treatment of Complex Silver-Ore at the Lucky Tiger Mine, El Tigre, Sonora," AIME *Trans.*, XLIII (1912), pp. 471–507; M. Peña, "La mina 'El Tigre,' Sonora," *Bol. min.*, V (Feb. 1918), 190–194; B. Rubio, "La mina 'El Tigre,'" *Bol. min.*, XXVII (Feb. 1929), 101–102.

95. James W. Gerard, *My First Eighty-Three Years* (New York, 1951), pp. 154–155; *E&MJ*, LXXV (Apr. 18, 1903), 607; (May 16, 1903), 760; (June 13, 1903), 902; LXXVI (Aug. 15, 1903), 254; (Dec. 24, 1903), 979; LXXVIII (July 28, 1904), 155; CXII (Sept. 24, 1921), 510; *Min. Mag.*, II (Feb. 1910), 111–112; Anon., "Reseña minera del Estado de Jalisco," *Bol. min.*, XXII (Oct. 1926), 195.

96. H. M. Chance, "The Taviche Mining District near Ocotlan, State of Oaxaca, Mexico," AIME *Trans.*, XXV (1904), pp. 886–892; *E&MJ*, LXXV (May 23, 1903), 794; LXXVIII (Aug. 11, 1904), 235.

97. J. Fred Rippy, "Investments of Citizens of the U.S. in Latin America," *Journal of Business*, XXIII (Jan. 1949), 17–21.

98. D. Barlow, "United States Enterprises in Mexico," Bur. of Foreign Commerce, Dept. of State, *Commercial Relations of the United States with Foreign Countries*, I (Oct. 29, 1902), pp. 433–503.

99. L. M. Gottschalk, "Large Investments of Foreign Capital Have Been Made," Bur. of Manufactures, Dept. of Commerce and Labor, *Monthly Consular and Trade Reports*, No. 321 (June 1907), pp. 124–125.

100. Southworth and Holms, *El directorio*, p. 19.

101. *Ibid.*, p. 17.

102. The largest of these were: British and Mexican Trust (£500,000); Esperanza Mining Co. [with heavy American interests] (£455,000); Mexican Mining

and Industrial Co. (£153,750); San Carlos Gold, Zacatecas (£100,000); and W. S. Pearson and Co. (£1,500,000). Several of these enterprises, however, were either paper concerns or had large interests in fields other than mining. ("Review of British Mining Investments in Mexico," *Mex. Min. J.* [Jan. 1909], 14.) Also see *E&MJ*, XC (Oct. 1, 1910), 664; and XCI (Feb. 25, 1911), 412.

103. Banco Central Mexicano, *Las sociedades anónimas de México*, Año I, 1908 (Mexico, 1908), pp. 317–323.

104. Marion Letcher, "Wealth of Mexico," Bur. of Foreign and Domestic Commerce, Dept. of Commerce and Labor, *Daily Consular and Trade Reports*, 15th year, III, No. 168 (July 18, 1912), p. 416.

105. Thompson opined that only the nationality of the company was taken into account, and in making his division in 1920, based upon information from private sources, the share of the British increased greatly at the Americans' expense. (Wallace Thompson, *Trading with Mexico* [New York, 1921], pp. 97–98.)

106. 66th Congress, 2d Session, *Senate Reports*, No. 645.

107. Cleona Lewis, *America's Stake in International Investments*, pp. 583–584, 608–609, 613–614. Also see Rippy, "Investments of Citizens of the U.S.," 21n.

108. For British difficulties during this period see Tischendorf, *Gt. Br. and Mex.*, pp. 22–31. For details on the 16 companies see *ibid.*, p. 148.

109. Rippy, *British Investments in Latin America*, pp. 32, 34, 40, 46, 47, 54–56; Tischendorf, *Gt. Br. and Mex.*, pp. 71, 78–86 (for small companies). For a list with some details of British companies organized from 1895 to 1910, see *ibid.*, pp. 150–164; Rippy, "The British Investment Boom of the 1880's in Latin-American Mines," *Inter-American Economic Affairs*, I (Mar. 1948), 72–73; Rippy, "The Peak of British Investment in Latin-American Mines," *ibid.*, II (Summer 1948), 42.

110. Rippy, "French Investments in Latin America," *Inter-American Economic Affairs*, II (Autumn 1948), 64; Rippy, "French Investments in Mexico," *ibid.*, II (Winter 1948), 10.

111. Southworth and Holms, *El directorio*, p. 15.

112. Quoted in *Mex. Min. J.* (Dec. 1908), 11.

CHAPTER 6

1. Southworth, *Minas de México*, p. 6.

2. Francisco Bulnes, *The Whole Truth About Mexico* (New York, 1916), pp. 121–123, 138.

3. Turner, *Barbarous Mexico*, pp. 13–15.

4. *Proyecto de Ley Minera; Escrito de remisión* (Mexico, 1907). The "Escrito" was signed by Rodolfo Reyes; the "Proyecto" by E. Martínez Baca, J. L. Requena, Rodolfo Reyes, Joaquín M. Ramos, and Manuel Ortega Espinosa. This pamphlet was privately reprinted in 1909 as *Primer proyecto de Ley Minera presentado al Señor Ministro de Fomento* (Mexico: Imp. y Lib. de Inocencio Arriola, 1909) with the authors of the *Proyecto* given credit for authorship. This edition had a short foreword signed by Rodolfo Reyes and J. L. Requena, and included an excerpt from

Reyes' thesis "La agricultura y la ley minera" as an appendix. For editions of the drafts and the final law itself, see Vance and Clagett, *Guide to the Law . . . of Mexico,* pp. 207–209.

5. *Proyecto de Ley Minera,* pp. iv–vi; and Art. 33, pp. 10–11.

6. *Ibid.,* Art. 2F, p. 4; Art. 38, pp. 12–13; and Art. 46, pp. 14–15.

7. *Ibid.,* pp. xxxi–xxxiv; Arts. 166–177, pp. 43–46.

8. Printed in *Mexican Year Book for 1908,* pp. 510–511; *Mex. Min. J.* (July 1908), 9–10. The various intermediary drafts and their preambles can be found in "Proyecto de la Ley Minera de los Estados Unidos Mexicanos, presentado al Señor Presidente de la República y discutido y modificado en Consejo de Ministros," *Memoria ... de* [*Secretaría de*] *Fomento, Colonización e Industria, 1908–1909* (Mexico, 1910), pp. 179–237.

9. Dublán and Lozano, *Legislación mexicana, 1856–60,* VIII, p. 95; M. de la Peña, *El dominio directo del soberano en las minas de México,* I, pp. 141–144.

10. *Min. Mag.,* I (Sept. 1909), 27.

11. *Min. & Sci. Press,* XCVII (Aug. 1, 1908), 135–136. For a fuller development of these ideas, see *La nueva Ley Minera y su Reglamento* (Mexico, 1910), pp. 597–613. Another lengthy defense of the articles was presented by Fernando Solis Cámara, *Los artículos 141 y 144 del proyecto de Ley Minera* (Mexico, 1908).

12. *Mex. Min. J.* (Nov. 1907), 10; (July 1908), 9–10; (Aug. 1908), 9–10; (Sept. 1908), 9–10; (Nov. 1908), 9. While the Federal Water Law of 1910 made no distinction between individuals, it limited the grant of concessions to "companies organized under the laws of Mexico, and such Mexican associations, public or private, as have legal capacity to enjoy such grants." (H. N. Branch, "Concessions; A Brief Analysis," *Mexican Year Book for 1922,* pp. 225–226.)

13. Cámara de Diputados, Comisión primera de Fomento, *Dictamen de las comisiones unidas primera y segunda de Fomento que consulta la Ley Minera de los Estados Unidos Mexicanos* (Mexico, 1908).

14. *Nueva Ley Minera,* pp. 7–33. This volume contains the entire debate on the law as well as the texts and a number of studies and commentaries.

15. Forms for filing claims were described in J. P. Flynn and W. B. Baggaly, "Denouncing Mineral Lands in Mexico," *E&MJ,* XCII (July 22, 1911), 159; *Mexican Year Book for 1913,* pp. 97–99; and Frederick F. Barker and R. Reyes, *The Mining Laws of Mexico* (Mexico, 1910), pp. 24–28.

16. *Nueva Ley Minera,* pp. 400–404, 410.

17. For the complete debate on this point, see *Nueva Ley Minera,* pp. 387–425, 454–459. For the complicated mechanics of the procedure, see Barker and Reyes, *Mining Laws of Mexico,* pp. 20–21. Also see the comments in *Mex. Min. J.* (Dec. 1909), 15–16; and *Min. Mag.,* II (June 1910), 427.

18. Anon., "Estudio Legislativo," *Nueva Ley Minera,* pp. 544–545.

19. "Dictamen de las comisiones unidas," *ibid.,* pp. 30–31; Address of Calero to the Chamber, *ibid.,* pp. 35–38.

20. "Estudio Legislativo," *ibid.,* p. 552.

21. *Ibid.,* p. 234.

22. Barker and Reyes, *Mining Laws of Mexico,* p. 36.

23. For the totals of the votes, see *Nueva Ley Minera,* pp. 84, 173, 186, 247, 263–264, 323, 331, 362, 386, 426, 463.

24. Rickard, *Journeys,* pp. 23, 93–94; *Mex. Min. J.* (Sept. 1911), 15; Banco Central Mexicano, *Las sociedades anónimas de México* (1908), pp. 288–289; *Mexican Year Book for 1913,* pp. 92–93; J. C. Zárate, "Visita a la Fábrica Nacional de Dinamita y Explosivos," *Boletín de industrias,* 2a. época, I (July–Sept. 1922), 4; H. N. Branch, "Concessions," p. 237; Special Correspondence, *E&MJ,* LXXXIX (Jan. 8, 1910), 117.

CHAPTER 7

1. Rickard, *Journeys*, p. 101.

2. H. G. Elwes, "Points about Mexican Labor," *E&MJ*, XC (Oct. 1, 1910), 662; C. W. Hall, "Requisites of Successful Mine Operations," *Min. & Met.*, VI (June 1925), 288; Letter, W. R. Wade to *E&MJ*, CXVIII (Aug. 2, 1924), 183; Wagner, *Bullion to Books*, p. 134.

3. Presidential address to AIME meeting at Mexico City, Nov. 9, 1901, AIME *Trans.*, XXXII (1902), cxxiv–cxxv.

4. E. K. Judd, "Wages and Welfare," in Robert Peele (ed.), *Mining Engineers' Handbook* (New York, 1927), pp. 1536–37.

5. Personal communication to author, June 13, 1955.

6. Cámara Nacional de Minería (hereinafter cited as Cám. Nac. de Min.), *Circ.* 699, Memo. to the Secretaría de Hacienda (May 18, 1932). Also see *Bol. min.*, IX (Mar.–Apr. 1920), 314. The predilection of American workers to leave work for hunting and fishing has caused labor difficulties north of the border. (*New York Times* [Dec. 16, 1948], p. 51.)

7. One of the most complete and level-headed discussions of the Mexican laborer about 1900 can be found in Walter E. Weyl, "Labor Conditions in Mexico," *Bulletin of the Department of Labor*, No. 38 (Jan. 1902), pp. 12–22.

8. Interview with T. A. Rickard in *Interviews with Mining Engineers*, p. 339. Also see F. W. Ruttencutter, "Difficulties of Pumping at Veta Grande," *E&MJ*, CXXIV (Oct. 15, 1927), 616. A number of interesting comments on Mexican labor in the Aguascalientes and Monterrey smelters in the late 1890's were made by O. H. Hahn, "On the Development of Silver Smelting in Mexico," pp. 267–268.

9. R. E. Chism, "Sierra Mojada, Mexico," AIME *Trans.*, XV (1886–87), pp. 586–587.

10. J. W. Malcolmson, "The Erection of Silver-Lead Smelting Works in Mexico," in J. Forrest (ed.), *Smelting Processes*, p. 61; and Collins, "Smelting Processes," p. 159. For the same reason, the use of processes in which interruptions would be less destructive upon equipment than the cooling of furnaces was advocated. (T. H. Clemes, "The Lixiviation of Silver Ores," Institution of Civil Engineers [London], *Minutes of Proceedings*, CXXV [1896], p. 96.)

11. Martin, *Mexico's Treasure-House*, p. 63; Rickard, *Journeys*, pp. 102–103; M. Romero, *Mexico and the U.S.*, p. 542.

12. E. A. H. Tays, "Present Labor Conditions in Mexico," *E&MJ*, LXXXIV (Oct. 5, 1907), 622. Also see Comisión Monetaria Mexicana, *Actas de las juntas generales* (Mexico, 1904), pp. 46, 48, 53.

13. E. D. Trowbridge, *Mexico, Today and Tomorrow* (New York, 1920), p. 263.

14. W. E. Weyl, who felt that the difference between agricultural and industrial wages was "not very great," has a chart of wage rates in "Labor Conditions in Mexico," p. 55. For an interesting dollars-and-cents comparison of Mexican and United States workers, see Malcolmson, "Mining in Mexico, 1902," *E&MJ*, LXXV (Jan. 3, 1903), 35. Matías Romero insisted that on a production-cost basis, Mexican labor cost as much as American labor. His comments comparing American and Mexican workers are noteworthy. (*Mexico and the U.S.*, pp. 495–543.) J. W. Malcolmson believed that Mexican labor was dear "on account of its inefficiency and untrustworthiness." He estimated that it would take "about 5 [Mexicans] 11 hours

to get through the work that 2 English navvies do in 9 or 10 hours." High supervision costs were another burden. ("The Erection of Silver-Lead Smelting Works," Institution of Civil Engineers, (London), *Minutes,* CXII (1893), p. 171.)

15. Anon., "A Typical Wage Scale," *Mex. Min. J.* (July 1908), 19. Also see, R. T. Hill, "The Guanajuato Mining District," *E&MJ,* LXXVII (Apr. 21, 1904), 643; and J. MacDonald, "A Labor Chart for the Management of Mining and Milling Operations (at Guanajuato)," AIME *Trans.,* XXXIX (1908), pp. 664–667.

16. Manuel M. Contreras, *Reseña de los trabajos de la Sociedad Mexicana de Minería* (Mexico, 1884), Appendix Table ii.

17. E. Martínez Baca, "Historical Sketch," AIME *Trans.,* XXXII (1902), pp. 521–522; *Mexican Year Book for 1920-1921,* p. 344; Rickard, *Journeys,* pp. 100, 135; Weyl, "Labor Conditions," *passim;* Comisión Monetaria, *Actas,* p. 42.

18. C. H. Grabill, "Inefficiency and Poor Food of Mexican Miners," *E&MJ,* CIX (Feb. 14, 1920), 451.

19. Letter, Dr. G. F. Campbell to *E&MJ,* CIX (May 8, 1920), 1056–57; Weyl, "Labor Conditions," pp. 15–16, 66–76.

20. P. C. Hanna, "Zinc Industry in Mexico," *Mex. Min. J.* (Nov. 1909), 17–18.

21. Ingersoll, *In and Under Mexico* (New York, 1924), pp. 117–118; *E&MJ,* CXVIII (July 12, 1924), 72.

22. Letter, W. R. Wade to *E&MJ,* CXVIII (Aug. 2, 1924), 183. See Mark R. Lamb, "The Gentle Art of Appreciation," *E&MJ,* XCI (Feb. 11, 1911), 325, for some general remarks on the situation.

23. Ingersoll, *In and Under Mexico,* pp. 117–118.

24. Angel de la Garza Brito, "La anquilostomasia en el Estado de Hidalgo," *Boletín de industria, comercio y trabajo* (Sección de trabajo), I (Oct. 1918), 138-141.

25. E. D. Trowbridge, *Mexico,* p. 278.

26. A. H. Rogers, "Character and Habits of the Mexican Miner," *E&MJ,* LXXXV (Apr. 14, 1908), 701.

27. *Mex. Min. J.* (Apr. 1912), 16; (Dec. 1912), 45; B. Burwell, "Pachuca, Home of the Patio Process," *E&MJ,* CXVIII (Nov. 8, 1924), 729. Also see Ingersoll, *In and Under Mexico,* pp. 130–133.

28. Ernest Gruening, *Mexico and its Heritage* (New York, 1928), p. 345. W. H. Triplett of Peñoles has written to the author: "According to my experience the niggardliness of accident compensation has been grossly exaggerated. The companies were pretty tight all right but as the years went by, both medical attention and compensation improved. If an injured man was paid off completely and discharged, he, in nearly every instance, spent his compensation in a few weeks or months or some one got it away from him and he was left destitute. Whenever possible, a crippled man was given employment as a watchman, warehouseman or a job that would keep him in food. I have seen companies try with varying success in aiding many unfortunates. I mention my experience only to show that there are other angles to the question...." (Personal communication to the author, June 13, 1955.)

29. IMMM, *Indus. min. de Méx.: Edo. de Mich.,* pp. 68–69. For the system used at San Rafael in Pachuca, see E. Girault, "La beneficencia privada en la negociación minera de San Rafael y Anexas de Pachuca," IMMM, *Informes,* I (Dec. 1909), pp. 129-132.

30. E. Ludlow, "The Coal Fields of Las Esperanzas, Coahuila, Mexico," AIME *Trans.,* XXXII (1902), pp. 144–145, 147.

31. There was a fairly widespread effort to bring in Chinese and Japanese for work in mines at this time. See *E&MJ,* LXXV (Jan. 31, 1903), 200; (May 16, 1903), 760; LXXVI (Aug. 29, 1903), 325; (Oct. 10, 1903), 533; LXXVII (June 30, 1904), 1056; LXXVIII (Aug. 11, 1904), 235. The Anglo-Mexican Mining Co. at Culiacán, Sinaloa, had an interesting experience importing Chinese in 1889. (Tischendorf, *Gt. Br. and Mex.,* pp. 79–81.)

32. E. Fraser-Campbell, "The Management of Mexican Labor," *E&MJ*, CXI (June 3, 1911), 1104–5; Ingersoll, *In and Under Mexico*, p. 40. At Fresnillo during the 1930's, two-thirds of the men were on contract or task systems. See J. H. Ashley, "Working Sulphide Ores at Fresnillo," *E&MJ*, CXXXVII (June 1936), 284.

33. W. W. Shelby, "Mexican Contract Labor, Day's Pay and Task," *E&MJ*, CXIV (Sept. 30, 1922), 587; Fred McCoy, "Mexican Labor on Concrete Work," *E&MJ*, XCII (Sept. 16, 1911), 555.

34. Ingersoll, *In and Under Mexico*, p. 40.

35. E. Fraser-Campbell, "Management of Mexican Labor," 1105.

36. *Ibid.*, 1104; Rickard, *Journeys*, pp. 102–103; J. W. Bear, et al., "In an Adit Heading at Ojuela—Averaging 714 Feet per Month," *E&MJ*, CXXVI (July 14, 1928), 49–50. Also see Ingersoll's allegations concerning pay practices at Nacozari. (*In and Under Mexico*, pp. 44–45.)

37. Rickard, *Journeys*, p. 114.

38. F. J. Gamboa, *Commentaries*, Chap. xxiv, Par. 4. Ore stealing by American miners in the West was also scandalous; see *E&MJ*, XCV (Apr. 12, 1913), 771; T. A. Rickard, "Ore Theft," *E&MJ*, CXL (Dec. 1939), 37–39, and CXLI (Jan. 1940), 44–47.

39. Martin, *Mexico's Treasure-House*, p. 68.

40. Rickard, *Journeys*, p. 167; and also see *Bol. min.*, XIII (Apr. 1922), 482; *E&MJ*, CXLI (Dec. 1940), p. 86.

41. G. L. Sheldon, "High Grading," *E&MJ*, XCVI (Nov. 15, 1913), 933; also see Anon., "Adobe Furnaces in the Sonora Valley," *E&MJ*, XCI (Feb. 25, 1911), 418; Rickard, *Journeys*, p. 115.

42. Shepherd, *Silver Magnet*, pp. 219–221.

43. Cámara Minera de México (hereinafter cited as Cám. Min. de Méx.), *Circ.* 99 (Aug. 15, 1937); *Min. Mag.*, XXXIV (1926), 85–89; *E&MJ*, CXXIII (Mar. 5, 1927), 416; CXLIII (Sept. 1942), 101.

44. See the experience of O. J. Langendorf, a mine superintendent in Parral, Chih., described in U.S. State Department, *For Rel. of the U.S., 1913*, p. 891. During World War II a mine in central Mexico suffered continual shortages of drill bits while a store a few miles away had a larger stock of the company's bits than the mine stockroom! Tired of periodically repurchasing its own property, the company ordered bits by carload lots in order to have them stamped with its private mark.

45. Editorial, "Labor Legislation in Mexico," *E&MJ*, CXIV (Sept. 9, 1922), 422.

46. Tomás Reyes Retana, "Estudio sobre huelgas," *Boletín de industria, comercio y trabajo* (Sec. de trabajo), II (Jan.–June 1919), 54; M. Clark, *Organized Labor in Mexico*, p. 10.

47. Tays, "Present Labor Conditions in Mexico," 624.

48. Martin, *Mexico's Treasure-House*, pp. 62–66. Also see Rickard, *Journeys*, p. 108; O'Connor, *Guggenheims*, pp. 326–327; *E&MJ*, LXXV (June 6, 1903), 869; LXXVI (Aug. 22, 1903), 287; (Sept. 5, 1903), 366; (Sept. 12, 1903), 403.

49. S. Traylor, *Out of the Southwest*, pp. 66–71; Marcosson, *Metal Magic*, p. 52; Guggenheim, *William Guggenheim*, pp. 81–83.

CHAPTER 8

1. Reyes' platform was printed in Francisco Bulnes, *The Whole Truth About Mexico*, pp. 121–126. Madero's platform is in his book *La sucesión presidencial en 1910*, pp. 206–208.

2. E. I. Bell, *The Political Shame of Mexico*, pp. 48, 89–96; *Min. Mag.*, II (June 1910), 426.

3. "Reglamento de policia y seguridad en los trabajos de las minas," *Diario oficial*, CXXII, No. 39 (Oct. 17, 1912).

4. Henry Lane Wilson, *Diplomatic Episodes in Mexico, Belgium and Chile* (New York, 1927), pp. 240, 285–288.

5. *Ibid.*, p. 230.

6. *E&MJ*, XCVII (May 2, 1914), 928. Controlling only the northwest at the time, Carranza forced the American personnel to leave the Sonora copper mines. The full story of Woodrow Wilson's Mexican policy has not yet been written. Three important studies are Robert Quirk's two books, *The Mexican Revolution, 1914–15; The Convention of Aguascalientes* (Indiana University Press, 1960); *An Affair of Honor* (University of Kentucky Press, 1962); and Charles C. Clendenen, *The United States and Pancho Villa* (Cornell University Press, 1961).

7. *Mex. Min. J.* (May 1913), 16; (Oct. 1913), 471; (Nov. 1913), 521; (Dec. 1913), 569; *E&MJ*, XCVII (Apr. 25, 1914), 880; W. F. McCaleb, *Public Finances of Mexico*, pp. 203, 205–206.

8. *E&MJ*, XCVI (Nov. 29, 1913), 1039; (Dec. 6, 1913), 1194; *For. Rel. of the U.S., 1914*, pp. 763–764; O'Connor, *Guggenheims*, p. 334.

9. *E&MJ*, XCVII (Jan. 24, 1914), 253.

10. For the effect of this fighting upon the mining industry, see Anon., "Mexican Mining in 1913," *E&MJ*, XCVII (Jan. 10, 1914), 137–140; Anon., "Mining in Mexico in 1914," *E&MJ*, XCIX (Jan. 9, 1914), 122–124. The full story of this period is to be found in Quirk, *The Mexican Revolution, 1914–15* and Clendenen, *The U.S. and Pancho Villa*.

11. *E&MJ*, XC (Dec. 10, 1910), 1181; XCI (Jan. 7, 1911), 68; (Jan. 28, 1911), 243; (May 6, 1911), 925. However, see the penetrating analysis of D. E. Woodbridge, "The Mexican Disorders," *E&MJ*, XCI (Feb. 4, 1911), 263–264.

12. Anon., "Editorial Correspondence," *E&MJ*, XCI (May 6, 1911), 925.

13. *Mex. Min. J.* (July 1911), 38.

14. *Ibid.*, 16.

15. *E&MJ*, XCII (July 8, 1911), 83; (July 29, 1911), 209; K. Thomas, "Mining in Mexico in 1911," *E&MJ*, XCIII (Jan. 6, 1912), 77–79; *Mex. Min. J.* (Sept. 1911), 35.

16. *E&MJ*, XCI (Apr. 8, 1911), 736; (May 6, 1911), 925; *For. Rel. of the U.S., 1912*, 910–926.

17. *Mex. Min. J.* (Feb. 1912), 15.

18. Lic. Antonio Ramos Pedrueza, Director del Depto. del Trabajo, in *Boletín del Departamento del Trabajo*, Año I (July 1913), 33–34.

19. B. Newman, "Present Labor Conditions in Mexico," *E&MJ*, XCII (Oct. 7, 1911), 689.

20. *E&MJ*, XCI (Feb. 4, 1911), 293; (Apr. 8, 1911), 736; (May 6, 1911), 925; (June 17, 1911), 1229; XCII (July 8, 1911), 88; (July 15, 1911), 132; (July 22, 1911), 180; (July 29, 1911), 209; (Aug. 5, 1911), 280; (Aug. 19, 1911), 372; (Sept. 2, 1911), 466; XCIV (Sept. 28, 1912), 612; XCV (Jan. 4, 1913), 40; O'Connor, *Guggenheims*, pp. 332–333; Wagner, *Bullion to Books*, pp. 152–153; *Mex. Min. J.* (Nov. 1911), 36; (Jan. 1912), 46; (Aug. 1912), 43; *E&MJ*, XCIV (July 27, 1912), 186; (Dec. 28, 1912), 1247.

21. Wagner, *Bullion to Books*, p. 155.

22. *Mex. Min. J.* (Aug. 1912), 42.

23. *E&MJ*, XCIV (Sept. 21, 1912), 522; (Oct. 26, 1912), 812; XCV (May 5, 1913), 890–891. For a slightly different version of this incident, see D. Pletcher, "An American Mining Company in the Mexican Revolutions of 1911–1920," *Journal*

of Modern History, XX (Mar. 1948), 24–25. Also see *E&MJ,* XCV (Apr. 12, 1913), 771; 109, (Apr. 24, 1920), 987. For accounts of raids in Chihuahua, Sonora, and Durango, see *E&MJ,* XCV (Feb. 24, 1912), 389, 424; (Mar. 2, 1912), 476; (Mar. 9, 1912), 484; (Mar. 16, 1912), 574; (Apr. 6, 1912), 686.

24. Trowbridge, *Mexico,* pp. 159–160.

25. For the closedown of the Aguascalientes smelter, see *Mex. Min. J.* (Sept. 1913), 451.

26. Anon., Mexican Mining in 1913," *E&MJ,* XCVII (Jan. 10, 1914), 137–140; Anon., "Mining in Mexico in 1914," *E&MJ,* XCIX (Jan. 9, 1915), 122–124; and *E&MJ,* XCVII (Jan. 17, 1914), 199; (Jan. 24, 1914), 241; (Apr. 25, 1914), 880; XCVIII (Oct. 31, 1914), 808; Anon., "Coppers," *E&MJ,* CIII (Jan. 6, 1917), 8. For an excellent survey, see D. Pletcher, "An American Mining Company in the Mexican Revolutions," pp. 19–26.

27. *E&MJ,* XCV (June 11, 1913), 136; XCVI (Aug. 6, 1913), 314; XCVII (Jan. 24, 1914), 241; XCVIII (Oct. 31, 1914), 808; Cleland, *Phelps Dodge,* pp. 197–199.

28. Will Davis, *Experiences and Observations of an American Consular Officer,* p. 176.

29. See Davis, *Experiences, passim,* and *E&MJ, passim.* Also see *For. Rel. of the U.S., 1916,* pp. 677–682; and J. E. Clennell, "Among the Mexican Rebels," *Min. Mag.,* XXXIII (Oct. 1925), 213–220.

30. Hamilton Fyfe, *The Real Mexico* (New York, 1914), pp. 25, 41, 81; C. F. Williams, "Driving a 1200-Foot Waste-Pass," *E&MJ,* CXVI (Aug. 11, 1923), 227; Marcosson, *Metal Magic,* pp. 232, 234–237; O'Connor, *Guggenheims,* pp. 335–336; Trowbridge, *Mexico,* p. 279; *E&MJ,* XCVII (June 27, 1914), 1308; XCVIII (July 4, 1914), 5; XCIX (Apr. 3, 1915), 627; CI (Jan. 1, 1916), 8–9; (Apr. 8, 1916), 651; CIII (Mar. 17, 1917), 470.

31. *E&MJ,* XCIX (Mar. 27, 1915), 582; CII (Sept. 16, 1916), 502; Marcosson, *Metal Magic,* p. 238.

32. *Mex. Min. J.* (Mar. 1914), 134; (Mar. 1916), 73; *E&MJ,* CIII (June 30, 1917), 1174; CIV (July 7, 1917), 38; (July 28, 1917), 190; Anon., "Facts for the Stockholder. XIV—Greene-Cananea Copper Company," *E&MJ,* CXV (Apr. 21, 1923), 738; Arthur Notman, "Comparative Earning Power of Capital Invested in the Copper Industry of the Western Hemisphere," *E&MJ,* CXV (June 30, 1923), 1146.

33. *E&MJ,* CII (Dec. 9, 1916), 1040; (Dec. 23, 1916), 1112.

34. *Mex. Min. J.* (Jan. 1916), 14; *E&MJ,* CI (May 27, 1916), 944.

35. *Min. Mag.,* XX (Apr. 1919), 320.

36. *Bol. min.,* I (June 15, 1916), 375; *Mex. Min. J.* (Mar. 1916), 73; *E&MJ,* CI (Jan. 22, 1916), 181; (May 13, 1916), 869.

37. *Mex. Min. J.* (Mar. 1914), 132; *E&MJ,* CV (Mar. 2, 1918), 429; CVI (Dec. 21, 1918), 1063; F. W. Baker to Camp Bird Ltd. Shareholders, *Min. Mag.,* XXII (1920), Company Meetings and Reports Section.

38. For photographs and accounts of railroad destruction, see *E&MJ,* XCV (Jan. 25, 1913), 237; and F. W. Powell, "The Railroads of Mexico," *Mexican Year Book for 1920–1921,* pp. 174–175. Also O. Hardy, "The Revolution and the Railroads of Mexico," *Pacific Historical Review,* III (1934), 249–269.

39. R. G. Cleland, ed., *Mexican Year Book for 1920–1921,* p. 277; Marcosson, *Metal Magic,* pp. 238–245; Anon., "The Future of Mexican Mining," *E&MJ,* CVII (Feb. 1, 1919), 239. For details of these arrangements see C. A. Grabill, "Ore-buying in Mexico," *E&MJ,* CIX (Mar. 20, 1920), 694–697.

40. S. Jennings, "Symposium on the High Cost of Mining, Milling and Smelting," *E&MJ,* CIII (Feb. 3, 1917), 219; *E&MJ,* CX (Sept. 4, 1920), 492.

41. Anon., "Mining in Mexico Today," *E&MJ,* CVII (Jan. 25, 1919), 176–177.

42. Anon., "The Mexican Problem," *E&MJ*, CVII (May 10, 1919), 831. For the experience of one company in Sonora, see Pletcher, "An American Mining Company in the Mexican Revolutions," pp. 22–25.

43. *E&MJ*, XCVIII (Aug. 8, 1914), 273; (Oct. 10, 1914), 670.

44. *Mex. Min. J.* (Oct. 1914), 243; (Nov. 1914), 287; (Dec. 1914), 340; *E&MJ*, XCIII (Apr. 13, 1912), 734; (June 8, 1912), 1150; XCVI (Nov. 1, 1913), 849; XCVII (May 2, 1914), 915; XCVIII (Sept. 19, 1914), 541. For changes in the dynamite tariff doing away with the Díaz-protected monopoly, see *Colección de leyes, decretos, circulares, acuerdos y desposiciones referentes a la minería* (hereinafter cited as *Col. de leyes, 1918*), Mexico, 1918, pp. 209–210, 238–239, 249, 251.

45. For a complete survey see Edwin W. Kemmerer, *Inflation and Revolution in Mexico's Experience of 1912–1917* (Princeton, N. J., 1940).

46. *An. de estad. min., 1922*, p. 130.

47. Davis, *Experiences,* pp. 121–128; Trowbridge, *Mexico,* pp. 192–193. For examples of forced loans see *For. Rel. of the U.S., 1914,* pp. 758–763. Cananea imported some $400,000 in silver dollars from China to keep its properties operating. (Pletcher, "An American Company," p. 24.)

48. For a rather outrageous incident at Guadalajara, see Davis, *Experiences,* pp. 223–233; *E&MJ*, CII (Aug. 12, 1916), 318.

49. Trowbridge, *Mexico,* p. 162; *E&MJ*, CXVI (Dec. 13, 1913), 1138.

50. Villa never could understand "the law of supply and demand" in determining value. For a famous anecdote on this topic, see Marcosson, *Metal Magic,* p. 233; Trowbridge, *Mexico,* p. 193.

51. Grabill, "Ore-buying in Mexico," 694–697; Decree of March 29, 1917, *Col. de leyes, 1918*, pp. 250–251.

52. *E&MJ*, XCIX (May 15, 1915), 875; *For. Rel. of the U.S., 1915,* pp. 909–912.

53. S. Ramirez, "Informe sobre el estado de actividad de las negociaciones mineras en Pachuca y Real del Monte," *Bol. min.,* III (May 1, 1917), 453; Anon., "Conditions in Mexico," *E&MJ*, CII (Aug. 19, 1916), 340; S. Jennings, "Symposium," 218; *E&MJ*, CII (July 22, 1916), 529.

54. E. J. Smith, "Concreting the Barron Shaft in Pachuca, Mexico," *E&MJ*, CI (Apr. 15, 1916), 676–679.

55. Report from *Argus de Paris* (Jan. 4, 1917), reprinted in *Bol. min.,* III (Mar. 15, 1917), 288–290. For production figures, see T. S. Saunders, "Las Dos Estrellas Gold Mine," *Min. Mag.,* XXV (Aug. 1921), 89.

56. *Diario de los debates* (del Constituyente), I, pp. 608–609. Also see *E&MJ*, CVIII (Aug. 30, 1919), 375; L. G. Aguirre, "Informe referente al estado de actividad que guardan las principales negociaciones mineras del Estado de Guanajuato," *Bol. min.,* III (Feb. 15, 1917), 174.

57. Anon., "Mining in Mexico in 1916," *E&MJ*, CIII (Jan. 6, 1917), 78.

58. Gibbon, *Mexico Under Carranza,* pp. 148–150; *Mex. Min. J.* (Oct. 1913), 499; *E&MJ*, XCVI (Sept. 13, 1913), 519; (Sept. 20, 1913), 557; *For. Rel. of the U.S., 1914,* p. 761.

59. Letter, F. F. Sharpless to *E&MJ*, CVII (June 7, 1919), 1007–8.

60. 66th Cong., 2d Sess., *Senate Reports,* No. 645, pp. 17–18, 93. Also see 62nd Cong., 2d Sess., Senate Committee on Foreign Relations, *Revolutions in Mexico* (Washington, D.C., 1913). For a description of some depredations in 1916 see *For. Rel. of the U.S., 1916,* pp. 650–683.

61. Wallace Thompson, *Trading With Mexico,* p. 99.

62. Lewis, *America's Stake in Foreign Investments,* pp. 203–204.

63. See the petition presented by William Loeb, Vice-President of ASARCO, to the Mexican-American Commission in 1916 on behalf of 45 mining companies, *E&MJ*, CII (Sept. 30, 1916), 609; (Oct. 21, 1916), 762–763.

64. *E&MJ*, CXVII (Feb. 2, 1924), 195.

65. *E&MJ*, CXXII (Oct. 9, 1926), 588; (Dec. 4, 1926), 907.

66. George A. Chamberlain, *Is Mexico Worth Saving?* (Indianapolis, 1920), pp. 62–63.

CHAPTER 9

1. Signed at Hermosillo, Sonora, and printed in Secretaría de Hacienda y Crédito Público, *Decretos, circulares, y demás disposiciones expedidas por el gobierno constitucionalista por conducto de la Secretaría de Hacienda desde abril 1913 hasta diciembre 1915* (hereinafter cited as *Decretos, etc., 1913–1915*), Mexico, 1916, p. 192. Also see *Col. de leyes, 1918*, pp. 214–215, 217–218; *E&MJ*, XCV (June 20, 1913), 1259.

2. *For. Rel. of the U.S., 1914*, pp. 730–740; Circ. No. 1, Nov. 26, 1914, Vera Cruz, in Decretos, etc., *1913–1915*; *Col. de leyes, 1918*, pp. 214–215; *E&MJ*, XCV (June 20, 1913), 1259; XCVII (Jan. 24, 1914), 241; Paul W. Meyers, "The Reclamation of Mexican Mining Titles," *E&MJ*, CXII (Oct. 29, 1921), 685–687.

3. Meyers, "Reclamation of Mexican Mining Titles," 408.

4. *Decretos, etc., 1913–1915*, pp. 227, 321; *Col. de leyes, 1918*, pp. 82–88, 95–97, 105–106; Gobierno provisional de la República Mexicana, *Recopilación de las circulares, reglamentos y acuerdos expedidas por las secretarías de estado adscritas a la Primera Jefatura del Ejercito constitucionalista* (Mexico, 1916), pp. 178–201; *For. Rel. of the U.S., 1914*, pp. 723–730; *Mex. Min. J.* (Sept. 1914), 200–201; (Oct. 1914), 243–244; Carlo de Fornaro, *Carranza and Mexico* (New York, 1915), p. 91; Blas Urrea (pseudo. of Luis Cabrera), *La herencia de Carranza*, quoted in Miguel Quintana, *Los ensayos monetarios*, pp. 128–130; Anon., "Mining in Mexico in 1916," *E&MJ*, CIII (Jan. 6, 1917), 77.

5. *For. Rel. of the U.S., 1914*, pp. 720–723.

6. Reprinted in translation in *Mining and Engineering World*, XLII (Apr. 10, 1915), 687–688 and *E&MJ*, XCIX (Apr. 10, 1915), 668–669.

7. *For. Rel. of the U.S., 1915*, pp. 893, 895–899, 901–902, 903–908, 909 ff., 922, 924; Clendenen, *The U.S. and Pancho Villa*, pp. 160–162; Frederick Dunn, *Diplomatic Protection of Americans in Mexico* (New York, 1933), pp. 328–329.

8. Villa's confiscation threat is discussed in detail in Clendenen, *The U.S. and Pancho Villa*, pp. 165–166, 183–186; and Quirk, *The Mexican Revolution*, pp. 283–284. Also see *E&MJ*, XCVII (May 2, 1914), 928; XCVIII (Nov. 14, 1914), 890; *For. Rel. of the U.S., 1915*, pp. 926–931, 931–935, 938–940; Wagner, *Bullion to Books*, pp. 151, 168–169, 172–176; Hugh L. Scott, *Some Memories of a Soldier* (New York, 1928), pp. 513–516; O'Connor, *Guggenheims*, p. 335; Marcosson, *Metal Magic*, pp. 232–233.

9. *For Rel. of the U.S., 1915*, pp. 946–947. For protests of miners' associations representing companies in central Mexico, see *ibid.*, pp. 959–963.

10. *E&MJ*, XCVIII (Sept. 5, 1914), 449; C (Oct. 23, 1915), 698; CI (Jan. 15, 1916), 151 (for an eyewitness account of the Santa Ysabel massacre); Nathaniel and Sylvia Weyl, *The Reconquest of Mexico* (New York, 1939), pp. 49–55; Cleland, *Phelps Dodge*, pp. 198–199.

11. Saltillo, June 29, 1914, in *Col. de leyes, 1918*, pp. 216–217.

12 Decree No. 25, Apr. 24, 1914, in *Decretos, etc., 1913-1915,* pp. 20–21, 460.

13. *Ibid.,* p. 207.

14. Saltillo, July 1, 1914, *ibid.,* p. 222.

15. *Col. de leyes, 1918,* pp. 227–228, 230–231, 242, 247–248, 252–253, 257–258.

16. *For. Rel. of the U.S., 1916,* pp. 725–727, 729.

17. *Col. de leyes, 1918,* pp. 153–154, 158–159, 197–198, 241–242; *Bol. min.,* III (Apr. 15, 1917), 413 (trans. in *For. Rel. of the U.S., 1917,* pp. 1053–54); Depto. de Minas, Circ. No. 5, *ibid.,* V (Mar.–Apr. 1918), 398–401; (May–June 1918), 643–646; P. W. Meyers, "The Reclamation of Mexican Mining Titles," *E&MJ,* CXII (Sept. 10, 1921), 406–407.

18. Gobierno provisional de la nación, *Codificación de los decretos del C. Venustiano Carranza* (Mexico, 1915), pp. 186–187; *Col. de leyes, 1918,* pp. 92–94 (trans. in *E&MJ, C* [Oct. 23, 1915], 688).

19. This new feature was difficult to enforce. Furthermore, mine agents were unfamiliar with the system, and therefore a number of "clarifying circulars" had to be sent out, *Col. de leyes, 1918,* pp. 230, 232, 253; Circ. 836 of the Dirección General de Timbre (Feb. 22, 1919), *Bol. min.,* VII (Mar.–Apr. 1919), 342.

20. Letter, E. A. H. Tays to *E&MJ,* XCIX (May 22, 1915), 913; C (Dec. 25, 1915), 1038. For the role of the State Department, see *For. Rel. of the U.S., 1915,* pp. 936–938, 940–946, 959–963.

21. C. Díaz Dufoo, *México y los capitales extranjeros,* pp. 458–460.

22. Letter, F. Roel to *E&MJ,* C (Oct. 16, 1915), 647–648. The *Mexican Mining Journal* (Sept. 1915), 311, expressed essentially the same view.

23. Address to the International Engineering Congress, San Francisco, 1916, reprinted in *Mex. Min. J.* (May 1916), 160–164. Clendenen points out that Villa's tax decree "was issued after consultation with representatives of the mining industry; presumably the rates agreed upon were the maximum that could be extorted without killing the goose. . . . Carranza's decree, issued without any reference to the industry, laid extortionate export taxes. . . ." (*The U.S. and Pancho Villa,* p. 162.)

24. *For. Rel. of the U.S. 1915, loc. cit.* Note 20 above.

25. *Codificación de los decretos del C. Venustiano Carranza,* pp. 250–251; *Decretos, circulares, etc., 1913-1915,* pp. 159–160 (trans. in *E&MJ, C* [Oct. 23, 1915], 688); *For. Rel. of the U.S., 1915,* pp. 899–901, 910, 923, 925, 931–932; *For. Rel. of the U.S., 1916,* pp. 720–721, 733, 736; F. S. Dunn, *The Diplomatic Protection of Americans in Mexico,* p. 328.

26. *For. Rel. of the U.S., 1916,* pp. 709–719.

27. *Col. de leyes, 1918,* pp. 108–113; *Bol. min.,* I (1916), 329–330.

28. Anon., "Mining in Mexico in 1916," *E&MJ,* CIII (Jan. 6, 1917), 77.

29. *For Rel. of the U.S., 1917,* p. 1040; Anon., "What Mexico Needs, By an American Citizen Residing in Mexico," *E&MJ,* CVIII (Oct. 11, 1919), 614.

30. José Ignacio González, *Codificación de leyes y órdenes aduaneras vigentes* (Mexico, 1918), pp. 38–39, 39–40; *Bol. min.,* V (Feb. 1918), 242; *For. Rel. of the U.S., 1916,* pp. 738–740; *For. Rel. of the U.S., 1917,* pp. 1039, 1040–41.

31. *E&MJ,* XCVI (July 5, 1913), 44; (July 19, 1913), 140; (Dec. 20, 1913), 1194; XCIX (Apr. 10, 1915), 667; (Apr. 24, 1915), 753; Anon., "Mining in Mexico in 1915," *ibid.,* CI (Jan. 8, 1916), 116–117; (June 17, 1916), 1091; *For. Rel. of the U.S., 1914,* pp. 718–720; *For. Rel. of the U.S., 1915,* p. 920; *ibid., 1916,* pp. 776–787; *ibid., 1917,* pp. 1072–78. In 1919 the United States Consul in Chihuahua reported that 400 confiscated properties in that state alone were being returned to their former owners, not including those formerly held by Creel, Terrazas, Orozco, or the Huerta "interests," which were still retained by the government. (*E&MJ,* CVII [May 3, 1919], 779.)

32. *Bol. min.,* I (June 15, 1916), 363–364; II (July 1, 1916), 23, 29–30; *For. Rel.*

Notes 329

of the *U.S., 1916,* pp. 720–721, 722, 723–724.

33. *For. Rel. of the U.S., 1916,* pp. 722–723, 728; *Bol. min.,* II (Oct. 1, 1916), 400–401; *Col. de leyes, 1918,* pp. 123–125.

34. *Bol. min.,* II (Sept. 1, 1916), 268–270 (trans. in *E&MJ,* CII [Sept. 30, 1916], 600); II (Nov. 1, 1916), 525; III (June 15, 1917), 74; III (May 1, 1917), 470.

35. *Bol. min.,* II (Oct. 1, 1916), 402–405; *Col. de leyes, 1918,* pp. 126–130; trans. in *For. Rel. of the U.S., 1916,* pp. 731–733; and *E&MJ,* CII (Oct. 14, 1916), 718.

36. *Bol. min., loc. cit.; Col. de leyes, 1918,* pp. 132–133. Although not explicitly stated, the decree of Nov. 14, 1916, which suspended the forced working decree for three months, declared that quotas would be assigned only to mines not in operation by that date.

37. *For. Rel. of the U.S., 1916,* pp. 734–738; Wendell C. Gordon, *The Expropriation of Foreign-Owned Property in Mexico* (Washington, D.C., 1941), p. 144.

38. *Col. de leyes, 1918,* pp. 133–134; *Bol. min.,* III (Mar. 1, 1917), 247; *For. Rel. of the U.S., 1916,* pp. 737–738.

39. *E&MJ,* CII (Oct. 14, 1916), 731; (Nov. 18, 1916), 924; CIII (Mar. 3, 1917), 398; *For. Rel of the U.S., 1917,* pp. 1039–40, 1041–52.

40. *E&MJ,* CIII (Mar. 10, 1917), 440; (Mar. 17, 1917), 480; (Apr. 14, 1917), 688; (Apr. 28, 1917), 743; *Bol. min.,* III (Feb. 15, 1917), 187.

41. H. V. Winchell, "Mining Law," in Robert Peele, (ed.), *Mining Engineers' Handbook* (New York, 1927), p. 1074; P. X. Stoffel, "Recent Mexican Mining Decrees," *E&MJ,* CXVI (Sept. 15, 1923), 451.

42. *Col. de leyes, 1918,* pp. 156–157; *Bol. min.,* III (Apr. 15, 1917), 412.

43. Letter, Carranza to Eliseo Arredondo of the Mexican Embassy in Washington, Feb. 3, 1915, reprinted in Felix F. Palavicini, *Un nuevo congreso constituyente* (Veracruz, 1915), p. 3.

44. See F. F. Palavicini, *Un nuevo congreso constituyente;* and L. Melgarejo Randolf and J. Fernandez Rojas, *El congreso constituyente de 1916 y 1917* (Mexico, 1917), pp. 115–117. The articles comprising Palavicini's pamphlet were reprinted by him in his *Historia de la Constitución de 1917* (hereinafter cited as *Hist. de la Cons. de 1917*), 2 vols. (Mexico, 1938), I, pp. 21–42. Also see Frank Tannenbaum, *Mexico's Agrarian Revolution* (Washington, D.C., 1930), pp. 165–172; Eyler N. Simpson, *The Ejido,* pp. 53–55, 62–63, 78; Djed Borques (pseudo. for Juan de Díos Bojórquez), *Crónica del constituyente* (hereinafter cited as Bojórquez, *Crónica*), Mexico, 1938, pp. 88–91. Many of the social ideas of the Constitution of 1917 were anticipated by the so-called anti-Carranza Convention of Aguascalientes: Quirk, *The Mexican Revolution, 1914–1915, passim.*

45. Melgarejo Randolf and Fernandez Rojas, *El congreso constituyente,* pp. 117–132, for the decrees in full.

46. *Ibid.,* pp. 136–137.

47. Palavicini, *Hist. de la Cons. de 1917,* I, pp. 131, 143.

48. Bojórquez, *Crónica,* p. 222; Andrés Molina Enríquez, *Esbozo de la historia de los primeros diez años de la revolución agraria de México* (hereinafter cited as *Rev. agrar.*), 5 vols. (Mexico, 1932–36), V, p. 179. Palavicini replied that the stenographers were quite capable men, and if the deputies in charge of the *Diario* had exercised more care "they would have avoided many omissions. . . ." (*Hist. de la Cons. de 1917,* II, p. 626).

49. *Diario de los debates del Congreso Constituyente* (hereinafter cited as *Diario*), 2 vols. (Mexico, 1916–17), I, pp. 260–270.

50. Bojórquez, *Crónica,* p. 222.

51. According to Molina Enríquez, *Rev. agrar.,* V, p. 176. Rouaix declared, however, that Carranza never interfered (Pastor Rouaix, "Genesis del artículo

ventiseite de la constitución política de 1917" [hereinafter cited as "Gen. del art. 27"], *Memoria del Segundo Congreso Mexicano de Ciencias Sociales* [Mexico, 1946], IV, pp. 184–190), and that Molina Enríquez's charge is the result of his "active imagination . . . inspired in [anti-Carranza] political passion." (Rouaix in Palavicini, *Hist. de la Cons. de 1917*, I, pp. 607–610.) In any event, Bojórquez agrees with Rouaix that the drafts presented to the convention were hammered out in open consultation with anyone free to offer suggestions and take part in the discussion. (Bojórquez, *Crónica*, pp. 230–233, 559; Rouaix in Palavicini, *Hist. de la Cons. de 1917*, I, p. 610.)

52. Molina Enríquez, *Rev. agrar.*, V, p. 172.

53. *Diario*, I, p. 737.

54. Bojórquez, *Crónica*, p. 599.

55. *Diario*, II, pp. 262, 607–623. The explanatory introduction is on pages 261–263; the text of the article itself as submitted is on pp. 263–265; the revisions inserted between January 13th and 23rd are in the version on pp. 602–604.

56. Rouaix, "Gen. del art. 27," pp. 181–183; Rouaix in Palavicini, *Hist. de la Cons. de 1917*, I, pp. 601–607.

57. Molina Enríquez hints quite broadly that he was the true author of Article 27 in *Rev. agrar.*, V, pp. 172–179. Rouaix declares that Molina Enríquez's work was unusable, perhaps because his "was a talent very unequal in its manifestations and its works." ("Gen. del art. 27," p. 184; Rouaix in Palavicini, *Hist. de la Cons. de 1917*, p. 610.) For Rouaix's list of the men whom he considers contributed the most, see Rouaix in Palavicini, *Hist. de la Cons. de 1917*, I, p. 608. He categorically denies the article was solely an Obregonista work. (*Ibid.*, p. 610.) Bojórquez, an Obregonista himself, generally agrees with Rouaix. For changes between the draft and the final version, see *Diario*, II, pp. 773–775, and Appendix, pp. xxxi–xxxiii. The article was not too well worded, and one commentator points out that the mining sections can only be understood by reference to the Mining Code of 1884, in which the various terms were carefully used and closely defined. (Rouaix, "Gen. del art. 27," pp. 203–204; and commentary of Lic. Carlos Sánchez Mejorada, "Costeabilidad de substancias minerales bajo la legislación especial de minería," *Bol. de min. y pet.*, XVII [Oct. 1945], pp. 3–10.)

58. *Diario*, II, Appendix, p. xxx.

59. Rouaix, "Gen. del art. 27," pp. 190–201; *Diario*, II, pp. 772–773.

60. *Diario*, II, pp. 786–788, 788–792, 794, 797, 811–812; Palavicini, *Hist. de la Cons. de 1917*, pp. 83–84.

61. The *Diario* records the passage as unanimous; Molina Enríquez wrote that he heard a number of dissenting votes from rightist "criollos." (*Rev. agrar.*, V, p. 179.)

62. F. Roel and Antonio R. Ortiz, "El artículo 123 de la Constitución de 1917 y su influencia sobre las industrias minera y metalúrgica; Consideraciones presentadas al Congreso por la Sección de Industria Minera," monografo núm. 5, *Primer Congreso Nacional de Industriales organizado bajo el patrocinio de la Secretaría de Industria, Comercio y Trabajo* (Mexico, 1917); Genaro P. García, Tomás R. Retana, et al., "El artículo 123 de la constitución federal; Dictamen presentado al Congreso por la comisión respectiva," monografo núm. 12, *ibid.*

63. F. Viesca Lobaton, Adolfo Martínez, et al., *El artículo 27 constitucional (Constitución de 1917); Dictamen de la comisión nombrada por el Primer Congreso Nacional de Industriales* (Mexico, 1917). See esp. pp. 49–76, 78–87, 109–110 and 111–114.

64. Secretaría de Industria, Comercio y Trabajo, Depto. de Minas, *Proyecto de Ley Minera* (no place of publication, 1917–18); also in Secretaría de Fomento, *Boletín oficial*, Epoca 4, I (Mar. 1917), pp. 373–379.

CHAPTER 10

1. Charts, *Bol. min.,* IX (May–June 1920), 628; X (July–Aug. 1920), 56.
2. *E&MJ,* CIV (Sept. 29, 1917), 580; (Oct. 13, 1917), 635.
3. R. G. Cleland, "Natural Resources," in *Mexican Year Book for 1920–1921,* p. 279.
4. *E&MJ,* CIV (Nov. 3, 1917), 806.
5. L. Duncan, "Copper Operation of the Compagnie du Boleo," *E&MJ,* CIV (Sept. 8, 1917), pp. 415–417; I. Lagunas, "Informe sobre 'Compañía del Boleo,'" *Boletín de industria, comercio y trabajo,* Sección de trabajo, V (July–Sept. 1920), 6.
6. Anon., "Mining in Mexico," *E&MJ,* CV (Jan. 12, 1918), 120–121; Anon., "Mining in Mexico in 1918," *E&MJ,* CVII (Jan. 11, 1919), 112–113; CVII (May 17, 1919), 896; G. Montes de Oca, "Informe general sobre ... Guerrero," *Bol. min.,* IX (Mar.–Apr. 1920), 282–314.
7. *E&MJ,* CVI (Aug. 8, 1918), 270.
8. *E&MJ,* CVII (Jan. 11, 1919), 112; (Mar. 8, 1919), 464; (Mar. 22, 1919), 536; Letter, B. R. Bates to *E&MJ,* CVII (May 10, 1919), 837; (May 31, 1919), 963; CXIV (Aug. 19, 1922), 311.
9. *E&MJ,* CIII (May 5, 1917), 813; (June 23, 1917), 1130; CIV (Sept. 22, 1917), 540; (Nov. 3, 1917), 814; CV (Jan. 12, 1918), 67; (Feb. 9, 1918), 308; (Mar. 23, 1918), 576; CVII (Mar. 22, 1919), 537; (May 17, 1919), 871; Marcosson, *Metal Magic,* pp. 203–214.
10. *E&MJ,* CXXII (Oct. 16, 1926), 623; F. Lundberg, *America's Sixty Families,* p. 204.
11. J. Ibarra, "El Estado de Coahuila, Junio de 1919," *Bol. min.,* XI (Jan. 1921), 13; G. Montes de Oca, "La planta metalúrgica de Peñoles," *Bol. min.,* XII (Nov. 1921), 542.
12. *Mex. Min. J.* (Jan. 1915), 28.
13. L. Jiménez, "El Mineral de Agujita, Coahuila," *Bol. min.,* XVI (July–Sept. 1923), 29; Gibbon, *Mexico Under Carranza,* pp. 150–151 gives some fanciful background.
14. *E&MJ,* CIII (June 16, 1917), 1088.
15. A. B. Parsons, "Heath Steele," *E&MJ,* CXXVI (Nov. 17, 1928), 778; G. Montes de Oca, "La planta metalúrgica de Peñoles," 559; and W. H. Triplett, communication to the author, June 13, 1955.
16. J. Ibarra, "Informe sobre la Cia. Minera 'La Constancia,' S.A.," *Bol. min.,* VII (May–June 1919), 507; J. Ibarra, "Informe sobre ... la Cia. Metalúrgica de Torreón," *Bol. min.,* VIII (Sept.–Oct. 1919), pp. 358–362. For a description of Peñoles' rolling stock, see G. Montes de Oca, "La fundición número 2, Monterrey," *Bol. min.,* XIV (Aug. 1922), 168.
17. Ibarra, "El Estado de Coahuila," 13–16.
18. Amendment to the tariff schedule of July 31, 1916, in *Bol. min.,* VI (July–Aug. 1918), 70.
19. *Col. de leyes, 1918,* pp. 270–280; *Bol. min.,* V (Mar.–Apr. 1918), 393–398; trans. in *E&MJ,* CVI (Sept. 28, 1918), 589. Also see *E&MJ,* CVI (Sept. 7, 1918), 438.

20. *Bol. min.,* VI (July–Aug. 1918), 71–72.

21. *Ibid.,* VII (Mar.–Apr. 1919), 341.

22. *Ibid.,* XXI (Jan. 1926), 58.

23. F. Roel and A. Ortiz, "El decreto del 27 de septiembre de 1917, relativo a la exportación de metales y minerales," monográfo núm. 9, *Primer Congreso Nacional de Industriales* (Mexico, 1917).

24. *Col. de leyes, 1918,* pp. 259–261; J. I. González, *Codificación de leyes y órdenes aduaneras vigentes,* pp. 50–51; *Bol. min.,* IV (Sept. 1, 1917), 252–253; *E&MJ,* CIV (Oct. 6, 1917), 623. For the decree regulating enforcement, see *Bol. min.,* V (May–June 1918), 643. Various earlier decrees were united into the tax law of April 26, 1918.

25. Trowbridge, *Mexico,* pp. 252–253; *E&MJ,* CIV (Oct. 20, 1917), 736; (Oct. 27, 1917), 776; (Nov. 11, 1917), 852; (Nov. 17, 1917), 891.

26. Secretaría de Hacienda y Crédito Público, *Ley de impuestos a la minería y su reglamento* (Mexico, 1919); *Bol. min.,* VII (May–June 1919), 580–584; VIII (July–Aug. 1919), 78–95; English trans. in *E&MJ,* CVIII (Aug. 2, 1919), 186–188.

27. *Bol. min.,* VIII (July–Aug. 1919), 78. A 10 per cent surcharge was added to all import and export taxes on February 27, 1920, to build a fund to pay the external debt. This surcharge has been continued to the present. (*Bol. min.,* IX [Mar.–Apr. 1920], 393–394.)

28. *Ibid.,* IX (Jan.–Feb. 1920), 66–67; X (July–Aug. 1920), 103–104; XI (Jan. 1921), 94–95; *E&MJ,* CVIII (Dec. 13–20, 1919), 914; (Dec. 27, 1919), 964.

CHAPTER 11

1. *E&MJ,* CXIV (Oct. 14, 1922), 693; E. P. Crawford, "Conditions in Western Mexico Invite Confidence," *E&MJ,* CXVI (Sept. 8, 1923), 408. For the specific case of the Promontorio mine, see *E&MJ,* CXI (Jan. 8, 1921), 79; (Feb. 19, 1921), 365.

2. A. B. Parsons, "The Situation at the Mines," *E&MJ,* CXV (May 12, 1923), 864; *E&MJ,* CI (Jan. 8, 1916), 116; CV (Feb. 9, 1918), 308; CVI (Sept. 7, 1918), 467; (Sept. 14, 1918), 512; CVIII (Sept. 13, 1919), 489; CIX (Mar. 6, 1920), 630; CXI (June 4, 1921), 963; CXII (Aug. 20, 1921), 311; (Aug. 27, 1921), 353; (Oct. 1, 1921), 553; (Oct. 15, 1921), 631; CXIV (Sept. 23, 1922), 563; (Oct. 7, 1922), 650; CXV (Mar. 21, 1923), 727; CXVII (Apr. 26, 1924), 700.

3. *E&MJ,* CVIII (Sept. 20, 1919), 526.

4. J. C. Pickering, "Mexico, A Field for Investment," *E&MJ,* CXX (Dec. 5, 1925), 893.

5. *E&MJ,* CVIII (Aug. 2, 1919), 195; (Aug. 9, 1919), 251; (Aug. 16, 1919); 293; (Nov. 1, 1919), 748; (Dec. 6, 1919), 884; (Dec. 13–20, 1919), 919; CIX (Jan. 24, 1920), 292; (Jan. 31, 1920), 305; (Mar. 20, 1920), 721; (Apr. 24, 1920), 987; (May 7, 1921), 789; (June 5, 1920), 1288; (June 12, 1920), 1333; CX (July 17, 1920), 132; (Sept. 11, 1920), 537; (Oct. 16, 1920), 786; CXVIII (Aug. 23, 1924), 311; F. Reynoso, "La Cia. 'The Peregrina Mining and Milling Co.,' Gto., Gto.," *Bol. min.,* X (July–Aug. 1920), 4–11; J. Aurelio García, "La mina de San Rafael, Pachuca, Hgo.," *ibid.,* X (Sept.–Oct. 1920), 273; Marcosson, *Metal Magic,* pp. 194–196.

6. C. A. Grabill, "Ore-Buying in Mexico," *E&MJ*, CIX (Mar. 20, 1920), 694–697.

7. H. H. Taft, "The Sierra Madre of Northwestern Mexico," *E&MJ*, CXIII (Jan. 14, 1922), 49–50. Some independents used adobe furnaces with an ore capacity of about a ton a day. See C. A. Grabill, "Primitive Smelting," *E&MJ*, CIX (Apr. 17, 1920), 926–927.

8. This analysis is summarized from Grabill, "Ore-Buying in Mexico," 696–697.

9. *Ibid.*, 697; G. Montes de Oca, "Informe general de Guerrero," *Bol. min.*, IX (Mar.-Apr. 1920), 314.

10. For references for these strikes, see Note 24 below.

11. *E&MJ*, CX (July 31, 1920), 228–229; *Bol. min.*, X (July–Aug. 1920), 103–104.

12. *E&MJ*, CX (Sept. 11, 1920), 541; (Oct. 9, 1920), 736; (Dec. 24, 1920), 1145.

13. *E&MJ*, CX (Dec 4, 1920), 1104; (Dec. 18, 1920), 1189; Great Britain, Department of Overseas Trade, Norman King, *Report on Financial and Economic Conditions in Mexico, 1920–1921* (London, 1921), p. 7.

14. *Bol. min.*, XI (Jan. 1921), 94–95.

15. *Ibid.*, 93; *E&MJ*, CXI (Jan. 8, 1921), 79.

16. *Bol. min.*, XI (May 1921), 738.

17. *Ibid.* (Apr. 1921) 546–547; (June 1921), 883.

18. For references for this paragraph see Note 24 below.

19. P. X. Stoffel, correspondence to *E&MJ*, CXIV (Oct. 7, 1922), 622; (Oct. 14, 1922), 693.

20. *Bol. min.*, XII (Sept. 1921), 355–356; (Oct. 1921), 480.

21. *E&MJ*, CXII (Aug. 20, 1921), 306–307; (Sept 3, 1921), 382; (Oct. 8, 1921), 562–563.

22. *E&MJ*, CXII (Sept. 24, 1921), 510.

23. C. Bruchhold and E. Villafaña, "La planta de flotación de Mapimí," *Bol. min.*, XXIV (Oct. 1927), 231–232.

24. References for the general developments from 1920 through 1923 are as follows: *E&MJ*, CX (Nov. 6, 1920), 919; (Nov. 13, 1920), 960; (Nov. 27, 1920), 1056; (Dec 4, 1920), 1100; (Dec. 11, 1920), 1145; (Dec. 25, 1920), 1229, 1234, 1236; CXI (Jan. 8, 1921), 79, 80; (Jan. 15, 1921), 121; (Jan. 22, 1921), 184–185; (Jan. 29, 1921), 244; (Feb. 5, 1921), 282; (Feb. 12, 1921), 326; (Feb. 19, 1921), 365; (Mar. 5, 1921), 442; (Mar. 12, 1921), 486; (Mar. 26, 1921), 562; (Apr. 2, 1921), 603; (Apr. 9, 1921), 642; (Apr. 16, 1921), 690; (Apr. 23, 1921), 742; (May 7, 1921), 805; (May 21, 1921), 885; (June 4, 1921), 963; (June 11, 1921), 1003; CXII (July 2, 1921), 30, 31; (July 9, 1921), 69; (Aug. 6, 1921), 225; (Aug. 13, 1921), 271; (Aug 20, 1921), 311; (Sept. 3, 1921), 388; (Sept. 10, 1921), 431; (Sept. 17, 1921), 472; (Sept. 24, 1921), 511; (Oct. 8, 1921), 591; (Oct. 29, 1921), 712; (Dec. 3, 1921), 911; (Dec. 31, 1921), 1069; CXIII (Jan. 28, 1922), 184; (Feb. 4, 1922), 221; (Feb. 11, 1922), 261; (Feb. 18, 1922), 305; (Apr. 29, 1922), 741; (May 27, 1922), 935; (June 3, 1922), 973; (June 24, 1922), 1111; CXIV (Aug. 5, 1922), 253; (Aug. 12, 1922), 279; (Aug. 19, 1922), 338; (Sept. 23, 1922), 563; (Sept. 30, 1922), 605; (Nov. 4, 1922), 827; CXV (Feb. 3, 1923), 248; CXVI (Nov. 3, 1923), 784; (Dec. 29, 1923), 1131; CXVIII (Nov. 8, 1924), 744, 749; (Dec. 20, 1924), 992; A. B. Parsons, "Mexican Mines Install Equipment," *E&MJ*, CXXI (Jan. 16, 1926), 122; J. E. Clennell, "Among the Mexican Rebels," *Min. Mag.*, XXXIII (Oct. 1925), 213–220; C. J. Barber, "Among the Mexican Bandits," *ibid.*, XXXIV (Feb. 1926), 85–89.

25. C. L. Bradbury, "Charcas, an Ancient District in San Luis Potosí," *E&MJ*, CXVI (Dec. 15, 1923), 1031–34.

26. *Bol. min.*, XV (Apr. 1923), 522–523.

27. *Ibid.*, XVI (July–Sept. 1923), 146–147, 149.

28. King, *Report on Mexico*, p. 7.

29. H. H. Taft, "Caduca," *E&MJ*, CXXI (Feb. 20, 1926), 325; G. C. Harding, "Critique," *ibid.*, (Mar. 13, 1926), 449; Stoffel, "Recent Mexican Mining Decrees," *E&MJ*, CXVI (Sept. 15, 1923), 451.

30. *Bol. min.*, X (Sept.–Oct. 1920), 362; (Nov.–Dec. 1920), 672–673; trans. in *E&MJ*, CX (July 31, 1920), 230. Also see *E&MJ*, CX (Aug. 7, 1920), 280.

31. *E&MJ*, CX (Aug. 21, 1920), 379; (Sept. 11, 1920), 541; (Oct. 9, 1920), 736–737; (Oct. 30, 1920), 883; (Nov. 13, 1920), 960–961. The dilemma of small mineowners working their way out of the labyrinth of Mexican law is illustrated by Paul W. Meyers' "The Reclamation of Mexican Mining Titles," *E&MJ*, CXII (Sept. 10, 1920), 406–409; (Oct. 29, 1920), 685–687.

32. *E&MJ*, CXIII (May 27, 1922), 935.

33. For the decrees issued and comments on the development of this policy, see *Bol. min.*, XIII (Jan. 1922), 105 (decree of Jan. 7, 1922); XIII (Apr. 1922), 526–528 (Mar. 6, 1922); XIV (Nov. 1922), 712–714 (Oct. 5, 1922); XVI (July–Sept. 1923), 147–149 (June 13, 1923); *ibid.*, 152–153 (Sept. 6, 1923); *ibid.*, 153 (Sept. 11, 1923); XVI (Oct.-Dec. 1923), 378–379 (Oct. 22, 1923); XXI (Apr. 1926), 192 (Mar. 9, 1926); XXI (May 1926), 258–259 (Mar. 23, 1926); XXI (June 1926), 344–345 (Apr. 28, 1926); *E&MJ*, CXIII (Mar. 18, 1922), 462; (May 20, 1922), 887; CXVI (Sept. 15, 1923), 451–452; CXVII (Apr. 26, 1924), 700; CXXI (Apr. 3, 1926), 577; Cám. Nac. de Min., *Circ.* 177, (Mar. 12, 1926).

34. *E&MJ*, CXII (Aug. 27, 1921), 325.

35. *Bol. min.*, XII (Dec. 1921), 719; XIII (Jan. 1922), 104–105; XVII (Jan.–June 1924), 16–17; XVIII (Nov. 1924), 227–228; XIX (May 1925), 163-164; (June 1925), 229–230; XXI (Mar. 1926), 113–114; (June 1926), 344.

CHAPTER 12

1. For the early history of the process, see Theodore J. Hoover, *Concentrating Ores by Flotation* (London, 1914), pp. 42–67; A. B. Parsons, *The Porphyry Coppers*, pp. 450–454; T. A. Rickard, "The History of Flotation," *Min. & Sci. Press*, CXIV (Mar. 24, 1917), 404.

2. R. A. Wagstaff, "Flotation and Lead Smelting: The Blast Furnace," AIME *Trans.*, LXXIX (1928: Flotation Practice), pp. 25–27.

3. *E&MJ*, LXXXIX (Jan. 22, 1910), 244. For a description of an early unidentified mill, see "Flotation in a Mexican Mill," *Min. & Sci. Press*, CXI (July 24, 1915), 122–126. Also see A. W. Edelin, "An Appreciation of Walter M. Drury," *E&MJ*, CXLVII (Nov. 1946), 93.

4. *E&MJ*, CIV (July 28, 1917), 159–162.

5. H. E. Megraw, *The Flotation Process* (New York, 1918), pp. 262–263; S. Ramirez, "Informe sobre el tratamiento de los minerales por flotación en las compañías mineras 'Pachuca y Real del Monte' y 'Santa Gertrudis,' Hidalgo," *Bol. min.*, III (May 1, 1917), 445–452; Anon., "Mining in Mexico in 1916," *E&MJ*, CIII (Jan. 6, 1917), 76; *E&MJ*, CVII (Jan. 4, 1919), 15; H. W. von Bernewitz, "Flotation in the Treatment of Gold and Silver Ores," *E&MJ*, CXXIV (Oct. 22, 1927), 657.

6. *Bol. min.*, XVIII (Nov. 1924), 225–227; *E&MJ*, CXXVI (Dec. 1, 1928), 883; B. Rubio and C. Bruchhold, "La planta de beneficio de 'The Cananea Consolidated Copper Co.,' en Cananea, Son.," *Bol. min.*, XXVIII (Dec. 1929), 486; H. R. MacMichael, "Silver-Lead Smelting Progress in Chihuahua, Mexico," *Min. & Met.*, XIV (Feb. 1933), 93–94; Marcosson, *Metal Magic*, p. 201.

7. J. Castanedo, "La evolución de la metalurgia en México," *Bol. min.*, XXIV (Oct. 1927), 212–216; Anon., "La flotación, sus fundamentos científicos y porvenir," *Bol. min.*, XXV (Jan. 1928), 3–6; Anon., "El desarollo de la flotación en el país," *Bol. min.*, XXXVIII (Aug. 1929), 83–84; *E&MJ*, CXXVIII (Oct. 12, 1928), 577.

8. C. Bruchhold, "Necesidad de un laboratorio experimental de flotación en el país," *Bol. min.*, XXIV (Dec. 1926), 419–420; Anon., "El sistema de flotación como subsidiario de la industria minera en pequeña escala," *Bol. min.*, XXIII (May 1927), 333–334; C. Bruchhold, "Pequeñas plantas de flotación," *ibid.*, 344–353; J. Aurelio García, "La planta de flotación 'El Calavario,' Zacualpán, México," *Bol. min.*, XXIII (Feb. 1927), 32–40; and see editorial comment, *Bol. min.*, XXI (Feb. 1926).

9. Anon., "Nuevos recursos de la minería—Antiguas minas que se tenían por agotados, vuelvan a tener nueva vida," *Bol. min.*, XXII (Dec. 1926), 462–463.

10. C. L. Bradbury, "Charcas, An Ancient District in San Luis Potosí," *E&MJ*, CXVI (Dec. 15, 1923), 1031–34.

11. J. Ibarra, "Informe acerca de la 'Planta calcinadora' perteneciente a la 'International Ore Co.,' S.A., Saltillo, Coah.," *Bol. min.*, VI (Nov.–Dec. 1918), 691–696.

12. W. R. Ingalls, "Foreign Zinc-Smelting Capacities and Prospects," *E&MJ*, CVII (Feb. 1, 1919), 227–228; *E&MJ*, CVII (Feb. 22, 1919), 359.

13. *E&MJ*, CXIX (Mar. 7, 1925), 420.

14. G. Montes de Oca, "La metalurgia del zinc en México; La planta calcinadora perteneciente a la 'International Ore & Smelting Co.,'" *Bol. min.*, XI (Apr. 1921), 492–500; *E&MJ*, CXVII (Apr. 5, 1924), 577; R. B. Brinsmade, "Taxco," *E&MJ*, CXIX (June 27, 1925), 1053; Cám. Nac. de Min. *Circ.* 50 (Oct. 24, 1924).

15. By far the best survey of the zinc industry up to the time of the introduction of flotation is M. Perogordo y Lasso, "La industria del zinc en México," *Bol. min.*, XVIII (Sept. 1924), 92–110. For an individual case, see "Consultation Section," *E&MJ*, CXVI (Nov. 24, 1923), 905.

16. Brinsmade, "Taxco," 1050; Anon., "La industria del zinc en México," *Bol. min.*, XVIII (Sept. 1924), 70–71; D. V. Navarro, "El contigente del Depto. de Minas ... en la exposición del informe presidencial objectivo," *Bol. min.*, XXVII (Feb. 1929), 78; W. R. Ingalls, *World Survey of the Zinc Industry* (New York, 1931), pp. 10–11.

17. Marcosson, *Metal Magic*, pp. 152–153; *Bol. min.*, XXIX (Jan. 1930), 7. For abortive plans to open an electrolytic smelter, see A. Zentner, "World Developments in Electrolytic Zinc," *Min. & Met.*, X (Nov. 1929), 528.

18. For a list of zinc producers and the export destination of their output, see *Bol. min.*, XXV (May 1928), 300–307.

19. H. A. Guess (Vice-Pres., ASARCO), "Lead Mining Makes Highest Production," *E&MJ*, CXXI (Jan. 16, 1926), 83; J. Castanedo, "La minería en el país y el incremento que ha adquirido en los últimos años," *Bol. min.*, XXIII (May 1927), 337–343.

20. Letters, A. Spencer Cragoe to *E&MJ*, CXVI (Dec. 1, 1923), 949; 123, (Feb. 19, 1927), 330; remarks of R. A. Varden in Inst. of Min. and Met. (London), *Trans.*, XIII (1903–4), pp. 142–144.

21. *E&MJ*, LXXV (Feb. 7, 1903), 239; (May 9, 1903), 723; (June 6, 1903),

869–70; 123, (Feb. 19, 1927), 330.

22. *Min. Mag.*, II (Apr. 1910), 303; VIII (Apr. 1913), 241; *E&MJ*, LXXXIX (Apr. 16, 1910), 95; (May 17, 1913), 989. For the financial structure and ownership of San Francisco del Oro, see "The Union Corporation Report," in Co. Mtngs. & Repts. Sec., *Min. Mag.*, Vols. XXVI, XXXII, XXXIV, XXXVIII, XL; *E&MJ*, CXXIII (Jan. 22, 1927); CXXIV (Sept. 17, 1927), 466.

23. *Min. Mag.*, XXI (Sept. 1919), 138; XXII (Apr. 1920), 202; and "The Union Corporation" and "San Francisco Mines of Mexico" Reports in Co. Mtngs. & Repts. Sec., *Min. Mag.*, Vols. XX and XXII.

24. "The Union Corp.," Co. Mtngs. & Rept. Sec., *Min. Mag.*, Vols. XXIV, XXVI, XXVIII, XXXII, XXXIV, XXXVI; "San Francisco Mines," Co. Mtngs. & Rept. Sec., *Min. Mag.*, Vols. XXVIII, XXX, XXXII, XXXIV, XXXVI; *Min. Mag.*, XXIV (May 1921), p. 256; W. A. Doman, "San Francisco Mines," *ibid.*, XXVIII (Jan. 1923), 8; (Mar. 1923), 194; (Apr. 1923), 202; XXXII (Feb. 1925), 128; XXXVI (Feb. 1927), 128; *E&MJ*, CXI (Apr. 16, 1921), 683–684; W. A. Doman, "San Francisco Mines," *ibid.*, CXV (Mar. 10, 1923), 465; Pickering, "Mexico, A Field for Investment," 892; CXV (Apr. 14, 1923), 685; CXXIII (Jan. 22, 1927), 163; CXXV (May 19, 1928), 832.

25. Anon., "Las actividades de la 'San Francisco Mines of Mexico,' Ltd.," and J. Martínez, "Las minas y planta de San Francisco," *Bol. min.*, XXII (Aug. 1926), 59–61, 62–70; J. Horcasitas, "Las minas de la Unidad Clarines de la 'San Francisco Mines of Mexico,' Ltd.," *Bol. min.*, XXIV (July 1927), 45–48.

26. "San Francisco Mines," Co. Mtngs. & Repts. Sec., *Min. Mag.*, Vols. XXXVIII, XL, XLII, XLIV, XLVI (1928–32); XLVIII (Feb. 1933), 128; *E&MJ*, CXXXI (Feb. 23, 1931), 194; A. W. Hahn, "Flotation of Oxidized Lead-Silver Ores," AIME *Trans.*, LXXIX (1928: Flotation Practice), pp. 189–191; J. Horcasitas, "La planta de flotación y concentración de la 'San Francisco Mines of Mexico Co.,' Ltd.," *Bol. min.*, XXXI (Apr. 1931), 97–104.

27. A. H. Hubbell, "Mining in Mexico Today," *E&MJ*, CXXXVII (Mar. 1936), 119–136; Anon., "The San Francisco del Oro Mine," *ibid.* (Aug. 1936), 381; J. González Reyna, *La industria minera en el Estado de Chihuahua* (Mexico, 1946), pp. 86–87; *Min. Sur.*, VI (Apr. 1939), 16; XII (Mar. 1945), 13–14.

28. Anon., "New Flotation Technique," *E&MJ*, CXLVII (May 1946), 69; E. Just, "Vistas of Mexican Mining," *E&MJ*, CXLVII (Oct. 1946), 77; Anon., "San Francisco del Oro Metallurgy," *Min. World*, X (May 1948), 16–18.

29. J. F. Rippy, *British Investments in Latin America*, p. 100.

30. *Min. Sur.*, VIII (June 1941), 18; E. Just, "Vistas of Mexican Mining, II: San Francisco del Oro—A British Enterprise," *E&MJ*, CXLVII (Oct. 1946), 77.

31. US BuMines, *1950 Materials Survey: Lead* (Washington, D.C., May 1951), p. An III-50; US BuMines, *Min. Yrbk.* (1953), I, p. 1301; *E&MJ*, CLVII (Aug. 1956), 188; CLVIII (May 1957), 140; *Min. World*, XIV (Aug. 1952), 75; Anon., "Tabling and Flexibility Make a Unique New Mill," *Min. World*, XVI (May 1954), 44–48.

32. E. Honigman, "El futuro del mineral de Santa Eulalia, Chih.," *Bol. min.*, IV (Oct. 1, 1917), 358–366; S. Ramirez, "Informe sobre las compañías 'El Potosí Mining Co.,' y 'Chihuahua Mining Co.,' Ltd.," *Bol. min.*, VII (Mar.–Apr. 1919), 261–265; Anon., "La industria del zinc en México," *Bol. min.*, XXI (Apr. 1926), 125–194 (esp. pp. 172, 174); C. Bruchhold, "La flotación de minerales oxidados en México; Hacienda de San Guillermo, 'Cia. Industrial El Potosí,'" *Bol. min.*, XXV (Apr. 1928), 245–246; *E&MJ*, LXXXIX (Jan. 22, 1910), 244; (Jan. 29, 1910), 292; XC (Oct. 15, 1910), 787; XCII (Nov. 18, 1911), 1012; CXVII (Apr. 19, 1924),

659; H. A. Walker, "Diamond Drilling in the El Potosí Mine," *E&MJ*, CXIV (Nov. 18, 1922), 896; CXXVII (June 29, 1929), 1053.

33. J. Horcasitas, "La planta de flotación de la 'Cia. Industrial El Potosí,' S.A.," *Bol. min.*, XXVII (Jan. 1929), 27–33; *E&MJ*, CXXVII (Feb. 2, 1929), 210; (June 29, 1929), 1053; *Min. World*, XX (June 1958), 87.

34. AIME *Trans.*, LXXIX (1928), pp. 151–174, 235–252.

35. For notes and descriptions of these plants see: J. W. Malcolmson, "Mining in Mexico in 1902," *E&MJ*, LXXV (Jan. 3, 1903), 35–36; *E&MJ*, CVIII (Oct. 25, 1919), 708; CXVI (July 28, 1923), 167; (Dec. 29, 1923), 1105; CXVII (Apr. 19, 1924), 659; CXVIII (Sept. 20, 1924), 445–454; CXXI (Apr. 3, 1926), 576; (Apr. 10, 1926), 598; (June 12, 1926), 980; CXXII (Aug. 28, 1926), 329; (Oct. 23, 1926), 644; (Nov. 6, 1926), 741; CXXIII (Jan. 22, 1927), 124–125; CXXIX (May 8, 1930), 477; (June 23, 1930), 627; CXXX (Oct. 9, 1930), 351; *Bol. min.*, XXII (Dec. 1926), 482–485, 474–475; XXIV (Oct. 1927), 231–236; XXIV (Nov. 1927), 264–269; XXIV (Dec. 1926), 454–460; XXV (Jan. 1928), 13; XXV (Apr. 1928), 222–228; 246–249; XXV (May 1928), 328–334; XXVI (Sept. 1928), 184–187; XXVI (Dec. 1928), 488–499; XXVIII (Aug. 1929), 83; XXVIII (Dec. 1929), 461–464.

36. *E&MJ*, CVIII (Oct. 25, 1919), 708; CIX (June 5, 1920), 1288; (June 12, 1920), 1333; CX (Oct. 16, 1920), 786; CXVI (Dec. 29, 1923), 1133, 1137; CXVII (Mar. 15, 1924), 459; (Apr. 19, 1924), 659; (May 23, 1925), 861; CXXVIII (Nov. 2, 1929), 688; *Bol min.*, XXII (July 1926), 405; XXV (Feb. 1928), 87–99; Marcosson, *Metal Magic*, p. 201.

CHAPTER 13

1. G. Butler Sherwell, *Mexico's Capacity to Pay* (Washington, D.C., 1929), p. 38.

2. Depto. de Minas, *An. de estad. min., 1923*, pp. 72–73; *1924*, pp. 161–165; *1925*, pp. 160–163.

3. *America's Stake in International Investments*, pp. 583–584. For other estimates see: N. King, *Report on Economic and Financial Conditions in Mexico, 1920–1921*, p. 7; E. C. Vuxton (Great Britain, Department of Overseas Trade), *Report on the Economic and Financial Conditions in Mexico, November, 1927* (London, 1928), pp. 16–17; Max Winkler, *Investments of United States Capital in Latin America* (Boston, 1928), pp. 224–225; *E&MJ*, CX (Aug. 21, 1920), 375; CXV (June 16, 1923), 1081; CXXIII (Feb. 5, 1927), 258.

4. Paul D. Dickens, *American Direct Investments in Foreign Countries*, U.S. Department of Commerce, Bureau of Foreign and Domestic Commerce, Information Bulletin No. 731 (Washington, D.C., 1930), pp. 18–19, 21.

5. Rippy, *British Investments in Latin America*, pp. 55–56.

6. A. B. Parsons, "William Loeb, of A.S.&R., Sees Improved Industrial Relations," *E&MJ*, CXXVI (Oct. 13, 1928), 566–567; O'Connor, *Guggenheims*, pp. 337–338; Marcosson, *Metal Magic*, Chaps. x and xi.

7. *E&MJ*, CXIV (July 8, 1922), 71; CXV (May 5, 1923), 816; (June 9, 1923), 1034; CXVI (Oct. 13, 1923), 647; CXVII (Jan. 19, 1924), 99; A. B. Parsons,

"New A.S.&R. Projects in Mexico Involve $10,000,000 for Construction," *E&MJ*, CXVIII (Nov. 15, 1924), 786–787; CXXIII (Mar. 5, 1927), 416; CXXXI (Feb. 23, 1931), 190; W. J. Jennie and R. F. Spooner, "Zinc Smelting in Mexico," *E&MJ*, CXXXI (June 22, 1931), 558; *Bol. min.*, XXIX (Jan. 1930), 7; Marcosson, *Metal Magic*, pp. 215–216, 218–219, 220–224.

8. *E&MJ*, CXIII (May 20, 1922), 887; A. B. Parsons, "New A.S.&R. Projects in Mexico," 786–787; Marcosson, *Metal Magic, pp.* 279–280; G. Montes de Oca, "La 'Cia. Carbonífera de Sabinas,' S.A.," *Bol. min.*, XX (Dec. 1925), 253–288.

9. *E&MJ*, CIX (Mar. 20, 1920), 721; (Apr. 24, 1920), 987; (June 12, 1920), 1333; CXI (June 4, 1921), 963; CXII (Aug. 27, 1921), 353; CXIV (Dec. 23, 1922), 1131; CXV (May 5, 1923), 812; CXVI (July 21, 1923), 109; (Oct. 13, 1923), 647; CXVIII (Dec. 13, 1924), 948; CXXI (Jan. 9, 1926), 61–62; Marcosson, *Metal Magic*, pp. 193–196; *An. de estad. min.*, 1925, 184–187.

10. *E&MJ*, CVIII (Dec. 13–20, 1919), 920; CXV (June 30, 1923), 1167; CXVI (July 14, 1923), 75; (Sept. 22, 1923), 516; (Oct. 13, 1923), 647; A. B. Parsons, "New A.S.&R. Projects in Mexico," 786–787; Marcosson, *Metal Magic*, 211–214; G. Montes de Oca, "La planta de flotación de 'Tiro General' ... ," *Bol. min.*, XXI (Mar. 1926), 105–112.

11. *E&MJ*, CXVI (Sept. 29, 1923), 560; CXVII (May 31, 1924), 895. For a description of Peñoles' pre-1920 holdings, see J. Ibarra, "El Estado de Coahuila," *Bol. min.*, XI (Jan. 1921), 13–16.

12. *E&MJ*, CXII (Aug. 13, 1921), 271; CXIV (Nov. 4, 1922), 827; CXVI (July 28, 1923), 168; CXVII (May 31, 1924), 895; CXVIII (Aug. 9, 1924), 228; CXIX (Apr. 18, 1925), 663; (May 16, 1925), 816; CXXI (Feb. 27, 1926), 381; CXXIII (Jan. 22, 1927), 163–164; (Apr. 16, 1927), 661; CXXVI (Sept. 1, 1928), 325–329; (Sept. 8, 1928), 370–375; (Oct. 6, 1928), 550.

13. *E&MJ*, CVI (Sept. 7, 1918), 467; (Sept. 14, 1918), 512.

14. "Camp Bird," Co. Mtngs. & Repts. Sec., *Min. Mag.*, XXII (1920); XXIV (1921). Also see *Min. & Sci. Press*, CXIX (Sept. 13, 1919), 355–356.

15. For the starting financial arrangements, see "The Mexican Corporation," Co. Mtngs. & Repts. Sec., *Min. Mag.*, XX (1919); "Camp Bird," Co. Mtngs. & Repts. Sec., *ibid.*, XXII (1920); *E&MJ*, CVIII (Sept. 20, 1919), 523–524; CXIII (Jan. 14, 1922), 79.

16. *Min. Mag.*, XXI (Nov. 1919), 261; "Camp Bird," Co. Mtngs. & Repts. Sec., *Min. Mag.*, XXII (1920); *E&MJ*, CVIII (Dec. 6, 1919), 879–880.

17. *Min. Mag.*, XXIX (July 1923), 3–4 and Co. Mtngs. & Repts. Sec.

18. *Ibid.*, XXIII (Dec. 1920), 330; XXXIII (Nov. 1925), 264; Co. Mtngs. & Repts. Sec., XXIV (1921); XXXIII (1925).

19. *Ibid.*, XXIV (May 1921), 317; "Mex. Corp.," Co. Mtngs. & Repts. Sec., XXIV (1921); "Camp Bird," Co. Mtngs. & Repts. Sec., XXVI (1922).

20. *Ibid.*, XXVI (Jan. 1922), 8; XXVII (Dec. 1922), 328; *E&MJ*, CXV (Jan. 27, 1923), 204; CXVII (Mar. 15, 1924), 459; CXX (July 25, 1925), 147.

21. *Ibid.*, XXXI (Dec. 1924), 328 and "Mex. Corp.," Co. Mtngs. & Repts. Sec., XXXVII (Dec. 1927), 405–406; "Mex. Corp.," Co. Mtngs. & Repts. Sec., XXXIV, XXXV, XXXVII (1925, 1926, 1927); XLI (Oct. 1929), 200; XLII (Jan. 1930), 61, 62; XLIII (Dec. 1930), 381–382; "Mex. Corp.," Co. Mtngs. & Repts. Sec., XLIV (1931); *E&MJ*, CXXIII (Jan. 1, 1927), 35; CXXX (Dec. 23, 1930), 629.

22. *Min. Mag.*, XXXV (Dec. 1926), 328; XXXVII (Dec. 1927), 405–406; XLII (Jan. 1930), 62; XLIII (Dec. 1930), 383; XLV (July 1931), 8; "Camp Bird," Co. Mtngs. & Repts. Sec., XXXIV, XXXV, XXXVII, XL (1926, 1927, 1929).

23. *E&MJ*, CXVI (July 7, 1923), 33; (Oct. 27, 1923), 735; CXVII (Apr. 26, 1924), 700; (June 28, 1924), 1054; CXX (Dec. 5, 1925), 906.

CHAPTER 14

1. *E&MJ*, CXIX (May 30, 1925), 900; CXX (Sept. 19, 1925), 467.

2. W. L. Vail, "Mexico City Letter," *E&MJ*, CXX (Sept. 19, 1925), 468.

3. Although urged officially to inscribe themselves in the Register as early as 1925 ("Reglamento," July 21, 1925, *Bol. min.*, XX [Aug. 1925], 76–77), as late as 1929 demands for registration were still being repeated. See G. S. López, "El Registro Público de Industrias Minerales, su finalidad y ventajas," *Bol. min.*, XXIV (Sept. 1927), 139–141; "Tarifa para el cobro de los derechos de inscripción en el Registro Público de Industrias Minerales (Mar. 5, 1929)," *Boletín de industrias minerales* (hereinafter cited as *Bol. de indus. min.*), VI (Apr. 1929), 359–360; *ibid.* (June 1929), 519; Cám. Nac. de Min., *Circs.* 287 (Apr. 29, 1927), 333 (July 29, 1927), and 366 (Nov. 4, 1927); *E&MJ*, CXXIV (Aug. 6, 1927), 228; (Aug. 27, 1927), 348; (Oct. 29, 1927), 706; A. Terrones Benítez, "Mining and the Government in Mexico," *E&MJ*, CXXXVII (May 1936), 243.

Calles' changes weighed most heavily on the smaller mineowners, most of whom were Mexicans. Paradoxically, at the same time the *Boletín Minero,* the official publication of the Department of Mines, deprecated the traditional role of the small miner. It pointed out editorially that production from the one-hectare fundos was sporadic and insignificant when compared to the gigantic and efficient productivity of power machinery used in mass mining and beneficiating. The editorial concluded that the demise of the small companies was natural and government policy should encourage enterprises able to economically work low-grade deposits and guarantee regular workings. (Anon., "Bosquejo sobre la apreciación de los negocios mineros," and "La gran industria se impone en minería," *Bol. min.*, XIX [Feb. 1925], 41–43; Anon., "La economía de las grandes compañías mineras," *ibid.*, XX [Nov. 1925], 195–196.)

4. "Ley organica de la fracción 1 del artículo 27 de la Constitución general (Mar. 22, 1926)," *Bol. de indus. min.*, I (Nov. 1926), 51–56; *E&MJ*, CXX (Oct. 31, 1925), 683; S. J. Jennings, "Gold and Silver Mining," *E&MJ*, CXXI (Jan. 16, 1926), 86; and the assurances of W. D. Thornton to stockholders of Greene-Cananea, *E&MJ*, CXXI (May 29, 1926), 873.

5. *Circ.* 29, Sec. de Industria, Comercio y Trabajo, *Bol. Min.*, XXI (Jan. 1926), 58; reprinted in Cám. Nac. de Min., *Circ.* 166 (Feb. 8, 1926); also see *E&MJ*, CXXI (Mar. 20, 1926), 501. For a survey of the status of foreign investors, see Frederick F. Barker, "Mexican Mining Concessions," *Southern California Law Review,* V, No. 1 (Oct. 1931), 7–8.

6. A. B. Parsons, "The Mexican Situation," *E&MJ*, CXXI (Feb. 13, 1926), 278.

7. *Diario de los debates,* II, p. 772. For an excellent succinct discussion of these concepts, see Barker, "Mexican Mining Concessions," 1–8.

8. Samuel Guy Inman, *Intervention in Mexico* (New York, 1919), p. 109.

9. *Bol. min.*, XVIII (Nov. 1924), 172–174. While the Díaz regime was willing to accept a concessionaire's property rights to "ore in place," post-Revolutionary governments have emphatically rejected that right. In their eyes, "ore in place" belongs to the State under the Constitution, and a company has a right only to what it can bring to the surface while the concession is in force.

10. F. González Roa, *Las cuestiones fundamentales de actualidad en México* (Mexico, 1927), p. 32.

11. F. González Roa, "Régimen constitucional del subsuelo; Estudio presentado al Segundo Congreso Jurídico Nacional," *Boletín del petróleo*, XIV (Sept. 1922), 264. For further discussions of this point, see González Roa, "Régimen," 253–254; González Roa, *Las cuestiones*, pp. 15–16, 33–34; G. Fernandez Castillo, *La propiedad y la expropiación en el derecho mexicano actual* (Mexico, 1939), p. 34; Oscar Morineau, *Los derechos reales y el subsuelo en México* (Mexico, 1948), *passim;* Alberto Vásquez del Mercado, *Concesión minera y derechos reales* (Mexico, 1946), *passim.*

12. Barker, "Mexican Mining Concessions," 1–3.

13. Roscoe B. Gaither, *Expropriation in Mexico: The Facts and the Law* (New York, 1940), pp. 149–150.

14. A. Molina Enríquez, *Revolución agraria*, IV, p. 68.

15. As with many fundamental legal concepts, the definition and scope of the terms *derecho real* and *derecho personal* are still subjects of debate. See O. Morineau, *Derechos reales;* and A. Vásquez del Mercado, *Concesión minera.*

16. For this interesting document, see: Comisión de la Secretaría de Industria ... integrada por los señores ingenieros Carlos Sellevier, Luis C. Caveaga, Teodoro Flores y José Aurelio García, "Estudio de los artículos 1° y 2° de la Ley Minera vigente," *Boletín del petróleo*, XVIII (Aug.–Sept. 1924), 136–145; Oct. 1924, 223–238.

17. *E&MJ*, CXIX (May 30, 1925), 900. Also see *E&MJ*, CXVII (May 31, 1924), 898.

18. See Note 2 above; and *E&MJ*, CXX (Nov. 21, 1925), 831; CXXI (Jan. 23, 1926), 180.

19. Cám. Nac. de Min., Annex to *Circ.* 224 (Sept. 25, 1926); *E&MJ*, CXXI (Apr. 3, 1926), 577; (May 8, 1926), 777.

20. Stenographic record of the *Junta celebrada en la tarde del día 30 de julio de 1926 entre la comisión nombrada por la Secretaría de Industria ... y la designada por los representantes de los intereses mineros ... para tratar acerca de las observaciones hechas ... al reglamento de la Ley de Industrias Minerales,* in Cám. Nac. de Min., *Circ.* 224 (Sept. 25, 1926).

21. Editorial, "La nueva Ley de Industrias Minerales," *Bol. min.*, XXI (June 1926), 273–274.

22. "Ley de Industrias Minerales," *Bol. min.*, XXI (June 1926), 325–343; "Reglamento," *ibid.*, XXII (Aug. 1926), 71–110. For an excellent résumé in English, see E. M. Burton, "Provisions of the Mexican Mining Law of 1926," *E&MJ*, CXXIII (Mar. 19, 1927), 486–487.

23. J. Castanedo, "Conferencia dada en la Escuela de Verano, en Agosto de 1928," *Bol. min.*, XXVI (Sept. 1928), 176–177; D. V. Navarro, "Algunas de los factores económicas que han influido en el desarrollo de la industria minera en México," *Bol. min.*, XXVII (Feb. 1929), 93.

24. For the routine in filing a claim, see "Instrucciones para solicitantes de lotes mineros," *Bol. min.*, XXIII (Apr. 1927), 269–311. For a comparison with the procedure followed under the old law, see "Manera de obtener y conservar la propiedad minera en México," in "La industria del zinc en México," *Bol. min.*, XXI (Apr. 1926), 136–137.

25. "Ley de Industrias Minerales," Arts. 150–157; "Comprobación de producción mínima," *Bol. min.*, XXVII (Feb. 1929), 85–89; D. V. Navarro, "El contigente del informe presidencial objetivo," *Bol. min.*, XXVII (Feb. 1929), 82.

26. P. Wooton, "News from Washington," *E&MJ*, CXXII (July 3, 1926), 26.

27. *El Universal* (Sept. 5 and 8, 1926), reprinted in Cám. Nac. de Min., *Circ.* 221 (Sept. 21, 1926); *ibid.*, 220, Sept. 13, 1926; *E&MJ*, CXXII (Oct. 23, 1926), 668.

28. Depto. de Minas, *Circ.* 8230 (Apr. 23, 1927), reprinted in Cám. Nac. de

Min., *Circ.* 286 (Apr. 25, 1927); *E&MJ,* CXXIII (Feb. 12, 1927), 300.

29. Cám. Nac. de Min., *Circ.* 368T (Nov. 13, 1927); *E&MJ,* CXXV (Apr. 28, 1928), 711.

30. Cám. Nac. de Min., *Circ.* 425 (June 29, 1928).

31. Anon., "La industria minero-metalúrgica en el año de 1926,' *Bol. min.,* XXV (Mar. 1928), 124; J. Castanedo, "Diversas legislaciones que en materia de minería han regido en México," *Bol. min.,* XXIII (Apr. 1927), 247; Editorial, "La Ley de Industrias Minerales no hostiliza, ante al contrario ayuda a los mineros en pequeño," *Bol. min.,* XXV (May 1928), 283–285; and see Note 4 above.

32. S. F. Eaton, "Five Hundred Miles Through Mexico on Muleback," *E&MJ,* CXXIV (Aug. 6, 1927), 221–222.

33. Anon., "La influencia del 'Factor Humano' en los accidentes de las minas," *Bol. min.,* XXIII (Apr. 1926), 237–239.

34. "Las sanciones a los infractores del Reglamento de Policia Minera, según el Reglamento de la Ley de Impuestos Minerales," *Bol. min.,* XXII (Aug. 1926), 57–59. For a review of the history of the law of 1912 and its failures, see Anon., "La labor de la Secretaría de Industria en relación con la seguridad de la vida del minero," *Bol. min.,* XXI (Mar. 1926), 91–93.

35. *Bol. de indus. min.,* III (Aug. 1927), 71.

36. *Bol. min.,* XIX (Apr. 1925), 135–136; XXV (Mar. 1928), 119–121; XXVI (Oct. 1928), 223; *Bol. de indus. min.,* IV (Mar. 1928), 247–248; V (Oct. 1928), 340; Cám. Nac. de Min., *Circ.* 445 (Sept. 28, 1928).

37. The article "El resultado de la campaña de seguridad en la industria minero-metalúrgica," *Bol. min.,* XXVII (Jan. 1929), 3–4, has an excellent summary of the advances made. A listing of all articles on safety in the *Boletín minero* between 1926 and 1930 would require a lengthy catalogue.

38. *An. de estad. min.,* 1927, p. 540; *1929 y 1930,* p. 321; *1932,* p. 274.

39. Anon., "Las responsibilidades en las minas," *Bol. min.,* XIX (June 1925), 175–177; XIX (Jan. 1925), 3–4, 31–35, 38; *E&MJ,* CXIX (Jan. 31, 1925), 223.

40. Cám. Nac. de Min., *Circ.* 111 (May 16, 1925); Anon., "Las compañías mineras deben ayudar a los estudiantes," *Bol. min.,* XX (Dec. 1925), 241–242.

41. A. B. Parsons, "The Mexican Situation," 283.

42. *Bol. min.,* XX (Dec. 1925), 298; *E&MJ,* CXXV (May 19, 1928), 832.

43. Marjorie R. Clark, *Organized Labor in Mexico,* pp. 117-118.

44. E. Gruening, *Mexico and its Heritage,* p. 344. For a background on Pachuca labor relations, see *E&MJ,* CX (Jan. 13, 1920), 967.

45. Gruening, *Mexico,* pp. 345–347; Sec. de Industria, *La industria ... durante la gestión administrativa del Señor Gral. Plutarco Elias Calles* (Mexico, 1928), III, *passim; E&MJ,* CXXII (July 24, 1926), 151; CXXV (Apr. 7, 1928), 588.

46. For references to analyses of these laws, see International Labor Office, *La legislación social en América Latina* (Geneva, 1929), II, pp. 614–625; Vincente Lombardo Toledano, *Bibliografía del trabajo y la previsión social en México* (Mexico, 1938).

47. For the text of the Guanajuato law, see *Boletín de industrias, comercio y trabajo* (Sección de trabajo), V (Oct.–Dec. 1920), 38–42; *E&MJ,* CXII (July 2, 1921), 30. For a summary of a similar law in Chihuahua, see *E&MJ,* CXIII (May 27, 1922), 935; CXIV (Sept. 2, 1922), 414–417. Also see Gruening, *Mexico,* pp. 345–346; Anon., "Mexico Trying out System of Labor Arbitration," *E&MJ,* CXII (Sept. 3, 1921), 385; *E&MJ,* CXIII (Feb. 11, 1922), 261; (June 10, 1922), 1017; CXIX (Jan. 31, 1925), 223; (Feb. 7, 1925), 262; (May 30, 1925), 900; CXX (July 4, 1925), 27; CXXI (Mar. 20, 1926), 501; CXXIII (Jan. 15, 1927), 81; CXXIV (Nov. 5, 1927), 742.

48. Gruening, *Mexico,* p. 347.

49. *E&MJ,* CXX (Aug. 8, 1925), 228; CXXIV (Aug. 13, 1927), 266.

50. Sec. de Industria, *La industria,* III, p. 514.

51. *Ibid.,* p. 515; Clark, *Organized Labor,* p. 115.

52. *Diario oficial,* XLI, No. 13 (Mar. 15, 1927); XLI, No. 23 (Mar. 28, 1927); *Bol. de indus. min.,* II (Apr. 1927), 293–294; Cám. Nac. de Min., *Circ.* 297 (Mar. 29, 1927); III (Oct. 1927), 215–216, 217–233; Sec. de Industria, *La industria,* III, pp. 509–529, has all pertinent texts.

53. Juan de Díos Bojórquez, "El sindicalismo y la Revolución," *Memoria del Primer Congreso Mexicano de Derecho Industrial* (Mexico, 1934), Appendix No. 1, pp. 15–16.

54. *Ibid.,* p. 16; Clark, *Organized Labor,* p. 115; for a list of early decisions, see Sec. de Industria, *La industria,* III, pp. 403–429.

55. *E&MJ,* CXXV (Jan. 7, 1928), 30; (Jan. 14, 1928), 70; CXXVIII (Jan. 12, 1929), 71; (Apr. 20, 1929), 656; (May 4, 1929), 736; CXXVIII (Aug. 17, 1929), 267; Miguel Lanz Duret, *Derecho constitucional mexicano* (Mexico, 1931), p. 406.

56. Anon., "Passage of Labor Law Now Almost Certain, Retards New Mining Ventures," *E&MJ,* CXXVIII (Oct. 19, 1929), 641; *E&MJ,* CXXVIII (Aug. 3, 1929), 190); (Aug. 31, 1929), 374.

57. *E&MJ,* CXXXII (Sept. 14, 1931), 228. Rather than outline the many provisions of this code, most of which are not germane to this study, the reader is referred to J. W. F. Dulles, *Yesterday in Mexico* (Austin, Tex., 1961), pp. 513–514, for a summary.

58. Joaquín Ramirez Cabanas C., "Los ingresos federales de México durante los años 1876–1936," *Revista de Hacienda,* II (Apr. 1938), 15.

59. Sec. de Industrias, *La industria,* I, p. 217; Juan de Díos Bojórquez, *Sonora, Sinaloa y Nayarit; Estudio estadístico y económico social elaborado por el Departamento de Estadística Nacional, Año de 1927* (Mexico, 1929), pp. 262–263.

60. A. B. Parsons, "Mexican Situation," 282–283; Marcosson, *Metal Magic,* pp. 242–244.

61. See the report of Coverdale and Colpitts, Consulting Engineers, *The National Railways of Mexico,* rendered on Sept. 17, 1929, to the International Committee of Bankers on Mexico. At the time 65 per cent of the railway trackage was controlled by Ferrocarriles Nacionales. Also see *E&MJ,* CXII (Sept. 3, 1921), 383; CXX (Sept. 19, 1925), 468; (Nov. 21, 1925), 831; CXXI (June 12, 1926), 958; CXXII (Nov. 6, 1926), 742; CXXIII (Apr. 9, 1927), 615; CXXIV (Aug. 6, 1927), 219.

62. *E&MJ,* CXI (Jan. 1, 1921), 31; (Feb. 19, 1921), 365; CXIII (Jan. 28, 1922), 184; CXIV (Sept. 30, 1922), 605; (Oct. 7, 1922), 650; CXV (Feb. 10, 1923), 290; (Apr. 7, 1923), 639; CXVII (Apr. 19, 1924), 657; CXXI (May 1, 1926), 739; CXXIV (Aug. 6, 1927), 218; (Aug. 20, 1927), 308; CXXVI (July 21, 1928), 111; (Oct. 6, 1928), 550; J. Campa, "El distrito de Taxco, Guerrero," *Bol. min.,* XV (Jan. 1923), 6–7.

63. *E&MJ,* CXIX (Jan. 31, 1925), 223; CXXII (Sept. 4, 1926), 389.

64. *E&MJ,* CXXV (Mar. 17, 1928), 466; (Apr. 14, 1928), 631; (Apr. 21, 1928), 670; (June 16, 1928), 989; CXXVIII (Aug. 10, 1929), 228.

65. Anon., "La industria metalúrgica en México," *Bol. min.,* XIV (Sept. 1922), 302; Anon., "Los caminos y las minas," *ibid.,* XIX (May 1925), 139–141; *E&MJ,* CXII (Aug. 20, 1921), 311; Anon., "Mining in Nayarit," *E&MJ,* CXVII (Jan. 26, 1924), 184; CXX (Oct. 17, 1925), 630.

66. *E&MJ,* CXIX (Feb. 14, 1925), 298; CXX (Dec. 5, 1925), 906; CXXIII (May 14, 1927), 815; CXXVI (Aug. 25, 1928), 312; (Sept. 1, 1928), 352; CXXVIII (Aug. 17, 1929), 267; (Oct. 19, 1929), 641; Eaton, "500 Miles Through Mexico," 219–220.

67. José Herrera y Lasso, *La fuerza motriz en México* (Mexico, 1927), p. 228.

68. José Herrera y Lasso, *La industria eléctrica* (Mexico, 1933), pp. 37, 50.

69. *La indus. eléc.,* pp. 88–89.

70. Herrera y Lasso, "El consumo de energía que hace la industria minera y metalúrgica," *La fuerza motriz,* pp. 113 ff; Chap. vii, pp. 149–157.

71. Anon., "Los paros y readjustes en las minas de Chihuahua," *Bol. min.,* XXVIII (Dec. 1929), 455–456; *E&MJ,* CXXVI (July 28, 1928), 151; CXXVIII (Sept. 21, 1929), 485; (Oct. 5, 1929), 562; (Nov. 2, 1929), 714; (Nov. 30, 1929), 868; CXXIX (Feb. 24, 1930), 209; *Min. Mag.,* XLII (Feb. 1930), 72; and "San Francisco Mines of Mexico," in Co. Mtngs. & Repts. Sec.; W. E. Washburn, "Electric Power," in San Francisco Mines of Mexico number of the *E&MJ,* CXXXVII (Aug. 1936), 411–413.

72. *E&MJ,* CXXVIII (Oct. 5, 1929), 562; (Nov. 2, 1929), 714; CXXIX (Feb. 8, 1930), 144; *Moody's Manual of Investments, Public Utilities, 1929,* p. 1447; *1930,* pp. 1514–15.

CHAPTER 15

1. See the discussion of D. V. Navarro, "El contigente del Depto. de Minas ... en la exposición del informe presidencial objectivo," *Bol. min.,* XXVII (Feb. 1929), 81–82.

2. Parker T. Handy, "Silver," in J. E. Spurr and F. E. Wormser, (eds.), *The Marketing of Metals and Minerals* (New York, 1925), p. 170.

3. *E&MJ,* CXIV (Oct. 28, 1922), 782; CXVIII (July 19, 1924), 106; CXXV (Mar. 24, 1928), 509. For complete coinage figures, see *An. de estad. min., 1922,* p. 130; *1929 y 1930,* p. 349.

4. *E&MJ,* CXII (Aug. 27, 1921), 325; Anon., "Mexican Silver to Supply Orient?" *E&MJ,* CXIII (May 27, 1922), 941; D. H. Leavens, *Silver Money,* p. 158. Also see *E&MJ,* CXXIII (Mar. 12, 1927), 455; Quintana, *Los ensayos monetarios,* pp. 135–172.

5. Editorial, "La situación de la plata en México," *Bol. min.,* XXII (Nov. 1926), 277, 283; *E&MJ,* CXXII (Nov. 13, 1926), 787.

6. *E&MJ,* CXXII (Oct. 30, 1926), 707; (Nov. 6, 1926), 744; (Nov. 20, 1926), 829; Anon., "Mexican Mines," *E&MJ,* CXXIII (Jan. 22, 1927), 163; (Feb. 5, 1927), 258.

7. *E&MJ,* CXXII (Dec. 4, 1926), 907; CXXIII (Jan. 1, 1927), 35; (Feb. 5, 1927), 258.

8. C. H. Crane, "Lead," *E&MJ,* CXXV (Jan. 21, 1928), 85–86; Crane, "Lead," *E&MJ,* CXXIX (Feb. 8, 1930), 114.

9. M. J. Elsing, "Lead, Zinc, Copper and the Tariff," *Min. & Met.,* XIII (Oct. 1932), 449–450; A. B. Parsons, "London's Influence on Domestic Lead and Zinc Prices," *E&MJ,* CXXI (Mar. 13, 1926), 469–470; I. H. Cornell, "Lead," in Spurr and Wormser, *Marketing,* pp. 99–100; F. E. Wormser, "Lead Market in an Excellent Position," *E&MJ,* CXV (Mar. 17, 1923), 516; Wormser, "Lead Market Is Exceptional," *E&MJ,* CXVI (Oct. 27, 1923), 744; Wormser, "The Lead Shortage," *E&MJ,* CXVII (Mar. 5, 1923), 469; Wormser, "The Rise in Metal Prices," *E&MJ,* CXVIII (Dec. 20, 1924), 99; US BuMines, *1950 Materials Survey: Lead* (Washington, D.C., 1951), pp. V–10–11.

10. Crane, "Lead," *E&MJ,* CXXV (Feb. 8, 1930), 114.

11. US BuMines, *Lead, 1950*, pp. V–10–11, VI–84; William Y. Elliott, et al., *International Control in the Non-Ferrous Metals*, pp. 622–636.

12. Wormser, "The American Zinc Institute," *E&MJ*, CXIII (May 13, 1922), 821; Anon., "Zinc Mining in Mexico," *E&MJ*, CXIV (Nov. 4, 1922), 794; Elsing, "Lead, Zinc, Copper and the Tariff," 450.

13. Ingalls, *World Survey of the Zinc Industry*, pp. 84, 107.

14. US Dept. of Comm., Bureau of Foreign and Domestic Trade, *World Survey of the Zinc Industry*, Trade Information Bulletin 246 (Washington, D.C., 1924), p. 48; *E&MJ*, CXII (Aug. 20, 1921), 311; CXVII (Mar. 22, 1924), 499; CXVIII (Nov. 8, 1924), 749; (Dec. 20, 1924), 992; CXIX (Mar. 7, 1925), 420; CXXIII (Apr. 2, 1927), 579; CXXVI (Nov. 17, 1928), 794; *Bol. min.*, XXIII (Jan. 1927), 13.

15. J. Castanedo, "La explotación de cobre en México," *Bol. min.*, XXIV (July 1927), 5 ff.

16. Benjamin B. Wallace and L. R. Edminster, *International Control of Raw Materials* (Washington, D.C., 1930), pp. 259–262; W. Y. Elliott et al., *International Control in the Non-Ferrous Metals*, pp. 433–445; S. Peña, "La mina 'La Colorada' perteniciente a 'The Cananea Consolidated Copper Co.,' S.A.," *Bol. min.*, XXXI (June 1931), 181; *E&MJ*, CXVIII (July 19, 1924), 105; (Sept. 20, 1924), 474; CXXI (Jan. 16, 1926), 122; CXXIII (Mar. 5, 1927), 416; CXXXIII (Aug. 1932), 453; CXXXIV (Feb. 1933), 88; (July 1933), 309; US Tariff Comm., *Latin America as a Source of Strategic and other Essential Materials*, Report No. 144, 2nd Ser. (Washington, D.C., 1941), pp. 53–66.

17. *E&MJ*, CXXIV (Sept. 17, 1927), 466; (Sept. 24, 1927), 508.

18. *E&MJ*, CXXII (Nov. 6, 1926), 744; CXXIV (Aug. 6, 1927), 228.

19. *E&MJ*, CXXIII (Apr. 16, 1927), 661.

20. *E&MJ*, CXXIV (Oct. 22, 1927), 668; Navarro, "El contigente del informe presidencial," 82.

21. *E&MJ*, CXXV (Apr. 21, 1928), 670; CXXVI (Sept. 29, 1928), 508.

22. *E&MJ*, CXXVII (Feb. 16, 1929), 295; (Apr. 6, 1929), 574; (May 11, 1929), 775; CXXVIII (Nov. 16, 1929), 791; CXXIX (June 7, 1930), 578.

23. *Bol. min.*, XVIII (Aug. 1924), 47–53.

24. The participation of the municipalities had been decreed as early as January 24, 1923. The decree provided that the increments on the basic tax occasioned by the law's progressive rates were to be turned over to the municipality. See *Bol. min.*, XVI (July–Sept. 1923), 150–151; and Cám. Nac. de Min., *Circ.* 11 (Mar. 11, 1924).

25. *Bol. min.*, XVII (Jan.–June 1924), 16–17; Cám. Nac. de Min., *Circ.* 43 (June 26, 1924); *E&MJ*, CXVIII (July 26, 1924), 150.

26. The organization of a Chamber had been suggested as early as 1917. (F. Roel and A. Ortiz, "Organización de Cámaras de Minería," Monograph No. 10, *Primer Congreso Nacional de Industriales*, pp. 181–191.) Chihuahua organized a Chamber in 1922. (Cámara nacional de minería del Estado de Chihuahua, *Estatuos* [Chihuahua, 1922]; *E&MJ*, CXIII [Feb. 4, 1922], 215.) The national chamber's bylaws were drawn up in 1923, and a charter was granted the next year. Its organizers were a blue-ribbon collection of influential mine spokesmen. (*E&MJ*, CXVII [Sept. 29, 1923], 564.)

27. The terms of the loan were 920,000 pesos, guaranteed by the Commission, at 17 per cent interest. (Cám. Nac. de Min., *Circs.* 46 [July 3, 1924]; 58 and attachments [Aug. 16, 1924]; and 97 [Feb. 10, 1925], sheets 14–15; *E&MJ*, CXVIII [July 19, 1924], 106; [July 26, 1924], 150; [Dec. 20, 1924], 992; Decree of Aug. 13, 1924, *Bol. min.*, XVIII [Nov. 1924], 227–228.)

28. *Bol. min.*, XX (July 1925), 31–34.

29. Cám. Nac. de Min., *Circ.* 124 (June 25, 1925); *E&MJ*, CXX (Aug. 18, 1925), 228.

30. *Bol. min.*, XXI (May 1926), 223–246.

31. *Ibid.*, XXII (Aug. 1926), 115–123.

32. Cám. Nac. de Min., *Circ.* 235b (Oct. 22, 1926); *E&MJ*, CXXII (Nov. 20, 1926), 829.

33. *E&MJ*, CXXIII (Mar. 12, 1927), 455.

34. *Bol. de indus. min.*, II (June 1927), 387–398; Cám. Nac. de Min., *Circ.* 304 (May 30, 1927); 456 (Nov. 6, 1928).

35. *Bol. de indus. min.*, VIII (Jan. 1930), 5–17. For English summaries of this law, see *E&MJ*, CXXIX (Jan. 9, 1930), 46; (Feb. 24, 1930), 210.

36. This clause was implemented by *Circ.* 24–8–101 of the Sec. de Hacienda (Mar. 3, 1930), *Bol. de indus. min.*, VIII (Apr. 1930), 321. Also see *Circ.* 24–4–14, *Boletín de concesiones mineras* (hereinafter cited as *Bol. de conc. min.*), II (Feb. 1931), 53. For state tax aid, see *E&MJ*, CXXIII (Jan. 15, 1927), 108; CXXV (Jan. 14, 1928), 70.

37. The law restricted the discount given to silver when the price was below 57 cents to refined silver, bullion, and all impure forms except flotation concentrates. On February 11, 1931, the privilege was extended to all silver obtained from complex ores, "since the value of copper, lead, and zinc has diminished." (*Bol. de conc. min.*, II [Mar. 1931], 113–114.)

38. For example, see *E&MJ*, CXIII (June 3, 1922), 974, wherein the Ministry of Finance ordered the state of Durango to repeal its mine production tax.

39. See the state of Zacatecas' law of Dec. 27, 1926, in the state's *Diario oficial*, XIX, No. 52, reprinted in Cám. Nac. de Min., *Circ.* 266 (Feb. 17, 1927).

40. *Bol. min.*, XIX (Jan. 1925), 36.

41. Alejandro Carrillo, *Mexico's Resources for Livelihood* (The Hague, 1938), 21.

42. *An. de estad. min., 1929 y 1930*, p. 352.

43. *Bol. min.*, XVIII (Nov. 1924), 203–210, 210–217; XIX (Jan. 1925), 36–38; (Mar. 1925), 101–103; XX (July 1925), 30; Anon., "El impuesto sobre utilidades y la minería," *Bol. min.*, XVIII (Nov. 1924), 171–172; Cám. Nac. de Min., *Circs.* (1924–25), *passim*.

44. *E&MJ*, CXX (Sept. 19, 1925), 468.

45. Parsons, "The Mexican Situation," pp. 280, 287.

46. *Min. & Met.*, XI (Nov. 1930), 506.

47. *E&MJ*, CXXX (Oct. 23, 1930), 414; H. M. Bratter, "Silver," *E&MJ*, CXXXI (Feb. 9, 1931), 99; CXXXII (Aug. 10, 1931), 132. An attempt to change the tax scale in 1931 met with such a storm of protest that it was repealed immediately after its promulgation. (*E&MJ*, CXXXII [Sept. 14, 1931], 228.) For a detailed listing of the miners' complaints against Mexican taxes, see *E&MJ*, CXXIX (June 7, 1930), 578.

CHAPTER 16

1. *E&MJ*, CXXIV (Dec. 3, 1927), 907.

2. Genaro García, *La situación de la industria minera* (Mexico, 1929); also see *E&MJ*, CXXVII (Feb. 9, 1929), 255.

3. *E&MJ*, CXIX (May 9, 1925), 774; (May 30, 1925), 900; CXXII (Nov. 20,

1926), 825; CXXIII (Feb. 5, 1927), 258; CXXIV (Nov. 5, 1927), 742; CXXV (Jan. 7, 1928), 30; CXXVI (July 21, 1928), 111; CXXVIII (Oct. 12, 1929), 597; *Bol. min.*, XXIX (Jan. 1930), 8; E. Villafaña, "Los trabajos de 'The Guanajuato Consolidated Mining and Milling Co.,'" *ibid.*, XXVII (June 1929), 426–432; E. Villafaña, "Las minas del Cia. Min. 'El Cubo,'" *ibid.*, XXXI (May 1931), 125–127.

4. *Min Mag.*, XXVIII (June 1923), 332; XLIV (Jan. 1931), 8; XLVI (Jan. 1932), 8; *E&MJ*, CXV (June 9, 1923), 1036; CXVI (Dec. 29, 1923), 1133; CXVIII (Sept. 6, 1924), 389; (Nov. 1, 1924), 703; E. Castelazo, "El mineral de Cuale, Edo. de Jalisco," *Bol. min.*, XIX (May 1925), 157–158.

5. *Min. Mag.*, XXXII (Feb. 1925), 128; XXXIV (Jan. 1926), 8; XXXVI (Feb. 1927), 127; XXXVII (Nov. 1927), 274; *E&MJ*, CXXIII (Mar. 5, 1927), 416; (May 7, 1927), 778; CXXVI (Sept. 1, 1928), 352; (Sept. 15, 1928), 428; CXXVII (Mar. 16, 1929), 456; C. Bruchhold, "Las plantas de 'The Mexico Mines of El Oro,' Ltd.," *Bol. min.*, XXV (May 1928), 328–334.

6. *Min. Mag.* XXXVI (Apr. 1927), 200; XXXVII (Dec. 1927), 406; XXXIX (Nov. 1928), 270; XLI (Nov. 1929), 264; Vol. XL, Co. Mtngs. & Repts. Sec., *E&MJ*, CXIII (Jan. 7, 1922), 36; CXVI (Dec. 29, 1923), 1137; CXXII (Sept. 25, 1926), 509; CXXIV (Oct. 1, 1927), 547; CXXXIX (July 1938), 77; CXLIV (Feb. 1943), 144; Anon., "La planta metalúrgica de 'El Oro Mining and Railway Co.,' Ltd.," *Bol. min.*, IX (May–June 1920), 592–608.

7. *E&MJ*, CXXV (May 5, 1928), 751; CXXVI (Nov. 10, 1928), 765; (Dec. 8, 1928), 920.

8. M. López Núñez, "La mina Dos Estrellas," and "La planta metalúrgica [de] Dos Estrellas," *Bol. min.*, XXVI (Dec. 1928), 478–487, 500–505; *E&MJ*, CX (Oct. 2, 1920), 699; CXVI (Dec. 29, 1923), 1131; CXXV (June 2, 1928), 910; (Sept. 14, 1929), 447; (Nov. 2, 1929), 716; CXXIX (Jan. 19, 1930), 45; CXXX (July 10, 1930), 43.

9. *E&MJ*, CXXIV (Dec. 17, 1927), 987; CXXV (Mar. 31, 1928), 553; CXXVI (Aug. 18, 1928), 272; CXXIX (Mar. 24, 1930), 320; (Apr. 24, 1930), 424.

10. *E&MJ*, CXXVI (Aug. 18, 1928), 272; (Dec. 15, 1928), 959; CXXIX (May 8, 1930), 479.

11. *E&MJ*, CXXIV (Nov. 26, 1927), 867; CXXVIII (Dec. 14, 1929), 493.

12. *E&MJ*, CXXVII (Apr. 20, 1929), 656; CXXVIII (Aug. 31, 1929), 374; (Nov. 23, 1929), 826.

13. *E&MJ*, CXXVII (June 15, 1929), 973; CXXVIII (Oct. 12, 1929), 597; CXXXI (May 25, 1931), 479; W. A. Wasley, "The Mexican Gambusino in El Tigre," *Min. & Met.*, XIV (Apr. 1933), 187.

14. *E&MJ*, CXXVI (Nov. 10, 1928), 764; (Nov. 24, 1928), 845; CXXXI (Jan. 12, 1931), 38.

15. M. Santillan, "Estudio geológico sobre el mineral de Pachuca," *Bol. min.*, XXXI (Feb. 1931), 29–41 (quote from p. 39); trans. in *E&MJ*, CXXXI (May 25, 1931), 482.

16. *E&MJ*, CXXIII (June 18, 1927), 1019.

17. *E&MJ*, CXXIV (July 30, 1927), 189; (Sept. 3, 1927), 384; (Oct. 15, 1927), 624; (Dec. 17, 1927), 987; (Dec. 24, 1927), 1029; CXXV (Jan. 7, 1928), 30; (Jan. 21, 1928), 131; *Bol. min.*, XXV (Jan. 1928), 13.

18. *E&MJ*, CXXVII (Mar. 23, 1929), 493; (Apr. 6, 1929), 574; (Apr. 13, 1929), 616; (Apr. 20, 1929), 656; (Apr. 27, 1929), 696; CXXVIII (Aug. 31, 1929), 374; S. D. Strauss, "The Mining Industry of Mexico," *E&MJ*, CXXIX (Feb. 8, 1930), 144.

19. S. D. Strauss, "Mining in Latin America," *E&MJ*, CXXXI (Feb. 9, 1931), 128.

20. US Tariff Comm., *Foreign Trade of Latin America* (Washington, D.C., 1942), Pt. II, p. 43.

21. *E&MJ*, CXXX (July 24, 1930), 92; (Aug. 9, 1930), 147; (Aug. 23, 1930), 194; (Sept. 8, 1930), 247, 249; (Sept. 25, 1930), 306; (Oct. 23, 1930), 410; (Nov. 24, 1930), 540; CXXXI (June 22, 1931), 574, 580.

22. *E&MJ*, CXXIX (Mar. 8, 1930), 265; CXXX (Sept. 25, 1930), 300, 302; (Oct. 23, 1930), 410; CXXXI (Jan. 26, 1931), 79; (Mar. 9, 1931), 239; (Apr. 13, 1931), 334; CXXXII (Sept. 14, 1931), 229, 233; (Sept. 28, 1931), 274, 277; (Dec. 28, 1931), 548; CXXXIII (Jan. 1932), 63; (Feb. 1932), 120; (Apr. 1932), 244; (May 1932), 303; (June 1932), 359; (July 1932), 408; (Nov. 1932), 599; (Dec. 1932), 646; *Min. Mag.*, XLIII (Oct. 1930), 200; XLV (Nov. 1931), 264; XLVI (Mar. 1932), 136; Cleland, *Phelps Dodge*, pp. 241–243.

23. *E&MJ*, CXXXIII (Apr. 1932), 244; S. Turner, "Improved Outlook for Gold and Silver," *Min. & Met.*, XV (Jan. 1934), 7.

24. *E&MJ*, CXXXIV (Feb. 1933), 88.

25. *Bol. min.*, XXX (July–Aug. 1930), 4–22. For a review of the law as well as Mexican mining terminology, see Frederick F. Baker, "Mexican Mining Concessions," *Southern California Law Review*, V, No. 1 (Oct. 1931), 1–8.

26. "Exposición de motivos de la Ley Minera de las Estados Unidos Mexicanos y su reglamento," *Bol. min.*, XXX (Sept.–Oct. 1930), 85.

27. The Instituto de Geología offered to do free assays for all cateo concession holders. (*Bol. de conc. min.*, III [Oct. 1931], 308; IV [Apr. 1932], 241.) The regulations governing the granting and working of cateo concessions, issued on June 30, 1931, were rather strict. (*Ibid.*, III [Aug. 1931], 112–114.)

28. "Exposición," 91–92. The amounts to be invested were set in the Reglamento, Arts. 130–131. Also see A. Terrones Benítez, "Mexico Spurs Inactive Mine Owners," *E&MJ*, CXXXVII (Dec. 1936), 608.

29. Feuerlein and Hannon, *Dólares en la América Latina*, pp. 100–106; *E&MJ*, CXXXII (Sept. 14, 1931), 228; CXXXVIII (Feb. 1937), 77.

30. *Diario oficial*, LXXV, No. 52 (Jan. 30, 1933); *Bol. de pet. y min.*, I (July 1933), 134.

31. *Diario oficial*, LXXXII, No. 17 (Jan. 20, 1934); LXXXV, No. 53 (Aug. 31, 1934).

32. Cám. Nac. de Min., *Circ.*, no number (Sept. 4, 1934).

33. *Diario oficial*, LXXII, No. 1 (May 2, 1932); *Bol. min.*, XXXIII (May 1932), 159–165.

34. By an oversight, mines held under titles granted before 1909 were omitted, necessitating an additional decree. See *Diario oficial*, LXXII, No. 29 (June 4, 1932).

35. Cám. Nac. de Min., *Circ.* 693 (Observations to members), May 4, 1932; *Circ.* 699 (Memo. to the Sec. de Hacienda), May 18, 1932; *Diario oficial*, LXXIII, No. 51 (Aug. 29, 1932). Also see *ibid.*, LXXIV, No. 1 (Sept. 1, 1932); LXXVI, No. 8 (Jan. 10, 1933).

36. *Diario oficial*, LXXXV, No. 53 (Aug. 31, 1934).

CHAPTER 17

1. *Plan Sexenal del P. N. R.* (Mexico, 1936), pp. 52–56, 171.
2. *E&MJ*, CXXXVI (Jan. 1935), 45.
3. O'Connor, *Guggenheims*, pp. 339–340.

4. A. S. Everest, *Morgenthau, The New Deal, and Silver* (New York, 1950), *passim,* for a discussion of the politics of the silver purchase program.

5. For an official expression of Mexico's approval of this policy, see Depto. de Estudios Económicos, Secretaría de la Economía Nacional, *Apuntes acerca del porvenir de la minería en México* (Mexico, 1935), mimeo.

6. A. H. Hubbell, "The Mining Industry South of the Rio Grande," *E&MJ,* CXXXVII (Feb. 1936), 71. American producers were also caught unprepared, *E&MJ,* CXXXVI (Jan. 1935), 30.

7. A. Notman, "Mineral Economics," *Min. & Met.,* XIX (Jan. 1938), 22.

8. Everest, *Morgenthau,* pp. 80–82; D. H. Leavens, *Silver Money,* pp. 283–284.

9. *Diario oficial,* LXXXIX, No. 50 (Apr. 27, 1935); XC, No. 18 (May 25, 1935); Leavens, *Silver Money,* 284; *E&MJ,* CXXXVI (May 1935), 242–243; US Tariff Comm., *Foreign Trade of Latin America,* Pt. II, Vol. 2, p. 37.

10. Everest, *Morgenthau,* pp. 82–84; Leavens, *Silver Money,* p. 327; A. H. Hubbell, "Mexico," *E&MJ,* CXL (Feb. 1939), 62.

11. *Diario oficial,* C, No. 8 (Jan. 1, 1937); C, No. 31 (Feb. 2, 1937); *Bol. de pet. y min.,* VI (Jan. 1937), 11–12; *E&MJ,* CXXXVIII (Feb. 1937), 109; J. B. Glenn, "The Economic Renaissance of Mexico," *Bankers' Monthly,* CXXIX (Dec. 1934), 611.

12. *Diario oficial,* LXXXVIII, No. 1 (Jan. 1, 1935); *E&MJ,* CXXXVI (Feb. 1935), 88.

13. I. M. Zaragoza, "La disvalorización del peso determina un severo golpe a [la industria minera] en México," *Excelsior,* Mexico City (Aug. 6, 1948); reprinted in Cám. Min de Méx., *Circ.* 2614 (Aug. 7, 1948).

14. *Diario oficial,* LXXXIX, No. 38 (Apr. 13, 1935); XC, No. 19 (June 1, 1935); *Bol. de pet. y min.,* IV (Mar. 1935), 19; IV (June 1935), 16–17; Great Britain, Dept. of Overseas Trade, Joseph Pyke, *Economic Conditions in Mexico* (London, 1936), p. 15.

15. Anon., "Mexico and Her Relation to American Defense," *Journal of Commerce,* CLXXXV (Aug. 27, 1940), 29, 34–35; *Min. & Met.,* XX (Aug. 1939), 384; E. Gnoseclose, "Revival In Mining and Other Evidence of a New Prosperity in Mexico," *The Analyst* (Sept. 27, 1935), 430; Depto. Autónomo de Prensa y Publicidad, Commentary Ser. No. 3, *American Investments in Mining* (Mexico, 1938), unpaged; *Min. Sur.,* III (Oct. 1935), 25.

16. Gnoseclose, "The Revival In Mining," 430.

17. Secretaría de la Economía Nacional, *Memoria, 1933,* pp. 96–97; *E&MJ,* CXXXIV (May 1933), 218; (July 1933), 309; (Dec. 1933), 531; CXXXV (Feb. 1934), 83–84; (Mar. 1934), 135; (Aug. 1934), 377, 378; CXXXVI (Apr. 1935), 196; (Aug. 1935), 415; (Oct. 1935), 525; (Nov. 1935), 579; *Min. Sur.,* II (Jan. 1935), 25; III (Oct. 1935), 25.

CHAPTER 18

1. Lázaro Cárdenas, *Policies of the Present Administration of Mexico* (Mexico, 1936), pp. 15–16.

2. *E&MJ,* CXXXVI (Feb. 1935), 88.

3. A. Terrones Benítez, "Mining and the Government in Mexico," *E&MJ,* CXXXVII (May 1936), 242.

4. Feuerlein and Hannon, *Dólares en la América Latina,* pp. 100–106. An inter-

esting union tactic to force wage raises was to insist that low-grade ore be left in place and only high-grade ore be mined. Therefore, wages could be raised out of the increased profits. (*Min. Sur.*, II [Aug. 1935], 17.)

5. Asociación Mexicana de Minería (hereinafter cited as Aso. Mex. de Min.) *Circ.* 408 (Jan. 31, 1938); *Min. & Met.*, XVIII (May 1937), 250; *E&MJ*, CXXXV (Feb. 1934), 89. For difficulties besetting American engineers working abroad, see F. MacCoy, "Advice to Those Seeking Employment in Latin America," *E&MJ*, CXXIX (May 23, 1930), 502.

6. *Consulto* of the Departamento de Trabajo, *Revista mexicana del trabajo* (Nov.-Dec. 1937), 288. For protests against the employment of Mexicans in the United States, see *E&MJ*, XCVIII (Nov. 4, 1914), 890; CXXVIII (Sept. 14, 1929), 419–420; CXXXV (Apr. 1934), 187.

7. Quoted in J. L. Hyde, "Mexican Attitude Toward Foreign Investment," *Min. & Met.*, XIX (Aug. 1938), 356.

8. A. Terrones Benítez, "Mexico Spurs Inactive Mine Owners," *E&MJ*, CXXXVII (Dec. 1936), 608.

9. *Bol. de pet. y min.*, XV (Mar. 1944), 15; *Diario oficial*, CXLII, No. 30 (Feb. 7, 1944); Cámara Minera de México, "Ponencia ... sobre reforma a los artículos 18 de la Ley Minera y 131 de su Reglamento," in PCMN, *Memoria*, pp. 139–143. Also see *ibid.*, pp. 145–149.

10. SEN, *Memoria de septiembre de 1936 a agosto de 1937* (Mexico, 1937), pp. 47–88; Cám. Nac. de Min., *Circ.* 1682 (Sept. 3, 1936); *Circ.* 1718 (Oct. 3, 1936); *E&MJ*, CXXXVII (Oct. 1936), 530; *Min. Sur.*, IV (Oct. 1936), 30; (Nov. 1936), 21–22. On Nov. 7th, the Cámara issued a 25-page critique on the proposed law. (*Circ.* 1752.)

11. Cám. Min. de Méx., *Circ.* 61 (July 13, 1937); *Circ.* 73 (July 24, 1937); *E&MJ*, CXXXVIII (Feb. 1937), 109.

12. Cám. Min. de Méx., *Circ.* 101 (Aug. 26, 1937).

13. Cám. Min. de Méx., *Circ.* 221 (Apr. 22, 1938).

14. *Diario oficial*, CI, No. 8 (Mar. 9, 1937); CI, No. 22 (Mar. 25, 1937); *Bol. de pet. y min.*, VI (Mar. 1937), 15–16. A government agreement to accept without limit coupons from depreciated 40-year Internal Debt Bonds in payment for all taxes except that on gold or those payable in gold lessened the burden a little. See *Diario oficial*, C, No. 14 (Jan. 18, 1937); and Aso. Mex. de Min., *Circ.* 31 (Jan. 20, 1937).

15. Julio Ocádiz Arnaud, "Impuesto sobre la producción de plata," *Revista de Hacienda*, I (Oct. 1937), 3; Carleton Beals, "Sharing the Wealth Mexican Style," *Barron's* (Dec. 6, 1937), 8.

16. See chart: "Valor de la producción minero-metalúrgica. Impuestos pagados y Remanente a los productores—Años 1937 a 1945," printed by the Cám. Min. de Méx. in the pamphlet of Raúl Madero, *La minería atraviesa por una crisis muy seria* (Mexico, 1946), p. 16. This chart was later revised but the proportion of the value of production paid in taxes, which ranged from 21 per cent up to 33 per cent, still remained the same.

17. Hubbell, "The Mining Industry South of the Rio Grande," *E&MJ*, CXXXVII (Feb. 1936), 71.

18. *E&MJ*, CXXXVIII (Nov. 1937), 82; C. L. Jones, "Mexico Robs American Investors," *Magazine of Wall Street* (Apr. 9, 1938), 829, 867.

19. *E&MJ*, CXXXIX (May 1938), 80.

20. *Ibid.*; W. C. Gordon, *Expropriation of Foreign-Owned Property in Mexico*, p. 150. For a detailed description of the labor troubles at this time, see Chap. XIX, pp. 192–99.

21. *Min. & Met.*, XIX (Aug. 1938), 356; *E&MJ*, CXXXIX (Dec. 1938, 79);

CXLII (Aug. 1941), 156; E. Hodiger, "The Impact of War on Mexico's Economy," *Foreign Policy Reports* (June 15, 1943), 79.

22. The viewpoint of Secretary Morgenthau and the Treasury in the following section is taken from Everest, *Morgenthau*, pp. 84–93. For Ambassador Josephus Daniel's attitude and role see his autobiography, *Shirt-Sleeve Diplomat* (Chapel Hill, N.C., 1947), Part VI; and E. David Cronon, *Josephus Daniels in Mexico* (Madison, Wis., 1960), Chaps. vii–x.

23. Leavens, *Silver Money*, pp. 328–329; Leavens, "Silver [1939]," *E&MJ*, CXL (Oct. 1939), 37; Beals, "Sharing the Wealth Mexican Style," 9. For a trenchant critique of United States policy, see Frank L. Kluckhohn, *The Mexican Challenge* (New York, 1939), pp. 50–51, 247, *passim*.

24. Leavens, "Silver [1939]," 37; *E&MJ*, CXXXIX (May 1938), 80; Hubbell, "Mexico [1938]," *E&MJ*, CXL (Feb. 1939), 62.

25. "Mexico," *Journal of Commerce*, 31; US Dept. of Comm., Bur. of Foreign and Domestic Trade, *Foreign Trade of the United States in 1938* (Washington, D.C., 1939), Pt. II, pp. 24–25.

26. *Diario oficial*, CIX, No. 34 (Aug. 9, 1938). Wendell C. Gordon and Frank L. Kluckhohn insist that the tax was part of a scheme to raise the $1,000,000 a year needed to settle America citizens' agrarian claims. Because of the role played by Americans in the major export (minerals), it was literally a tax levied on one group of Americans to pay other Americans. (Gordon, *Expropriation*, p. 148; Kluckhohn, *Mexican Challenge*, pp. 66–67.) Ana Mekler directly disputes this view and defends the government's action. (*El impuesto de aforo . . . sus repercusiones en la exportación* [Mexico, 1942].)

27. Armando Servin A., "El significado del impuesto del 12% sobre las exportaciones," *Revista de Hacienda*, II (Nov. 1938), 5; Rodolfo M. Ortega, "El impuesto de 12% sobre las exportaciones," *ibid.*, II (Aug. 1938), 3.

28. Cám. Min. de Méx., *Circ.* 276 (July 8, 1938).

29. Cám. Min. de Méx., *Circ.* 292 (Aug. 4, 1938); *Circ.* 284 (July 16, 1938); *Diario oficial*, CIX, No. 14 (July 16, 1938).

30. *Diario oficial*, CIX, No. 35 (Aug. 10, 1938).

31. Cám. Min. de Méx., *Memorandum sobre la ley en estudio que establece un impuesto del 12% sobre las exportaciones, presentado por la Cámara Minera de México al Señor Secretario de Hacienda*, *Circ.* 286 (July 20, 1938); *Min. & Met.*, XIX (Oct. 1938), 449; A. Servin A., "El significado del impuesto del 12%," 6; Hubbell, "Mexico [1938]," 62. For a complete listing of the official tax rates for the major metals from Dec. 1938 to Jan. 1940, see Hubbell, "Mexico [1939]," *E&MJ*, CXLI (Feb. 1940), 66. A critique of the tax from the mineowners' point of view is in C. Pérez Duarte, "Mexican Mining Must Have Tax Relief," *E&MJ*, CXLVI (Dec. 1945), 98–99.

32. Cám. Min. de Méx., *Circ.* 655 (July 29, 1939).

33. *Min. Sur.*, VIII (May 1941), 25, 30.

34. H. M. Bratter, "Silver," *E&MJ*, CXLI (Feb. 1940), 43–44; Everest, *Morgenthau*, 93–94.

35. Hubbell, "Mexico [1939]," 66.

36. Bratter, "Silver," *E&MJ*, CXLII (Feb. 1941), 43–45.

37. *E&MJ*, CXL (Sept. 1939), 77.

38. *Diario oficial*, CXVII, No. 19 (Nov. 23, 1939); *E&MJ*, CXL (Nov. 1939), 82; Hubbell, "Mexico [1939]," 67; Hubbell, "Mexico [1940]," *E&MJ*, CXLII (Feb. 1941), 67; "Mexico," *Journal of Commerce*, 30; *Min. Sur.*, VII (Oct. 1939), 20; (Nov. 1939), 18–19, 24; IX (Jan. 1942), 31.

39. Hubbell, "Mexico [1940]," 67.

40. Figures originally compiled by A. Terrones Benítez cited in G. González

Reyna, "Consideraciones sobre los problemas de la minería en México," PCMN, *Memoria,* p. 503.

41. A. Terrones Benítez, "Mexico," *E&MJ,* CXLIII (Aug. 1942), 100. (Since San Francisco del Oro was British owned, listing all large mines as American is questionable.) Also see Anon., "Decline of Mexican Mining," *E&MJ,* CXLII (June 1941), 31. For a full statement of the position of the small miners, see Anon., "Convention of Small Miners in Mexico City," *Min. Sur.,* IV (Oct. 1936), 22–25; and "Declaration of Principles of Small Miners," *ibid.,* 27.

42. Hubbell, "Mining South of the Rio Grande," 72; Gnoseclose, "Revival in Mining," 430.

43. Editorial, *E&MJ,* CXLII (Oct. 1941), 31. In Mexico, the *E&MJ* was accused of bias and unfairness in its analysis of Mexico's troubles. See G. Ortega, "Comentarios erróneos de la situación de la minería en México," *Bol. de min. y pet.,* XIII (July 1941), 13–14.

44. G. García Lozano and Raúl Madero, "Impulso a la minería," *Bol. de min. y pet.,* XIII (Aug.–Dec. 1941), 12.

45. E. Villaseñor, "El problema de la escasez de moneda fraccionaria," *Investigación económica,* Tercer trimestre (1943), 214.

46. *E&MJ,* CXXXVII (Dec. 1936), 627–629.

47. William P. Rawles, *The Nationality of Commercial Control of Minerals* (New York, 1933), *passim.*

48. E. Atlanis Patiño, "La riqueza de México," 50.

49. US Tariff Comm., *Foreign Trade of Latin America,* Pt. II, Vol. 2, pp. 17–18.

50. US Dept. of Comm., Bur. of Foreign and Domestic Trade, Economic Ser. No. 20, R. L. Sammons and M. Abelson, *American Direct Investments in Foreign Countries,* 1940 (Washington, D.C., 1942), pp. 12–13, 24.

51. *Min. Sur.,* III (Apr. 1936), 19; (June 1936), 26.

52. *Min. Sur.,* IX (Jan. 1942), 16.

53. Banco de México, S.A., *Vigesimasexta asamblea general ordinaria de accionistas y undecima asamblea general extraordinaria de accionistas* (Mexico, 1948), pp. 54–55. For another survey of the "Mexican Investment Balance Sheet" in 1938, the reader is referred to Cleona Lewis, *The United States and Foreign Investment Problems,* Brookings Institution (Washington, D.C., 1948), p. 321.

54. *E&MJ,* CXXXVI (Mar. 1935), 152; CXXXVII (Mar. 1936), 157; (Oct. 1936), 530.

55. Depto. de Estudios Económicos, SEN, *Geografía económica del Estado de Hidalgo,* pp. 300–301.

56. *E&MJ,* CXXXVIII (Sept. 1937), 80; CXL (July 1939), 78.

57. Raúl Madero, *La minería atreviesa por una crisis muy seria,* pp. 9–10. Also see C. Pérez Duarte, *La situación de la industria minera* (Mexico, 1945), pp. 6–7.

CHAPTER 19

1. *Min. Sur.,* II (Jan. 1935), 27; Hubbell, "Mining South of the Rio Grande," 70.

2. Hyde, "Mexican Attitude," 356–357.

3. Unless otherwise noted, the rest of this section is taken from Faustino Roel, "Labor Laws and Mining in Mexico," *Min. & Met.,* XVIII (Feb. 1937), 114–116 and (Mar. 1937), 148–150, one of the best summaries of Mexican mine labor law.

Also see the comments and experiences of J. E. Harding, Manager of the Anexas de Nuevo Año Mine, "Salvaging a $300,000 Investment in a Lower California Gold Mine," *Min. & Met.*, XVIII (Aug. 1937), 379; and W. E. Wiegand, "Labor Relations [at San Francisco del Oro] Governed by Collective Contract," *E&MJ*, CXXXVII (Aug. 1936), 417–419. For the situation at a later date, see E. Just, "Mexico Is Strangling Its Mining Industry," *E&MJ*, CXLVII (June 1946), 77–78. Postwar conditions were similar: US Dept. of Comm., Bur. of Foreign Commerce, World Trade Information Service, *Economic Reports* (Pt. 1, No. 55–78), "Establishing a Business in Mexico," (July 1955), pp. 14–17.

4. *Min. Sur.*, IV (Nov. 1936), 37.

5. *E&MJ*, CXIV (Sept. 30, 1922), 604; Aso. Mex. de Min., *Circ.* 397 (Jan. 1938).

6. Wiegand, "Labor Relations," 419. In 1944 the Supreme Court ruled that a miner must show up drunk three times in order to give cause for discharge. (*Min. Sur.*, XII [Oct. 1944], 11.)

7. Depto. del Trabajo, *Revista del Trabajo,* III, 61; Pan-American Union, Div. of Labor and Social Information, *Employment of United States Citizens in Latin America* (Washington, D.C., 1945), p. 5; *Min. Sur.*, XI (Sept. 1944), 14; S. F. Eaton, "Five-Hundred Miles Through Mexico on Muleback," *E&MJ*, CXXIV (Aug. 6, 1927), 221.

8. US Dept. of Comm., "Establ. a Business in Mexico" (July 1955), p. 15 and citations to the *Diario oficial,* XCIX, No. 42 (Dec. 31, 1936), and CLXXII, No. 19 (Jan. 24, 1949); *Min. Sur.*, III (Apr. 1936), 23; (May 1936), 22.

9. Roel, "Labor Laws," 115.

10. Hubbell, "Economic Reform Program Hampers Mining Operations," *E&MJ*, CXXXVIII (Feb. 1937), 76.

11. *Diario oficial*, XCVI, No. 38 (June 25, 1936).

12. Roel, "Labor Laws," 148.

13. *E&MJ*, CXLIII (Jan. 1942), 84; *Min. Sur.*, VI (July 15, 1939), 15; *E&MJ*, CXLVI (Jan. 1945), 122. In 1945 the Supreme Court ruled that the plaintiff must prove that he was on company business when an injury occurred and that lung diseases must be attested to by a specialist. This ruling was made in a case in which a widow sued the Dos Carlos mining cooperative. (*Min. Sur.*, XII [May 1945], 14.)

14. Roel, "Labor Laws," 148. On April 1, 1934, a General Office of Industrial Hygiene was set up under the Dept. of Public Health. Starting work in 1935, this office worked on the problems of inspecting and prescribing standards for rescue equipment, safety devices, operation procedures, transit systems, and ventilation. (*Min. Sur.*, IV [Oct. 1936], 18.)

15. *Min. Sur.*, IV (Aug. 1937), 24.

16. C. J. Barber, "Silver Mining in Mexico: Real del Monte," *Mine and Quarry Engineering* (Aug. 1939), 266.

17. *E&MJ*, CXLII (July 1941), 84; *Min. Sur.*, III (Sept. 1936), 24–25; Ingersoll, *In and Under Mexico*, pp. 87–88, 229–230.

18. *E&MJ*, CXL (Nov. 1939), 82.

19. *E&MJ*, CXXXVII (Aug. 1936), 433.

20. Depto. del Trabajo circulars reprinted in Cám. Min. de Méx., *Circ.* 325 (Sept. 21, 1938); Aso. Mex. de Min., *Circ.*, 754 (Jan. 2, 1939); *Min. Sur.*, II (Mar. 1935), 23; VI (June 1939), 18; (July 1939), 16; XI (Oct. 1943), 19; *Min. World,* IX (June 1947), 67. Also see US Dept. of Comm., "Establ. a Business in Mexico" (July 1955), p. 14 and Notes 55 and 56 for more information.

21. Sec. 3, Art. III, Ley Federal del Trabajo; *E&MJ*, CXL (June 1939), 80–81; *Min. Sur.*, VI (June 15, 1939), 14.

22. For some company problems in running these schools, see *Min. Sur.*, III (Apr.

1936), 22; (May 1936), 25; IV (May 1937), 32; (June 1937), 34; IX (May 1942), 16.

23. For the companies' traditional attitude, see C. F. Willis, "Notes on the Housing Problem," *E&MJ*, CVII (May 17, 1919), 864–865; Ingersoll, *In and Under Mexico, passim.*

24. Anon., "William Loeb of A.S.&R. Sees Improved Industrial Relations," *E&MJ*, CXXVI (Oct. 13, 1928), 566.

25. *Min. Sur.,* IV (May 1937), 32; editorial, "Standard Contracts for Large Operators," *ibid.* (Aug. 1937), 21; (Aug. 1937), 30; (Sept. 1937), 21; V (Oct. 1937), 35, 40; P. C. Escalante, "A Law Contract in the Mining Industry," *ibid.* (Nov. 1937), 22, 34; (Dec. 1937), 27; (Jan. 1938), 30, 31; editorial, "The American Smelting and Refining Conflict," *ibid.* (Mar. 1938), 33–34; (Apr. 1938), 28.

26. Roel, "Labor Laws," 114.

27. Aso. Mex. de Min., *Circ.* 23 (Jan. 14, 1937); *E&MJ*, CXXXVI (July 1935), 358; *Min. & Met.,* XVII (Mar. 1936), 157. Also see *E&MJ* and *Min. Sur., passim.* for these years.

28. *Diario oficial,* CXI, No. 49 (Dec. 31, 1938).

29. Abuse of the rules was not uncommon; see Hubbell, "Mining South of the Rio Grande," 70–71.

30. Under President Avila Camacho, the looseness of the labor law's provisions was recognized, and a bill to change the law in regard to strikes was introduced. (*Min. Sur.,* VIII [Mar. 1941], 16.)

31. Hubbell, "Mining South of the Rio Grande," 71; Hubbell, "Mexico [1938]," 61; Hubbell, "Mexico [1939]," 66. In 1937, the Supreme Court fixed the rate for labor on the weekly rest day at triple time. (*Min. Sur.,* IV [June 1937], 34.)

32. Hubbell, "Mexico [1938]," 61.

33. Hubbell, "Mexico [1941]," *E&MJ*, CXLIII (Feb. 1942), 68–69.

34. *Min. Sur.,* X (Jan. 1943), 16; *E&MJ*, CXLIV (Mar. 1943), 108; (May 1943), 116; (Nov. 1943), 160.

35. *Min. Sur.,* VIII (June 1941), 17.

36. *E&MJ*, CXXXVIII (Apr. 1937), 209; CXL (Nov. 1939), 82; CXLI (Oct. 1940), 80; CXLIV (Jan. 1943), 100; (May 1943), 116; (June 1943), 120; (Dec. 1943), 146–147; *Min. Sur.,* X (May 1943), 26; (Aug. 1943), 31; XI (Nov. 1943), 23.

37. Instituto de investigaciones económicas, Universidad Autónomo de México, *Las cooperativas de consumo organizadas sindicalmente en México* (Mexico, 1944), pp. 24–26, 28, 30–42, 44–45, 51.

38. *Min. Sur.,* III (Sept. 1936), 17; VIII (Apr. 1941), 20; Genaro González Reyna, "Consideraciones sobre los problemas de la minería en México," PCMN, *Memoria,* pp. 505–508.

CHAPTER 20

1. *E&MJ*, CXXVI (Nov. 10, 1928), 764; CXXVIII (July 27, 1929), 152.

2. Osvaldo Gurría Urgell, SEN, *Tendencias de la Secretaría en relación con el fomento y nacionalización de la minería; Trabajo presentado a la X° Convención Nacional de Ingenieros* (Mexico, 1934). Also see G. García Lozano, "El fomento de la minería en México," *Anales del Primer Congreso Panamericano de Ingenería de Minas y Geología* (Santiago de Chile, 1942), V, pp. 2161–69.

3. Gurría Urgell, *Tendencias,* p. 7.

4. *Ibid.,* p. 16. Also see P. E. Ellsworth, *Chile, An Economy in Transition* (New York, 1945), pp. 14, 17, 25.

5. A. Glyka, "Mining Cooperative Societies; Their Advantages and Disadvantages," *Min. Sur.,* II (Jan. 1935), 13–14.

6. *E&MJ,* CXXXIII (Dec. 1932), 646; CXXXIV (June 1933), 264; (July 1933), 309; CXXXV (June 1934), 277; CXXXVI (Apr. 1935), 196; *Min. Sur.,* II (Jan. 1935), 21; (June 1935), 26.

7. A. H. Hubbell, "Economic Reform Program Hampers Mining Operations," *E&MJ,* CXXXVIII (Feb. 1937), 77.

8. *E&MJ,* CXXXIX (Jan. 1938), 86.

9. A. H. Hubbell, "Mexico [1938]," *E&MJ,* CXL (Feb. 1939), 61, 66. Also see Instituto de Investigaciones Económicos de la Universidad Nacional, *La legislación sobre cooperativas en México* (Mexico, 1943), pp. 115–117; Wendell Gordon, *The Expropriation of Foreign-Owned Property in Mexico,* p. 149; and Frank Kluckhohn, *The Mexican Challenge,* p. 225.

10. "Mexico and Her Relations to American Defense," *Journal of Commerce* (New York), CLXXXV, No. 14,319, Sec. 2 (Aug. 27, 1940), p. 17.

11. SEN, *Memoria, 1934,* pp. 199–212; *Bol. min.,* XXXV (May–June 1933), 117–122.

12. SEN, *Memoria, 1934, loc. cit.*

13. *Mexican Year Book, 1920–1921,* p. 222.

14. *Bol. de pet. y min.,* I (Aug. 1933), 292–293. Although this decree exempted cooperatives from a number of taxes, several others still had to be paid.

15. Inst. de Invest. Eco., *Legislación sobre cooperativas,* pp. 67–73.

16. Socs. Coops. de Prod. Min. Met. San Rafael, M. M. Santa Fé de Gto., No. 1, Minerales y Metales, Mineros de Esmeralda, Mineros de Coah., Mineros de Sierra Mojada, Minera El Bote, Minerales San Juan de Matanzas, Min. Met. La Noria, "Ponencia ... relativa a subsidios que deben regir en la actividad minera cooperativa," PCMN, *Memoria,* pp. 195, 199–201; *ibid.,* pp. 351–354.

17. P. C. Escalante, "Mexican Mining Cooperatives," *Min. Sur.,* V (Aug. 1938), 14; *Min. Sur.,* V (Sept. 1938), 10, 11; *E&MJ,* CXXXIX (Nov. 1938), 77; (Dec. 1938), 80.

18. Delegación del Gobierno del Estado de Hidalgo, "Ponencia," PCMN, *Memoria,* pp. 181-184; Escalante, "Mex. Min. Coops.," 14; *Min. Sur.,* VI (May 1939), 15–16.

19. Inst. de Invest. Eco., *Legislación sobre cooperativas,* p. 71.

20. *E&MJ,* CXLIX (Apr. 1948), 141–142.

21. In regard to ore treatment plants and cooperatives, see *E&MJ,* CXXXV (Aug. 1934), 378; (Dec. 1934), 570; CXXXVI (Jan. 1935), 45; CXXXVIII (Sept. 1937), 80; CXL (May 1939), 80; (July 1939), 78. For other aid see SEN, *Memoria, Sept. 1936–Aug. 1937,* p. 33; *E&MJ,* CXXXIX (Dec. 1938), 80; CXL (July 1939), 78; CXLII (Jan. 1941), 85; CXLIV (Jan. 1943), 100.

22. *E&MJ,* CXXXIX (Dec. 1938), 80; CXL (July 1939), 78; CXLII (Jan. 1941), 85; CXLIII (Mar. 1942), 90; CXLIV (Jan. 1943), 100; SEN, *Memoria, Sept. 1936–Aug. 1937,* p. 33.

23. *E&MJ,* CXLI (Feb. 1940), 122.

24. *E&MJ,* CXLI (Dec. 1940), 86; CXL (May 1939), 79–80. For a critical analysis of the situation, see P. C. Escalante, "Mexican Mining Cooperatives," 14.

25. *E&MJ,* CXL (Dec. 1939), 82.

26. *Min. Sur.,* VIII (Oct. 1940), 26.

27. *Ibid.* (Sept. 1941), 18; X (Nov. 1942), 23, 24, 26; *E&MJ,* CXLIII (Dec. 1942), 109.

28. *Min. Sur.,* XI (May 1944), 20, 22.

29. For Promontorio's history, see *E&MJ,* CXXXVII (Jan. 1936), 39; CXXXIX

(Jan. 1938), 86; CXLIII (July 1942), 99; CXLIV (Apr. 1943), 120; *Min. Sur.,* V (Dec. 1937), 29; IX (Oct. 1941), 21; (June 1942), 18. For Guanajuato's history, see *E&MJ,* CXXXVII (May 1936), 263; (June 1936), 313; CXXXVIII (Nov. 1937), 82; CXXXIX (Dec. 1938), 79; CXL (Jan. 1939), 84; (Feb. 1939), 112.

30. *E&MJ,* CXXXVI (Feb. 1935), 88; (June 1935), 306; (Aug. 1935), 415; CXXXVII (Mar. 1936), 157; (June 1936), 313; CXXXVIII (Aug. 1937), 435; (Sept. 1937), 80; *Min. & Met.,* XIX (Aug. 1938), 363.

31. SEN, Depto. de Estudios Económicos, *Geografía económica del Estado de Hidalgo,* p. 106. For the passing of the San Rafael company, see *E&MJ,* CXXXIX (Aug. 1938), 97; *Min. Sur.,* V (July 1938); 28; IX (Mar. 1942), 14, 20; (Apr. 1942), 16; *E&MJ,* CXLVI (Nov. 1945), 150.

32. *E&MJ,* CXXXVIII (July 1937), 369; *Min. Sur.,* IV (July 1937), 28, 33–34.

33. *E&MJ,* CXXXVIII (Nov. 1937), 82; (Dec. 1937), 82; SEN, *Geografía de Hidalgo,* p. 106; *Min. Sur.,* IV (Sept. 1937), 23; V (Dec. 1937), 31.

34. *E&MJ,* CXLI (Mar. 1940), 79; CXLII (Dec. 1941), 85; CXLIII (Jan. 1942), 85; *Min. Sur.,* V (Jan. 1938), 28; (Mar. 1938), 29; (June 1938), 24; VII (Nov. 1939), 20; VII (Feb. 1940), 18–19. The Labor Department had to warn the cooperatives as a group that they had to obey the safety regulations strictly and that the Department would exercise a closer watch over their mines and old equipment following several serious accidents. (*E&MJ,* CXLII [Jan. 1942], p. 85.)

35. *Min. Sur.,* VII (Nov. 1939), 13; (Apr. 1940), 16; VIII (Dec. 1940), 21; IX (July 1942), 15; X (June 1943), 18.

36. *E&MJ,* CXXXIX (Jan. 1938), 86; (May 1938), 80; (Aug. 1938), 97; CXLI (Mar. 1940), 79; CXLII (Jan. 1941), 86; CXLIII (June 1942), 107; (Sept. 1942), 102; CXLIV (Oct. 1943), 132; (Nov. 1943), 161; *Min. Sur.,* XI (Dec. 1943), 24; (Jan. 1944), 17.

37. *Min. Sur.,* XII (June 1945), 18; (Aug. 1945), 16; XIII (Nov. 1945), 22; *Mining World,* VIII (Aug. 1946), 75.

38. D. Olguín Díaz, "Ponencia presentada por la Sociedad Cooperativa Limitada Minera de Producción 'Dos Carlos,' S.C.L.," PCMN, *Memoria,* pp. 359–361.

39. *E&MJ,* CXLVI (Sept. 1945), 148; CL (Sept. 1949), 142; (Nov. 1949), 148; CLI (July, 1950), 120; CLIV (Oct. 1953), 192; *Mining World,* XIII (May 1951), 55; XV (Dec. 1953), 76.

40. For details of the settlement, see *Min. Sur.,* V (June 1938); 24; VII (Mar. 1940), 17.

41. Felipe Bracho Valle and Manuel Franco López, "Estudio técnico de las propiedades mineras y planta de 'El Cedro,' de la Cooperativa Minera 'Las Dos Estrellas,' en El Oro y Tlalpujahua, Michoacan," *Bol. de min. y pet.,* XVI (June 1945), 3–9; (July 1945), 11–43; (Sept. 1945), 3–57, is a complete survey, comparing the results of private and cooperative management of the mine and analyzing the reasons for the cooperative's failure. Another study was made in 1946–47 surveying the position of the cooperative and its future prospects: S. J. Vicente Juárez, "El problema de la cooperativa minera," PCMN, *Memoria,* pp. 371–372. Also see, *E&MJ,* CXXXVIII (Apr. 1937), 209; (May 1937), 262; (June 1937), 315; (July 1937), 369; CXXXIX (Mar. 1938), 81; (May 1938), 80; CXLI (Mar. 1940), 79; CXLIII (Apr. 1942), 102; CXLVI (Sept. 1945), 148; (Dec. 1945), 152; *Min. Sur.,* V (Mar. 1938), 32; IX (Mar. 1942), 18; XI (May 1944), 17–19; XIII (Nov. 1945), 15.

42. S. J. Vicente Juárez, *op. cit.; E&MJ,* CXLVII (June 1946), 154.

43. *E&MJ,* CXLVIII (July 1947), 148. Reworking old dumps in the area helped. See M. Villafaña, "El tratamiento de los jales de Tiro México en El Oro," Primer Convención Inter-Americana de Recursos Minerales, *Memorias* (hereinafter cited as PCIARM, *Memorias*), Mexico, 1952, pp. 108–111.

44. G. González Reyna, "Consideraciones sobre los problemas de la minería en

México," PCMN, *Memoria,* pp. 499, 507–508; *Min. Sur.,* X (Sept. 1943), 26.

45. *E&MJ,* CXL (Apr. 1939), 79; (Oct. 1939), 81; CXLVIII (Mar. 1941), 92–93; CXLIII (June 1942), CVII (Aug. 1942), 153; A. Terrones Benítez, "Mexico," *E&MJ,* CXLIII (Aug. 1942), 100; CXLVI (June 1945), 152; *Min. Sur.,* VIII (Sept. 1940), 13; (Feb. 1941), 15; IX (Apr. 1942), 16; (June 1942), 24; XII (May 1945), 13; W. H. Triplett, communication to author, June 13, 1955.

46. *E&MJ,* CXL (June 1939), 80; (Oct. 1939), 81.

47. Anon., "Mexico," *E&MJ,* CXXXIX (Feb. 1938), 61; Hubbell, "Mexico," *E&MJ,* CXL (Feb. 1939), 61; "Mexico," *Journal of Commerce,* 19.

48. *Min. Sur.,* IX (Mar. 1942), 20; *E&MJ,* CXLIII (Jan. 1942), 85.

49. *E&MJ,* CXLIII (May 1942), 91.

50. *E&MJ,* CXL (Dec. 1940), 81; Hubbell, "Mexico," *E&MJ,* CXLII (Feb. 1941), 67; *Min. Sur.,* VII (July 1940), 11; IX (Apr. 1942), 18. For an excellent succinct statement of the cooperatives' inherited weaknesses as outlined by representatives of the cooperatives, see: "El punto de vista cooperativa," in "El problema nacional de la minería [1946]," *Conferencias de mesa redonda presididas durante su campaña electoral por el lic. Miguel Alemán,* pp. 224–225.

51. W. H. Triplett, communication to author, June 13, 1955.

52. For examples see *Min. Sur.,* VII (Nov. 1939), 15, 16; Promontorio mines, *ibid.,* V (Dec. 1937), 29; IX (Oct. 1941), 21; (June 1942), 18; Los Azules, *ibid.,* VIII (Feb. 15, 1941), 24; IX (Oct. 1941), 18; Maguarichic, *ibid.,* VIII (Dec. 1940), 24; XI (Sept. 1944), 14; La Naica, *ibid.,* VII (Apr. 1940), 20; (Aug. 1940), 24; IX (Aug. 1942), 15.

53. *Technological Audit of Selected Mexican Industries* (Chicago, 1946), p. 41.

54. *Ibid.,* p. 21. Mexico's producers' cooperatives troubles were not unique. See Pan American Union, Division of Labor and Social Welfare, *Labor Trends and Social Welfare in Latin America, 1939–1940* (Washington, D.C., June 1941), p. 58.

55. Socs. Coops. de Prod. Min. Met. San Rafael et al., "Ponencia," pp. 352–353; *Min. Sur.,* VI (June 1939), 14–15.

56. From a manuscript "Industria minera" by M. T. de la Peña, lent to the author by Srta. Cristina Zárate.

57. "Mexico," *Journal of Commerce,* 19; P. C. Escalante, "Cooperative Plan Spreads in Mining," *Min. Sur.,* VII (Apr. 1940), 12.

58. *E&MJ,* CXLIII (Aug. 1942), 100.

CHAPTER 21

1. "Mexico," *Journal of Commerce,* 17.

2. Madero, *La minería atraviesa por una crisis muy seria,* pp. 20–21.

3. G. González Reyna, "Consideraciones sobre los problemas de la minería en México," PCMN, *Memoria,* pp. 497–499.

4. Anon., "Convention of Small Miners," *Min. Sur.,* IV (Oct. 1936), 22–25; "Declaration of Principles of the Convention of Small Miners," *ibid.,* 27; *ibid.,* VII (Mar. 1940), 16.

5. *Bol. de conc. min.,* V (Oct. 1932), 301.

6. *Ibid.* (Nov. 1932), 381–382.

7. *Ibid.* (Nov. 1932), 382; (Dec. 1932), 497; VI (Jan. 1933), 5.

8. *Ibid.* (Jan. 1933), 3.

9. Cf. *ibid.,* VI (Apr. 1933), 210–211; (May 1933), 357; (June 1933), 455; *Bol. de pet. y min.,* I (July 1933), 54, 135–136; (Aug. 1933), 295–296; (Sept.

1933), 441; (Oct. 1933), 561–562; (Nov. 1933), 653; (Dec. 1933), 793; II (Jan. 1934), 50–52; (Feb. 1934), 50–52.

10. *Bol. de pet. y min.,* I (Aug. 1933), 294; (Sept. 1933), 441.

11. Gurría Urgell, *Tendencias de la SEN,* p. 15.

12. Sec. II, Art. 126.

13. *Diario oficial,* LXXXIX, No. 51 (Apr. 29, 1935); *Bol. de min. y pet.,* IV (Apr. 1935), 33–34; A. Terrones Benítez, "Mining and the Government in Mexico," *E&MJ,* CXXXVII (May 1936), 243.

14. *Bol. de pet. y min.,* IV (June 1935), 17.

15. *Diario oficial,* XCVIII, No. 16 (Sept. 19, 1936); *E&MJ,* CXXXVIII (Oct. 1937), 82.

16. A. Terrones Benítez, "Mining and the Government in Mexico," 244.

17. *Bol. de pet. y min.,* IV (June 1935), 18; (Oct. 1935), 29; V (Jan. 1936), 143; (July 1936), 175; VII (Oct. 1937), 11; IX (July 1938), 10; XIV (Oct. 1943), 6–7; *Min. Sur.,* XI (Nov. 1943), 21.

18. *Bol. de pet. y min.,* IVB (Nov. 1935), 16; V (Feb. 1936), 21; (July 1936), 175; (Aug. 1936), 15; (Dec. 1936), 9; VII (Oct. 1937), 11; VIII (Apr. 1938), 21; IX (July 1938), 9–10; (Aug. 1938), 10; (Sept. 1938), 9; (Oct. 1938), 13; X (Feb. 1939), 21.

19. *Seis años de gobierno al servicio de México, 1934–1940* (Mexico, 1940), pp. 208–209; Anon., "Trabajos [del] Depto. de Minas ... septiembre de 1940 a julio de 1941," *Bol. de min. y pet.,* XIII (Aug.–Dec. 1941), 3–4.

20. *Diario oficial,* CII, No. 20 (June 3, 1937); CXII, No. 3 (Jan. 4, 1939).

21. *Ibid.,* CXIV, No. 9 (May 12, 1939).

22. Toca No. 8681/39, reprinted in Aso. Mex. de Min., *Circ.* 1402 (Nov. 12, 1940).

23. *Diario oficial,* CXXX, No. 13 (Jan. 16, 1942); *Bol. de min. y pet.,* XIII (Aug.–Dec. 1941), 27–35; (Apr.–June 1942), 8; XIV (June 1943), 14; (Sept. 1943), 6; (Dec. 1943), 5.

24. *Min. Sur.,* XI (Mar. 1944), 17.

25. *Diario oficial,* CXIX, No. 28 (Apr. 2, 1940).

26. *Diario oficial,* CXVII, No. 34 (Dec. 11, 1939); *E&MJ,* CXLII (Oct. 1941), 92.

27. *Bol. de min. y pet.,* XVI (Aug. 1945), 3; (Sept. 1945), 64–65; XVII (Dec. 1946), 12.

28. A. Glyka, "Exhaustible Reserves and Resources," *Min. Sur.,* II (Mar. 1935), 10–11. Also see Erich W. Zimmermann, *World Resources and Industries* (New York, 1951), Chap. xlix for an exhaustive analysis of this topic. John Hickey in his article, "Barriers to Inter-American Trade: The Economics of Self-Pity," *Inter-American Economic Affairs,* X (Summer 1956), 25–46, has some scathing comments on Latin American conservation and nationalist policies.

29. *E&MJ,* CXXVII (Jan. 5, 1929), 31; CXXXV (Aug. 1934), 378; (Dec. 1934), 570; CXXXVI (Jan. 1935), 45; (Mar. 1935), 152; *Min. Sur.,* III (Jan. 1936), 25.

30. *E&MJ,* CXXXVII (Oct. 1936), 530; CXL (Mar. 1939), 76; *Min. Sur.,* II (Sept. 1935), 25; *Diario oficial,* CI, No. 30 (Apr. 3, 1937).

31. *E&MJ,* CXXXVIII (Feb. 1937), 109.

32. *E&MJ,* CXXVI (Sept. 1935), 471; CXXXVIII (July 1937), 369; *Memoria de la SEN de septiembre de 1936 a agosto de 1937,* p. 23.

33. *Min. Sur.,* II (Sept. 1935), 24–25; *E&MJ,* CXXXVI (Oct. 1935), 525; *Diario oficial,* CXII, No. 21 (Jan. 25, 1939); for an excellent short history of the Comisión and the background to its founding, see G. García Lozano, "El fomento de la minería en México," *Anales del Primer Congreso de Ingenería de Minas y Geologia* (Santiago de Chile, 1942), V, 2161–69.

34. Germán García Lozano and Raúl Madero, "Impulso a la minería; labora-

torios y pequeñas plantas de beneficio," *Bol. de min. y pet.,* XIII (Aug.–Dec. 1941), 11–16; *E&MJ,* CXL (July 1939), 78.

35. Raúl Madero and J. J. Falomir (Manager and Sub-Manager, respectively), *Informe que presenta a C. Sec. de la Economía Nacional la gerencia de la Comisión de Fomento Minero sobre la labor desarrollada por esta institución desde que fundaba* (hereinafter cited as *Informe Com. de Fom. Min.*). Typewritten copy dated August 29, 1944, unpaged. The Comisión graciously lent this report to the author for examination.

36. *Seis años de gobierno al servicio de México,* p. 211. For the mineral reserves granted directly to the Comisión, see *Bol. de min. y pet.,* XII (Jan.–Apr. 1942), 28, 30–31; Cám. Min. de Méx., *Circ.* 871 (July 2, 1940). For a complete description of the holdings of the Comisión, see *Bol. de min. y pet.,* XV (Dec. 1944), 4–7; XVI (Jan. 1945), 3–6; (Mar. 1945), 3–6; (Apr. 1945), 15–17; and Ing. Norberto de la Rosa y Salgado, "Ponencia," PCMN, *Memoria,* pp. 484–486 (short list reproduced in Appendix 4) and pp. 487–494 (for a map and detailed description).

37. *Seis años de gobierno,* p. 212; *E&MJ,* CXLI (June 1940), 81, 212.

38. *Informe Com. de Fom. Min.*

39. *Bol. de min. y pet.,* XV (July 1944), 3–5; N. de la Rosa y Salgado, "Ponencia," pp. 491–492.

40. D. Contreras, "Informe sobre la Unidad Tecamachalco," *Bol. de min. y pet.,* XVI (Apr. 1945), 15–17 (reprinted in PCMN, *Memoria,* pp. 515–521); *Informe Com. de Fom. Min.;* García Lozano and R. Madero, "Impulso a la minería," 13–15; Cám. Min. de Méx., *Circ.* 883 (July 25, 1940). For a good technical survey, see T. L. Johnson, "Mexico's Ore Testing Laboratory," *E&MJ,* CXLIX (Apr. 1948), 95; Anon., "Laboratorio experimental de minerales en México," *Revista minera y petrolera,* XV (June 15, 1948), 43.

41. Costo Iturbe, "Datos generales y de operaciones de las plantas metalúrgicas de la Comisión de Fomento Minero; Unidad Guanajuato," *Bol. de min. y pet.,* XVI (Jan. 1945), 3–5; *Informe Com. de Fom. Min.; E&MJ,* CXL (May 1939), 80; (July 1939), 78; *Min. Sur.,* VIII (May 1940), 17.

42. *Informe Com. de Fom. Min.;* C. Rosete Mateos, "Comisión de Fomento Minero: Unidad Tlalpujahua," *Bol. de min. y pet.,* XVI (Mar. 1945), 11–16.

43. *Informe Com. de Fom. Min.;* A. H. Múñoz, "Las unidades de la Comisión de Fomento Minero; Unidad Altar," *Bol. de min. y pet.,* XV (Dec. 1944), 4–7; *E&MJ,* CXL (Nov. 1939), 81; CXLII (May 1941), 85.

44. *Informe Com. de Fom. Min.; E&MJ,* CXLIII (Sept. 1942), 102; CXLIV (Feb. 1943), 145.

45. *Informe Com. de Fom. Min.* For a statement of the Comisión's proposed scope of activities, see M. Villafaña Barajos, "Colaboración de la Comisión de Fomento Minero para el PCMN," *Memoria,* pp. 339–340. This discussion gives no actual figures or estimates of success.

CHAPTER 22

1. A. J. Powers, "Mexico's Trade Trends," *For. Comm. Wkly.* (Nov. 9, 1940), 236; *Min. Sur.,* VII (July 1940), 17; VIII (Oct. 1940), 27, 32.

2. US Tariff Comm., *Foreign Trade of Latin America,* Pt. II, Vol. 2, p. 62; *E&MJ,* CXL (Jan. 1939), 85; CXLI (July 1940), 82.

3. C. H. Crane, "The Future of Lead and Zinc Markets," *Min. & Met.* (Oct. 1940), 466; *Min. Sur.,* VII (Nov. 1939), 11; US BuMines, *Lead, 1950,* p. VI–84.

4. *Min. Sur.*, VII (Aug. 1940), 18, 19; VIII (Oct. 1940) 19–20, 32; (Nov. 1940), 22; (Dec. 1940), 25; (Mar. 1941), 17–18; (Apr. 1941), 18–19.

5. *Min. Sur.*, VIII (Feb. 1941), 19, 22; (Mar. 1941), 18; (Apr. 1941), 24; (May 1941), 20; (July 1941), 17; *E&MJ*, CXLII (Mar. 1941), 91–92; A. H. Hubbell, "Mexico," *E&MJ*, CXLIII (Feb. 1942), 68–69.

6. Bratter, "Silver," *E&MJ*, CXLII (Feb. 1941), 55.

7. *Min. Sur.*, VII (Dec. 1939), 14–15.

8. *Ibid.*, VIII (Sept. 1941), 28.

9. Hubbell, "Mexico," *E&MJ*, CXLIII (Feb. 1942), 68; P. C. Escalante, "The Eloquence of Figures," *Min. Sur.*, VIII (May 1941), 16; *ibid.* (Sept. 1941), 24.

10. *Min. Sur.*, VIII (Feb. 1941), 17.

11. *Bol. de min. y pet.*, XIII (Aug.–Dec. 1941), 22–24; *Commercial and Financial Chronicle* (July 19, 1941), 328 (hereinafter cited as *Comm. & Fin. Chr.*); Pan American Union *Bulletin* (Nov. 1941), 671–672.

12. *E&MJ*, CXLIII (Mar. 1942), 89.

13. *E&MJ*, CXLII (Dec. 1941), 84; *The Economist* (Nov. 29, 1941), 658; Howard F. Cline, *The United States and Mexico* (Cambridge, Mass., 1953), pp. 248–249.

14. For an expression of American dissatisfaction with these terms, see editorial, *E&MJ*, CXLII (Dec. 1941), 32.

15. *Bol. de min. y pet.*, XIII (Jan–Mar. 1942), 3; *E&MJ*, CXLII (Dec. 1941), 84; Bratter, "Silver," *E&MJ*, CXLII (Feb. 1941), 55; Leavens, "Silver," *E&MJ*, CXLIII (Feb. 1942), 56; Everest, *Morgenthau*, pp. 94–96.

16. A. M. Bateman, "Wartime Dependence on Foreign Minerals," *Economic Geology*, XLI (June–July 1946), 308.

17. Bateman, "Wartime Dependence," 309; *E&MJ*, CXLIII (June 1942), 41; C. W. Vaupell, "Mexico," *ibid.*, CXLIV (Feb. 1943), 88. For comments on the reciprocal trade treaty and workings of the wartime arrangements, see the *New York Times* (Dec. 24, 1942), 25; (Sept. 21, 1943), 9; (July 13, 1944), 3.

18. US BuMines, *Lead, 1950*, pp. S–21, IV–34, IV–35; F. Cutler, "Yield on U.S. Direct Investments Abroad," *For. Comm. Wkly.*, XXIX (Oct. 18, 1947), 7; *E&MJ*, CXLIV (Jan. 1943), 77; S. M. Anderson, "Latin American Minerals' Role During the War Years," *For. Comm. Wkly.*, XXIII (June 8, 1946), 5.

19. Vaupell, "Mexico," 88.

20. *E&MJ*, CXLIII (June 1942), 108; (July 1942), 98; D. C. Mackallor, "Mexican Operations [of Eagle-Picher]," *E&MJ*, CXLIV (Nov. 1943), 106; *E&MJ*, CXLIV (July 1943), 53; R. H. Ramsey, "Zinc Refining Steps Ahead," *E&MJ*, CXLIV (Aug. 1943), 62–67; Marcosson, *Metal Magic*, p. 154.

21. *E&MJ*, CXLVI (Jan. 1945), 122; *Min. Sur.*, XI (May 1944), 20.

22. *Min. Sur.*, VII (Dec. 1939), 11; XII (Mar. 1944), 13; *E&MJ*, CXLIII (May 1942), 91.

23. *E&MJ*, CXLIII (Sept. 1942), 101; CXLIV (July 1943), 117; (Sept. 1943), 114; CXLVI (Apr. 1945), 161–162; *Min. Sur.*, VIII (Aug. 1941), 29; IX (May 1942), 15; L. B. Clark, "Mexico in 1944," *For. Comm. Wkly.*, XX (July 28, 1945), 58; H. F. Cline, *The U.S. and Mexico*, p. 273.

24. *Min. Sur.*, XII (May 1944), 13.

25. *Ibid.*, IX (May 1942), 26; (June 1942), 21; (Aug. 1942), 23, 26; (Sept. 1942), 16, 26.

26. *Ibid.*, X (Dec. 1942), 21; (Jan. 1943), 14; *E&MJ*, CXLIV (Feb. 1943), 144; (Mar. 1943), 108; (May 1943), 116.

27. *Min. Sur.*, X (July 1943), 27.

28. *Ibid.*, VIII (June 1941), 25, 28, 30.

29. Anon., "Wage Increases in Mexico, Sept. 1943," *Monthly Labor Review* (Dec. 1943), 1221–23; L. B. Clark, "Mexico in 1943," *Mexican-American Review*, XII

(Sept. 1944), 70; *For. Comm. Wkly.*, XIII (Nov. 20, 1943), 19; XVI (July 15, 1944), 32; *Min. Sur.*, XI (Dec. 1943), 21, 23; *E&MJ*, CXLIV (Nov. 1943), 160; CXLVI (Oct. 1945), 144; CXLVII (Jan. 1946), 132.

30. *E&MJ*, CXLIV (Oct. 1943), 131.

31. *Business Week* (July 15, 1944), 32–34; *Min. Sur.*, XI (Apr. 1944), 21–22; (May 1944), 15–16, 19–20, 22; (June 1944), 22; (July 1944), 13, 14, 16, 22; (Aug. 1944), 16; XII (July 1945), 22; *For. Comm. Wkly.*, XVI (July 15, 1944), 10; (Aug. 12, 1944), 14; XVIII (Dec. 30, 1944), 23.

32. *Min. Sur.*, VIII (Feb. 1941), 11; XI (Oct. 1943), 32; (Mar. 1944), 21; *E&MJ*, CXLVI (Apr. 1945), 161.

33. *Bol. de min. y pet.*, XV (Mar. 1944), 15; *Diario oficial*, CXLII, No. 30 (Feb. 7, 1944); Cám. Min. de Méx., "Ponencia ... sobre reforma a los artículos 18 de la Ley Minera y 131 de su Reglamento," PCMN, *Memoria*, pp. 139–143 (and also see pp. 145–149).

34. *Bol. de min. y pet.*, XV (Aug. 1944), 3; XVI (Feb. 1945), 4; (Mar. 1945), 17; XVII (Feb. 1946), 11; (Apr. 1946), 8; A. Terrones Benítez, "Mexico Exempts Old Titles as to Assessment Work," *E&MJ*, CXLVIII (May 1947), 79–80.

35. See Notes 33 and 36; *Bol. de min. y pet.*, XVII (Feb. 1946), 11; *Min. Sur.*, XI (Feb. 1944), 17–19; (Mar. 1944), 14; (Aug. 1944), 22; (Sept. 1944), 16; *E&MJ*, CXLVI (Feb. 1945), 181; CXLVII (Feb. 1946), 159.

36. *Bol. de min. y pet.*, XV (Mar. 1944), 15; (Sept. 1944), 3; *Diario oficial*, CXLII, No. 30 (Feb. 7, 1944); *Min. Sur.*, XI (Aug. 1944), 22.

37. Hubbell, "Mexico [1941]," *E&MJ*, CXLIII (Feb. 1942), 69.

38. *Bol. de min. y pet.*, XIII (July 1942), 10.

39. *Min. Sur.*, X (June 1943), 23.

40. *Ibid.*, XI (Oct. 1943), 19.

41. J. González Reyna, "Consideraciones sobre los problemas de la minería en México," PCMN, *Memoria*, pp. 503–504.

42. *Bol. de min. y pet.*, XIII (Aug. 1942), 15 (reprinted from *Min. Sur.* [June 1942], 4).

43. *E&MJ*, CXLIII (Nov. 1942), 100; C. W. Vaupell, "Mexico," *E&MJ*, CXLIV (Feb. 1943), 88.

44. *Bol. de min. y pet.*, XIII (Sept. 1942), 3–4; *E&MJ*, CXLIII (Dec. 1942), 109; Vaupell, "Mexico," 88.

45. US Tariff Comm., *Mining and Manufacturing Industries in Mexico* (Washington, D.C., 1946), pp. 35, 83; *New York Times* (Aug. 11, 1943); *Comm. & Fin. Chr.* (Aug. 19, 1943), 694; *E&MJ*, CXLIV (Oct. 1943), 133.

46. For sample denunciations of this tax, see *Min. Sur.*, IX (Jan. 1942), 146; and C. Pérez Duarte, "Mexican Mining Must Have Tax Relief," *E&MJ*, CXLVI (Dec. 1945), 96–99. (This article appeared in Mexico as a pamphlet, *La situación de la industria minera*, published by the Cámara Minera de México in Sept. 1945.)

47. See *For. Comm. Wkly.*, XIX (Mar. 31, 1945), 27; *E&MJ*, CXLVI (Feb. 1945), 180.

48. C. Pérez Duarte, "Mexican Mining," *loc. cit.*; *La situación*, p. 13; and *Bol. de min. y pet.*, XIV (Oct. 1943), 5. Also see "El problema nacional de la minera" in *Conferencias de mesa redonda presididas durante su campaña electoral por el licenciado Miguel Alemán*, pp. 233–236.

49. *The Economist* (London), CXLVIII (Mar. 10, 1945), 323.

50. *Min. Sur.*, XII (June 1945), 21–22; *E&MJ*, CXLVI (July 1945), 141–142; D. H. Leavens, "Silver," *E&MJ*, CXLVII (Feb. 1946), 74.

51. *For. Comm. Wkly.*, XX (Nov. 3, 1945), 13, 25; M. Burgin, "Latin America's Economy as World Conflict Ended," *ibid.*, XXIV, (July 2, 1946), 4; H. H. Wanders, "What Caused Foreign Silver to Jump to 71.11 Cents," *E&MJ*, CXLVI (Nov. 1945),

81; *ibid.* (Oct. 1945), 104; (Nov. 1945), 150; D. H. Leavens, "Silver," *ibid.*, CXLVII (Feb. 1946), 74.

52. D. S. Cole, "Business Conditions in Mexico in 1945," *Commercial Intelligence Journal*, LXXIV (Feb. 23, 1946), 165.

53. C. F. Carson, "Financial Developments in Latin America, 1945," *For. Comm. Wkly.*, XXIII (Apr. 27, 1946), 48.

54. *Min. Sur.*, XIII (Oct. 1945), 18.

55. For an analysis of the results, see Banco de México, S.A., *Vigesimacuarta assemblea general ordinaria de accionistas* (Mexico, 1946), pp. 59–61. Also see *Min. Sur.* (Dec. 1945), 16; Cole, "Mexico in 1945," 165; *E&MJ*, CXLVI (Nov. 1945), 73; *For. Comm. Wkly.*, XXII (Jan. 19, 1946), 26.

56. *E&MJ*, CXLVI (Dec. 1945), 151.

57. *Ibid.* (Nov. 1945), 150; (Dec. 1945), 151; CXLVII (Jan. 1946), 132; (Mar. 1946), 144; *Min. Sur.*, XIII (Dec. 1945), 17; (Mar. 1946), 13; *For. Comm. Wkly.*, XXII (Mar. 22, 1946), 46.

58. *Min. Sur.*, XI (Mar. 1944), 14, 15–17; A. L. Ransome, "Lead," *E&MJ*, CXLI (Feb. 1945), 100; US BuMines, *Lead, 1950*, p. S–21; Cole, "Mexico in 1945," 165.

59. *E&MJ*, CXLVI (Feb. 1945), 136; (June 1945), 152; Clark, "Mexico in 1944," *For. Comm. Wkly.*, XX (July 28, 1945), 13; *Min. Sur.*, XII (Aug. 1945), 22.

60. Cole, "Mexico in 1945," 165; *E&MJ*, CXLVI (Oct. 1945), 144; (Nov. 1945), 150; CXLVII (Feb. 1946), 159; (Apr. 1946), 142; *Min. Sur.*, XIII (Nov. 1945), 14; *For. Comm. Wkly.*, XXI (Nov. 10, 1945), 33.

61. C. F. Carson, "Decline of Latin American Gold and Exchange Holdings During 1947," *For. Comm. Wkly.*, XXX (Mar. 20, 1948), 7.

62. Report of the National Bank of Mexico reprinted in *E&MJ*, CXLVI (Mar. 1945), 142; Cole, "Mexico in 1945," 165.

63. See A. T. Stephan, "Mexico—Its Economic and Financial Policy," *Comm. & Fin. Chr.*, CLVIII (Dec. 30, 1943), 2634 ff, for a complete survey of Mexico's activities in this field; and *Min. Sur.*, XI (May 1944), 20.

64. Sylvia P. Bernstein, "Latin American Price Trends," *For. Comm. Wkly.*, XXIV (July 27, 1946), 9.

CHAPTER 23

1. For example, see the papers presented in the *Conferencias de mesa redonda presidadas durante su campaña electoral por el licenciado Miguel Alemán*, Chap., "El problema nacional de la minería," and at the First National Mining Congress in 1948 (PCMN, *Memoria*, pp. 165–170, 213–229, 311–313, 497–513). Also see *E&MJ*, CLI (Apr. 1950), 152; CLIV (Jan. 1953), 160–161; (Feb. 1953), 228; (Nov. 1953), 172.

2. A. J. Terrones, Jr., address to the Institute of Geology, Oct. 7, 1955, printed as "Mexican Mining Engineer Says That Excessive Taxation Could Strangle Mining," *E&MJ*, CLVI (Dec. 1956), 115.

3. See the recommendation of the National Institute for the Investigation of Mineral Resources, a government organ, to the official candidate for President, A. Ruiz Cortines, in the summer of 1952. (*E&MJ*, CLIII [Aug. 1952], 156.)

4. Terrones, "Mexican Mining Engineer," *loc. cit.*

5. See Howard F. Cline, *The United States and Mexico*, Chap. xiv, "Revolution and World War II."

6. See Stanford Mosk, *Industrial Revolution in Mexico* (Berkeley, Calif., 1950).

7. For an exposition of a businessman's fear of nationalism, nationalization, exchange difficulties, labor laws, and wage inflation, see H. Bancroft, "To Encourage Investment Latin America Must Vitalize Inter-American Conference Resolutions," *E&MJ*, CXLVII (Jan. 1946), 52–57.

8. See Cline, *U.S. and Mexico*, pp. 333–386.

9. Miguel Alemán, *Program of Government: Presidential Campaign in Mexico, 1946–1952*, pp. 43–44.

10. *Conferencias de mesa redonda presididas durante su campaña electoral por el licenciado Miguel Alemán*, Chap., "El problema nacional de la minería."

11. For this committee and its predecessor, see *Min. Sur.*, XII (Oct. 1944), 13; and *For. Comm. Wkly.*, XXXVIII (Mar. 27, 1950), 23–24.

12. *E&MJ*, CLIII (Aug. 1952), 156; *Min. World*, XIV (Aug. 1952), 65.

13. *E&MJ*, CLIX (Aug. 1958), 157, 159.

14. Report of the Combined Mexican Working Party (of the International Bank for Reconstruction and Development and Mexican representatives), *The Economic Development of Mexico* (hereinafter cited as Intl. Bk., *Eco. Dev. of Mex.*), Baltimore, 1953, p. 43, and Appendix Tables 3 and 63. The figures for 1951–54 have been compiled by J. G. Maddox, "The Growth of the Mexican Economy," American Universities Field Staff *Report* (June 14, 1956), pp. 12–13. The bank's treatment of smelters leaves much to be desired. (See Appendix III, p. 293.)

15. Intl. Bk., *Eco. Dev. of Mex.*, p. 43.

16. *Ibid.*, p. 115.

17. UN, Dept. of Economic and Social Affairs, *Non-Ferrous Metals in Underdeveloped Countries* (Doc. No. E/2798/ST/ECA/36), New York, 1956, p. 56. This UN study defines "minerals" as antimony, copper, lead, manganese, and zinc. The rapid increase of exports of cotton and coffee at extremely attractive prices partially accounts for this shift. Figures compiled by the International Bank include petroleum and perhaps gold and silver. The figures for more or less equivalent years are: 1939, 65.3%; 1948, 37.5%; 1950, 33.0% (*Eco. Dev. of Mex.*, Table 130).

18. Banco de México, *25a. asamblea general ordinaria de accionistas* (Mexico, 1947), p. 18. Also see La Oficina de Estudios Especiales del Comité de Aforos y Subsidios al Comercio Exterior, "Problemas de comercio exterior," *Memoria del Segundo Congreso Mexicano de Ciencias Sociales*, III, pp. 205–206.

19. H. Bratter, "Mexico's Tax Jumble," *E&MJ*, CXLIX (Oct. 1948), 93; L. B. Clark, "Mexico," *For. Comm. Wkly.*, XXXIV (Jan. 31, 1949), 5.

20. G. Kalmanoff, "Mexico's Economy in 1946," *For. Comm. Wkly.*, XXVII (Apr. 26, 1947), 5–6; *ibid.*, XXXIII (Oct. 16, 1948), 19; L. B. Clark, "Mexico Faces 1950," *ibid.*, XXXVIII (Jan. 23, 1950), 5.

21. US BuMines, *Minerals Yrbk., 1953*, I, pp. 667–668, 1300; Anon., "Mexico," *For. Comm. Wkly.*, LI (Mar. 15, 1954), 3.

22. Intl. Bk., *Eco. Dev. of Mex.*, pp. 40, 124–125. Also see the suggestions of Ing. Adrian Esteve reported in *E&MJ*, CLI (Apr. 1950), 152.

CHAPTER 24

1. For example, see H. H. Wanders, "Lead," *E&MJ*, CXLVI (Aug. 1945), 91; F. E. Wormser, "Lead," *ibid.*, CXLVII (Feb. 1946), 76–77; US BuMines, *Lead, 1950*, p. S–7; editorial, "Time of Crisis," *E&MJ*, CLIV (Feb. 1953), 71.

2. This topic has been the subject of numerous debates and studies. It has been discussed at length by W. G. Fritz ("Natural Resources," Chap. xxi) and J. F. Dewhurst ("Needs vs. Resources," Chap. xxvi, esp. pp. 939–940) in J. Frederick Dewhurst, *America's Needs and Resources: A New Survey* (New York: Twentieth Century Fund, 1955); Erich W. Zimmermann, *World Resources and Industries,* Chaps. xxv, xlix, and l (particularly for a discussion of concepts); Paul M. Tyler, *From the Ground Up* (New York, 1948), Chaps. x and xi. The views of the U.S. State Department were discussed by Charles P. Taft ("The Concerns of the U.S. With Mineral Resources," *U.S. Dept. of State Bulletin,* XII [Jan. 28, 1945], 129–132); Paul H. Nitze ("Minerals as a Factor in U.S. Foreign Economic Policy," *ibid.,* XVI [Feb. 16, 1947], 300–302); and T. C. Mann ("Foreign Relations Aspect of the Lead and Zinc Problem," *ibid.,* XXXIX [Oct. 13, 1958], 583–584). Government analyses (of varying degrees of "officialness") are: E. W. Pehrson, "Our Mineral Resources and Security," *Foreign Affairs,* XXVIII (July 1945), 644–657; Staffs of the Bureau of Mines and Geological Survey, *Mineral Position of the United States* (Appendix to the "Investigation of Natural Resources," Hearings before a subcommittee of the Committee on Public Lands, U.S. Senate, 80th Cong., 1st Sess., May 15, 16 and 17, 1947—Washington, D.C., 1947); The President's Materials Policy Commission, William S. Paley, Chairman, *Resources for Freedom: A Report to the President* (Washington, D.C., 1952), 5 vols.; Public Advisory Board for Mutual Security (D. W. Bell, Acting Chairman), *A Trade and Tariff Policy in the National Interest* (Washington, D.C., 1953); U.S. Tariff Comm., *Lead and Zinc Industries; Report on Investigation* (Report No. 192, 2d Ser.), Washington, D.C., 1954; US Tariff Comm., *Lead and Zinc: A Report to the President* (Washington, D.C., 1958); U.S. Senate, 83rd Cong., 2nd Sess., Report No. 1627, Minerals, Materials and Fuels Subcommittee of the Committee on Interior and Insular Affairs, *Accessibility of Strategic and Critical Materials to the United States in Time of War and for Our Expanding Economy* (Washington, D.C., 1954); and Commission on Foreign Economics Policy (Clarence B. Randall, Chairman), *Report to the President and Congress* (Washington, D.C., 1954).

3. J. González Reyna, "Consideraciones sobre los problemas de la minería en México," PCMN, *Memoria,* pp. 510–511.

4. US Tariff Comm., *Lead and Zinc Industries,* p. 69.

5. Intl. Bk., *Eco. Dev. of Mex.,* p. 41.

6. *E&MJ,* CL (Oct. 1949), 142.

7. "Mexican Business," *For. Comm. Wkly.,* LIV (Oct. 24, 1955), 23.

8. *Barron's,* XXXIV (Mar. 1, 1954), 27–28; XXXV (Aug. 22, 1955), 1; (Dec. 5, 1955), 39–40, XXXVI (June 18, 1956), 39–40; *E&MJ,* CLIX (Feb. 1958), 113.

9. The 4-cent excise tax on copper (reduced to 2 cents a pound by the Geneva Trade Agreement) was suspended in April, 1947 until June 30, 1950. Reimposed on July 1, 1950, it was suspended again on May 22, 1951 retroactive to April 1, 1951. Suspensions have been extended to June 30, 1958. (ABMS, *Yrbk.* [1957], p. 136.)

10. US BuMines, *Lead, 1950,* pp. V–15–17, S–7; A. L. Ransome, "Lead," *E&MJ,* CXLVI (Feb. 1945), 100; H. H. Wanders, "Lead," *ibid.* (Aug. 1945), 91; F. E. Wormser, "Lead," *ibid.,* CXLVII (Feb. 1946), 76–77.

Between 1946 and 1956, American mine output of lead increased 5 per cent while zinc mine output fell 6 per cent. Outside the U.S. lead mine output rose by 122 per cent and zinc by 138 per cent. (US Tariff Comm., *Lead and Zinc Report,* p. 15.) Part of this difference can be attributed to the resumption of mining in devastated areas after 1946.

11. US BuMines, *Lead, 1950,* pp. S–7, IV–32–34.

12. *Ibid.,* p. V–7.

13. US BuMines, *Zinc, 1950,* pp. S–10–11, IV–41, V–11, VI–79–80.

14. US BuMines, *Lead, 1950,* p. IV–35; US Tariff Comm., *Lead and Zinc Industries,* pp. 109, 119.

15. Intl. Bk., *Eco. Dev. of Mex.,* p. 41.

16. *Min. World,* XI (Apr. 1949), 36; (Sept. 1949), 56, 60; *For. Comm. Wkly.,* XXXV (June 20, 1949), 24–25.

17. *For. Comm. Wkly.,* XXXV (Apr. 18, 1949), 29; (June 20, 1949), 24–25; *Min. World,* XI (June 1949), 31; *E&MJ,* CL (May 1949), 129; L. B. Clark, "Mexico," *For. Comm. Wkly.,* XXXVIII (Jan. 23, 1950), 5.

18. *For. Comm. Wkly.,* XXXVIII (Mar. 27, 1950), 33; XXXIX (May 29, 1950), 22; *E&MJ,* CLI (May 1950), 140.

19. *For. Comm. Wkly.,* XL (July 17, 1950), 20; (Aug. 28, 1950), 5; *E&MJ,* CLI (Aug. 1950), 107; (Oct. 1950), 140–141; R. L. Ziegfeld, "Lead," *ibid.,* CLIII (Feb. 1952), 82; US BuMines, *Zinc, 1950,* p. IV–41.

20. *For. Comm. Wkly.,* XL (Aug. 7, 1950), 26; XLII (Mar. 19, 1951), 5; XLV (Dec. 24, 1951), 13.

21. F. E. Wormser, "The Lead Industry Under Government Controls," *Comm. & Fin. Chr.,* CLXXV (Feb. 28, 1952), 870; US Tariff Comm., *Lead and Zinc Industries,* pp. 119, 122, 169, 171.

22. "Mexico Holds Price Line Despite U.S. Lead Ceiling," *Barron's,* XXXI (Oct. 15, 1951), 26. Also see *Min. World,* XIV (Jan. 1952), 25.

23. "Foreign Lead Price Sags," *Barron's,* XXXI (Dec. 31, 1951), 27.

24. *For. Comm. Wkly.,* XLVIII (Oct. 27, 1952), 15; XLIX (Apr. 6, 1953), 16–19; US Tariff Comm., *Lead and Zinc Industries,* pp. 120–124, 275, 277 (for lead); 170–174, 304–307 (for zinc).

25. "North American Zinc-Lead Mines React to Depressed Market," *E&MJ,* CLIII (Dec. 1952), 158.

26. *E&MJ,* CLIV (June 1953), 171; (Dec. 1953), 121; CLV (Sept. 1954), 191–192; (Oct. 1954), 166–168; CLVI (June 1955), 155.

27. Intl. Bk., *Eco. Dev. of Mex.,* p. 42.

28. For short analyses of the silver market, see: "Silver . . . Mainly a Common Commodity," in Rotterdamsche Bank, N.V., *Quarterly Review* (Aug. 1952), 5–41; Y. S. Kedari, "World Trends in Silver Since 1945," Reserve Bank of India *Bulletin,* VII (Dec. 1953), 971–985; H. Bratter, "Silver Marks Time," *E&MJ,* CLII (Aug. 1951), 65–67; "Mine Output Too Small to Meet Silver Demands," *Barron's,* XXXIII (Feb. 9, 1953), 35–36.

29. "The stabilization of the price of silver in the international market is due in great part to the policy followed by the Bank of Mexico in respect to this matter; the bank intervened in said market when conditions required it." (Banco de México, *32a. asamblea general ordinaria de accionistas* [Mexico, 1954], p. 50.)

30. *E&MJ,* CXLVII (July 1946), 92; (Aug. 1946), 102. For an analysis of the silver situation at this time, see Anon., "Shortage of Silver," *Economist,* CLI (Aug. 10, 1946), 222–223. In anticipation of the rise Mexico had stopped coining silver in March. (*E&MJ,* CXLVII [Apr. 1946], 142.)

31. *Min. World,* VIII (Sept. 1946), 85; *E&MJ,* CXLVII (Sept. 1946), 124–125; (Oct. 1946), 117; (Dec. 1946), 131–132; D. H. Leavens, "Silver," *E&MJ,* CXLVIII (Feb. 1947), 78; *Min. Sur.,* XIV (Dec. 1946), 20.

32. *E&MJ,* CXLVIII (Mar. 1947), 130; (July 1947), 99; D. H. Leavens, "Silver," *ibid.,* CXLIX (Feb. 1948), 73; Anon., "Silver Adjusts Itself," *Economist,* CLI (Dec. 14, 1946), 960–961.

33. *E&MJ,* CXLVIII (Apr. 1947), 149; (May 1947), 127–128; (July 1947), 99, 146; (Oct. 1947), 140; D. H. Leavens, "Silver," *E&MJ,* CXLIX (Feb. 1948), 74; *Min. World,* IX (Aug. 1947), 69; X (Oct. 1948), 52; *Min. Sur.,* XIV (Sept. 1947);

F. Roberts, "U.S. Silver Off Market," *Barron's*, XXVII (Oct. 6, 1947), 29–30; *For. Comm. Wkly.*, XXXIII (Oct. 16, 1948), 19.

34. *For. Comm. Wkly.*, XXXIII (Oct. 16, 1948), 19; and for details, D. H. Leavens, "Silver," *E&MJ*, CL (Feb. 1949), 74; H. Bratter, "Mexico's Tax Jumble," *E&MJ*, CXLIX (Oct. 1948), 92–94. Also see Notes 35 and 36 below.

35. *Min. World*, X (Oct. 1948), 52.

36. Leavens, "Silver [Feb. 1949]," *loc. cit.; E&MJ*, CL (Mar. 1949), 125.

37. Leavens, "Silver [Feb. 1949]," *loc. cit.;* Leavens, "Silver," *E&MJ*, CLI (Feb. 1950), 80; *Min. World*, XI (Feb. 1949), 31.

38. Leavens, "Silver [Feb. 1950]," *loc. cit.*

39. Anon., "Mexican Bank to Market Silver Barter Coin," *E&MJ*, CL (July 1949), 154; Leavens, "Silver [Feb. 1950]," 80.

40. Leavens, "Silver [Feb. 1950]," 80. Also see *E&MJ*, CL (May 1949), 145; (Oct. 1949), 142; (Nov. 1949), 148; *Min. World*, XI (Oct. 1949), 30; (Nov. 1949), 28; *Foreign Trade*, VI (Oct. 29, 1949), 796. By the end of 1952, silver coinage for Saudi Arabia alone reached about $40,000,000. (*For. Comm. Wkly.*, XLV [Dec. 24, 1951], 13.) Also see *E&MJ*, CLII (Mar. 1951), 118; (Aug. 1951), 128; (Oct. 1951), 148; (Dec. 1951), 152; CLIII (Apr. 1952), 157; (Aug. 1952), 156–157; and H. M. Bratter, "Silver," *ibid.*, CLIV (Feb. 1953), 76–77 ff.

41. *E&MJ*, CLII (Jan. 1951), 122; Anon., "Silver Demand Pushes Market Near U.S. Peg," *Barron's*, XXXI (Jan. 22, 1951), 41. One correspondent inferred that Mexico stopped silver shipments at this time for fear of a United States price freeze at 72 cents during the Korean War. (*Min. World*, XIII [Jan. 1951], 43.)

42. D. H. Leavens, "Silver," *E&MJ*, CLII (Feb. 1951), 78.

43. Rotterdamsche Bank, "Silver," 18.

44. W. F. Boericke, "Silver Price Appears to Have Hit Ceiling," *Barron's*, XXXI (July 30, 1951), 21; D. H. Leavens, "Silver," *E&MJ*, CLIII (Feb. 1952), 78–79.

45. Anon., "Mexico Mints Hard Money," *For Comm. Wkly.*, XLV (Dec. 24, 1951), 13; *E&MJ*, CLII (Nov. 1951), 106; Anon., "Mexican Government Justified New Peso Rate," *For. Comm. Wkly.*, LI (June 14, 1954), 5.

46. H. Bratter, "Silver Marks Time," *E&MJ*, CLII (Aug. 1951), 65–67; Anon., "Silver Purchase Act Today," *Bankers Monthly*, LXXII (Sept. 1955), 48–50. Also see *New York Times* (July 19, 1955) for a defense of the Act by Felix E. Wormser, Assistant Secretary of the Interior.

47. Anon., "Silver Galore," *Economist* (London), CLXXVI (July 23, 1955), 327–328; *Barron's*, XXXV (Apr. 4, 1955), 3 ff; H. Bratter, "Silver as Money; Monetary Fund Makes World Survey," *E&MJ*, CL (Jan. 1949), 79–80; Kedari, "World Trends in Silver Since 1945," *loc. cit.* Lend-Lease silver began to return to the U.S. in 1956. Returns were spotty; the United Kingdom paid practically all of its debt, India and Pakistan about half, and others asked for extensions. It has been noted that practically all of this silver has been obtained from demonetized coins, thus not only making unnecessary the purchase of new silver but destroying as well potential future markets.

48. Rotterdamsche Bank, "Silver," 5–9.

49. "A Story of Money Too Good to Last," *New York Times* (Feb. 19, 1956).

50. *Ibid.*

51. Bratter, "Silver Marks Time," *loc. cit.*

52. *E&MJ*, CLVIII (Mar. 1957), 165.

53. Bratter, "How Profitable Is Gold Mining?" *ibid.*, CL (Mar. 1949), 76–77.

54. *For. Comm. Wkly.*, XIX (Mar. 31, 1945), 27; *E&MJ*, CXLVI (Feb. 1945), 180. See above, Chap. 24.

55. *Min. World*, VIII (Sept. 1946), 89.

56. *Comm. and Fin. Chr.*, CLXVI (July 3, 1947), 19.

57. *Bol. de min. y pet.*, XX (Aug. 1949), 30; *For. Comm. Wkly.*, XXXII (Aug. 28, 1948), 23; XXXIV (Feb. 14, 1949), 21; XXXVII (Oct. 31, 1949), 27; XXXVIII (Feb. 13, 1950), 21–22; XXXIX (Apr. 3, 1950), 25; *E&MJ*, CXLIX (Nov. 1948), 142; CL (Dec. 1949), 128; CLIII (Mar. 1952), 154; CLV (June 1953), 173.

CHAPTER 25

1. Intl. Bk., *Eco. Dev. of Mex.;* International Bank, *The International Bank for Reconstruction and Development, 1946–1953* (Baltimore, 1954), pp. 190–191.

2. Intl. Bk., *Eco. Dev. of Mex.*, p. 16.

3. *Ibid.*, pp. 17–18.

4. *Ibid*, pp. 42–43.

5. UNECLA, *Economic Bulletin for Latin America*, II (Feb. 1957), 33 (Table 24); *E&MJ*, CLVII (Jan. 1956), 72. (The UNECLA figures set mine employment at about 97,000, but it includes petroleum workers.)

6. This discussion has drawn heavily on González Reyna, "Consideraciones," pp. 497–499.

7. C. Pérez Duarte, "Los problemas"; S. Escamilla, "Ponencia."

8. Un grupo de mineros de Cimarron Chico, Jalisco, "Ponencia," PCMN, *Memoria,* pp. 451–452; La Asociación de Mineros en Pequeño de Hidalgo del Parral, Chih., "Ponencia," *ibid.*, pp. 171–174; R. Licona, "Ponencia de la Asociación Minera de Chihuahua," *ibid.*, p. 273.

9. R. A. Beals, "Will Taxation Destroy the Mining Industry in Mexico?" *Min. Engin.*, VII (Feb. 1955), 128; "Higher Taxes, Reduced Output Hampers Mexican Mining," *E&MJ*, CLVI (May 1955), 120, 122.

10. Starting Aug. 1957, the *Bol. de min. y pet.* began publishing serially the Mining Law in force with notes on the dates of the various amendments.

11. For example, see the owners' complaints in *Conferencias de mesa redonda,* pp. 216–218.

12. *Diario oficial*, CLIV, No. 21 (Jan. 25, 1946); reprinted in *Bol. de min. y pet.*, XVI (Feb. 1946), 11. For a summary of the various methods of obtaining concessions, including those in the mineral reserves, see F. Peraza, "Formas de adquirir concesiones mineras en la República Mexicana," PCIARM, *Memoria*, pp. 141–142.

13. *Diario oficial* CXLVIII, No. 20 (Jan. 24, 1945), and CLXVI, No. 3 (Jan. 5, 1948); *Bol. de min. y pet.*, XVI (Apr. 1946), 8; XIX (Feb. 1948), 3.

14. *E&MJ*, CXLVIII (July 1947), 148; CXLIX (Mar. 1948), 138.

15. *Bol. de min. y pet.*, XVII (Dec. 1946), 12–13.

16. "Proyecto de reforma a la Ley Minera y su Reglamento, en lo referente a comprobación de trabajos regulares," *Bol. de min. y pet.*, XXIV (May 1952), 3–4.

17. Cleona Lewis, *The United States and Foreign Investment Problems*, Brookings Institution (Washington, D.C., 1948), pp. 136–137 and citations; *For. Comm. Wkly.*, XXVIII (Aug. 9, 1947), 16; XXIX (Dec. 20, 1947), 17; A. Terrones Benítez, "Mexico Exempts Old Titles," *E&MJ*, CXLVIII (May 1947), 79–80; US Dept. of Comm., Office of International Trade, *Factors Limiting U.S. Investment Abroad* (Washington, D.C., 1953), p. 37; US Dept. of Comm., "Establishing a Business in Mexico" (July 1955), p. 3.

18. W. P. Shea, "The Price of Lead, 1956–1975," *E&MJ*, CLVII (Sept. 1956), 86–87. Also see Shea, "What Price Lead, 1953–75?" *ibid.*, CLIV (Dec. 1953), 81;

and complaints in *Conferencias de mesa redonda*, pp. 213–214. Also see E. Just, "Mexico," *E&MJ*, CXLVII (June 1946), 80; editorial, "For Mexican Mining—A Great Opportunity," *E&MJ*, CLVIII (Jan. 1957), 67; E. Prieto López, et al., "Dictamen que rinde la Comisión Dictaminadora sobre ponencias relativos a cuestiones fiscales," PCMN, *Memoria*, pp. 250–265. A UN study stated that "in 1952 approximately 30 per cent of the gross value of mining output went into the public purse." See United Nations, Dept. of Economic and Social Affairs, *Non-Ferrous Metals in Under-Developed Countries* (hereinafter cited as UN, *Non-Ferrous Metals*), p. 110.

19. Beals, "Taxation in Mexico," 127–128. In 1954, the Fresnillo Co. set its tax bill at 29 per cent. (*Ibid.*, 128.) The US Bureau of Mines has estimated that the larger lead and zinc workings pay, in production and export taxes, over 20 per cent of the value of their export sales. (*Minerals Yrbk., 1953*, I, p. 1300.)

20. Intl. Bk., *Eco. Dev. of Mex.*, p. 43; UN, *Non-Ferrous Metals*, p. 110. For an excellent summary, with examples of the methods used in calculating taxes of all sorts, see S. Peña, "Impuestos sobre la minería en México," PCIARM, *Memorias* (1951), pp. 143–162.

21. Prieto López, "Dictamen," pp. 250–254. Also see "Trabajo presentado ... como colaboración de la Comisión de Fomento Minero," *ibid.*, 231–237; T. A. Lagos, et al., "Ponencia," *ibid.*, pp. 185–192; and *Conferencias de mesa redonda*, pp. 213–214, 218, 220.

22. "The tax levied on this exploitation is, therefore, in effect, a recovery by the Nation of a portion of its own patrimony in consideration of the privilege granted to private individuals of the exploitation of national resources." (J. K. Burnham, "Mining Taxes in Mexico," US BuMines, *Mineral Trade Notes*, Spec. Suppl. No. 25 to Vol. XXVI, No. 4 [Apr. 1948], 2.) Also see United Nations, Economic and Social Council, Fiscal Commission, *Taxation in Capital-Exporting and Capital-Importing Countries of Foreign Private Investment: Foreign Investment in Mexico* (Doc. No. E/CN.8/69/Add. 2), New York, Apr.–May 1953, (hereinafter cited as UN, *Taxation in Mexico*), p. 24.

23. Excellent surveys of the Mexican tax situation in the late 1940's and early 1950's can be found in J. K. Burnham, "Mining Taxes in Mexico," 1–17; Burnham, "Addenda to Mining Taxes in Mexico," *ibid.*, Spec. Suppl. No. 31 to Vol. XXVIII, No. 5 (May 1949), 1–7; UN, *Taxation in Mexico*, pp. 12–26; and US Dept. of Comm., "Establ. a Business in Mexico" (July 1955), pp. 6–14. H. Bratter in "Mexico's Tax Jumble," *E&MJ*, CXLIX (Oct. 1948), 92–94, gives an inclusive list of the various types of taxes to which businesses in Mexico are subject.

24. For the method of calculating this tax, with examples, see Burnham, "Mining Taxes in Mexico," pp. 3–5. Burnham also notes that the tax is levied on the assay content, not the recoverable content—for which the smelter pays—and is based on the New York price, not the smelters' Mexica price. Silver was extended a rebate subsidy between Sept. 1946 and Jan. 1956 as part of a government–labor–industry compromise settlement to split the price rise that year. (Burham, 11–12.) Also see Intl. Bk., *Eco. Dev. of Mex.*, p. 105; Beals, "Taxation in Mexico," 127–128; C. Pérez Duarte, "Mexican Mining Must Have Tax Relief," *E&MJ*, CXLVI (Dec. 1945), 96–99; and remarks of G. Serrano, President of the Mexican Mining Chamber, "Taxing Metal Output and Exports in Mexico," *Metals*, XVIII (Dec. 1947), 12–16.

25. The International Bank study team believed these methods to be ineffective in aiding the opening of new areas because of transportation and power shortages. As a general subsidy, it had little effect on the small-scale segments because the rate was based on the large-scale producers' ability to pay. (*Eco. Dev. of Mex.*, p. 45.)

26. *Bol. de min. y pet.*, XXIII (Jan. 1951), 45. For the method of fixing rates, see Burnham, "Mining Taxes in Mexico," pp. 5–7, and Burnham, "Addenda," p. 3, for a critique of the method. See above, Chap. 17 for a detailed discussion of the

effect of exchange devaluation. It is demonstrated at length in H. Bratter, "Mexico's Tax Jumble." Bratter's implicit contention that the remaining windfall profits are too small to speak of is rejected by the Mexican government. He does make a point when he writes: "Since the Mexican system of taxing mine output takes advantage from the government's standpoint of rises in income in terms of either Mexican or foreign currencies . . . the miners 'get it both ways.'"

27. UN, *Taxation in Mexico*, p. 23; *E&MJ*, CXLIX (May 1948), 146; Just, "Mexico," 80; Intl. Bk., *Eco. Dev. of Mex.*, p. 44; E. Prieto López, "Reducción de impuestos para fomentar el aprovechamiento de minerales de baja ley," PCMN, *Memoria*, pp. 239–241.

28. Serrano, "Taxing Metal Output"; Prieto López, "Dictamen." Also see Pérez Duarte, *La situación de la industria minera*, p. 12; *E&MJ*, CLIII (Sept. 1952), 164, 187–188; Burnham, "Mining Taxes in Mexico," p. 3.

29. Intl. Bk., *Eco. Dev. of Mex.*, p. 44; UN, *Taxation in Mexico*, pp. 3–4, 24.

30. Intl. Bk., *Eco. Dev. of Mex.*, p. 44.

31. US Tariff Comm., *Lead and Zinc Industries*, pp. 350–351.

32. Pérez Duarte, *La situación*, pp. 9–10.

33. For the dates of minor changes, see *Bol. de min. y pet.*, XIV (Apr. 1943), 14. For the gold tax, see *ibid.*, XIV (Oct. 1943), 5.

34. *Min. World*, XV (Oct. 1953), 85; XVII (Aug. 1955), 78.

35. *E&MJ*, CL (Jan. 1949), 124; (Oct. 1949), 142; *Min. World*, XI (Apr. 1949), 45; C. W. Wright, "What Chance Has Foreign Capital in Mexico?" *E&MJ*, CLV (Mar. 1954), 98–99; *For. Comm. Wkly.*, XL (Sept. 11, 1950), 17.

36. *Bol. de min. y pet.*, XXV (Sept. 1953), 7–9.

37. UN, *Taxation in Mexico*, pp. 6–7.

38. *Min. World*, XV (Oct. 1953), 53, 85; (Nov. 1953), 82; XVI (Feb. 1954). R. A. Beals has written that of $60,000,000 collected in production taxes in 1954, some $2,000,000 (about 24,000,000 pesos) was returned. ("Taxation in Mexico," 130.)

39. *E&MJ*, CLV (Dec. 1954), 150.

40. *Diario oficial*, CCXIII, No. 53 (Dec. 31, 1955). An English translation is in US BuMines, *Mineral Trade Notes*, Spec. Suppl. No. 48 to Vol. XLII, No. 1 (Jan. 1956).

41. *Diario oficial*, CLV, No. 31 (Apr. 5, 1946); *For. Comm. Wkly.*, XXIII (Apr. 27, 1946), 34; *Min. Sur.*, XIII (June 1946), 15. The export of gold having been prohibited, it was subject to a special "supplementary production tax" decreed on Aug. 26, 1943, to replace the export tax. (Burnham, "Mining Taxes in Mexico," pp. 8–9.)

42. *For. Comm. Wkly.*, XXIX (Dec. 20, 1947), 16; XXX (Mar. 6, 1948), 17; *E&MJ*, CXLIX (Feb. 1948), 157. For methods of calculation see Burnham, "Mining Taxes in Mexico," pp. 16–17.

43. See esp. Burnham, "Addenda," pp. 1–3; and *For. Comm. Wkly.*, XXXIII (Oct. 30, 1948), 19; (Dec. 6, 1948), 23–24; (Dec. 13, 1948), 26; XXXIV (Jan. 17, 1949), 23; (Jan. 31, 1949), 5; XXXVI (Aug. 8, 1949), 18; XXXVII (Nov. 14, 1949), 15; XXXVIII (Jan. 16, 1950), 18; XL (Sept. 11, 1950), 17; XLVIII (Dec. 1, 1952), 19; (Dec. 22, 1952), 27; XLIX (Feb. 9, 1953), 11; LI (Jan. 18, 1954), 3; (Jan. 25, 1954), 20; *E&MJ*, CXLIX (Oct. 1948), 142; (Dec. 1948), 145; CL (Oct. 1949), 142; CLI (Jan. 1950), 125.

44. *Diario oficial*, CCI, No. 50 (Dec. 31, 1953), with the bylaws in *ibid.* (Feb. 10, 1954). This law is summarized in US Dept. of Comm., "Establ. a Business in Mexico" (July 1955), pp. 6–11.

45. Intl. Bk., *Eco. Dev. of Mex.*, pp. 17–18; *Conferencias de mesa redonda*, pp. 214–215.

46. Excellent discussions of this point are to be found in UN, *Non-Ferrous Metals*,

pp. 103–105; and Cám. Min. de Méx., "Ponencia ... sobre transportes ferrocarrileros," PCMN, *Memoria*, pp. 291–294.

This view has been "stood on its head" by E. Moyo Porras in an article, "Los transportes y la minería" *(Revista de economía, XVI* [May 1953], 142–146) which takes the position that since the railroads were built originally for the export of raw materials to the U.S., mining has had an encouragement vouchsafed other segments of the economy. And since the industry produces only 8.6 per cent of the national income and employs only 1.8 per cent of the economically active population, it has little call for more help in view of the internal communications needs of the nation. The logic of nationalism is ofttimes bewildering.

47. Intl. Bk., *Eco. Dev. of Mex.,* pp. 39, 125. *Ibid.,* pp. 89–93, and Tables 90–103, give a fine analysis and summary of this problem. Much of the following information is drawn from this source.

48. *Ibid.,* pp. 16–18.

49. See above, Chap. 22, notes 22 and 23. Also see A. E. Stuntz, "Mexican Rails," *For. Comm. Wkly.,* XXIV (Sept. 21, 1946), 5, for a rather laudatory write-up.

50. C. Lewis, *The U.S. and Foreign Investment Problems,* p. 115 n.

51. For example, see *For. Comm. Wkly.,* XXXIII (Oct. 16, 1948), 19; and *E&MJ,* CXLIX (May 1948), 146; CLI (Mar. 1950), 134; and González Reyna, "Consideraciones," pp. 500–501. For notes on rate increases, see *Min. Sur.,* XII (Jan. 1945), 14; *For. Comm. Wkly.,* XXI (Dec. 29, 1945), 16; XLVIII (Nov. 24, 1952), 27; *E&MJ,* CXLVI (Apr. 1945), 161; CXLVII (Jan. 1946), 132; CXLVIII (Mar. 1947), 132; (Sept. 1947), 133; CL (Jan. 1949), 124; (Feb. 1949), 166–167; (Mar. 1949), 125; CLI (June 1950), 136; (Aug. 1950), 164; CLIII (Apr. 1952), 157–158; *Min. World,* XIV (June 1952), 53; (Dec. 1952), 65.

52. *For. Comm. Wkly.,* XXV (Oct. 5, 1946), 18; *Min. World,* XI (May 1949), 33, 49; (Sept. 1949), 57.

53. *E&MJ,* CXLVII (Dec. 1946), 132–133. This argument was still based upon those advanced by Moisés T. de la Peña before the war. Also see his article, "La industria minera en México," *Investigación económica,* 1944, 1st quarter, 21–27. For an excellent discussion of the various factors entering into the fixing of railroad rates by product, line, distance, etc., see Carlos Villafuerte, *Ferrocarriles* (Mexico, 1959), pp. 210–232.

54. *E&MJ,* CLI (Aug. 1950), 164; CLII (June 1951), 140; (Oct. 1951), 150; 82nd Cong., 2nd Sess., House Comm. on Foreign Affairs, The Inter-American Study Mission, *Report ... pursuant to H. Res. 28,* H. Rept. No. 1454 (Washington, D.C., 1952), pp. 23–24; *Min. World,* XV (Apr. 15, 1953), 111; XVI (Apr. 15, 1954), 78. Also see the *For. Comm. Wkly.* for the years 1953 to the present, *passim.*

55. For a survey of Mexican highway routes, see US Dept. of Comm., Bureau of Foreign Commerce, World Trade Information Service, *Utilities Abroad* (Pt. 4, No. 56–13), "Highways of Mexico" (Sept. 1956).

56. *Min. Sur.,* VII (Apr. 1940), 24; VIII (Mar. 1941), 24; IX (Dec. 1941), 29, 30, 31, 33; (Mar. 1942), 21; (Aug. 1942), 23; X (Nov. 1942), 19; (Dec. 1942), 19; (Jan. 1943), 16; (May 1943), 23; XI (Oct. 1943), 18, 19; (Nov. 1943), 19–20; (June 1944), 16–17; *E&MJ,* CXLVII (Mar. 1946), 146; *Min. World,* XII (Nov. 1950), 47; Intl. Bk., *Eco. Dev. of Mex.,* p. 45.

57. Intl. Bk., *Eco. Dev. of Mex.,* pp. 16–17. González Reyna reached the same conclusion. ("Consideraciones," p. 500.) Also see statement of G. P. Serrano, President of the Mexican Mining Chamber, *Min. World,* XIII (Aug. 1951), 49, 51.

58. UN, *Non-Ferrous Metals,* p. 110. Also see *Min. World,* XII (Nov. 1950), 47; XIV (Oct. 1952), 68. This program, "of some assistance to the small miner," could only succeed if there was a simultaneous improvement in the railway situation.

(UNECLA, *Economic Survey of Latin America, 1951-52*, p. 203.)

59. *Min. Sur.*, VII (July 1940), 13; *E&MJ*, CL (Jan. 1949), 124. For an interesting exposition of the uses of airplanes by mines in mountain regions, see a series of articles by George Law, "Primitive and Modern Mountain Transportation," *Min Sur.*, II (Feb.-June 1935), *passim.*

60. *E&MJ*, CXLVIII (Mar. 1947), 132; CXLIX (Jan. 1948), 124; CLV (Mar. 1954), 177; *Min. Sur.*, XIV (Sept. 1947), 20; *Min. World*, XIV (Aug. 1952), 76; XV (Dec. 1953), 77; XVI (Nov. 1954), 68; XVIII (Feb. 1956), 84-85; (Oct. 1956), 88.

61. González Reyna, "Consideraciones," pp. 501-502; Intl. Bk., *Eco. Dev. of Mex.*, p. 45; *Min. World*, XIII (Nov. 1951), 60. For a survey of this problem in general in Latin America, see UNECLA, *Energy in Latin America* (Geneva, 1957).

62. UN, *Non-Ferrous Metals*, p. 105; *Min. World*, XVI (Apr. 15, 1954), 78.

63. Banco de México, *35a. asamblea general ordinaria de accionistas*, pp. 93-94.

64. M. Villafaña Barajas (Manager, CFM), "Colaboración de la CFM," PCMN, *Memoria*, pp. 338-339. For a discussion of the role of mining banks in general, see UN, *Non-Ferrous Metals*, pp. 120-121.

65. Cia. Minera Metalúrgica, S.A. de Mazatlán, Sinaloa, "Ponencia: Otro de tantos motivos por los cuales carece de crédito la industria minera," *ibid.*, pp. 309-310; Villafaña, "Colaboración," pp. 338-339; J. Sifuentes, "Refracciones a la minería," *ibid.*, p. 315.

In any case, private mine financing must be a high interest proposition. The First National City Bank of New York calculates that the value of money in Mexico fell from an index of 100 in 1947 to 49 in 1957 (a drop of almost 7 per cent a year), with government bonds in 1957 yielding 10.32 per cent. (*Monthly Letter* [June 1958], 71.) When the risk of mining is added to these interest rates, they rise to back-breaking heights.

66. L. Latapí, "Ponencia presentada ... en representación del Crédito Minero y Mercantil, S.A.," *ibid.*, pp. 305-307; Cia. Minera Metalúrgica, "Ponencia," pp. 309-310.

67. See the "Ponencias" in *ibid.*, pp. 309-336.

68. Villafaña, "Colaboración," pp. 337-338, 343-344.

69. "Dictamen sobre crédito a la minería," *ibid.*, pp. 345-347.

70. *Ibid.*, p. 347.

71. Intl. Bk., *Eco. Dev. of Mex.*, p. 187. Also see *ibid.*, p. 38.

72. A confusing Mexican report to the UN's Economic Committee for Latin America states "that in 1941 sixteen companies, accounting for more than 80 per cent of the country's total mining production in 1947, were owned by United States capital." See UN, Dept. of Eco. and Social Affairs, *Foreign Capital in Latin America* (Doc. No. E/CN.12/360), New York, 1955, p. 112 and note. It should be noted that U.S. and Mexican figures are not comparable. In 1950, the Bank of Mexico estimated total foreign direct investment in mining at 967,387,000 pesos (about $112,000,000), while the U.S. Department of Commerce reported American direct investments at $121,000,000 for that year. (*Ibid.*, p. 111; US Dept. of Comm., Office of Business Economics, *Direct Private Foreign Investments of the United States, Census of 1950; A supplement to the Survey of Current Business*, Washington, D.C., 1953.) J. F. Rippy sets British investment in Mexican mining at the end of 1949 at £3,000,000. ("English Investments in Mexico," *Journal of Business*, XXV [Oct. 1952], 243.) For more details also see his *Br. Investments in Latin America*, pp. 55-56. Also see Just, "Mexico," 76-77. The Mexican Government bought Real del Monte for a reported $2,060,000. (US BuMines, *Minerals Yearbook, 1947*, p. 575.)

Ricardo Samaniego D. estimates that out of 207 companies engaged in mining, 63 of them, producing 73.24% of the Mexican output, are foreign-owned. Mexicans own privately 101 mines with 12.60% of the output; cooperatives hold 10 with 4.01%; and the Mexican government holds 3 (including Real del Monte) with 10.15%. While Mexicans produce over half the gold and 40% of the silver, foreign domination of copper and zinc exceeds 97% and of lead it comes to almost 90%. ("¿Saqueo de los minerales mexicanos?" *Revista de economía*, XV, No. 9 [Sept. 1952], 292–293.)

73. Banco de México, S.A., *33a. asamblea general ordinaria de accionistas* (Mexico, 1955), pp. 82–83.

74. Intl. Bk., *Eco. Dev. of Mex.*, p. 38.

75. *Ibid*, pp. 186–188.

76. Banco de México, S.A., *33a. asamblea general ordinaria*, p. 78; *35a. asamblea* (Mexico, 1957), p. 91.

77. US Dept. of Comm., Office of Business Economics, *U.S. Investments in the Latin American Economy* (Washington, D.C., 1957), p. 144; UN, Dept. of Eco. and Soc. Affairs, *Foreign Capital in Latin America*, p. 111; S. Pizer and F. Cutler, "International Investments and Earnings," *Survey of Current Business*, XXXV (Aug. 1955), p. 16, Table 3. Also see US Dept. of Comm., Office of Business Economics, *Foreign Investments of the United States, 1950*, pp. 48–49, Tables 12 and 13.

78. *Ibid.* For a general discussion of this problem in the Mexican economy, see UN, *Non-Ferrous Metals*, pp. 112–117.

79. S. Pizer and F. Cutler, "International Investments and Earnings," *Survey of Current Business* (hereinafter referred to as *Sur. Cur. Bus.*), XXXV (Aug. 1955), 18, Table 5. As an example of subsidiary reinvestment we have the statement of Standard Oil of New Jersey that while on a "net outflow" basis their total investment in 1956 was set at $289,000,000, actually new investments, including the search for oil, came to $686,000,000. (E. G. Collado and J. F. Bennett, "Private Investment and Economic Development," *Foreign Affairs*, XXXV [July 1957], 632–633.)

80. The 1950 census of U.S. direct foreign investments gave the following figures for U.S. holdings and earnings in Mexican mining in millions of dollars: total investment (book value), 120.5; foreign investments in securities and surplus, 7.0; net earnings after foreign income tax, 24.5; U.S. share of net earnings, 21.7; total U.S. income receipts, 17.9; U.S. share in undistributed profits of foreign corporations, 3.7; and direct investment capital movements, inflow of 8.1. (US Dept. of Comm., *Direct Foreign Private Investments, 1950*, p. 60, Table 28.) The 1953 estimate was $13,000,000 in income receipts and $4,000,000 in reinvested subsidiary earnings. (Pizer and Cutler, "Foreign Investments," *Sur. Cur. Bus.*, XXXIV [Nov. 1954], 13, Table 10.)

81. US Dept. of Comm., *U.S. Investments in the Latin American Economy*, pp. 141–142.

82. See articles in *Comm. & Fin. Chr.*, CLXV (Apr. 24, 1947), 2201 ff; and CLXXVI (Oct. 23, 1952), 1521.

83. UN, *Foreign Capital in Latin America*, p. 14.

84. Intl. Bk., *Eco. Dev. of Mex.*, p. 44.

85. UN, Dept. of Economic and Social Affairs, *Taxation in Capital-Exporting and Capital-Importing Countries of Foreign Private Investment in Latin America: U.S. Income Taxation of Private U.S. Investments in Latin America* (ST/ECA/18), New York, 1953; UN, *Taxation in Mexico*, pp. 7–11, US Dept. of Comm., *Direct Foreign Private Investments, 1950*, p. 30; UN, *Foreign Capital in Latin America*, pp. 26–27.

86. *Direct Foreign Private Investments, 1950*, p. 17.

87. UNECLA, *Economic Survey of Latin America, 1953*, p. 23, Table 9; UNECLA, "Changes in Employment Structure in Latin America, 1945–55," *Economic*

Bulletin for Latin America, II (Feb. 1957), 21 (Table 9), 22 (Table 10), 26 (Table 17), 33 (Table 24); UN, *Non-Ferrous Metals,* p. 100. (It is difficult to compare statistics from different sources concerning "mine labor." The figures used by the International Bank study cover only labor actually engaged in mining, omitting workers in the metallurgical industries, while the ECLA figures used in the text are distorted by the inclusion of petroleum workers.)

88. See above, Chap. 19; US. Dept. of Comm. "Establ. a Business in Mexico" (July 1955), pp. 14–17; and US Dept. of Comm., *Investing in Mexico,* pp. 85–91. Also see Beals, "Taxation in Mexico," 128.

89. *Diario oficial,* CXXXVI, No. 15 (Jan. 19, 1943), and CLXXII, No. 48 (Feb. 28, 1949); US Dept. of Comm., "Establ. a Business in Mexico" (July 1955), p. 16; *For. Comm. Wkly.,* XXI (Nov. 10, 1945), 35.

90. Sec. de Economía, Dir. Gen. de Estadística, *México en Cifras, 1952,* Plate No. 18.

91. Just, "Mexico," 77–78.

92. Beals, "Taxation in Mexico," 129; Just, "Mexico," 78.

93. *Conferencias de mesa redonda,* pp. 215–216.

94. *Ibid.,* pp. 220-223.

95. González Reyna, "Consideraciones," pp. 505–508; *Min. World,* VIII (May 1946), 65; *E&MJ,* CLIV (Jan. 1953), 98–99.

96. Banco de México, *35a. asamblea general,* pp. 78–79. Diego G. López Rosado and Juan F. Nayola Váquez ("Los salarios reales en México, 1939–1950," *Trimestre económico,* XVIII, No. 2 [April 1951], 201–209) claim that workers as a group have lost in purchasing power while employers have gained.

97. *Conferencias de mesa redonda,* pp. 215–216.

98. Intl. Bk., *Eco. Dev. of Mex.,* p. 148.

99. "The Growth of the Mexican Economy," American Universities Field Staff *Report* (June 14, 1956), pp. 22–24.

100. See Chaps. 22 and 24; *Min. Sur.,* XIII (Dec. 1945), 17; (Feb. 1946), 16; (Apr. 1946), 14; *E&MJ,* CXLVII (Jan. 1946), 132; (Feb. 1946), 159; (Apr. 1946), 141–142; (June 1946), 153–154; (July 1946), 134; *For. Comm. Wkly.,* XXII (Mar. 23, 1946), 46.

101. *E&MJ,* CXLIX (Apr. 1948), 103; (May 1948), 146–147; (July 1948), 105; (Sept. 1948), 146; (Oct. 1948), 142; *For. Comm. Wkly.,* XXXI (Apr. 3, 1948), 14; (May 1, 1948), 22; XXXIII (Oct. 16, 1948), 19; *Revista minera y petrolera,* XV (June 1948), 13; *Min. World,* XI (Jan. 1949), 54; (Apr. 1949), 36.

102. *For. Comm. Wkly.,* XXXV (June 20, 1949), 24–25; L. B. Clark, "Mexico Faces 1950," *ibid.,* XXXVIII (Jan. 23, 1950), 5; *Min. World,* XI (Apr. 1949), 36; (Sept. 1949), 57, 60; XII (Apr. 15, 1950), 78.

103. *E&MJ,* CLI (Feb. 1950), 170; (May 1950), 140; (June 1950), 134, 136; (July 1950), 119; (Aug. 1950), 164, 165; (Dec. 1950), 151; CLII (May 1951), 144; (June 1951), 140; *Min. World,* XII (July 1950), 51; *For. Comm., Wkly.,* XXXIX (May 29, 1950), 22; XLI (Nov. 6, 1950), 15; XLII (Jan. 15, 1951), 15; UN, Economic and Social Council, ECLA, *Economic Survey of Latin America, 1950: Recent Trends and Events in Mining* (Doc. No. E/CN.12/217/Add. 12), p. 103.

104. *E&MJ,* CLII (May 1951), 144; (June 1951), 139; (July 1951), 209; *Min. World,* XIII (Feb. 1951), 51; (May 1951), 52; (July 1951), 50.

105. Banco de México, *31a. asamblea ordinaria de accionistas* (Mexico, 1953), p. 27; *32a. asamblea* (Mexico, 1954), p. 31; *E&MJ,* CLIV (Mar. 1953), 162; CLV (Aug. 1954), 158; CLVI (June 1955), 172, 174; *For. Comm. Wkly.,* XLIX (June 15, 1953), 3; LII (Aug. 23, 1954), 7.

106. Banco de México, *31a. asamblea,* p. 27; *For. Comm. Wkly.,* LII (Sept. 9,

1954), 6. In 1944 the average wage in mining was reported as 1800 pesos (about $370) per year. (*México en Cifras, 1952*, Plate No. 17.)

107. La delegación del Gobierno del Estado de Hidalgo, "Ponencia," PCMN, *Memoria*, pp. 181–182.

108. See PCMN, *Memoria, passim,* and esp. pp. 350–383; also *Conferencias de mesa redonda*, pp. 224–225.

109. For example, see *E&MJ*, CXLVI (Feb. 1945), 180; CXLVII (May 1946), 130; CLIV (Mar. 1953), 162; CLV (July 1954), 157; *Min. World*, XIII (June 1951), 62; ABMS, *Yrbk., 1957*, pp. 1–3.

110. M. M. Saavedra, "La minería y sus problemas actuales," *Investigación económica*, IX (2nd Quarter, 1949), 193.

111. E. Just, "Mexico," 78.

112. *E&MJ*, CXLVII (May 1946), 130.

113. *Bol. de min. y pet.*, XXIV (Apr. 1953), 121–122; (Aug. 1953), 72; XXVI (June 1955), 9–25, 29; (July 1955), 9–10; XXVII (Apr. 1956), 114; XXVIII (Feb. 1957), 11; (Apr. 1957), 11; (May 1957), 13; (June 1957), 13; (Sept. 1957), 15; (Dec. 1957), 11; XXIX (Apr. 1958), 11; (June 1958), 19, 21.

114. *Min. Sur.*, XIII (Mar. 1946), 18.

115. *E&MJ*, CLI (June 1950), 130; *Min. World*, XV (Apr. 1953), 67.

116. *Diario oficial*, CCXIII, No. 53 (Dec. 31, 1955).

117. International Cooperation Administration (ICA), *Mexico, Monthly Progress Report*, Sept. 1955 (US BuMines files); *E&MJ*, CLV (Mar. 1954), 177.

118. *E&MJ*, CXLVI (Sept. 1945), 148; CLV (Mar. 1954), 177; CLVI (Mar. 1955), 165, 167; *Min. World*, XII (Dec. 1950), 47; XVI (Jan. 1954), 72; (June 1954), 75; (Aug. 1954), 65; XVIII (Mar. 1956), 69.

119. *Min. World*, XI (Sept. 1949), 53; ICA, *Mexico*, p. 4.

120. *Min. World*, XIII (Sept. 1951), 53.

121. ICA, *Technical Cooperation Progress in Mineral Resources, Annual Report, 1955* (June 26, 1956), pp. 2–3 (US BuMines files); Inter-American Study Mission, *Report . . . pursuant to H. Res. 28*, H. Rept. No. 1454 (Washington, D.C., 1952), pp. 22–23, 36; *E&MJ*, CLI (Mar. 1950), 134; A. Probert, "Point IV," *Min. Engin.*, IV (July 1952), 664–665.

122. See the series of articles on this topic in PCMN, *Memoria*, pp. 429–440; *E&MJ*, CXLVII (Mar. 1946), 144, 146; CXLVIII (May 1947), 86–87; CXLIX (Sept. 1948), 146.

123. González Reyna, "Consideraciones," pp. 501–502; Un grupo de mineros de Cimarron Chico, Jalisco, "Ponencia," PCMN, *Memoria*, pp. 451–452; US Dept. of Comm., "Establ. a Business in Mexico" (July 1955), pp. 17–18.

124. González Reyna, "Consideraciones," pp. 503–504, 511–512; Just, "Mexico," 77; A. J. Terrones, Jr., "Mexican Mining Engineer," *E&MJ*, CLVI (Dec. 1955), 115.

125. For excellent short surveys of Mexico's resources in this area, see J. González Reyna, "Los yacimientos de minerales radioactivos de México y su exploración," and T. Flores, "Los recursos de minerales no-metalicos de México," PCIARM, *Memoria*, pp. 288–293, 325–348.

Glossary

OF SPANISH TERMS

Amparo—literally, "protection." A court order halting an executive agency from enforcing a legal requirement believed to be an invasion of individual or private rights. Sometimes compared to an injunction or the invalidation of a law by the United States Supreme Court.

Buscón—literally, "seeker," a prospector. May be applied to a solitary worker or to a group of men working together in such tasks as cleaning out a mine, working a rich ore "pip," or robbing pillars. (See *gambusino*, below.)

Caduca—"To be forfeit." Used to describe the legal status of a mine whose title has been revoked for failure to pay taxes or comply with some legal requirement.

Cámara Minera—Mining Chamber.

Cateo—A test; used in the term "cateo concession." This type of concession is taken before there are enough indications to warrant an exploration concession.

Científicos—literally, "the scientific ones." Refers to a group of men who, during the administration of President Díaz, counseled the government and believed that "scientific principles" could be used in governing Mexico.

Comisión de Fomento Minero (CFM)—Commission for Mining Development. An official agency with the objective of encouraging and aiding the mining industry in accordance with government policy.

Fondo—A mining claim. Includes one or more contiguous claim areas. (See *pertenencia*, below.)

Gambusino—Often used synonymously with *buscón* (see above), although this term tends to imply more strongly the prospecting function.

Hacendado—Large landowner; proprietor of a hacienda.

Hacienda de Beneficio—Beneficiation plant.

Hectare—Metric measurement of area, 100 meters by 100 meters, equal to 2.47 acres.

Ingeniero (Ing.)—Professional title of a graduate engineer.

Licenciado (Lic.)—Professional title of a graduate lawyer.

Pertenencia—Mine claim area measurement equal to one hectare (100 meters by 100 meters).

Reglamento—Bylaws detailing the more general provisions of a code.

Rurales—A federal police force organized during the Díaz administration. Usually assigned to rural areas and smaller towns, but also used during emergencies to quell riots and other disturbances.

Vara—Spanish linear measure, about 34 inches.

Glossary
OF ABBREVIATIONS

I. Companies, Associations, and Departments

ASARCO—American Smelting and Refining Company
Aso. Mex. de Min.—*Asociación Mexicana de Minería* (Mexican Mining Association)
ASSCO—American Smelters Securities Company
Cám. Min. de Méx.—*Cámara Minera de México* (Mexican Chamber of Mining)
Cám. Nac. de Min.—*Cámara Nacional de Minería* (National Mining Chamber)
CFM—*Comisión de Fomento Minero* (Commission for Mining Development)
CROM—*Confederación Regional de Obrera Mexicana* (Regional Confederation of Mexican Labor)
Dept. de Minas—*Departamento de Minas* (Department of Mines)
ECLA—Economic Commission for Latin America (an agency of the United Nations)
Guggenex—Guggenheim Exploration Company
IMMM—*Instituto mexicano de minas y metalurgia* (Mexican Institute of Mining and Metallurgy)
Inst. de Min. and Met.—Institution of Mining and Metallurgy (London)
Intl. Bk., *Eco. Dev. of Mex.*—International Bank for Reconstruction and Development, *Economic Development of Mexico*
IO&S—International Ore & Smelting Company
OPA—Office of Price Administration
PCIARM—*Primer Convención Inter-Americana de Recursos Minerales* (First Inter-American Convention on Mineral Resources)
PCMN—*Primer Congreso Minero Nacional* (First National Mining Congress)
SEN—*Secretaría de la Economía Nacional* (Ministry of the National Economy)
UN—United Nations
UNECLA—See ECLA
UNESCO—United Nations Economic and Security Council
US BuMines—United States Bureau of Mines
US Dept. of Comm.—United States Department of Commerce
USSR&M—United States Smelting, Refining, and Mining Company
US Tariff Comm.—United States Tariff Commission

II. Periodical Titles

AIME *Trans.*—American Institute of Mining, Metallurgical, and Petroleum Engineers, *Transactions*
ABMS *Yrbk.*—American Bureau of Metal Statistics *Yearbook* (New York)
An. de estad. min.—*Anuario de estadística minera* (*Annual of Mining Statistics*)
Bol. de conc. min.—*Boletín de concessiones mineras* (*Bulletin of Mining Concessions*)
Bol. de indus. min.—*Boletín de industrias mineras* (*Bulletin of Mining Industries*)
Bol. de min. y pet.—*Boletín de minas y petróleo* (*Bulletin of Mines and Petroleum*)
Bol. min.—*Boletín minero* (*Mining Bulletin*)

Comm. & Fin. Chr.—Commercial and Financial Chronicle
E&MJ—Engineering and Mining Journal
For. Comm. Wkly.—Foreign Commerce Weekly
Mex. Min. J.—Mexican Mining Journal
Min. & Met.—Mining and Metallurgy
Min. & Sci. Press—Mining and Scientific Press
Min. Engin.—Mining Engineering
Min. Mag.—Mining Magazine
Min. Sur.—Mineral Survey
Min. World—Mining World
Min. Yrbk.—Mineral Yearbook
Sur. Cur. Bus.—Survey of Current Business

Bibliography

THIS listing differs from the traditional forms for bibliography. Since the type of sources used in a work of this scope do not meaningfully lend themselves to classification by primary and secondary categories, or as public documents or periodicals, they have been presented instead in a functional listing by topic. Within topics certain subsections have been arranged chronologically for the sake of clarity. Furthermore, material not in the footnotes but which supplied broad background information, or which was not specifically used, has been included. To keep this bibliography within a reasonable length, sources appearing as articles in periodicals or transactions of societies which have been specifically cited in detail in the footnotes are omitted (with a few exceptions) along with certain minor items.

DICTIONARIES

The following dictionaries and glossaries have been found particularly useful in the interpretation of Spanish mining terms.

AMERICAN INSTITUTE OF MINING AND METALLURGICAL ENGINEERS (New York), *Transactions*, XXXII (1902). See pp. 573–603.

DAHLGREN, CHARLES B. *Historic Mines of Mexico.* Mexico: Oficina tipográfica de la Secretaría de Fomento, 1887. See pp. 15–19.

HALSE, EDWARD. *A Dictionary of Spanish, Spanish-American, Portuguese and Portuguese-American Mining, Metallurgical and Allied Terms.* London: C. Griffin, 1926.

NIETO, FELIX. *Apuntes en forma de diccionario por el minero práctico.* Zacatecas, 1891.

BIBLIOGRAPHIES

General Mexican Economy

BULLEJOS, JOSÉ. *Diez años de literatura económica: Bibliografía básica sobre la economía de México, 1943–1953.* Mexico: Universidad Nacional Autónoma de México (Instituto de Investigaciones Económicas), 1954.

———. *Bibliografía industrial de México, 1952–53.* Mexico: Banco de México (Oficina de Investigaciones Industrias), 1954.

———. *La bibliografía económica de México en 1954 y 1955.* Mexico: Banco de México (Departamento de Estudios Económicos), 1956.

CREEL LUJÁN, LUIS J. "Notes on Mexican Fiscal Literature," *Bulletin for International Fiscal Documentation* (Amsterdam: International Bureau of Fiscal Documentation), IV, No. 3 (1950), 91–104.

MEXICO. Dirección General de Estadística. (Secretaría de la Economía Nacional.) *Bibliografía mexicana de estadística.* 2 vols. Mexico: Talleres gráficos de la Nación, 1938.

Mexican Mining

AMERICAN INSTITUTE OF MINING AND METALLURGICAL ENGINEERS. *General Alphabetical and Analytical Index.* New York, 1936.

AGUILAR Y SANTILLÁN, RAFAEL. *Bibliografía geológica y minera de la República Mexicana.* (Instituto geológico *Boletín* 10.) Mexico: Oficina tipográfica de la Secretaría de Fomento, 1898.

————. *Bibliografía geológica y minera de la República Mexicana: Completada hasta el año de 1904.* Mexico: Impr. de la Secretaría de Fomento, 1908.

————. Mexico. Departamento de Minas. *Bibliografía geológica y minera de la República Mexicana, 1905–1918.* Mexico: Secretaría de Hacienda, 1918.

————. Mexico. Secretaría de la Economía Nacional. *Bibliografía geológica y minera de la República Mexicana.* Mexico: Talleres gráficos de la Nación, 1936.

STATISTICAL COLLECTIONS

Guides

MEXICO. Dirección General de Estadística. (Secretaría de la Economía Nacional.) *Informes sobre las principales estadísticas mexicanas.* Mexico: Talleres gráficos de la Nacíon, 1941.

Collections

AMERICAN BUREAU OF METAL STATISTICS. *Year Book.* Vols. I–XXXVII. New York, 1921–57.

MEXICO. Departamento de Minas. (Secretaría de Industria, Comercio y Trabajo.) *Anuario de estadística minera.* Mexico, 1923–33.

————. Fomento de Ministerio. *Informe y documentos para la estadística de la minería.* México: Oficina tipográfica de la Secretaría de Fomento, 1886.

————. Departamento de la Estadística Nacional. *Sonora, Sinaloa y Nayarit; Estudio estadístico y económico social. Año de 1927.* Mexico: Imprenta Mundial, 1928.

————. *Seis años de gobierno al servicio de México, 1934–1940.* Mexico, 1941.

SELLERIER, CARLOS. *Data Referring to Mexican Mining.* Mexico: F. P. Hoeck & Co., 1901.

UNITED NATIONS. Department of Economic and Social Affairs. (Economic Commission for Latin America.) *Economic Survey of Latin America, 1948——.* New York, 1950.

PHYSICAL FEATURES OF MEXICO

For a detailed listing see footnotes—especially first footnote to Chapter 1. Also see listings under "History" and "Economics."

CONGRÈS GEOLOGIQUE INTERNATIONAL. *Guide des excursions du Xᵉ Congrès Géologique International, México, 1906.* Mexico: Imprimiere du Ministère de Fomento, 1906.

FLORES, TEODORO. *Geología minera de la región N.E. del Estado de Michoacan* (1935). Mexico, 1946. (Published as Universidad Nacional Autónoma de México, "Instituto de Geología," *Boletín* 52.)

KUECHLER, JACOBO. *Los valles de Sabinas y Salinas.* Mexico: Impr. Imperial, 1866.

MEXICO. Departamento de Estudios Económicos. (Secretaría de la Economía Nacional.) *Geografía económica del Estado de Hidalgo.* Mexico: Talleres gráficos de la Nación, 1939.

——. Departamento de Estudios Económicos. (Secretaría de la Economía Nacional.) *Geografía económica del Estado de Nayarit.* Mexico: DAPP, 1939.

VILLAFANA, ANDRÉS. Mexico. Secretaría de Fomento. *Reseña minera de la región central y sureste del Estado de Jalisco.* Mexico, 1916.

WILSON, I. F., AND ROCHA, V. S. *Geology and Mineral Deposits of the Boleo Copper District, Baja California, Mexico.* (U.S. Geological Survey, Professional Paper 273.) Washington, D.C., 1955.

HISTORY AND POLITICS

General

CALDERON, FRANCISCO R. *La vida económica en la República restaurada.* Mexico: Editorial Hermes, 1955.

CALLCOTT, WILFRED H. *Liberalism in Mexico, 1857–1929.* Stanford, Calif.: Stanford University Press, 1931.

CHAVEZ OROZCO, LUIS. *Revolución industrial; Revolución política.* (Biblioteca del Obrero y Campesino, No. 28.) Mexico: DAPP, 1937.

CROSMAN, HERBERT A. "The Early Career of José Ives Limantour, 1854–1886." Unpublished Ph.D. dissertation, Harvard University (1949).

DAVIS, WILLIAM B. *Experiences and Observations of an American Consular Officer During the Recent Mexican Revolutions.* Chula Vista, Calif.: Privately printed, 1920.

DIAZ DUFOO, CARLOS. *Limantour.* 2d ed. Mexico: Impr. Victoria, 1922. (Translated into French as: *Les Finances du Mexique, 1892–1911; Limantour, l'homme et l'oeuvre.* Paris: Lib. Félix Alcan, 1926.)

DIFFIE, BAILEY W. *Latin American Civilization: Colonial Period.* Harrisburg, Pa.: Stackpole Bros., 1945.

DULLES, JOHN W. F. *Yesterday in Mexico: A Chronicle of the Revolution, 1919–1936.* Austin, Tex.: University of Texas Press, 1961.

FOSTER, JOHN W. *Diplomatic Memoirs.* 2 vols. Boston and New York: Houghton Mifflin Co., 1909.

GRUENING, ERNEST H. *Mexico and Its Heritage.* New York and London: The Century Co., 1928.

HARING, CLARENCE H. "American Gold and Silver Production in the First Half of the Sixteenth Century," *Quarterly Journal of Economics,* XXIX (May 1915), 433–479.

——. *The Spanish Empire in America.* New York: Oxford University Press, 1947.

KLUCKHOHN, FRANK L. *The Mexican Challenge.* New York: Doubleday, Doran & Co., Inc., 1939.

MARTIN, PERCY F. *Mexico of the Twentieth Century.* 2 vols. London: E. Arnold, 1907.

MEXICO. Secretaría de Industria, Comercio y Trabajo. *La industria, el comercio y el trabajo en México durante la gestión administrativa del Señor Gral. Plutarco Elias Calles.* 5 vols. Mexico, 1928.

PARKES, HENRY B. *History of Mexico.* 3d edition. Boston: Houghton Mifflin Co., 1960.

Ross, Stanley R. *Francisco I. Madero: Apostle of Mexican Democracy.* New York: Columbia University Press, 1955.

Scholes, Walter V. *Mexican Politics During the Juárez Regime, 1855–1872.* Columbia, Mo.: University of Missouri Press, 1957.

Turner, John Kenneth. *Barbarous Mexico.* Chicago: C. H. Kerr & Co., 1911.

Valadés, José C. *El porfirismo; Historia de un régimen.* 2 vols. Mexico: Antigua Libería Robredo, de J. Porrúa e hijos, 1941–48.

Weyl, Nathaniel and Sylvia. *The Reconquest of Mexico; The Years of Lázaro Cárdenas.* New York: Oxford University Press, 1939.

Economic History and Organization

Mining Industry (Contemporary Reports)

American Institute of Mining and Metallurgical Engineers (New York), *Transactions,* XXXII, 1902. (Entire volume on Mexico.)

Congrès Géologique International. *Compte Rendu de la Xe Session, México, 1906.* Mexico: Imprenta y fototípia de la Secretaría de Fomento, 1907.

Congreso Minero Nacional. *Memoria del Primer Congreso Minero Nacional.* México: Oficina de Prensa y Publicidad, Secretaría de Economía, 1948.

Frazer, Persifor. *Geological and Mineral Strikes in Nuero León and Coahuila, Mexico.* Philadelphia: Sherman & Co., 1884.

González Reyna, Genaro. "Consideraciones sobre los problemas de la minería en México," Primer Congreso Minero Nacional, *Memoria* (Mexico, 1948), 497–513.

———. *La industria minera en el Estado de Chihuahua.* (Comité directivo para la investigación de recursos minerales de México. *Boletín* 7.) Mexico, 1946.

———. *La industria minera en el Estado de Zacatecas.* (Comité directivo para la investigación de recursos minerales de México. *Boletín* 4.) Mexico, 1946.

———. *Riqueza minera y yacimientos minerales de México.* 3d ed. Mexico: Banco de México, 1956.

Instituto Mexicana de Minas y Metalurgia. *La industria minera de México.* (Parts 1–6 deal with the states of Hidalgo, Mexico, and Michoacan.) Mexico, 1911–12.

———. *Informes y memoria* ... 2 vols. Mexico, 1909–12.

Launay, C. "Mines et Industries Minières," in R. Bonaparte, L. Bourgeois, *et al.* (eds.). *Le Mexique au debût de XXe Siecle.* 2 vols. Paris: C. Delagrave, 1904.

Mexico. Departamento de Estudios Económicos. (Secretaría de la Economía Nacional.) *Apuntes acerca del porvenir de la minería en México.* Mexico: Multigrafos y mimeografos de la Sria., 1934–35.

Ortiz, Enrique. "Aspectos técnicos y económicos de la minería," *Investigación económica* (Third Quarter, 1942), 235–273.

Péna, Moisés T. de la. "La industria minera en México," *Investigación económica* (First Quarter, 1944), 21–62.

Primera Convención Interamericana de Recursos Minerales. *Memorias.* Mexico: Impr. Moctezuma, 1952.

Ramirez, Santiago. *Informe ... de su exploración en la Sierra Mojada....* Mexico: Impr. de F. Díaz de León, 1880.

Rickard, Thomas A. *Journeys of Observation.* San Francisco: Dewey Publishing Co., 1907.

Romero, Matías. *Geographical and Statistical Notes on Mexico.* New York and London: G. P. Putnam Sons, 1898.

Southworth, John R., and Holms, Percy G. *El directorio oficial minero de México.*

(Publicado bajo la autorización del gobierno.) Liverpool: Blake & Mackenzie, 1908.

SOUTHWORTH, JOHN R. *El Estado de sonora.* Nogales, Ariz.: The Oasis Printing and Publishing House, 1897.

———. *Las minas de México.* (Publicado bajo la autorización del gobierno.) Liverpool: Blake & Mackenzie, 1905.

———. *El territorio de la Baja California, México.* San Francisco: Press of the Hicks-Judd Company, 1899.

VILLAFAÑA, ANDRÉS, AND CASTANADO, JOSÉ. Dirección General de Minas y Petróleo. (Secretaría de la Economía Nacional.) *La industria minera-metalúrgica en México.* Mexico, 1941.

VILLAREAL, ARNULFO. *El carbon mineral en México.* Mexico: Editorial y Distribuidora Ibero-Americana de Publicaciones, 1953.

Mining Industry (*Historical Surveys*)

BARAGWANATH, JOHN. *Pay Streak.* New York: Doubleday, 1936.

BARGALLO, MODESTO. *La minería y la metalurgia en la América española durante la época colonial.* Mexico: Fondo de Cultura Económica, 1955.

BERNSTEIN, MARVIN D. "Colonel William C. Greene and the Cananea Copper Bubble," *Bulletin of the Business Historical Society* (Cambridge, Mass.), XXVI (Dec. 1952), 179–198.

———. "The Economic Organization of the Mexican Coal Industry," *Inter-American Economic Affairs,* V (Spring 1952), 73–91.

BIMSON, WALTER REED. *Louis D. Ricketts, 1859–1940, Mining Engineer, Geologist, Banker, Industrialist, and Builder of Arizona.* New York: Newcomen Society of England (American Branch), 1949.

CLELAND, ROBERT G. *A History of Phelps Dodge, 1834–1950.* New York: A. A. Knopf, 1952.

———. "The Mining Industry of Mexico: A Historical Sketch," *Mining and Scientific Press,* CXXIII (July 2, 1921), 13–20; (Nov. 5, 1921), 638–642.

CRESPO Y MARTINEZ, GILBERTO. *México; Industria minera; Estudio de su evolución.* Mexico: Oficina tipográfica de la Secretaría de Fomento, 1903.

DAHLGREN, CHARLES B. *Historic Mines of Mexico.* New York: Privately printed, 1883.

GARCÍA, TRINIDAD. *Los mineros mexicanos. Colección de artículos sobre tradiciones y narraciones mineras. ...* Mexico: Oficina tipográfica de la Secretaría de Fomento, 1895.

GARFIAS, V. R. "Historical Outline of Mineral Production in Mexico," American Institute of Mining and Metallurgical Engineers. *Transactions* (New York), CXXVI (1937), 346–355.

GERARD, JAMES W. *My First Eighty-Three Years in America: The Memoirs of James W. Gerard.* Garden City, N.Y.: Doubleday, 1951.

GUGGENHEIM, WILLIAM (under pseudo. GATENBY WILLIAMS), AND HEATH, CHARLES M. *William Guggenheim: The Story of an Adventurous Career.* New York: The Lone Voice Publishing Co., 1934.

HAMMOND, JOHN HAYS. *The Autobiography of John Hays Hammond.* 2 vols. New York: Farrar & Rinehart, Inc., 1935.

HOWE, WALTER. *The Mining Guild of New Spain and Its Tribunal General, 1770–1821.* Cambridge, Mass.: Harvard University Press, 1949.

INGERSOLL, RALPH M. *In and Under Mexico.* New York and London: The Century Co., 1924.

JENISION, H. A. C. "The Mining History of Mexico," *Engineering and Mining*

Journal, CXV (Feb. 24, 1923), 364–68; (March 3, 1923), 401–03.

MARCOSSON, ISAAC F. *Anaconda*. New York: Dodd, Mead & Co., 1957.

———. *Metal Magic: The Story of the American Smelting and Refining Company*. New York: Farrar, Straus, 1949.

MARTIN, PERCY F. *Mexico's Treasure-House (Guanajuato)*. New York: The Cheltenham Press, 1906.

MENDÍZABAL, M. O. DE. "Los minerales de Pachuca y Real del Monte en la época colonial," *El trimestre económico*, VIII, No. 2 (July–Sept. 1941), 253–309.

MOTTEN, CLEMENT G. *Mexican Silver and the Enlightenment*. Philadelphia: University of Pennsylvania Press, 1950.

O'CONNOR, HARVEY. *The Guggenheims: The Making of an American Dynasty*. New York: Covici, Friede, 1937.

PLETCHER, DAVID M. "An American Mining Company in the Mexican Revolution of 1911–20," *Journal of Modern History*, XX (Mar. 1948), 19–26.

———. *Rails, Mines and Progress: Seven American Promoters in Mexico, 1867–1911*. Ithaca, N.Y.: Cornell University Press, 1958.

RAMIREZ, SANTIAGO. *Noticia historica de la riqueza minera de México*. Mexico: Oficina tipográfica de la Secretaría de Fomento, 1884.

RICKARD, THOMAS A. *Man and Metals: A History of Mining in Relation to the Development of Civilization*. 2 vols. New York: Whittlesey House, McGraw-Hill Book Co., Inc., 1932.

RIVET, PAUL, AND ARSANDAUX, HENRI. *La métallurgie en Amérique précolombienne*. ("Université de Paris, Travaux et Memoires de l'Institut d'Ethnologie," XXXIX.) Paris, 1946.

SHEPHERD, GRANT. *The Silver Magnet: Fifty Years in a Mexican Silver Mine*. New York: E. P. Dutton & Co., Inc., 1938.

TAMAYO, J. L. "La minería de Nueva España en 1794," *El trimestre económico*, X, No. 2 (July–Sept. 1943), 287-319.

TRAYLOR, SAMUEL W. *Out of the Southwest*. Allentown, Pa.: G. P. Schlicher & Son, 1936.

WAGNER, HENRY R. *Bullion to Books*. Los Angeles: The Zamorano Club, 1942.

WEST, ROBERT C. *The Mining Community in Northern New Spain: The Parral Mining District*. Berkeley, Calif.: University of California Press, 1949.

Fiscal Policy and Taxes

ANDREW, A. PIATT. "The End of the Mexican Dollar," *Quarterly Journal of Economics*, XVIII (May 1904), 321–356.

DÍAZ DUFOO, CARLOS *Les finances du Mexique, 1892–1911* ... Paris: Lib. Félix Alcan, 1926.

———. *Una victoria financiera*. (Capítulos para la historia.) Paris: Lib. de la Vda. de Ch. Bouret, 1920.

GAMA, FELIPE DE LA. "Resumen de los egresos efectuados por el Gobierno Federal desde el año de 1876 hasta 1936," *Revista de Hacienda*, I, No. 3 (Nov. 1937), 3–20.

KEMMERER, EDWIN W. *Inflation and Revolution: Mexico's Experience of 1912–1917*. Princeton, N.J.: Princeton University Press, 1940.

———. *Modern Currency Reforms*. New York: The Macmillan Co., 1916.

MARTÍNEZ SOBRAL, ENRIQUE. *La reforma monetaria*. Mexico: Tipográfia de la Oficina Impresora de Estampillas, 1910.

McCALEB, WALTER F. *The Public Finances of Mexico*. New York: Harper & Brothers, 1921.

MEKLER, ANA. *El impuesto del aforo, el doce por ciento sobre el valor de aforo y sus repercusiones en la exportación.* (Colección "Nuevos Economistas," II.) Mexico: Editorial America, 1942.

MEXICO. Oficina de investigaciones económicas. (Secretaría de Hacienda y Crédito Público.) "El impuesto a la producción de plata," *Revista de Hacienda,* I, No. 5 (Jan. 1938), 3–17; No. 6 (Feb. 1938), 29–37; II, No. 1 (Mar. 1938), 13–23; No. 2 (Apr. 1938), 27–32.

OCÁDIZ ARNAUD, JULIO. "El impuesto sobre la producción de plata [1925–1937]," *Revista de Hacienda,* I, No. 2 (Oct. 1937), 3–16.

PLETCHER, DAVID M. "The Fall of Silver in Mexico, 1870–1910, and Its Effect on American Investment," *Journal of Economic History,* XVIII, No. 1 (Spring 1958), 33–55.

QUINTANA, MIGUEL A. *Los ensayos monetarios como consecuencia de la baja de la plata: La problema de la plata y el de la moneda de plata en el mundo y en México.* Mexico: Impr. Galas, 1931.

RAMÍREZ CABANAS C., JOAQUIM. "Los ingresos federales de México durante los años 1876–1936," *Revista de Hacienda,* II, No. 2 (Apr. 1938), 7–25.

TORRES GAITÁN, RICARDO. *Política monetaria mexicana.* Mexico: Librería Ariel, 1944.

Labor

CLARK, MARJORIE. *Organized Labor in Mexico.* Chapel Hill, N.C.: University of North Carolina Press, 1934.

GONZÁLEZ RAMÍREZ, MANUEL (ed.). *La huelga de Cananea.* (Vol. III: *Fuentes para la Historia de la Revolución Mexicana.*) Mexico. Fondo de Cultura Económica, 1956.

MEXICO. Departamento del Trabajo. *Boletínes* 1–8. Mexico, 1913–14.

RYNNING, CAPT. THOMAS H. *Gun Notches; the Life Story of a Cowboy-Soldier.* As told to Al Cohn and Joe Chisholm. New York: Frederick A. Stokes, 1931. (See material on Cananea strike, pp. 290–315.)

WEYL, WALTER E. "Labor Conditions in Mexico," *Bulletin of the Department of Labor,* No. 38, January 1902 (Washington, D.C., 1902), 1–94.

Railways

COVERDALE AND COLPITTS, Consulting Engineers, New York. "The National Railways of Mexico." (Mimeographed report rendered on Sept. 17, 1929 to the International Committee of Bankers in Mexico.)

GURZA, JAIME. *La política ferrocarrilera del gobierno.* Mexico: Tipográfia de la Oficina Impresora de Estampillas, 1911.

HARDY, O. "The Revolution and the Railroads of Mexico," *Pacific Historical Review,* III, No. 3 (Sept. 1934), 249–269.

MOYO PORRAS, EDMUNDO. "Los transportes y la minería," *Revista de economía,* XVI (May 1953), 142–146.

POWELL, F. W. "The Railroads of Mexico," *Mexican Year Book for 1920–1921.* Los Angeles: Mexican Year Book Pub. Co., 1922, pp. 163–188.

VILLAFUERTE, CARLOS. *Ferrocarriles.* ("Serie estructura económica y social de México.") Mexico: Fondo de Cultura Económica, 1959.

Fuel and Power

BRADLEY, J. R. *Fuel and Power in Latin America.* U.S. Department of Commerce. Bureau of Foreign and Domestic Trade. ("Trade Promotion Series," No. 126.) Washington, D.C., 1931.

GALARZA, ERNESTO. *La industria eléctrica en México.* Mexico: Fondo de Cultura Económica, 1941.

HERRERA Y LASSO, JOSÉ. Secretaría de Industria, Comercio y Trabajo. *La fuerza motriz en México.* Mexico: Talleres gráficos de la Nación, 1927.

————. *La industria de la generación de fuerza hidroeléctrica; Su fomento y reglamentación en México.* Departamento de Industrias. Mexico: Secretaría de Gobernación, Dirección de Talleres Gráficos, 1920.

————. *La industria eléctrica.* Mexico: Editorial Cultura, 1933.

LARA BEAUTELL, CRISTOBAL. *La industria de energía eléctrica.* Nacional Financiera. Mexico: Fondo de Cultura Económica, 1953.

RODRÍGUEZ MATA, EMILIO. *La generación y distribución de energía eléctrica.* Investigaciones Industriales del Banco de México, S.A. Mexico, 1953.

GOVERNMENT POLICY (OFFICIAL DECLARATIONS AND COMMENTARIES)

ALEMÁN, MIGUEL. *Program of Government: Presidential Campaign in Mexico.* (Edited and distributed by "Agrupación de Cuidadanos de México en el Extranjero.") San Antonio, Tex., 1946.

CÁMARA NACIONAL DE MINERÍA (and successors). *Circulares.* Mexico, 1924–43.

Conferencias de mesa redonda presidadas durante su campaña electoral por el lic. Miguel Alemán. Mexico: Cooperativa talleres gráficos de la Nación, 1949.

GARCIA, JENARO P. *La situación de la industria minera: Sintesis comparativa entre la producción y consumo de los principales metales.* Mexico, 1929.

GURRÍA URGELL, OSVALDO. "Tendencias de la Secretaría en relación con el fomento y nacionalización de la minería." (Trabajo presentado a la X° Convención Nacional de Ingenieros by the representative of the Departamento de Minas, Secretaría de la Economía Nacional. [Mimeographed].) Mexico, 1934.

"Junta celebrada en la tarde del día 30 de Julio de 1926, entre la comisión nombrada por la Secretaría de Industria, Comercio y Trabajo y la designada por los representantes de los intereses mineros de la República para tratar acerca de las observaciones hechas por esta última comisión, al reglamento de la Ley de Industrias Minerales." (Stenographic copy reprinted in mimeograph by the Cámara Nacional de Minería, Circular No. 224.) Mexico (Sept. 25, 1926).

MADERO, RAÚL, AND FALOMIR, J. J. "Informe que presenta a C. Sec. de la Economía Nacional la Gerencia de la Comisión de Fomento Minero sobre la labor desarrollada por esta institución desde que fundaba." (Typewritten copy [unpaged] dated [Mexico], Aug. 29, 1944.)

MADERO, RAÚL. *La minería atraviesa por una crisis muy seria.* Mexico: Cámara Minera de México, 1946. (Reprinted from the newspaper *Excelsior,* Feb. 22, 1946.)

PARTIDO NACIONAL REVOLUCIONARIO. *The Second Six-Year Plan, 1941–46.* Mexico, 1940.

————. *Plan Sexenal del P.N.R.* Mexico, 1934.

PÉREZ DUARTE, CONSTANTINO. *La situación de la industria minera.* Mexico: Cámara Minera de México, 1945.

PRIMER CONGRESO NACIONAL DE INDUSTRIALES *Informes.* (Sixteen monographs.) Mexico, 1917.

UNITED STATES—MEXICAN RELATIONS

CLENDENEN, CLARENCE C. *The United States and Pancho Villa: A Study in Unconventional Diplomacy.* Ithaca, N. Y.: Cornell University Press, 1961.

CLINE, HOWARD F. *The United States and Mexico.* Cambridge, Mass.: Harvard University Press, 1953.

"MEXICO AND HER RELATION TO AMERICAN DEFENSE," *The Journal of Commerce* (New York), CLXXXV, No. 14319, Sec. 2 (Aug. 27, 1940).

QUIRK, ROBERT E. *An Affair of Honor; Woodrow Wilson and the Occupation of Vera Cruz.* Lexington, Ky.: University of Kentucky Press, 1962.

ROMERO, MATÍAS. *Mexico and the United States.* New York and London: G. P. Putnam's Sons, 1898.

U.S. STATE DEPARTMENT. *Papers Relating to the Foreign Relations of the United States, 1913–1918.* Washington, D.C., 1920–30.

ECONOMICS AND TECHNOLOGY

GENERAL MINERAL ECONOMICS AND TECHNOLOGY

BATEMAN, ALAN M. *Economic Mineral Deposits.* New York: John Wiley & Sons, 1950.

BLONDEL, F. *L'économie du sous-sol dans les pays sous-développés.* Paris: Coll. Tiers-Monde, 1961.

HOOVER, HERBERT C. *Principles of Mining.* New York: Hill Publishing Co., 1909.

LEITH, CHARLES K. *The Economic Aspects of Geology.* New York: H. Holt and Co., 1921.

———. *World Minerals and World Politics.* New York: McGraw-Hill Book Co., Inc., 1931.

MARRIOTT, HUGH F. *Money and Mines; The Administration, Organisation and Economics of Precious and Non-Ferrous Metal Mines.* London: E. Benn Ltd., 1925.

TRYON, F. G., AND ECKEL, E. C. (eds.). *Mineral Economics. Lectures Under the Auspices of the Brookings Institution.* New York: McGraw-Hill Book Co., 1932.

U.S. BUREAU OF MINES. *Mineral Facts and Problems.* Bulletin 556. Washington, D.C., 1956.

ECONOMICS AND TECHNOLOGY OF METALS

General

BAIN, H. F. (ed.). *More Recent Cyanide Practice.* San Francisco: Mining and Scientific Press, 1910.

COLLINS, HENRY F. *The Metallurgy of Lead and Silver.* London: C. Griffin and Co., 1900.

CONGRESO PANAMERICANO DE INGENIERÍA DE MINAS Y GEOLOGÍA (Primero). *Anales.* Santiago de Chile, 1942.

Engineering and Mining Journal, LXIX–CLVI (New York: McGraw-Hill Publishing Co., 1900–55).

HOOVER, THEODORE J. *Concentrating Ores by Flotation.* London: The Mining Magazine, 1914.

INTERNATIONAL GEOLOGICAL CONGRESS, 20TH (Mexico, 1956). *Resumenes de los trabajos presentados.* Mexico, 1956.

JULIAN, H. FORBES, AND SMART, EDGAR. *Cyaniding Gold and Silver Ores.* London: Chas. Griffin and Co., 1907.

MEGRAW, HERBERT A. *The Flotation Process.* New York: McGraw-Hill Book Co., Inc., 1918.

Mining Engineering, I–VII (New York: American Institute of Mining and Metallurgical Engineers, 1949–55).

Mining and Metallurgy, I–XXIX (New York: American Institute of Mining and Metallurgical Engineers, 1924–48).

Mining Magazine, I–XLVII (London, 1910–32).

Mining World, VII–XVII (San Francisco, 1945–55).

PARSONS, ARTHUR B. *The Porphyry Coppers.* ("AIME, Rocky Mountain Fund Series.") New York, 1933.

RICKARD, THOMAS A. *Recent Cyanide Practice.* San Francisco: Mining and Scientific Press, 1907.

UNITED NATIONS. Department of Economic and Social Affairs. *Non-Ferrous Metals in Under-Developed Countries.* New York, 1956.

U.S. BUREAU OF MINES AND GEOLOGICAL SURVEY. *Mineral Resources of the U.S.* (Written by staff members.) Washington, D.C.: Public Affairs Press, 1948.

VON BERNEWITZ, M. W. *Cyanide Practice, 1910–1913.* San Francisco: Mining and Scientific Press, 1913.

ZIMMERMANN, ERICH W. *World Resources and Industries.* New York: Harper & Bros., 1951.

Mexican Developments

ARMOUR RESEARCH FOUNDATION OF ILLINOIS INSTITUTE OF TECHNOLOGY. *Technological Audit of Selected Mexican Industries with Industrial Research Recommendations.* Chicago, 1946.

CATRON, WILLIAM. U.S. Bureau of Mines. *Mining Methods, Practices and Costs of the Cananea Consolidated Copper Co., Sonora, Mexico.* (Information Circular No. 6247.) Washington, D.C., 1930.

FORREST, JAMES (ed.). *Smelting Processes.* (Comprising, Henry F. Collins, "Smelting Processes for the Extraction of Silver and Gold from Their Ores," and James W. Malcolmson, "The Erection of Silver-lead Smelting Works in Mexico.") London: The Institution [of Mining Engineers], 1893.

HAHN, OTTO H. "On the Development of Silver Smelting in Mexico," Institution of Mining and Metallurgy (London), *Transactions,* VIII (1899–1900), 231–303.

McCANN, FERDINAND. *Cyanide Practice in Mexico.* San Francisco: Mining and Scientific Press, 1912.

Mexican Mining Journal, V–XXI (Mexico, 1907–17).

MEXICO. Departamento de Minas. *Boletín de industrias minerales,* I–IX (Mexico, 1926–30).

———. Departamento de Minas. *Boletín minero,* I–XXXV (Mexico, 1916–33).

———. Secretaría de la Economía Nacional. *Boletín de petróleo y minas,* I–XI (Mexico, 1933–39). Changed to: Dirección General de Minas y Petróleo. *Boletín de minas y petróleo,* XI—— (Mexico, 1938——).

Mineral Survey, vols. I–X. (Mexico, 1934–44.)

MONTES DE OCA, GENARO. "Las plantas metalúrgicas mexicanas," *Boletín minero,* XIV (Sept. 1922).

UNITED NATIONS. Economic and Social Council. (Economic Commission for Latin America.) *Economic Survey of Latin America, 1950: Recent Trends and Events in Mining.* New York, 1951.

Silver

ADDICKS, LAWRENCE (ed.). *Silver in Industry.* New York: Reinhold Publishing Corp., 1940.

BLISS, DON C. *The Bombay Bullion Market.* U.S. Department of Commerce. Bureau of Foreign and Domestic Commerce. (Trade Information Bulletin No. 457.) Washington, D.C. (Feb. 1927).

EVEREST, ALLAN SEYMOUR. *Morgenthau, The New Deal and Silver.* New York: King's Crown Press, 1950.

LEAVENS, DICKSON H. *Silver Money.* (Cowles Commission for Research in Economics, Monograph No. 4.) Bloomington, Ind.: Principia Press, Inc., 1939.

LEONG, YAN SING. *Silver: An Analysis of Factors Affecting Its Price.* Washington, D.C.: The Brookings Institution, 1933.

ROTTERDAMSCHE BANK. "Silver . . . Mainly a Common Commodity," *Quarterly Review,* No. 2 (Aug. 1952), 5–41.

Lead and Zinc

INTERNATIONAL GEOLOGICAL CONGRESS, 18TH (London, 1948). *Report of the 18th Session, Great Britain, 1948.* (Part 7: "The Geology, Paragenesis, and Reserves of the Ores of Lead and Zinc.") London, 1950.

GENT, ERNEST V. *The Zinc Industry: A Mine to Market Outline.* New York: The American Zinc Institute, Inc., 1940.

INGALLS, WALTER R. *Lead and Zinc in the United States.* New York: Hill Publishing Co., 1908.

———. *World Survey of the Zinc Industry.* New York: Mining and Metallurgical Society of America, 1931.

SANTMEYERS, R. M. *The Lead Industry: In North America, South America and Oceania.* U.S. Department of Commerce. Bureau of Foreign and Domestic Commerce. (Trade Information Bulletin No. 368.) Washington, D.C., 1925.

U.S. BUREAU OF MINES. *Materials Survey: Lead.* Washington, D.C., 1951.

———. *Materials Survey: Zinc.* Washington, D.C., 1951.

U.S. DEPARTMENT OF COMMERCE. Bureau of Foreign and Domestic Trade. *World Survey of the Zinc Industry.* (Trade Information Bulletin No. 246.) Washington, D.C., 1924.

U.S. TARIFF COMMISSION. *Lead.* ("Tariff Information Surveys.") Rev. ed., Washington, D.C., 1921.

———. *Lead and Zinc Industries: Report of Investigation.* Report No. 192, 2d Ser. Washington, D.C., 1954.

———. *Lead and Zinc: Report to the President.* (Mimeographed.) Washington, D.C., Apr. 1958.

———. *The Zinc Industry.* ("Tariff Information Surveys.") Rev. ed., Washington, D.C., 1921.

Copper

INTERNATIONAL GEOLOGICAL CONGRESS, 16TH (Washington, D.C., 1933). *Copper Resources of the World.* 2 vols. Washington, D.C., 1935.

U.S. BUREAU OF MINES. *Materials Survey: Copper.* Washington, D.C., 1952.

U.S. FEDERAL TRADE COMMISSION. *Report of the Federal Trade Commission on the Copper Industry.* Washington, D.C., 1947.

WEED, W. H. *The Principal Copper Mines of the World.* New York: Hill Publishing Co., 1908.

GENERAL TRADE STUDIES

U.S. TARIFF COMMISSION. *The Foreign Trade of Latin America.* Report No. 146, 2d Ser. 3 vols. Rev. ed., Washington, D.C., 1942.

———. *Latin America as a Source of Strategic and Other Essential Materials.* Report No. 144, 2d Ser. Washington, D.C., 1941.

U.S. DEPARTMENT OF COMMERCE. Bureau of Foreign and Domestic Commerce. *Foreign Commerce Weekly,* I–LXXIII (Washington, D.C., 1940–55).

METAL TRADE STUDIES

ANON. "El caso de plomo y zinc," *Revista de comercio exterior,* III (Nov. 1953), 91–99.

SPURR, JOSIAH, AND WORMSER, FELIX E. (eds.). *The Marketing of Metals and Minerals.* (A series of articles by specialists.) New York: McGraw-Hill Book Co., 1925.

VALDIVIESO, MÁXIMO. "Situación del mercado internacional de metales: Oro y plata e industriales o básicos." *Revista de economía,* XVII, No. 4 (Apr. 15, 1954), 120–126.

THE ECONOMY OF MEXICO

General

BANCO DE MÉXICO. *Asamblea general ordinaria de accionistas.* Vols. XIII–XXIII. Mexico, 1945–55.

CARRILLO, ALEJANDRO. *Mexico's Resources for Livelihood.* The Hague: International Industrial Relations Institute, 1938.

GUMPEL, HENRY J. *Taxation in Mexico.* Boston: Little, Brown & Co., 1957.

INSTITUTE OF INTERNATIONAL FINANCE. *The Institute of International Finance, Bulletin No. 90. The Economic Position of Mexico.* New York: Institute of International Finance (Feb. 23, 1955).

Inter-American Economic Affairs. I–XI. Washington, D.C., 1946–56.

INTERNATIONAL BANK FOR RECONSTRUCTION AND DEVELOPMENT. *The Economic Development of Mexico.* (Report of the Combined Mexican Working Party.) Baltimore: Johns Hopkins Press, 1953.

LÓPEZ ROSADO, DIEGO, AND ROMERO KOLBEK, GUSTAVO. *Problemas económicos actuales de México.* Mexico: Escuela Nacional de Economía, 1954.

MEXICAN YEAR BOOK, THE. Robert G. Cleland (ed.). Los Angeles: Mexican Year Book Publishing Co., 1922–24.

MEXICO. Secretaría de Hacienda. *Mexican Year Book.* London: McCorquodale and Co., Ltd., 1908–14.

SHERWELL, G. BUTLER. *Mexico's Capacity to Pay: A General Analysis of the Present International Economic Position of Mexico.* Washington, D.C., 1929.

STURMTHAL, ADOLF. "Economic Development, Income Distribution and Capital Formation in Mexico." *Journal of Political Economy,* LXIII, No. 3 (June 1955), 183–201.

UNITED NATIONS. Economic Commission for Latin America. *El desequilibrio externo en el desarrollo económico de América Latina.* (Vol. II: *El caso de México*). Mimeographed. La Paz, 1957.

U.S. DEPARTMENT OF COMMERCE. Bureau of Foreign Commerce. (World Trade Information Service.) "Establishing a Business in Mexico," *Economic Reports,* Part 1, No. 55–78, Washington, D.C. (July 1955).

U.S. TARIFF COMMISSION. *Mining and Manufacturing Industries in Mexico.* Washington, D.C., 1946.

Mining and the Mexican Economy

ELUYAR, FAUSTO DE. *Memoria sobre el influjo de la minería en la agricultura, industria, población y civilización de la Nueva España, etc.* Madrid: Imprenta de Amarita, 1825.

SERRANO, GUSTAVO P. *Mining and Its Influence on the Progress and Development of Mexico.* Mexico, 1951.

INVESTMENTS

International Control of Minerals

AMERICAN INSTITUTE OF MINING AND METALLURGICAL ENGINEERS. *International Control of Minerals.* New York: McGraw-Hill Publishing Co., 1925.

ELLIOTT, WILLIAM Y., et al. *International Control in the Non-Ferrous Metals.* Bureau of International Research of Harvard University and Radcliffe College. New York: The Macmillan Co., 1937.

RAWLES, WILLIAM P. *The Nationality of Commercial Control of World Minerals.* New York: American Institute of Mining Engineers, 1933.

United States Investment Abroad

DICKENS, PAUL D. *American Direct Investments Abroad.* U.S. Bureau of Foreign and Domestic Commerce. (Trade Information Bulletin No. 731.) Washington, D.C., 1930.

———. *United States Foreign Investments.* U.S. Bureau of Foreign and Domestic Commerce. ("Economic Series," No. 1.) Washington, D.C., 1938.

FEUERLEIN, W., AND HANNAN, E. *Dólares en la América Latina.* Mexico: Fondo de Cultura Económica, 1944.

GOTTSCHALK, L. M. "Large Investments of Foreign Capital Have Been Made" (Bureau of Manufactures, Department of Commerce and Labor), *Monthly Consular and Trade Reports,* No. 321 (June 1907), 124–125.

LEWIS, CLEONA. *America's Stake in International Investments.* Washington, D.C.: The Brookings Institution, 1938.

———. *The United States and Foreign Investment Problems.* Washington, D.C.: The Brookings Institution, 1948.

SAMMONS, R. L., AND ABELSON, M. *American Direct Investments in Foreign Countries.* U.S. Bureau of Foreign and Domestic Commerce. ("Economic Series," No. 20.) Washington, D.C., 1942.

U.S. OFFICE OF BUSINESS ECONOMICS. U.S. Department of Commerce. *Survey of Current Business,* XXV–XL (Washington, D.C., 1945–60).

U.S. DEPARTMENT OF COMMERCE. Office of International Trade. *Factors Limiting U.S. Investment Abroad.* Washington, D.C., 1953.

———. Office of Business Economics. *Direct Private Foreign Investments of the United States, Census of 1950.* Washington, D.C., 1953.

———. Office of Business Economics. *U.S. Investments in the Latin American Economy.* Washington, D.C., 1957.

U.S. TREASURY DEPARTMENT. *Census of American-Owned Assets in Foreign Countries.* Washington, D.C., 1947.

Foreign Investments in Mexico

BARLOW, D. "United States Enterprises in Mexico" (Bureau of Foreign Commerce, Department of State), *Commercial Relations of the United States with Foreign Countries,* I (Oct. 29, 1902), 433–503.

DIAZ DUFOO, CARLOS. *México y los capitales extranjeros.* Paris: Lib. de la Vda. de Ch. Bouret, 1918.

ESPINOSA DE LOS REYES, JORGE. *Relaciones económicas entre México y los Estados Unidos, 1870-1910.* Mexico: Nacional Financiera, 1951.

LETCHER, MARION. "Wealth of Mexico" (Bureau of Foreign and Domestic Commerce, Department of Commerce and Labor), *Daily Consular and Trade Reports* (15th Year), III, No. 168 (July 18, 1912), 316.

RESENDIZ, SALVADOR ARREOLA. *Inversiones norteamericanas en México y sus consecuencias económicas.* Mexico: Universidad Nacional Autótoma de México, 1953.

RIPPY, J. FRED. *British Investments in Latin America, 1822-1949.* Minneapolis: University of Minnesota Press, 1959.

TISCHENDORF, ALFRED. *Great Britain and Mexico in the Era of Porfirio Díaz.* Durham, N.C.: Duke University Press, 1961.

UNITED NATIONS. Economic and Social Council, Fiscal Commission. *Taxation in Capital-Exporting and Capital-Importing Countries of Foreign Private Investment: Foreign Investment in Mexico.* New York (Apr.-May 1953).

U.S. DEPARTMENT OF COMMERCE. Bureau of Foreign Commerce. *Investment in Mexico: Conditions and Outlook for United States Investors.* Washington, D.C., 1955.

COOPERATIVES

MEXICO. Universidad Nacional. (Instituto de Investigaciones Económicas.) *Las cooperativas de consumo organizadas sindicalmente en México.* Mexico: Ediciones Minerva, 1944.

——. *La legislación sobre cooperativas en México.* Mexico: Impr. Universitaria, 1943.

LAW

General Interpretations of the Concept of Mining Law

BAINBRIDGE, WILLIAM A. *Treatise on the Law of Mines and Minerals.* Philadelphia: J. Campbell, 1871.

ISAY, RUDOLF. "Mining Law," *Encyclopaedia of the Social Sciences* (New York: The Macmillan Co., 1933), X, 513–517.

HOOVER, HERBERT C., AND L. H. "Notes on the Development of Mining Law," *Engineering and Mining Journal,* XCIV (Nov. 2, 1912), 823–825.

VAN WAGENEN, THEODORE F. *International Mining Law.* New York: McGraw-Hill Book Co., Inc., 1918.

VELARDE, CARLOS E. *La legislación minera en las repúblicas hispano-americanas. La propiedad minera; su orígen, caracteres y condición resolutoria.* Buenos Aires: Compañia Sud-Americana de Billetes de Banco, 1916.

Guides to Mexican Law

(See footnotes in pertinent sections of the text.)

VANCE, JOHN T., AND CLAGETT, HELEN L. *A Guide to the Law and Legal Literature of Mexico.* ("Latin American Series," No. 6.) Washington, D.C.: Library of Congress, The Law Library, 1945.

VANCE, JOHN T. *The Background of Hispanic-American Law; Legal Sources and Juridical Literature of Spain.* New York: Central Book Co., 1943.

General Collections of Mexican Law

DUBLÁN, MANUEL, AND LOZANO, JOSÉ MARIA (eds.). *Legislación mexicana o colección completa de las disposiciones legislativas expedidas desde la independencia de la República.* 42 vols. Edición Oficial. Mexico: Impr. del Comercio, 1876–1911. (From 1897 to 1904, the collection was edited by Adolfo Dublán and Adalberto A. Esteva. The volumes covering the years 1899–1910 were issued under the title: *Colección legislativa completa de la República Mexicana con todas las disposiciones expedidas para la federación, distrito federal y territorio ... continuación de la Legislación Mexicana de Dublán y Lozano.* The volume numbering is continuous.)

MACEDO, PABLO, AND MACEDO, MIGUEL S. *Anuario de legislación y jurisprudencia, sección de legislación; colección completa de decretos, circulares, acuerdos y demás disposiciones legislativas.* 15 vols. Mexico: Impr. de Francisco Díaz de León, 1884–99. (From 1894 to 1899, the *Anuario* was under the editorship of Miguel S. Macedo and Agustín Rodríguez.)

MEXICO. *Diario oficial; organo del gobierno constitucional de los Estados Unidos Mexicanos, I——,* Mexico, 1915——.

———. Secretaría de Industria, Comercio y Trabajo. *Documentos relacionados con la legislación petrolera mexicana.* 3 vols. Mexico, 1919–30. (Vol. III: *El Código de Minería* [en 1884].)

MEXICAN MINING LAW (TEXT AND COMMENTARIES TO 1917— LISTED CHRONOLOGICALLY)

Pre-1884

GAMBOA, FRANCISCO X. *Comentarios a las ordenanzas de minas, dedicados al católico rey, nuestro Señor, Don Carlos III.* Madrid: J. Ibarra, 1761.

———. *Commentaries on the Mining Ordinances of Spain: Dedicated to His Catholic Majesty, Charles III.* (Translated from the original Spanish by Richard Heathfield.) London: Langman, Rees, Orme, Brown & Green, 1830.

PEÑA, MANUEL DE LA. *El dominio directo del soberano en las minas de México y génesis de la legislación petrolera mexicana.* 2 vols. Mexico, 1928.

Ordenanzas de Minería y colección de las órdenes y decretos de esta materia. Nueva edición disputa por C. N. Paris and Mexico: Lib. de la Vda. de Ch. Bouret, 1881.

Code of 1884

MEXICO. *Código de Minería de la República Mexicana.* Edición de la Secretaría de Fomento. Mexico: Oficina tipográfica de la Secretaría de Fomento, 1884.

BEJARANO, PEDRO, et al. *Proyecto de Código de Minería formada por la comisión que nombró la Secretaría de Fomento.* Mexico: Oficina tipográfica de la Secretaría de Fomento, 1884.

RAMIREZ, SANTIAGO. *Apuntes para un proyecto de Código de Minería.* Mexico: Oficina tipográfica de la Secretaría de Fomento, 1884.

VALLARTA, IGNACIO LUIS. *El proyecto de Código de Minería.* Mexico: Imprenta Poliglota, 1884.

Law of 1892

MEXICO. *Ley Minera y Ley de Impuesto a la Minería.* Mexico: Oficina Impresora de Estampillas, Palacio Nacional, 1892.

CHISM, RICHARD E. *Encyclopedia of Mexican Mining Law.* Mexico: Impr. del Minero Mexicano, 1901.

LANDA Y ESCANDON, JOSÉ W. DE, et al. *Proyecto de Ley Minera de los Estados Unidos Mexicanos.* (Congreso de la Union. Cámara de diputados. [15 a]. Comisión de Código de Minería.) Mexico, 1892.

MARTÍNEZ BACA, EDUARDO. *Reseña historica de la legislación minera en México.* Mexico: Oficina tipográfica de la Secretaría de Fomento, 1901. Translated as "Historical Sketch of Mining Legislation in Mexico," in American Institute of Mining Engineers, *Transactions,* XXXII (1902), 520–565.

Law of 1910

REYES, RODOLFO, et al. *Proyecto de Ley Minera; Escrito de remisión.* Mexico: Imprenta y fototípia de la Secretaría de Fomento, 1907. (Also privately printed as *Primer proyecto de Ley Minera presentado al Señor Ministro de Fomento* [E. Martínez Baca, et al.] Mexico: Impr. y Lib. de Inocencia Arriola, 1909.)

SOLIS CÁMARA, FERNANDO. *Los Artículos 141 y 144 del proyecto de Ley Minera.* Mexico: Tipografía del Ing. Fernando Bustellos, 1908.

MEXICO. Cámara de Deputados, Comisión Primera de Fomento. *Dictamen de las Comisiones unidas primera y segunda de Fomento que consulta la Ley Minera de los Estados Unidos Mexicanos.* Mexico: Impr. de I. Paz, 1908.

———. Secretaría de Fomento. "Proyecto de la Ley Minera de los Estados Unidos Mexicanos, presentados al Señor Presidente de la República y discutido y modificado en Consejo de Ministros," *Memoria ... de [Secretaría de] Fomento, Colonización e Industria, 1908–1909* (Mexico, 1910), pp. 179–237.

"Discussión de la Ley en la Cámara de Diputados." *Nueva Ley Minera y su Reglamento (Ley Minera de 1909).* Mexico: Herrero y Hnos., 1910, pp. 7–463.

REYES, RODOLFO, AND BARKER, F. F. *The Mining Laws of Mexico . . . with an Introduction, Commentary, Cross-References and Alphabetical Index.* Mexico City: American Book and Printing Co., 1910.

Carranza Decrees

MEXICO. Gobierno Provisional de la República Mexicana. *Codificación de los decretos del C. Venustiano Carranza, Primer Jefe del Ejército Constitucionalista, encargado del poder ejecutivo de la Unión.* Mexico: Impr. de la Sec. de Gobernación, 1915.

———. Departamento de Minas. *Colección de leyes, decretos, circulares, acuerdos y disposiciones referentes a la minería.* Mexico, 1918.

———. Ministerio de Hacienda y Crédito Público. *Decretos, circulares y demás disposiciones emitados por el Gobierno constitucionalista por conducto de la Secretaría de Hacienda desde abril de 1913 hasta diciembre de 1915.* Mexico, 1916.

———. Secretaría de Hacienda y Crédito Público. *Decretos, circulares y reglamentos expedidos por la Secretaría de Hacienda y Crédito Público desde 26 de agosto de 1914 a 2 de noviembre de 1915.* Mexico, 1916.

————. Secretarías de Estado del Gobierno Provisional de la República Mexicana. *Recopilación de las circulares, reglamentos y acuerdos expedidos por las Secretarías de Estado, adscritas a la Primera Jefetura del Ejercito Constitucionalista.* Mexico: Impr. de la Sec. de Gobernación, 1916.

Constitution of 1917 (*Convention and Text*)

Constitución política de los Estados Unidos Mexicanos en vigor desde el 1° de mayo de 1917, con reformas y adiciones hasta la fecha. Mexico: Ediciones Cicerón, 1950.

"Mexican Constitution of 1917 Compared with the Constitution of 1857." (Translated by H. N. Branch.) Supplement to the *Annals of the American Academy of Political and Social Science.* Philadelphia (May 1917).

Bojorquez, Juan de Díos. (Under pseudo. Djed Borquez.) *Crónica del Constituyente.* Mexico: Ediciones Botas, 1938.

Mexico. Congreso Constituyente, 1916–17. *Diario de los debates del Congreso Constituyente.* 2 vols. Mexico: Imprenta de la Cámara de Diputados, 1922.

Melgarejo Randolf, L., and Fernandez Rojas; J. *El Congreso Constituyente de 1916 y 1917.* Mexico: Departamento de Talleres Gráficos de la Secretaría de Fomento, Colonización e Industria, 1917.

Palavicini, Felix F. *Historia de la Constitución de 1917.* 2 vols. Mexico, 1938.

Constitution of 1917 (*Commentaries on Property Rights and Expropriation*)

Barker, Frederick F. "Mexican Mining Concessions, with Special Reference to the Foreign Investor," *Southern California Law Review,* Vol. V, No. 1 (Oct. 1931), 1–8.

Botella Asensi, Juan. *La expropiación en el derecho mexicano.* Mexico, 1941.

Fernandez del Castillo, Germán. *La propiedad y la expropiación en el derecho mexicano actual.* Mexico: Cia. editora de revistas, 1939.

Gaither, Roscoe B. *Expropriation in Mexico: The Facts and the Law.* New York: William Morrow and Co., 1940.

González Roa, Fernando. *Las cuestiones fundamentales de actualidad en México.* Mexico: Impr. de la Sec. de Relaciones Exteriores, 1927.

————. *Régimen constitucional del subsuelo.* Mexico: Impr. Franco-Mexicana, 1922.

Gordon, Wendell C. *The Expropriation of Foreign-owned Property in Mexico.* Washington, D.C.: American Council on Public Affairs, 1941.

Lanz Duret, Miguel. *Derecho constitucional mexicano y consideraciones sobre la realidad política de nuestro régimen.* 4th ed. Mexico: Imprentas L. D., 1947.

The Mexican Expropriation Law and Cases in Which It Has Been Applied. Mexico: Editorial Polis, 1938.

Morineau, Oscar. *Los derechos reales y el subsuelo en México.* Mexico: Fondo de Cultura Económica, 1948.

Pena, Manuel de la. *Prolegómenos de la historia jurídica de la propiedad en México.* (Vol. I only was printed in the *Boletín de petróleo,* XVII–XX [1925], *passim.*)

————. *Retroactividad de la Constitución de 1917 y de la legislación de petróleo.* Mexico, 1920.

Primer Congreso Nacional de Industriales Comisión nombrado por. ... *El artículo 27 constitucional (Constitución de 1917).* Mexico, 1917.

Rippy, Merrill. *El petróleo y la Revolución Mexicana.* (Printed in *Problemas agrícolas e industriales de México,* Vol. VI, No. 3 [Mexico, 1954].)

Sánchez Mejorada y Rodrígueuz, Carlos. *Notas sobre evolución y tendencias actuales del derecho minero mexicano.* (Publicaciones de la Academia Mexicana de Jurisprudencia y Legislación.) Mexico, 1944.

———. *Algunas notas sobre la "Propiedad Minera" antes y después de la Constitución de 1917.* Mexico, 1947.

VÁSQUEZ DEL MERCADO, ALBERTO. *Concesión minera y derechos reales.* Mexico: Porrua Hnos. y Cia., 1946.

Mexican Mining Law (*Post-1917*)

(For detailed listings of laws in various government periodicals, see Chaps. XIV, XVI, XXI, and XXV.)

ANDRADE, MANUEL (ed.). *Leyes y reglamentos sobre aguas, bosques, colonización, minas y petróleo.* 2d ed. (Looseleaf.) Mexico: Información aduanera de México, 1943.

MEXICO. Departamento de Minas. *Proyecto de Ley Minera.* Mexico, 1918.

Index